D1510705

METHODS IN CANCER RESEARCH

Volume VI

Contributors to This Volume

PAUL BARTL

MICHAEL BEER

DIANNE D. BLACK

EDWARD BRESNICK

HARRIS BUSCH

YONG C. CHOI

HAROLD P. ERICKSON

LOUIS M. FINK

A. CLARK GRIFFIN

ERICH HECKER

THEODOR KOLLER

PEEYUSH K. LALA

CHARLES M. MAURITZEN

ARNOLD SCHWARTZ

FRED SNYDER

LOUIS A. SORDAHL

I. BERNARD WEINSTEIN

TOMIZO YOSHIDA

METHODS IN CANCER RESEARCH

Edited by

HARRIS BUSCH
DEPARTMENT OF PHARMACOLOGY
BAYLOR COLLEGE OF MEDICINE
HOUSTON, TEXAS

VOLUME VI

ACADEMIC PRESS   New York   London   1971

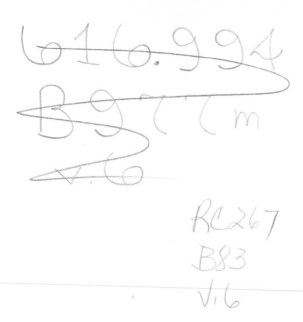

COPYRIGHT © 1971, BY ACADEMIC PRESS, INC.
ALL RIGHTS RESERVED
NO PART OF THIS BOOK MAY BE REPRODUCED IN ANY FORM,
BY PHOTOSTAT, MICROFILM, RETRIEVAL SYSTEM, OR ANY
OTHER MEANS, WITHOUT WRITTEN PERMISSION FROM
THE PUBLISHERS.

ACADEMIC PRESS, INC.
111 Fifth Avenue, New York, New York 10003

United Kingdom Edition published by
ACADEMIC PRESS, INC. (LONDON) LTD.
Berkeley Square House, London W1X 6BA

LIBRARY OF CONGRESS CATALOG CARD NUMBER: 66-29495

PRINTED IN THE UNITED STATES OF AMERICA

Contents

BIOLOGY

CHAPTER I. **Studies on Tumor Cell Population Kinetics**

Peeyush K. Lala

CHAPTER II. **Comparative Studies of Ascites Hepatomas**

Tomizo Yoshida

MAR 4 - 1971

CHAPTER III.   **Tumor Mitochondria**

Louis A. Sordahl and Arnold Schwartz

MOLECULAR BIOLOGY

CHAPTER IV.   **Protein Biosynthesis**

A. Clark Griffin and Dianne D. Black

CHAPTER V.   **Preparation of Macromolecules of Very High Specific Activity in Tumor Cells** *in Vitro*

Charles M. Mauritzen, Yong C. Choi, and Harris Busch

CHAPTER VI.   **Electron Microscopy of Nucleic Acids**

Michael Beer, Paul Bartl, Theodor Koller, and Harold P. Erickson

CHAPTER VII.   **Methods for Studying Mammalian Transfer Ribonucleic Acid**

I. Bernard Weinstein and Louis M. Fink

BIOCHEMISTRY

CHAPTER VIII.   **Regenerating Liver: An Experimental Model for the Study of Growth**

Edward Bresnick

CHAPTER IX.   **Glycerolipids in the Neoplastic Cell: Methodology, Metabolism, and Composition**

Fred Snyder

COCARCINOGENS

List of Contributors

Numbers in parentheses indicate the pages on which the authors' contributions begin.

PAUL BARTL, Hoffman-La Roche Inc., Nutley, New Jersey (283)

MICHAEL BEER, Department of Biophysics, The John Hopkins University, Baltimore, Maryland (283)

DIANNE D. BLACK, Department of Biochemistry, University of Texas, M. D. Anderson Hospital and Tumor Institute, Houston, Texas (189)

EDWARD BRESNICK, Department of Pharmacology, Baylor College of Medicine, Houston, Texas (347)

HARRIS BUSCH, Department of Pharmacology, Baylor College of Medicine, Houston, Texas (253)

YONG C. CHOI, Department of Pharmacology, Baylor College of Medicine, Houston, Texas (253)

HAROLD P. ERICKSON, Medical Research Council, Cambridge, England (283)

LOUIS M. FINK, Institute for Cancer Research, Departments of Medicine and Pathology, Columbia University College of Physicians and Surgeons, Francis Delafield Hospital, New York, New York (311)

A. CLARK GRIFFIN, Department of Biochemistry, University of Texas, M. D. Anderson Hospital and Tumor Institute, Houston, Texas (189)

ERICH HECKER, Biochemical Institute, German Cancer Research Center, Heidelberg, Germany (439)

THEODOR KOLLER, Laboratory for Electron Microscopy, Institute of Botany, Federal Institute of Technology, Zurich, Switzerland (283)

PEEYUSH K. LALA, Department of Anatomy, McGill University, Montreal, Quebec, Canada (3)

CHARLES M. MAURITZEN,* Department of Pharmacology, Baylor College of Medicine, Houston, Texas (253)

* Present address: Department of Biochemistry, University of Melbourne, Parkville, Victoria, Australia.

ARNOLD SCHWARTZ, Department of Pharmacology, Baylor College of Medicine, Houston, Texas (159)

FRED SNYDER, Medical Division, Oak Ridge Associated Universities, Oak Ridge, Tennessee (399)

LOUIS A. SORDAHL, Department of Pharmacology, Baylor College of Medicine, Houston, Texas (159)

I. BERNARD WEINSTEIN, Institute of Cancer Research, Departments of Medicine and Pathology, Columbia University College of Physicians and Surgeons, Francis Delafield Hospital, New York, New York (311)

TOMIZO YOSHIDA, Japanese Foundation for Cancer Research, Toshima-ku, Tokyo, Japan (97)

Preface

As noted in Volume V of "Methods in Cancer Research" important new techniques that apply to the cancer problem are being developed, thus, Volumes V and VI have been added to the four volumes originally planned for this treatise. In these volumes, special methods related to studies of molecular biology have been included, particularly those for studies on tRNA, DNA, and protein synthesis. In addition, special aspects of biology as related to the cell cycle, transplantation of ascites cells, and labeling procedures for RNA and proteins *in vitro* are incorporated. Moreover, special areas of regeneration, mitochondrial metabolism, and actions of croton oil are reviewed. The six volumes as now constituted cover a large segment of methods that are useful in cancer research not only for studies on cancer cells but for other cells active in growth.

It is apparent that even with six volumes this treatise is inadequate to cover all the topics that are important to cancer research. With the bibliographies that have been provided by the authors, and their interpretation, it is hoped that a sound base has been established for methods in cancer research that will prove both meaningful and useful to workers for many years to come.

HARRIS BUSCH

Houston, Texas
October, 1970

Contents of Other Volumes

VOLUME IV

BIOLOGY

CHAPTER I

STUDIES ON TUMOR CELL POPULATION KINETICS

PEEYUSH K. LALA

I. Introduction

Studies on cell population kinetics are aimed at understanding the dynamic events in the life history of a cell population, which take place in relation to time, space, morphology, and function. Vital data on cells relative to proliferation and differentiation, migration, fate, and loss, which represent the life history beyond the static histological picture, are obtainable through such studies. A "population" of cells may be defined either in reference to geography or spatial boundaries (such as organized tissues and solid tumors) or morphological and functional criteria (such as blood, blood-forming tissues, and leukemias). Use of different criteria in defining a population presents no limitation to performing kinetic studies.

Although a morphological recognition of the dynamic processes in cells dates back to the discovery of histological and cytological techniques, the concept of cell population kinetics had its origin in the recognition of the fact that a physiological marker of cellular proliferation—the process of mitosis—can be used as a tool in obtaining information about life history of cells (Leblond and Stevens, 1948). Following the introduction of colchicine as a mitosis-arresting (stathmokinetic) agent (Allen *et al.*, 1937; Leblond and Allen, 1937; Dustin, 1943; Eigsti and Dustin, 1955), it was possible to measure the rate of progress of cells into mitosis and, consequently, quantitate the rate of turnover or renewal of cells as reported in the excellent review by Leblond and Walker (1956). A second marker of cellular proliferation became available from the knowledge of the duplication of chromosomal material in a proliferating cell. Although it had been known for a long time that such duplication occurred before cell division, this was believed to take place during mitosis. The fact that deoxyribonucleic acid (DNA) replicates during the interphase rather than mitosis was brought to light by the introduction of two different techniques: (*1*) cytophotometric measurement of nuclear DNA in individual cells (e.g., by Walker and Yates, 1952) and (*2*) radioautographic identification of cells synthesizing DNA following the use of a labeled precursor. Studies by Howard and Pelc (1951, 1953) using [35]S- and ^{32}P-labeled precursors and by Lajtha *et al.* (1954) using [14]C- and ^{32}P-labeled precursors showed that DNA synthesis took place during only part of the interphase. This finding led to the concept of the mitotic "cell cycle" (see List of Symbols below) represented by four components as proposed by Howard and Pelc (1953): G_1 or the gap following mitosis and before DNA synthesis, S or the DNA synthetic phase, G_2 or the gap following DNA synthesis before mitosis, and M or the mitotic phase. A revolution in radioautographic studies of the cell cycle was brought about by the synthesis of the tritium-labeled nucleoside, thymidine (^{3}H TdR), a specific precursor for DNA, independently in U.S.A. (Taylor *et al.*, 1957) and in Belgium (Verly *et al.*, 1958). Although the specificity of thymidine provided a specific nuclear label, very short energy range of tritium β-particles helped in localization of silver grains over the nucleus in radioautograms, thus increasing its suitability as a label. Labeled thymidine provided a relatively permanent tag for observing the cell at any state because of the stability of nuclear DNA. Except for dilution of the label by cell division, it is carried by the cell until its DNA is lost either by cell death in most cell types or by the loss of nucleus in special cases such as red cells and lenticular cells. This made possible the tracing of the life history of a cell since its origin in relation to time or space, or, in other words, the study of "cell population kinetics."

The first collection of reports on various aspects of cell kinetics was the outcome of a conference, edited by Stohlman (1959). Subsequently a very profitable treatise resulted from a symposium on cell proliferation edited by Lamerton and Fry (1963). Among a few other publications on this subject, a recent monograph by Cleaver (1967) is an excellent review of the techniques as well as methods of analysis of data obtainable by them in the study of cell population kinetics. Application of available techniques to the study of tumor cell populations was initially somewhat slow, not primarily because of any underestimation of the importance of such studies, but rather of the unavailability of reproducible animal tumor systems that might be identifiable with the human situation. Although such difficulty has not been overcome, numerous valuable studies made in animal tumors and limited numbers of studies in human tumors have contributed significantly toward our understanding of the process of tumor growth. A number of elegant reviews on the subject are available for the interested readers: on the relationship of cell cycle to tumor growth (Baserga, 1965); on the cell kinetics of normal and malignant tissues (Lamerton and Steel, 1968; Patt, 1969; Bresciani, 1968); on the relationship of the cellular kinetics to radiation effects in normal and malignant tissues (Patt and Quastler, 1963; Patt, 1963; Gilbert and Lajtha, 1965); on the kinetics of tumor cell proliferation and its applications in tumor therapy (Mendelsohn, 1963, 1965, 1966; Mendelsohn and Dethlefsen, 1968); on cell population kinetics in human leukemias (Cronkite, 1967, 1968; Killmann, 1968a,b; Schiffer, 1968; Chervenick and Boggs, 1968); and on the biochemistry of cell cycle (Baserga, 1968; Prescott, 1968). Excellent publications on radioautographic techniques are also available (Boyd, 1955; Rogers, 1967; Feinendegen, 1967; Baserga, 1967).

LIST OF SYMBOLS FOR KINETIC PARAMETERS

Symbols used throughout this chapter were either adopted in the Guinnes symposium on cell proliferation, edited by Lamerton and Fry (1963), or are those generally accepted in literature by cell kineticists, some of which are modified by the author for the sake of uniformity.

Phases of cycle:
C = cell cycle
t_C = cell cycle time (does not include G_0 phase)
G_1 = pre-DNA-synthesis phase
t_{G_1} = time spent in pre-DNA-synthesis phase
S = DNA synthetic phase
t_S = DNA synthetic time
G_2 = post-DNA-synthesis phase
t_{G_2} = time spent in post-DNA-synthesis phase
M = mitosis
t_M = mitotic time
G_0 = phase of proliferative rest (Lajtha, 1963)
t_{G_0} = time spent in proliferative rest phase
N = total number in the population in any phase (the number in any phase is designated by a subscript, viz., N_C, N_S, etc.)

Fraction of the population at any defined state is given by the respective "index" (I) associated with a subscript for the state:
I_L = labeling index
I_S = DNA synthetic index (as given by flash ^{3}H TdR-labeling index)
I_M = mitotic index
I_P = proliferative index (growth fraction)

t_D = tumor doubling time
t_{PD} = potential doubling time (Steel, 1967, 1968)

Rates are designated k with a subscript:
k_B = "birth" rate
k_G = growth rate
k_L = rate of cell loss

ϕ = cell loss factor (Steel, 1967, 1968)

II. Types of Cell Populations

From the kinetic viewpoint, cell populations may be characterized in a number of ways. Leblond *et al.* (1959) classified tissues on the basis of two attributes: the extent of cellular proliferation and the extent of cell loss or replacement. Newborn (3-day-old) and adult (6-month-old) rats were sacrificed a few hours after injection of ³H TdR to determine the fraction of labeled cells in various tissues. This indicated the extent of proliferation. Some newborn animals labeled at 3 days were allowed to survive for 6 months and then the tissues were examined for labeled cells. This indicated the extent of cellular retention or loss. Based on these tests, three categories of cell populations were defined, although some tissues could not be clearly assigned to any category:

1. Stable or nongrowing populations. Tissues showing no proliferation in adulthood, but showing retention of labeled cells were assigned to this category, for example, muscular tissues. However, some tissues, such as large-sized cerebral neurons, did not show any labeled cells in formation and retention tests, indicating that cell proliferation stopped before 3 days after birth.

2. Expanding populations. In this category were included tissues (for example, liver parenchyma) that showed a small amount of cell proliferation as well as retention through adulthood.

3. Renewing populations. These included tissues showing substantial proliferation but no retention of labeled cells. The latter could result from loss of labeled cells or repeated division of labeled cells leading to nonrecognition of labeling at 6 months. Tissues such as epidermis and blood-forming organs, showed these characteristics.

Our present knowledge of tumors indicates that tumors would fit into the combined category of "expanding" and "renewing" populations.

A theoretical consideration of possible cell populations has been elegantly presented by Gilbert and Lajtha (1965) who combined the relative importance of three parameters—cell inflow, cell outflow, and cell division. Such consideration is very helpful in understanding the kinetic characteristics rather than practical classification of cell populations. Tumors when considered from such a viewpoint would possess the following attributes: (1) no cellular input from outside the population, (2) cell division partly for self-maintenance (thus having some "stem-type" character), and (3) cellular outflow (loss) either by death or migration. It will be illustrated later that the importance of the last-mentioned attribute, i.e., cell loss in tumors has only been appreciated relatively recently.

A very simple classification of cell populations often employed in practice results from a consideration of the population size:

a. *Steady state*—the population size or the cell number remains unchanged. Rather than a static situation, this implies a dynamic equilibrium between the cell input (including birth) and the cell output (including death). Cell renewal systems in adult animals as discussed by Leblond and Walker (1956), and Patt and Quastler (1963) represent such a steady state.

b. *Growing*—the population size is expanding; the cell input is higher than the cell output. Cell renewal systems in growing animals, growing tumors, and cell populations in tissue culture are typical examples.

c. *Decaying*—the population size is declining; the output from the population must exceed the input. Adult ovary, cell renewal systems following exposure to radiation or radiomimetic chemicals, dying tissue cultures, and regressing tumors following therapy illustrate this category.

III. Relevance of Tumor Materials to Kinetic Studies

In order to appreciate the significance as well as limitations of the kinetic studies in tumors, one needs to possess information about various aspects of the material which may influence the findings. An extremely wide range of tumors are in existence and possible materials may be separated by a variety of attributes as indicated below by question marks.

A. HUMAN TUMORS

1. Benign?
2. Malignant?

Primary? Secondary? Tissue of origin? Pathological classification and degree of differentiation? Clinical duration? Size? Treated? Untreated? Terminal? Having any recognized secretory function?

B. ANIMAL TUMORS OTHER THAN HUMAN

1. Spontaneous?

Truly spontaneous? Any known viral agent? Any known hormonal influence? Tissue of origin? Partly differentiated or anaplastic? Known human counterpart? Transplantable?

2. Experimentally induced?

Inducing agent—chemical, physical, viral? How long after induction? Transplantable?

3. Transplanted?

Solid? Ascitic? Original source? Number of transfers? Distinct subline with a fixed modality in chromosome number? Type of host? Dose of inoculum? Age of tumor? Size of tumor?

From the foregoing attributes that may widely separate one tumor material from the other, one might conclude that kinetic studies in animal tumors or isolated human tumors may not be applicable either to the understanding or to the cure of human cancer. Fortunately, investigations into a diverse range of animal and human materials have not only led to a gradual refinement of analytical tools, but have also revealed a number of features which seem fairly general. These will be considered later at the end of this chapter. Further kinetic studies using refined techniques in carefully chosen tumors should continue to produce valuable information if various factors that influence tumor behavior are taken into consideration and the findings are dealt with due reservations (Lamerton and Steel, 1968). In dealing with tumor materials, the following should be taken into account:

a. Special features related to spontaneous tumors. Secondary (metastatic) tumors may well differ from the primary source in growth rate depending on the secondary site; tissue of origin and the degree of differentiation or anaplasia may influence the growth characteristics a great deal. When a tumor shows some differentiation as observed in the parent tissue, its growth may still be influenced to some extent by humoral and other factors that act on the tissue of origin, and the relation of "proliferative" and "functional" compartments may be partly maintained. Carcinomas from skin, gut, or glandular epithelium provide some examples among solid tumors. Nonlocalized malignancies, such as various forms of leukemias, present rather striking illustrations of the situation. Age of a tumor is also an important factor influencing the growth rate as would be observed from the obtainable growth curves. Most human tumors, when first diagnosed are far advanced from the "exponential phase" if such a phase were present. Further, a tumor studied in a moribund patient in the terminal stage may not be representative of earlier growth conditions. Finally, treatment could substantially alter the growth parameters in a tumor.

b. Features associated with induced tumors. During experimental induction of tumors with various agents, the earlier tumors may behave artificially because of possibly altered tumor–host relationship resulting from changes in host environment. Such changes may be represented by a modification of "noncellular" environment or the host tissues themselves that formed the target of action of the inducing substance.

c. Factors special to transplanted tumors. (1) To obtain reproducibility in results, it is often necessary to perform repeated transfers of the original material in appropriate hosts. Although this would result in a "purer" tumor in terms of growth characteristics, such an aim is realized due to a protracted natural selection of faster-growing cells. In consequence, the tumor under study may lose its identity with the original tumor. (2) Tumor transplants in ascitic form may have different growth characteristics compared to the solid form. Ascitic transformation removes cells from dependence of stroma and vasculature and brings them nearer to tissue culture environments. Important information has been obtained by simultaneous studies on the same tumor cells both in ascitic as well as in solid tumor forms (Tannock, 1969; Lala, 1970b). (3) In transplanted tumors, the inoculum size and the age of transplant often jointly determine the population size and growth rate at any instant (Patt and Blackford, 1954; Lala and Patt, 1966; Lala, 1968b). These two basic parameters must be specified in any kinetic study, as cell cycle characteristics are very much dependent on them (Lala, 1968b). The best procedure would be to obtain the tumor growth curve, if possible, so that the particular kinetic study could be referable to the growth curve. If a full growth curve is not obtainable, an estimate of tumor growth rate should be made at the time of the study. Such information is essential to quantitate very important growth parameters such as the extent of cell loss (Lala and Patt, 1966; Steel *et al.*, 1966; Steel, 1967, 1968).

d. In studies related to any solid tumor, a knowledge of the structural organization is necessary. It may provide clues to the kinetics of spatial differentiation, if such a differentiation exists (Tannock, 1968). Even in the absence of any differentiation, a histological picture may provide information regarding spatial differences in proliferation rates within the tumor (Hermens and Barendsen, 1967) and possible reasons for such differences, viz., closeness to blood vessels and degree of oxygenation (Tannock, 1968).

e. It is also helpful to have some knowledge about the endogenous factors in the host that may influence growth of the tumor under study, such as immune mechanisms related to genetic differences in transplanted tumors (Hellström and Hellström, 1967; Southam, 1967; Klein, 1968) or hormonal environment of the host (Huggins, 1967; Dao, 1967; Currie, 1967; Jensen, 1967; Williams-Ashman, 1967; White, 1967) for any type of tumor, in which growth shows some hormonal influence.

IV. Parameters in Tumor Cell Population Kinetics

A. KINETIC PARAMETERS CONTROLLING GROWTH

As mentioned in Section II, for any population other than a truly static one (no birth, no loss), a change in the population size must result from the balance between the cellular input and output. For a growing tumor, the input which exceeds the output is due to cell birth within the population. The output represents loss either by cell death or migration and removal outside the population. For most localized tumors, cell death would represent the major pathway for loss. For an understanding of the cytokinetic mechanisms controlling tumor growth, one thus needs to quantitate the rates of formation ("birth" rate) and loss of cells. The birth rate, in turn, is controlled by two parameters: the fraction of proliferating cells and the mitotic cell cycle time of the proliferating cells. In other words, three parameters control the overall tumor growth at any instant (Lala and Patt, 1966; Lala, 1968b; Steel *et al.*, 1966; Lamerton and Steel, 1968): (*1*) the mean duration of the mitotic cell cycle (which exhibits some distribution function), (*2*) the proportion of proliferating cells within the population, designated as "growth fraction" by Mendelsohn (1960a, 1962a), and (*3*) the degree of cell loss from the population. The importance of measuring these parameters will be discussed later. As an example, a deceleration in the growth rate with increasing tumor mass in one line of Ehrlich ascites tumor was found to be due to (*1*) a gradual prolongation of the mitotic cell cycle and (*2*) a progressive decline in the growth fraction. The rate of cell loss did not change significantly except during the terminal stage (Lala and Patt, 1966; Lala, 1968b).

B. The Mitotic Cell Cycle

The interval between the end of one mitosis to the other is equated with one cell cycle time (see Fig. 1A). A new cell in cycle would thus progress in order from G_1 to S to G_2 to M phases. These components of the cell cycle will be considered below individually.

1. The G_1 Phase

Available data indicate that a decision on the part of the cell whether to recycle or decycle (either to a nondividing differentiated state or to a state of proliferative rest) is taken in G_1. A transition to the resting phase (G_0) has also been observed from G_2 to a small extent in some cell populations (Gelfant, 1962, 1963, 1966). Initiation of the process of DNA synthesis seems to be the most important event in G_1, and this seems to require the synthesis of ribonucleic acid (RNA) and proteins. Unfortunately, so far, no specific biochemical event leading to S has been characterized to provide a marker for G_1 (Baserga, 1968; Prescott, 1968). From some evidence during bacterial replication, it is believed that an initiator protein possibly acts as a trigger by bringing about the interaction between DNA and DNA polymerase (Prescott, 1968).

2. The S Phase

During S phase, the cell replicates its DNA content—an event specific for this phase. In addition, the cell also makes RNA and proteins. The requirement of protein synthesis seems to be important both for the initiation as well as for the continuation of DNA synthesis in mammalian cells. This has been explained by two different views

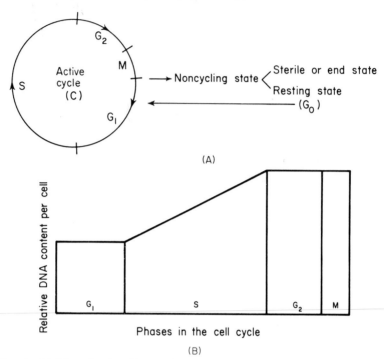

(A)

(B)

Fig. 1. (A) The mitotic cell cycle in mammalian cells showing the four phases. Arrow indicates the direction of progression of a cell through these phases in the cycle. At the end of mitosis, a cell may enter a new cycle or move into a noncycling state. The latter may represent either an end state or a phase of proliferative rest. (B) Relative deoxyribonucleic acid (DNA) content of a cell during progression through various phases in the cycle.

(Prescott, 1968): (*1*) that DNA synthesis in mammalian cells is dependent on concomitant histone synthesis unlike in bacteria (Robbins and Borun, 1967) or (*2*) that concomitant synthesis of initiator protein is needed to initiate an asynchronous replication of multiple replicons through the S phase of a cell. The latter interpretation seems to be more acceptable to cell biologists, and the number of possible replicating units has also been calculated for mammalian cells (Painter *et al.*, 1966). The rate of progress of a cell through DNA synthesis as represented by the linear doubling of DNA during the S period (Fig. 1B) represents a simplified average picture. Such a picture is consistent with the finding that, in a steady state, the average rate of movement of cells into DNA synthesis agrees well with the rate of movement out of DNA synthesis (Lala *et al.*, 1965). On the other hand, for an individual cell, DNA synthesis may not occur at a truly constant rate, as indicated from studies using different techniques (summarized by Cleaver, 1967).

For example, most mammalian cells show a rise and decline in the mean or median grain count over labeled mitotic figures following a pulse labeling with [3]H TdR (Lala, unpublished observations; Cleaver, 1964; Stryckmans et al., 1966). In general, there seems to be a rise in the rate of synthesis at the beginning and a considerable decline at the end of the S phase. This variation in the rate is not surprising, as elegant studies of DNA synthesis at the chromosomal level with labeled thymidine (Taylor, 1960; German and Bearn, 1961; Gilbert et al., 1962; Morishima et al., 1962; Bader et al., 1963; Mukherjee and Sinha, 1963, 1964, 1965; Lima-de-faria, 1964; German, 1964; Stubblefield, 1965) indicate not only an asynchrony in synthesis among chromosomes, which may show some characteristic pattern, but also an asynchrony among various sites in an individual chromosome. Some workers believe that the fluctuations in the rate of synthesis may, in extreme cases, lead to occasional brief pauses in DNA synthesis for an individual cell. Alpen and Johnston (1967) suggested this to explain the presence of a small number of cells with more than diploid DNA content not labeled with [14]C TdR in canine marrow. Hamilton (1969) supports this idea from the observation of occasional small dips in the plateau of labeled mitosis curves (the labeled mitosis technique is discussed in section VIII, A). These observations could also result from fluctuations of the size of intracellular thymidine pool. The significance of these interpretations, however, is that this would result in an incomplete labeling of the cells in the S phase with labeled thymidine. Examination of existing data on mitotic labeling and chromosome labeling in mammalian cells indicates that such a "nonlabeling" during DNA synthesis, even if existing in reality, would not be significant enough to influence kinetic interpretations to a major extent. Normal mammalian cells, once triggered into DNA synthesis appear to complete the process in preparation for division. They do not seem to spend time in "proliferative rest" midway through DNA synthesis. Although this may not be an impossibility in tumor cells, such behavior has not been detected for several tumor cell types (Cooper et al., 1966; Lala and Patt, 1968).

3. The G_2 Phase

The G_2 interval between completion of DNA synthesis and beginning of mitosis is in general considerably shorter than the S period, and no specific biochemical event has so far been detected in this phase. Both RNA as well as proteins are synthesized at this stage, and these seem to be prerequisites for initiation of the mitotic process (Donnelly and Sisken, 1967). Whatever the events may be in G_2, they must link the completion of chromosome replication with the chromosome segregation. There is good evidence that, during G_2, cells in some mammalian tissues may stay in a period of proliferative rest, as shown in the elegant series of experiments by Gelfant (1962, 1963, 1966). The most striking example is provided by basal cells in the epidermis.

4. The M Phase

The mitotic (M) phase represents the morphological process of chromosome segregation. Little is known about the molecular events leading to the morphological sequences observed in mitosis. There is some depression of protein synthesis and a marked decline (or cessation) of RNA synthesis in metaphase and anaphase followed by some recovery in telophase. Under normal conditions, the process of chromosomal segregation, once initiated, proceeds to completion. Occasionally, karyokinesis may be completed without accompanying cytokinesis leading to the formation of binucleate cells in normal as well as in malignant tissues.

Abnormal mitoses are not uncommon in tumor cells with an altered ploidy. Multipolar mitosis in polyploid cells or unequal chromosomal segregation in aneuploid cells are not infrequent. The latter, when it occurs in the absence of cytokinesis, may lead to a cell with two or more unequal nuclei (macro- and micronuclei). Grossly abnormal mitosis possibly leads to cell death and eliminates the cells with an unstable chromosomal constitution in the tumor cell population. Mitotic death may represent an important pathway for cell attrition in some tumors (Bennington, 1969; Lala, 1969, 1970a).

Mitoses may be observable to a variable extent depending on the type of cytological preparation. Usually early prophases and late telophases are difficult to score in routine smears—the former because of difficulty in identification, and the latter because of breakage of cells. It is always much safer from the point of view of reproducibility to score metaphases and anaphases.

C. The Phase of Proliferative Rest

This phase has been denoted as "G_0" phase (Lajtha *et al.*, 1962; Lajtha, 1963; Quastler, 1963) to distinguish it from the active cell cycle stage (see Fig. 1A). Cells in G_0 stage are fertile and retain their capability of entering active cell cycle, under proper conditions or stimuli. In measurements of the cell cycle time, it is the "active" cycle that is considered and G_0 stage is excluded. An ideal example of G_0 is provided by parenchymal liver cells that do not normally divide; they are triggered into cell cycle by partial hepatectomy, leading to regeneration. When regeneration is complete, cells go back to the G_0 phase. Another striking illustration is presented by the small lympho-cytes which are normally nondividing. Under proper immunological stimuli, either *in vitro* or *in vivo*, they are recruited into a state of active proliferation. For most systems, G_0 cells have postmitotic (G_1) DNA content. However, a number of cell populations (namely, epidermis) may contain cells with a premitotic DNA content in an arrested G_2 phase, which resembles G_0 (Gelfant, 1962, 1963, 1966). In kinetic studies it is often difficult to distinguish G_0 from a truly prolonged G_1, although in some experiments such distinction has been possible (Wolfsberg, 1964; Lala, 1968b; Brown, 1968). Nothing is known about the possible biochemical differences existing between G_0 and G_1. The G_0 concept dictates that a cell would rest in this phase indefinitely unless removed from this phase by some process, such as recycling (for example, lymphocytes and hepatocytes), death, or differentiation (as proposed for bone marrow stem cells by Lajtha *et al.*, 1962). Interested readers are referred to the elegant review by Epifanova and Terskikh (1969).

The significance of the presence or absence of a G_0 state in tumor cell populations is more than apparent, although such a knowledge may not be obtainable in many cases. Tumor therapy with commonly used agents acting on a specific stage of the cell cycle may leave the G_0 cells unharmed, which may be responsible for a tumor regrowth. In one line of Ehrlich ascites tumor, an increase in tumor age is associated with the movement of an increasing fraction of the population into G_0 state that has a postmitotic DNA content. Appropriate stimuli, such as ascites aspiration or retransplantation of a fraction of an older tumor into new hosts, promptly initiate cell cycle in these cells (Lala and Patt, 1966, 1968; Lala, 1968b). A similar situation may be mimicked by the small lymphoblasts in human acute leukemias. These cells are normally nonproliferating, but seem to feed into the proliferative blast cell compartment (Saunders and Mauer, 1969). If they represent a G_0 state, a relapse following therapy associated with an increased blast cell proliferation (Foadi *et al.*, 1967; Chan *et al.*, 1969) could be explained by a recruitment of these cells into cycle. Another line of Ehrlich ascites tumor, as reported by De Cosse and Gelfant (1968), shows a small proportion of cells arrested in G_2. Interestingly enough, such cells do enter mitosis when the host immune processes are suppressed with antilymphocyte serum, indicating that a G_2–G_0 transition may represent a defense mechanism on the part of the tumor cell from the host immune machinery. Further experiments are needed to test this possibility.

D. Age Distribution of Cells in the Cycle

For the purpose of computing "flow rates" of cells (also termed as "cell fluxes") through various stages in the cycle, one needs to know the expected distribution of population density along the cell cycle and

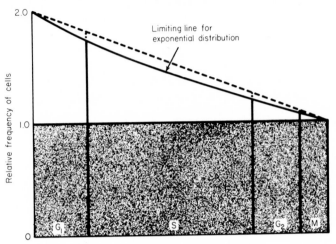

FIG. 2. Age distribution of cells along the cell cycle for two model cell populations. The rectangle (shaded) represents the expected distribution for a steady-state population. The total area, bound above by the continuous line and below by the abscissa passing through zero, represents the distribution for an exponentially growing population, where all cells are in cycle and there is no cell loss. For computational purposes, the upper limiting continuous line may be replaced by a straight line (broken) without introducing any significant error. Relative number of cells in any phase is given by the area limited on two sides by the vertical lines raised at the boundaries. (Adapted from Lala, 1968a by permission of Academic Press, Inc., New York.)

its components. Such distribution depends on the type of population under study. Figure 2 shows the distribution expected for steady-state cell renewal systems as well as for growing cell populations. In an idealized situation, ignoring any fluctuations in the proliferative activity that might cause synchrony, a steady-state system would dictate a rectangular distribution of cells along the cycle, where area represents population density. Frequency of cells in any particular stage of the cell cycle would then be proportional to the duration of the stage. For example:

$$I_M = t_M/t_C \qquad (1)$$

and

$$I_S = t_S/t_C \qquad (2)$$

Birth rate of the proliferating population would then be given by

$$k_B = 1/t_C = I_M/t_M = I_S/t_S \qquad (3)$$

All these relationships would not hold for a growing population. In an ideal expanding population showing exponential growth, where all the cells are in cycle and there is no cell loss, the population density shows a decline with age in the cycle (Fig. 2). Height of the density at the beginning of G_1 is 2 times that at the end of mitosis, because, with completion of each mitosis, two cells appear at the beginning of G_1. If one knows the duration of each phase of the cycle, the relative frequency of cells in each phase can be calculated graphically from the respective areas. The upper-limiting continuous line describes the exponential nature of the distribution. In practice, it hardly makes any difference if this line is replaced by a straight line in the linear plot, as represented by the broken line (Lala, 1968a). This is very helpful in making graphic measurements. As an alternative, the following equations [Eq. (4), Smith and Dendy, 1962; Eq. (5), Dawson and Field, 1964; Cleaver, 1965] may be used (for List of Symbols, see Section I):

$$I_M = t_M \ln 2/t_C \tag{4}$$

$$I_S = \{\exp(t_S \ln 2/t_C) - 1\} \exp(t_{G_2 + M} \ln 2/t_C) \tag{5}$$

Birth rate (k_B) of proliferating cells will then be given by

$$\ln 2/t_C = I_M/t_M \tag{6}$$

If one takes into account the variance in the cycle time and its components within the population, as found in practice, the age distribution during exponential growth slightly deviates from Fig. 2, mainly by lowering the height and producing a tail at the older end of the cycle (Powell, 1956; Sisken and Morasca, 1965) as shown in Fig. 6B (see Section VIII, A). However, for computational purposes, this may be ignored. Theoretical aspects of "age distribution" have been adequately considered by Johnson (1961), Cook and James (1964), Steel et al. (1966), Barrett (1966), and Cleaver (1967).

Practical problems that are faced with tumors are related to the fact that a tumor under study would seldom show a truly exponential growth; even if so, this may not mean that all the cells are in cycle, and there is no cell loss. An exponential growth may be exhibited by a tumor if the proliferating fraction and the rate of cell loss do not change over the period of observation (Lala and Patt, 1966). The effects of growth fraction and cell loss are to a certain extent predictable (Lala, 1968a).

a. Effects of growth fraction (I_P): if the growth fraction is less than unity, it means that with completion of each mitosis, less than two cells are added to the beginning of G_1. This would lower the height of population density at the beginning of G_1. Assuming for the moment that cell loss does not selectively take place from "in" or "out" of cycle, the height at the beginning of G_1, is given by the height at the end of mitosis multiplied by a, where

$$a = 1 + I_P \qquad\qquad (7)$$

(after Steel *et al.*, 1966). With a diminishing I_P, the distribution would approach a steady-state-type distribution, as indicated in Fig. 2.

b. Effects of cell loss from the population: if cell loss occurs at random from "in" or "out" of cycle, no change in the distribution will occur. If cell loss, for example, by death, occurs preferentially at mitosis, the effect would be to lower the height at the beginning of G_1 as in the case of a decline in growth fraction. If cell loss occurs exclusively outside the proliferative compartment, by itself it would have no influence on the distribution, except for changes in the effect of growth fraction as proposed in (a)—more cells would have to leave the proliferative compartment to maintain the growth fraction, and thus would lead to an additional lowering of the height at the beginning of G_1.

Thus, it would seem that the choice of the appropriate distribution of cell density along cycle needs a prior knowledge of parameters such as growth fraction and degree of cell loss. On the other hand, a knowledge of the distribution itself is useful in measuring these parameters. To bypass the dilemma, it may be advisable to use both a steady-state and an exponential distribution for computational purposes and see by how much the two assumptions differ (Lala and Patt, 1966). As a simple guideline, for fast growing tumors the growth of which is nearly exponential, an exponential distribution is acceptable without much error; on the other hand for very slow growing tumors, such as human tumors with long doubling times and a high magnitude of cell loss, as shown by Steel (1967), Refsum and Berdal (1967), and Iversen (1967), a steady-state distribution would be more acceptable.

E. MARKERS OF CELL PROLIFERATION

As already mentioned in the Introduction, two specific markers of the cell cycle are available: (*1*) a morphological marker for mitosis and (*2*) a radioactive marker for DNA synthesis. For radioautographic identification of DNA-synthesizing cells, ^{3}H-thymidine is the label most commonly employed, with ^{14}C-thymidine next in order. Cells in G_1 and G_2 cannot be distinguished except from measurements of nuclear DNA content of individual cells by microspectrophotometric technique. By this means, a proliferating cell population can be separated into three groups: (*a*) cells with G_1 or $2n$ DNA, (*b*) cells with G_2 or $4n$ DNA, and (*c*) cells with intermediate DNA values ($> 2n$ and

$< 4n$). Demarcation between these classes is not sharp, and the distinction can be improved by combining radioautography following ^{3}H TdR labeling in the same population to identify cells undergoing DNA synthesis. If the population represents a mixture of proliferating and nonproliferating cells, the latter cells usually show G_1 DNA values except where some cells may remain in an arrested G_2 phase (Gelfant, 1966). Thus, in a heterogeneous population, such as tumors, showing no morphological distinction between the proliferative and nonproliferative cells, DNA measurement alone is not adequate for structuring the cell cycle. On the other hand, when cell cycle parameters are measured independently, DNA measurement provides valuable information in identifying the status of noncycling cells relative to the cell cycle (Lala and Patt, 1968; Foadi et al., 1967; Frindel et al., 1969).

Application of ^{3}H TdR as a tool for the study of cell population kinetics in vivo needs a number of assumptions which have been explicitly pointed out by Cronkite et al. (1960). These assumptions have been critically reviewed by Cleaver (1967), and most of them are valid for most experimental situations. Three assumptions, the validity of which depends on the experimental situation are worth pointing out.

1. DNA synthesis destines a cell to divide. This has been found true for most normal tissues as well as for malignant tissues. However, a discovery of cells in G_2 arrest (Gelfant, 1966) warrants a critical examination of this assumption in each experiment. Such an arrest could be identified from kinetic data, such as the waves of labeled mitoses after pulse labeling with ^{3}H TdR. A certain degree of very slow DNA turnover, not associated with cell division and possibly indicative of a repair process has been postulated by Pelc (1963, 1964) to account for some labeled-thymidine uptake in nonrenewing or slowly renewing tissues. Even if this hypothesis were true, the degree of labeling is too small to jeopardize kinetic studies with thymidine labeling. In a rapidly renewing tissue, such as bone marrow, the degree of cell proliferation measured either from thymidine labeling index and DNA synthesis time or mitotic index and mitotic time shows a fairly close agreement between the two markers of cell proliferation (Lala et al., 1964).

2. There is no significant reutilization of labeled breakdown products. This is the most questionable assumption of all. Reutilization of thymidine-labeled breakdown products has been shown in vivo (Bryant, 1962; Hill, 1962; Rieke, 1962; Baserga and Kisieleski, 1963; Maruyama, 1964). Such reutilization was easily unmasked from 24 hours onward, following ^{3}H TdR labeling, when doses significantly higher than commonly employed in tracer studies were used (Bryant, 1965). It may be more significant in tumors (Steel, 1966), where the source of

salvage may be dying host cells as well as tumor cells, thus complicating pulse-labeling studies. These complications can be avoided by the use of a tracer dose and attributing less weight to data beyond 24 hours. Appropriate caution has to be exercised in analyzing data from chronic labeling experiments (Mendelsohn and Dethlefsen, 1968).

3. There is no significant radiation injury to cells on account of ^{3}H β-particles. This assumption is not valid above certain doses. For example, doses of ^{3}H TdR greater than 2 μcuries/gm were found to alter the cell cycle time of hepatocytes in growing liver (Post and Hoffman, 1965, 1967). This again, cautions against the use of a large dose.

An additional assumption, the validity of which has been recently subjected to some questions has already been mentioned, namely, that labeled thymidine is incorporated by all cells in the DNA synthetic phase. As has been pointed out, a possible nonlabeling of some cells in this phase does not seem to be of serious significance in most kinetic studies.

F. Growth Fraction

This nomenclature was proposed by Mendelsohn (1960a, 1962a) to denote the fraction of proliferating cells in the population. He introduced the concept that a tumor cell population, in spite of morphological homogeneity, may be heterogeneous in terms of proliferation because of an admixture of proliferating and nonproliferating cells. The growth fraction or the proliferative index (I_P) is an attribute of any cell population and is of particular importance in tumors where no morphological or geographic criteria may exist to distinguish proliferative (cycling) from the nonproliferative (noncycling) population. This parameter and the mean cell cycle time of the proliferating cells jointly determine the proliferation rate. What may be regarded as a direct outcome of the growth fraction concept in tumors are attempts to characterize the noncycling fraction—to understand whether such cells are fertile (G_0) cells or end cells (Lala and Patt, 1966, 1968; Lala, 1968b). Another outcome of the growth fraction concept is a new kinetic parameter proposed by Bresciani (1968)—the cell "distribution ratio," termed as the d ratio. Existence of a nonproliferating fraction in tumors dictates that at the end of each cell cycle, some of the "newborn cells" would leave the cycle and some would reenter the cycle; the d ratio is the ratio between the "recycling number"

$$\overleftarrow{(\eta)}$$

and the "decycling number"

$$\overrightarrow{(\eta)}$$

or η/η at any instant. An unlimited growth can only be generated where the d ratio is > 1. In the absence of changes in other kinetic parameters, such as the cell cycle time, this ratio bears a direct relationship to the growth fraction (I_p).

G. PROLIFERATING CELL VS. STEM CELL IN TUMORS

In normal renewing tissues, "stem" attribute is given to the cell that is capable of extensive proliferation and self-renewal. It may not have the potential for unlimited proliferation, as would be suggested by the clonal succession hypothesis proposed by Kay (1965) and also by the experimental findings of the decaying nature of the survival of successive bone marrow grafts (Barnes and Loutit, 1968). Proliferative ability of a cell in the tumor does not necessarily offer the stem characteristics to all such cells, although at least some proliferating cells must have these attributes for a continuing tumor growth. A knowledge of the stem cell content in a tumor should be an important parameter in constructing models for therapy. Unfortunately, at present there is no general means of directly measuring the degrees of growth potential in the proliferating tumor cells. Several techniques have been used to approach the problem, and some quantitation has been achieved in a number of transplantable rodent tumors.

Tumor cell transplantation using a serial dilution technique (Alexander, 1962) suggested that an average of 1.5 leukemic cells was capable of fatal tumor production in mice, and this finding has been supported by the transplant of a single cell using a micromanipulator for a variety of rodent tumor lines, such as leukemia in mice, Walker carcinoma in rats (Furth and Kahn, 1937; Schabel, 1968), and plasmacytoma in hamsters (Fortner et al., 1961). This would indicate that 100% of the cells in these tumors have stem characteristics. A different approach to measure stem cell content in a number of murine tumors by use of Till and McCulloch's spleen colony technique (Till and McCulloch, 1961) was undertaken in the same laboratory (Bruce and Vander Gaag, 1963; Bergsagel and Valeriote, 1968). This technique ascertains the cloning ability of a cell, and the colony-forming fraction of the population can also be approximated. Based on such studies, Bergsagel and Valeriote (1968) have proposed a model for plasma cell tumor proliferation in mice. Studies using this technique have been extremely valuable in screening chemotherapeutic agents, where a direct comparison can be made between the survival of the hemopoietic colony-forming cell and that of the clonogenic tumor cell (Bruce et al., 1966; Bruce, 1967; Bruce and Valeriote, 1968). Discovery of a G_0 state in some ascitic tumor cells which could revert to cycle (Lala and

Patt, 1968; Lala, 1968b) may be suggestive of a stem attribute; such cells increase in proportion in the older tumor, and are capable of stepping back into active cycle under proper stimulation, such as ascites aspiration and retransplantation. This possibly indicates that, if not all, most cells in this tumor may have the stem cell potential. Such a suggestion has recently been made by Saunders and Mauer (1969) from [3]H TdR-labeling studies of small lymphoblasts in acute leukemia.

Modal chromosome number is sometimes believed to represent the attribute of the stem line in a tumor, less stable chromosomal constitutions arising as a by-product of abnormal divisions; but in some experimental tumors, a definite mode may not be observed or a wide range of chromosome numbers may persist during the tumor growth (Agnish and Federoff, 1968). Several stem lines may coexist.

In partly differentiated tumors, it is sometimes possible to locate zones with succeeding grades of proliferation from [3]H TdR-labeling studies. This would indicate that only a fraction of the proliferating cells may serve as stem cells in such tumors.

H. "RATES" AND RELATED PARAMETERS CONCERNED WITH TUMOR GROWTH

1. Growth Rate (k_G)

Growth rate at any instant is expressed as the rate of expansion of the tumor (population) size per unit time. When growth is exponential, the slope of the growth curve defines the growth rate. However, most tumors do exhibit changes in growth rate with time. In these cases, the tangent to the growth curve at any instant is taken to represent the growth rate, ignoring any change in the growth rate during a very short interval.

Tumor doubling time (t_D) or the time taken for a doubling of the population size is dependent on the growth rate. It is given by the relationship:

$$t_D = \ln 2 / k_G \qquad (8)$$

This parameter usually increases with increase in tumor age. Population doubling time should not be confused with the cell cycle time (t_C), sometimes also referred to as "generation time." Such a confusion is present in many studies—these parameters are identical only when all the cells are proliferating and there is no cell loss.

2. Birth Rate (k_B)

Birth rate or the rate of production of new cells in the population is expressed as the fraction of the population reproduced per unit time.

This can be quantitated from the knowledge of the fraction in DNA synthesis (I_S) and DNA-synthesis time (t_S) or of the fraction in mitosis (I_M) and the mitotic time (t_M). For steady-state, it is given by Eq. (3), and for exponential growth by Eq. (6) (see Section IV, D above).

For a steady-state population, inverse of the birth rate gives the "turnover time." The latter may not be equated with the cell cycle time or generation time, unless all the cells are proliferating. In the case of growing populations, such as tumors, a similar (but not identical) parameter termed "potential doubling time" (t_{PD}) is introduced (Steel, 1968). This is calculated from birth rate from the relationship:

$$t_{PD} = \ln 2/k_B \qquad (9)$$

In the absence of any cell loss this equals the population doubling time (Steel, 1968).

3. Rate of Loss (k_L)

Rate of loss from the population is an important parameter regulating growth. In a large number of earlier kinetic studies in tumors, presence of this parameter was not taken into account. More recently this has been found to be a very significant factor in controlling growth rate in tumors (Lala and Patt, 1966; Steel et al., 1966; Steel, 1967, 1968; Iversen, 1967). It is expressed as the fraction lost per unit time. The only way to measure the overall rate of loss is from the discrepancy between the birth rate and the observed growth rate. Steel (1967, 1968) proposed to express the magnitude of cell loss as a fraction of the birth rate, termed "cell loss factor." This is given by

$$\phi = k_L/k_B \qquad (10)$$

This expression indicates the extent to which the process of cell loss is competing with the process of cell production. For most human tumors, observed clinically, cell loss could represent 54–99% of the production (Steel, 1967; Refsum and Berdal, 1967; Iversen, 1967).

Techniques for measuring the above-mentioned rates and related parameters are discussed later in more detail.

V. Kinetic Models for Tumors

It has already been emphasized that tumor growth is the net result of the balance between cell birth and cell death. Cell birth is influenced by the cycle characteristics of the proliferating cells as well as the growth fraction. Cycling cells, in turn, may not behave uniformly, and may constitute cells with various degrees of growth potential. For simplicity, proliferation may be considered to have two possible components—the stem and the nonstem components. Noncycling fraction, on the other hand, may be visualized to have two possible components—cells with growth potential (G_0) and sterile or end cells (see Fig. 1A). Cell loss (due to death, removal, or migration) may take place to varying extents from all these possible cellular compartments. The goal of an ideal kinetic study is to characterize all these possibilities, although this may not be achieved in practice. Several kinetic models that may be proposed on the basis of a combination of the above possibilities and used in practice are reviewed by Mendelsohn and Dethlefsen (1968):

1. Simple proliferative model. In this case, all the tumor cells are proliferating with a fairly uniform cell cycle and there is no cell loss. Growth is due to cell birth only, and is given by

$$\text{Growth rate } (k_G) = \text{birth rate } (k_B) = \ln 2/t_C \qquad (11)$$

or in other words, tumor doubling time $(t_D) = $ cell cycle time (t_C). This model is not applicable to most existing tumors; transplanted L1210 murine leukemia provides the closest example of this model, as reported by Skipper (1968a) and Schabel (1968).

2. Simple proliferative model with cell loss. In this model the probability of cell loss is added to model 1 and the rate of loss is considered uniform. Growth, in this case is given by

$$k_G = k_B - k_L \qquad (12)$$

in addition,

$$k_B = \ln 2/t_C \qquad (13)$$

3. Growth fraction model with no cell loss. Here the population has a nonproliferating fraction, and growth is represented by

$$k_G = k_B = \ln (1 + I_P)/t_C \qquad (14)$$

In this model the growth fraction (I_P) can be calculated from the knowledge of k_G and t_C (Reiskin and Berry, 1968). However, the assumption of no cell loss does not seem to be justified in most practical situations.

4. Growth fraction model with cell loss. Here the presence of cell loss may be complicated by the various modes of loss. It is often difficult to characterize the loss from the proliferative and the nonproliferative compartments separately and when no distinction is made between them, growth is given by Eq. (12):

$$k_G = k_B - k_L$$

where

$$k_B = \ln (1 + I_P)/t_C \qquad [\text{see Eq. (14)}]$$

A knowledge of k_G, I_P, and t_C allows a measurement of cell loss (Lala and Patt, 1966).

This seems to represent a practical model for most tumors. Within this model, a further analysis of the mode of cell loss is sometimes possible (Steel et al., 1966; Tannock, 1968), and further information on the status of noncycling cells (i.e., sterile or resting) may be obtained as well (Lala and Patt, 1968; Lala, 1968b) leading to appropriate modification of the model. In some instances, cells with proliferative ability may also be further characterized in terms of the fraction of stem or clonogenic cells (Bruce and Vander Gaag, 1963; Bergsagel and Valeriote, 1968).

VI. Tumor Growth Curves

A. SIGNIFICANCE OF GROWTH MEASUREMENT

Measurement of the size of the cell population extended over a period of time gives the most basic information about the tumor—the rate of growth. This parameter not only reflects the rate of the process of tumor expansion but also indicates how constant this process is over a span of the tumor age. Growth of any population, in general, does not remain unchanged. It often exhibits characteristic changes from rapid growth to slow growth and, occasionally, to no growth or even negative growth. A precise knowledge of the changes in growth rate is essential prior to the understanding of the reasons for such changes (Lala and Patt, 1966). Thus the construction of a growth curve is a prerequisite for any kinetic study in an experimental tumor, because a change in the growth rate is brought about by possible changes in three kinetic parameters—the cell cycle time, the growth fraction, and the rate of cell loss. Depending on the type of tumor, one or more of these parameters may exhibit characteristic changes with tumor age (Lala and Patt, 1966; Lala, 1968b, 1970b; Frindel et al., 1967, 1969; Lamerton and Steel, 1968; Wiebel and Baserga, 1968). Thus a measurement of any of these parameters in a tumor loses its significance without reference to the growth curve.

Although a growth curve is in most cases not obtainable in a human tumor, a crude measurement of the tumor growth rate over a short span is sometimes feasible. Such an estimate is needed for computing the rate of cell loss from the tumor (Lala and Patt, 1966; Steel et al., 1966; Steel, 1967, 1968). On the other hand, when growth can be quantitated for a relatively longer span, it may provide some crude information about growth rates in the past and predict the future by extrapolation.

B. Techniques for Quantitation of Tumor Growth

Precise growth measurement becomes increasingly difficult in the order from transplanted to induced to spontaneous animal tumors and is most difficult in the human situation. Techniques will be discussed in this order.

1. Transplanted Tumors

In transplanted tumors, one can control the inoculum size and an appropriate number of cells have to be used as well as a proper site has to be selected for inoculation. Transplantation techniques have been adequately considered in another volume (Liebelt and Liebelt, 1967) and will not be discussed here. In the case of solid tumors, tumor volume and tumor weight are the directly measurable parameters and these may sometimes be related to the approximate number of tumor cells. A very precise quantitation of the cell number is possible only in ascites tumors.

a. *Ascites Tumors.* Ascites tumor growth in mice following intraperitoneal inoculation of an appropriate number of tumor cells is easily measurable. Most commonly used inoculum sizes range from 10^6 to 10^7 cells, although other doses may be employed depending on the type of study. With 10^6 Ehrlich ascites tumor cells (near tetraploid line) inoculated into a 25-gm mouse, the animal survives about 2 weeks. Total number of tumor cells may be quantitated by aspiration of the total tumor with repeated washing of peritoneal space and performing the tumor cell count in the total volume of aspirate (Klein and Révész, 1953). As an alternative, an accurate measurement of the ascites volume may be obtained by a dye-dilution technique after intraperitoneal injection of a known concentration of Evans blue in a known volume of cell-free ascitic plasma (Patt *et al.*, 1953). A correction of total tumor cell counts from appropriate differential counts for the presence of nontumor cells is important, especially during early growth following a small inoculum size. A 25-gm mouse may contain 4–7×10^6 free, large nontumor cells (peritoneal and monocytic cells) in the peritoneal space (Lala and Patt, 1966). A typical growth curve for an Ehrlich ascites tumor in mice is presented in Fig. 3.

b. *Solid Tumors.* Measurements on solid tumors can be made in two ways: volume measurements and weight measurements. Volume measurement is the simplest way of obtaining a tumor growth curve by using a small number of animals. Volumes are calculated from measurements of three tumor dimensions, excluding skin thickness with vernier calipers, using appropriate formulas as dictated by the shape of the tumor, e.g., a sphere or an ellipsoid (Hermens and Barendsen,

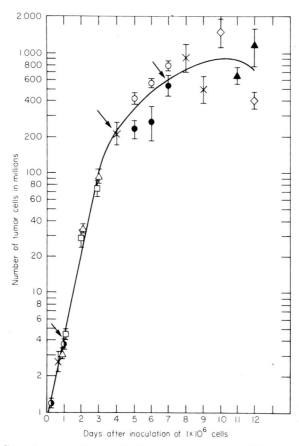

FIG. 3. Growth curve for an Ehrlich ascites tumor (with nearly tetraploid amount of deoxyribonucleic acid in postmitotic cells) in mice obtained with inoculation of 10^6 cells. Each point represents an average of tumor cell counts in 6 animals at sacrifice. Vertical lines indicate ± 1 standard error. Each symbol refers to growth with inocula from the same tumor donor. Arrows indicate stages chosen for kinetic studies. (Reproduced from Lala and Patt, 1966, courtesy of the National Academy of Sciences, U.S.A.).

1967; Dethlefsen *et al.*, 1968). With appropriate corrections, these volumes may also be converted into weights. Alternatively, one can measure the largest and the smallest superficial tumor diameters, and their products can be converted into tumor weight with appropriate calibration curves from pilot studies (Steel *et al.*, 1966). Various means of plotting data from caliper measurements have been used in different studies, such as plots of longest diameters (Mayneord, 1932), mean diameter (Brues *et al.*, 1939), tumor area (Mottram, 1935), or product of three dimensions (Hunter, 1955).

In small animals, such as mice, sacrifice of a large number of animals for constructing a growth curve from direct weight measurements of carefully dissected out tumors may not represent a problem. Such a growth curve is shown in Fig. 4 for solid tumors, obtained by subcutaneous inoculation of 10^7 Ehrlich ascites tumor cells into the thigh of mice.

Quantitation of cell number is extremely difficult in solid tumors. No cell dispersion technique is satisfactory enough for quantitation purposes. An assay procedure for total tumor cell number using

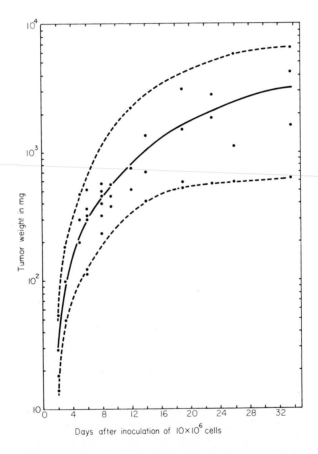

FIG. 4. Growth curve for solid tumors obtained with subcutaneous inoculation of 10^7 Ehrlich ascites tumor cells in the inner aspect of the thigh of mice. Inocula were obtained from a 7-day ascites tumor. Each animal had a single tumor that was dissected out and the weight of the freshly isolated tumor is represented by a single point. The continuous line is drawn to represent the best visual fit to the mean values. The dotted lines represent the upper and the lower limits in the growth curve.

[125]I-labeled iodouridine deoxyriboside (IUDR) in mice has been reported (Van Putten, 1968). In the author's laboratory, a 24-hour trypsinization procedure in cold, essentially the same as used in cell dispersion for monolayer culture (Merchant *et al.*, 1964), appeared to give a reasonably quantitative dispersion of tumors weighing between 0.5 to 10 gm. For tumors plotted in Fig. 4, 1 gm approximately represented 1.2×10^8 tumor cells. Cell dispersion techniques for obtaining viable cells are also available for use in quantitative transplantation studies with solid tumors (Reinhold, 1965; Carney and Malmgren, 1967).

In transplanted tumors, a variety of factors related to the tumor or the host may result in differences in the growth curves. Factors related to the tumor are size of the inoculum (Patt and Blackford, 1954; Lala, 1968b), occasionally age of the donor tumor that might influence the viable fraction, tumor subline or ploidy (Biczowa *et al.*, 1968), and generation of the transplant (Maruyama and Knuth, 1966; Frindel *et al.*, 1969). The host factors are strain of the host responsible for various degrees of immunological differences, age and even sex of the host (Vincent and Nicholls, 1967), and site of transplantation (Eichten and Maruyama, 1968).

2. Induced and Spontaneous (Solid) Tumors

Methods are the same as for the transplanted solid tumors, except for the fact that one has to be satisfied with the volume measurements only. The time parameter in the growth plot of a single tumor is expressed as the interval from the first measurement (Mendelsohn, 1965; Dethlefsen, *et al.*, 1968).

3. Human Tumors

For tumors in an accessible region, caliper measurements of dimensions would give the data on tumor volume. Radiological measurements have been made for growth evaluation in inaccessible areas. Of these, radiological shadows of metastatic lung carcinoma have been most extensively used for obtaining growth curves (Collins *et al.*, 1956; Collins, 1962; Schwartz, 1961; Spratt and Spratt, 1964; Spratt, 1965). Similar measurements have also been performed for primary lung tumors (Schwartz, 1961; Garland *et al.*, 1963; Spratt *et al.*, 1963). Radiological shadows of tumors in other areas, such as breast (Ingleby *et al.*, 1960), colon and rectum (Welin *et al.*, 1963), and skeleton (Spratt, 1965) have also been used for this purpose. The rate of change of gonadotropin production by trophoblastic tumors, such as chorionic carcinoma, is considered to provide an index of tumor growth (Bagshawe, 1968).

Steel and Lamerton (1966) have reviewed the existing data on growth rates in human tumors and concluded that the widely used practice of extrapolating assumed growth curves back to deduce the time of induction may not be justified.

C. MATHEMATICAL EXPRESSIONS FOR TUMOR GROWTH

In a conventional presentation of the tumor growth curve, the tumor size is plotted on a semilogarithmic scale against time. In most growth curves published so far, such a plot does not generate a straight line throughout the growth period, indicating a nonexponential nature of the growth. An exponential fit, if ever observed, is usually limited to the early growth period, following which a deceleration in growth is usually seen. A variety of mathematical formulations have been attempted to fit all or most of the growth curves in a large number of tumors, with the hope that a single mathematical expression should be able to discover the past history of growth or predict the future growth in an individual tumor.

Mayneord (1932) suggested that a continuous deceleration in the growth rate of a solid tumor can be expressed by a straight line fit of the tumor diameter or the cube root of the tumor volume against time. This expression was supported by Schrek (1935, 1936) and Haddow (1938) and was also used to explain ascites tumor growth by plotting the cube root of cell number against time (Klein and Révész, 1953). Patt and Straube (1956) observed that ascitic tumors gave a better fit to an exponential growth during the early stage, whereas a cube root fit could explain only the middle part of growth. Laird (1964, 1965) attempted to improve upon these expressions by proposing a modified exponential law of growth in which successive doublings occurred at increasingly longer intervals. The increase in the doubling times was more rapid than explained by an exponential law and was better represented by a Gompertz function. The mathematical expression of such function was given by

$$W/W_0 = \exp\left[A/a\,(1\text{-}\exp\,at)\right] \tag{15}$$

where W = tumor size at time t, W_0 = initial tumor size, and A and a are Gompertz constants. A is related to the initial slope of the growth curve and a is a retarding factor. The ratio A/a determines the number of tumor doublings before the growth curve reaches an asymptote. For a truly exponential growth, a is equal to zero and the function reduces to

$$W/W_0 = \exp At \tag{16}$$

Laird measured Gompertz constants for a variety of tumor growth curves reported in literature. A Gompertz function was also used by McCredie *et al.* (1965) and has been found to be applicable in other tumors (Dubin *et al.*, 1967). Curves presented in Figs. 3 and 4 can also be adequately explained by a Gompertz function.

An altogether different approach has been used by Mendelsohn and his associates (Mendelsohn, 1963; Dethlefsen *et al.*, 1968; Mendelsohn and Dethlefsen, 1968) who supposed that tumors of different types and under different circumstances could grow in different ways, for example, exponentially or as a cube root function or even linearly. They devised an expression that could explain such flexibility in behavior. Mendelsohn (1963) proposed the following equation:

$$dV/dt = kV^b \qquad (17)$$

where dV/dt is the growth rate, V is the tumor volume, k is a growth constant, and the exponent b defines the mode of growth. An integration of the above differential equation yields a growth function with three constants:

$$V^{1-b} = (1 - b)(kt + c) \qquad \text{when } b \neq 1 \qquad (18)$$

and

$$V = c \exp kt \qquad \text{when } b = 1 \qquad (19)$$

where c is proportional to the initial volume.

It is clear from Eq. (19) that for $b = 1$, dV/dt is proportional to V, or the growth becomes exponential. When $b = 0$, $dV/dt = k$ and growth is linear. When $b = 0.67$, the growth assumes a cube root function. In practice, any other value of b between 0 and 1 is possible, although most solid tumors exhibit a value of b nearer to 0.67 or a fit to a cube root function. To make an appropriate estimate of the exponent b, these authors used the help of a computer to generate a best straight-line fit of the normalized tumor volumes raised to the power $(1-b)$ plotted against time, as dictated by Eq. (18). They found that b was equal to 0.61 in the C3H mouse mammary tumors.

VII. Techniques for Quantitation of Tumor Cell Survival

For an evaluation of the effect of therapeutic agents on tumors, one needs to assay the survival or killing of tumor cells following exposure to such agents. This would permit a construction of dose–survival curves or an examination of the influence of cellular environments such as oxygen tension on tumor cell survival (Van Putten, 1968; Brown and Berry, 1968b). Essentially two techniques are available for quantitating the survival of transplantable tumor cells; both measure the survival of cells with tumorogenic or clonogenic capacity rather than the whole tumor population. Such information is valuable, because a therapist is primarily interested in the survival of cells that can reproduce a tumor.

A. TD_{50} TECHNIQUE

This is a technique of titration of tumor cells *in vivo* in which a serial dilution is employed to obtain inocula of different sizes, and the cell number required to produce 50% tumor-takes (TD_{50}) is calculated (Hewitt, 1953a,b; Hewitt and Wilson, 1959). This technique has been very effectively used in the measurements of tumor cell survival following irradiation (Hornsey and Silini, 1961a,b, 1962; Hewitt and Wilson, 1961; Kallman *et al.*, 1967; Van Putten, 1968; Kallman, 1968). Brown and Berry (1968b) have reviewed the dose–response curves for a large number of murine tumors irradiated under oxygenated or anoxic conditions.

The technique is summarized as follows. A single cell suspension of viable tumor cells is made in an appropriate medium (such as ice-cold Tyrode solution) to give a known cell concentration. The mother suspension is then serially diluted to give graded doses of inocula in a fixed volume. Several sites may be used for inoculation in one isogeneic host, several animals are used for each dilution, and a wide range of dilutions should be used to cover both sides of the expected TD_{50}. Animals are now observed over an appropriately long period for identifiable tumor-takes. A statistical estimate (Van Putten, 1968) of the TD_{50} is then made from the plot of percentages of tumor-takes against dose. Survival fraction of clonogenic tumor cells following exposure to an agent is given by the ratio TD_{50} (control)/TD_{50} (exposed).

B. SPLEEN COLONY TECHNIQUE

This technique is the same as originally used by Till and McCulloch (1961) for bone marrow cells and its application is limited to a number of murine tumors such as lymphomas, plasma cell tumors, and leukemia. Bruce and Vander Gaag (1963) extended this technique to assay clonogenic ability of murine lymphoma cells, and since that time it has been used to assay radiation survival (Bush and Bruce, 1964), to compare therapeutic effects on hemopoietic stem cells and clonogenic tumor cells in mice (Bruce and Meeker, 1965; Bruce *et al.*, 1966; Bruce and Valeriote, 1968), or to study growth and proliferation kinetics of tumor cells (Bergsagel and Valeriote, 1968; Wodinsky *et al.*, 1967).

Mice are injected intravenously with appropriate doses of tumor cells in single cell suspension and sacrificed at about a week following injection for scoring visible colonies on the surface of the spleen. There is a direct relationship between the inoculum size and the colony number;

it is also known that each colony is the result of cloning from a single cell. Thus the survival fraction of colony-forming tumor cells following exposure to various agents can be measured from the colony counts only following inoculation of a fixed cell number.

C. OTHER TECHNIQUES

Techniques other than above are not always as precise, although useful in many circumstances. The host survival time may be used as an index of the inoculated number of clonogenic tumor cells over a certain range of numbers, assuming that the tumor cells double at fixed intervals and kill the host when a critical cell population size is attained. These assumptions seem to be fairly valid over a practicable range of inocula in the case of a few murine tumors, such as L1210 leukemia (Skipper *et al.*, 1964; Skipper, 1968a; Schabel, 1968; Wodinsky *et al.*, 1967) and LSA ascitic lymphoma (Maruyama and Brown, 1964). A standard calibration curve may be obtained by injecting a range of inoculum sizes prepared by serial dilution and registering the host survival time with the tumorogenic doses. This may then be used as a reference to estimate the survival fraction in an experimental population of cells. Another technique may also be used to assay the surviving fraction, although such assay may not estimate the "clonogenic fraction." When a reproducible tumor growth curve can be obtained with a known inoculum size, and the curve extrapolates at zero time to the inoculum size, such extrapolation of growth curves obtained with treated tumor cells should give the viable number in the inoculum and the survival fraction can be calculated from this number.

The L1210 leukemia cells that permit a readily interchangeable growth *in vivo* and *in vitro* have been used for screening chemotherapeutic effects on survival *in vitro* (Wilkoff *et al.*, 1967, 1968a,b). Cell survival has been also estimated from their colony-forming ability in a soft agar gel (Himmelfarb *et al.*, 1967)—a method which might be comparable to the spleen colony technique *in vivo*.

VIII. Measurement of Cell Cycle Characteristics

A. ESTIMATION OF CELL CYCLE AND COMPONENTS

1. *"Labeled Mitosis" Technique*

This is the most widely used technique and it produces the largest amount of information about the cell cycle and its components available from one single study. The principles of cell cycle analysis from this method were introduced by Quastler and Sherman (1959) and are based on the fact that the duration of the mitotic phase is much shorter than the duration of DNA synthesis. In an asynchronous population having cells distributed throughout the cell cycle (see age distribution diagram, Fig. 2), cells in the S phase are labeled by a pulse-exposure to ^3H TdR, and the progression of this labeled cohort of cells is followed through the mitotic phase. Labeled thymidine, administered by intravenous or intraperitoneal route, is available for incorporation into the DNA-synthesizing cells only for less than an hour in most mammals (Hughes *et al.*, 1958; Rubini *et al.*, 1960; Chang and Looney, 1965). The availability time has also been found to be short in tumors (Staroscik *et al.*, 1964; Lala and Patt, 1966), thus allowing a "pulse" of labeling which is reasonably short compared to the S period, and for practical purposes may be taken as "instantaneous." A plot of the percentage of mitotic figures labeled at different time intervals following ^3H TdR injection generates a curve from which the cell cycle duration and its components can be measured.

In an idealized population of proliferating cells showing no variation in progression through the cell cycle, the percentage of labeled mitoses plotted against time would generate periodic trapezoid-shaped waves as indicated in Fig. 5A, and the phases can be measured as follows:

t_{G_2} = interval between ^3H TdR injection and the appearance of the first labeled mitotic figure

t_M = interval occupied by the ascending limb of the curve
= interval occupied by the descending limb of the curve

t_{S+L} = interval occupied by the plateau plus the interval occupied by the ascending or the descending limb, where L represents the length of the pulse-labeling. In practice, L is ignored

$t_{G_1+G_2}$ = interval between the zero points of the descending limb of the first wave and ascending limb of the second wave plus the duration of the pulse (t_L). The t_L is ignored in actual measurements

In practice, such ideal waves are seldom found because of various degrees of spread in phase durations which produce damping of the curves as indicated in Fig. 5B. This figure represents the actual measurements in the inner zone of tumor cords in a transplanted mouse mammary tumor (Tannock, 1968). Because of variations in G_2 phase, the ascending limb seldom reflects the mitotic duration only. Changes in slopes of the ascending limb of the first wave indicate the variations in progress through $G_2 + M$, and similarly changes in slopes of the descending limb represent variations in progress through $S + G_2 + M$. Construction of such slopes is often helpful in estimating the variances in the cycle phases (Cleaver, 1967).

Durations of the cycle phases as well as their degree of spread can be computed from an analysis of labeled mitosis curves by assuming

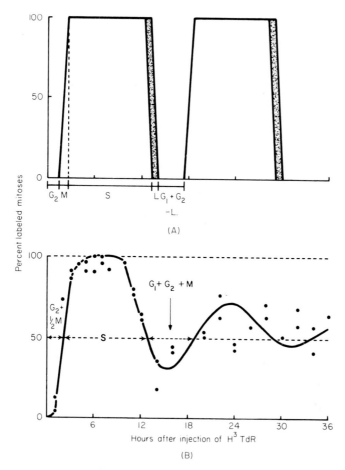

FIG. 5. Percentage of labeled mitoses as a function of time after a pulse label of ^{3}H-thymidine (TdR). (A) Ideal case for population with no intercell variation in the rate of progression through cell cycle. L = length of pulse labeling. This is short enough to be ignored in practice. For further explanation see text. (B) Actual case for tumor cells in the inner zone (nearest to the vascular supply) of the tumor cords in a mouse mammary tumor. The continuous line represents the best fit to the data, obtained with a computer assuming a log-normal distribution of the cell cycle phases. Median durations of the cell cycle and its phases are measured from the 50% intercepts in the waves (see text). (Redrawn from Tannock, 1968, courtesy of the author and the *British Journal of Cancer*.)

various types of statistical distributions such as normal (Quastler and Sherman, 1959), log-normal (Barrett, 1966), and Pearson Type III (Takahashi, 1966). The smooth line in Fig. 5B is a computer fit of the data assuming a log-normal distribution of the cycle phases. The distribution of cell cycle times obtained from Fig. 5B is shown in Fig. 6A, and the age distribution of cells in various cycle phases is plotted in Fig. 6B. From the last-mentioned figure, one can compare the expected exponential distribution (in the absence of variations in cycle phases) with the observed distribution. The largest variation is exhibited by cells in G_1.

There is some experimental evidence, primarily from *in vitro* observa-

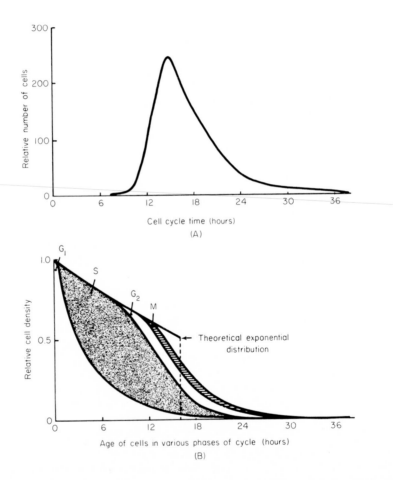

FIG. 6. (A) Distribution of the cell cycle times, computed from data in Fig. 5B. (Reproduced from Tannock, 1968, courtesy of the author and the *British Journal of Cancer.*) (B) Actual age distribution of cells along the cell cycle computed from data in Fig. 5B, compared to a theoretical exponential distribution. (Redrawn from Tannock, 1968, courtesy of the author and the *British Journal of Cancer.* Distribution in M phase is added to the original diagram, assuming 1 hour mitotic time.)

tions, against a normal distribution of cycle times. Sisken and Morasca (1965), using cinemicrographic techniques in exponentially proliferating human amnion cells observed that the generation time distribution was skewed to the right and the reciprocals of generation times or the rates of progress of cells through the cycle were normally distributed. A normal distribution of generation rates rather than times was also reported for bacteria (Kubitschek, 1962, 1966) and has also been found to give a best fit to the ^{3}H TdR-labeling data in rat bone marrow (Lord, 1968). Implications of a normal distribution of "rates" rather than "times" inkinetic studies have been discussed in detail by Quastler (1963).

Curves for labeled mitoses have received elaborate mathematical treatments by cell kineticists (Barrett, 1966; Takahashi, 1966; Trucco and Brockwell, 1968; Bronk, 1969; Bronk et al., 1968). The last-named authors suggested that rather precise information is available for the cycle time distributions from the decay in synchrony of the peaks of labeled mitosis waves.

Sophisticated mathematical treatments are not, however, always practicable or necessary for obtaining the basic information. Irrespective of the type of possible distribution, one can always measure the median times and also make some approximation of the minimum and maximum times by a visual analysis of the curves. These are given as follows:

median $t_{G_2 + (1/2M)}$ = interval from ^{3}H TdR administration to the 50% labeling point in the ascending limb of the first wave

median t_S = interval between the 50% labeling points in the ascending and descending limbs of the first wave

median $t_{G_1 + G_2 + M}$ = interval between the 50% labeling points in the descending limb of the first wave and ascending limb of the second wave

median t_C = interval between the 50% labeling points in the ascending limbs of the first and the second waves. It may also be measured as the interval between the midpoints of the plateaus for the first and the second waves

minimum t_{G_2} = interval between ^{3}H TdR injection and the appearance of the first labeled mitosis

minimum t_S = interval between the appearance of the first labeled mitosis and the onset of decline of the first plateau

minimum t_C = interval between the appearance of the first labeled mitosis and the onset of the second rise (indicating the second wave)

maximum $t_{G_2 + M}$ = interval between the ^{3}H TdR injection and the attainment of first maximum (in the ascending limb of the first wave) maximum t_C = interval between the attainment of first maximum (in the ascending limb of the first wave) and the attainment of a second maximum (in the ascending limb of the second wave)

Approximations of the minimum and the maximum durations of the cell cycle as indicated above are valid only when the variations affect all the phases of the cycle uniformly and are not compensatory in nature among the various phases.

Estimates of median times from Fig. 5B are $t_C = 16$ hours, $t_{G_1} = 3$ hours, $t_S = 10.7$ hours, and $t_{G_2 + M} = 2.3$ hours.

In some studies plateaus may be ill-defined and waves may show peaks rather than plateaus. In such cases, cell cycle time is best measured by the interval between the first and the second peak. In addition, the area under the first peak should measure the time of DNA synthesis (Mendelsohn, 1965). A plot of the median or mean grain count over the mitotic figure may also be helpful in such cases. The grain counts also show periodic waves for two reasons, namely, a declining ^{3}H TdR availability during the pulse-labeling time and a frequently observed higher DNA synthesis rate at the middle part of S (see Section IV,B, 2). In such cases, the interval between the two successive peaks in the grain count should give an approximate value of the cell cycle time.

2. Grain Count Halving Technique

In the absence of an adequate number of mitotic figures to construct labeled mitosis curves, grain counts on the interphase cells are sometimes employed to estimate the cell cycle time. At the outset, it should be mentioned that there are many pitfalls in this technique that may not always be coped with in practice and thus may lead to erroneous estimates. It should not be taken as a substitute for the labeled mitosis technique. It is assumed that number of grains over an individual cell is halved at mitosis, so that halving time for the average or median grain count should indicate the duration of the cell cycle (Killmann et al., 1963). However, the first halving of the labeled population takes place in less than one generation, as the labeled cells go through $S + G_2 + M$. Following this, however, halving should take place at intervals of a cell cycle time. Although in theory this seems sound, there are several practical problems. For example, weakly labeled cells, after division, may give rise to false negatives and artificially prolong the halving time. To compensate for such an artifact, appropriate corrections have been proposed (Killmann et al., 1963; Fried, 1968). Another problem is the effect of reutilization of label in any long-term experiment. This would artificially raise the grain count and prolong the halving time. An additional problem arises from the fact that certain cell populations, such as bone marrow cells or leukemic cell populations, may show a diminution of cell size in succeeding generations. For this reason, the initial average grain counts in the successive classes of proliferating cells may not be identical simply on account of the cell geometry. A larger precursor cell shows a higher grain count, and, in consequence, the grain count of the next generation of cells would not halve in one cycle time. This again may lead to an artificially long halving time. Finally, the most significant factor that may invalidate the technique in most tumor cell populations as well as leukemias is the possible existence of a continuous transition of cells from the proliferating to the nonproliferating state. Over the period of observation a significant number of labeled cells may move into a nonproliferative state and be retained in the population. As these cells may not be separable from the proliferating labeled population on morphological basis, the grain count halving time may again be artificially prolonged. In spite of the proposed refinements in computation of the generation time from a grain count halving (Fried, 1968), application of this technique to tumor cell populations may be of limited use, and many estimates of cell cycle time in tumors reported in literature using this technique may represent overestimates. The limitations and applicability of this technique have been discussed in a later publication by Fried (1969).

3. Repeated or Continuous Labeling Technique

This is a technique most suited to studies *in vitro* of tissue culture systems, where ^{3}H-thymidine can be left in the medium over a prolonged period for a continuous labeling of the cells synthesizing DNA (Yamada and Puck, 1961). For its application *in vivo*, one either needs to infuse ^{3}H TdR continuously into the circulation (Maloney *et al.*, 1962) or to give repeated injections of ^{3}H TdR at intervals shorter than the S period to label all the cells synthesizing DNA for a prolonged interval. The main drawback is that the total dose of ^{3}H TdR to be used may affect the kinetic characteristics because of irradiation of the nuclei with tritium β-rays (see Section IV,E).

Following a continuous or repeated labeling with ^{3}H TdR of growing cell populations such as tumors, a clear estimate of the cell cycle duration is possible only if all the cells in the population are proliferating. In such a case, 100% labeling of the total population will be achieved in a time equal to the combined duration of $G_2 + M + G_1$; 100% labeling of the mitotic figures is obtained in a period equal to the duration of $G_2 + M$. From the above two estimates, one can measure the duration of G_1 by subtraction. The S period may now be measured in three ways.

a. The flash-labeling index, registered at a short interval, for example, 0.5–1 hour following the initial administration of ^{3}H TdR, would give the fraction of the population in DNA synthesis (I_S). Now I_S, t_{G_1}, and

$t_{G_2 + M}$ as measured above should enable one to estimate the duration of S and hence, the whole cell cycle time, from a simple graphical technique using the age distribution diagram in Fig. 2. In this figure, the trapezoid represents the exponential distribution of cells in the cycle, area represents the relative number of cells in a particular phase, and the phase durations are given by approximate boundaries on the abscissa. Actual G_1 and $G_2 + M$ times may be used in this diagram to select an appropriate length of S period that would satisfy the agreement between the observed I_S and the graphically determined I_S. A similar, although not the same, simplified graphic approach has been reported by Okada (1967).

b. The S period can also be measured independently by a grain-counting procedure following continuous labeling (Maloney *et al.*, 1962). Maximal amount of labeling of a cell during one replicative cycle is related to a single replication of the total DNA content of the nucleus during the S period. Thus a saturation of grain count in an average cell would be achieved in a time equal to the S period. However, the passage of some labeled cells through mitosis during the experimental period would lead to some label dilution; besides, the labeled population will contain cells that might have begun or completed DNA replication during the labeling interval, and thus, lead to a less than maximal labeling. For these reasons, a plateau in the average grain count of labeled cells will be attained when the labeled population will contain predominantly those cells that have replicated the whole DNA content in the presence of label. As a result, the time taken for the saturation of an average grain count may overestimate t_S to a small extent. To avoid this error, Maloney *et al.* (1962) plotted the grain count of the "representative" cell rather than the average or median grain count. The representative cell was a cell sampled from the grain count distribution plot, which was separated from the "maximally" labeled cell by a fixed number of cells, but appreciably to the right-hand side of the cell with the median grain count. Such a correction may not be essential, as the accuracy achieved by this correction may be masked by other factors such as biological variations and possible radiation effects.

A crude estimation of the S period is also possible from the rate of increase of the labeling index, before a labeled cell goes through mitosis, i.e., during an interval $t_{G_2 + M}$. Such an estimate is ideally applicable to a steady-state population. The rate of increase in labeling $(\Delta I_L / \Delta t)$ indicates the rate of movement of cells into DNA synthesis. Thus, in a steady-state population having a rectangular distribution of cells along the cycle,

$$t_S = \frac{I_S}{\Delta I_L / \Delta t} \tag{20}$$

In an exponentially growing population, initially, when unlabeled cells in G_2 would go through mitosis, the population shows an increase in unlabeled cells, together with an increase in labeled cells due to a movement of cells into S. Since such a population contains more young cells than old, as indicated by the age distribution diagram (Fig. 2), the rate of entry into S exceeds the rate of cell division; thus there is a net increase in the labeling index. Following an interval longer than the duration of $G_2 + M$, the rate of increase of I_L should be slightly enhanced. However, in practical situations, such changes are barely noticeable, and a crude estimate of t_S may be made from Eq. (20). This equation would be more valid when a continuous or repeated labeling is combined with administration of colchicine or its derivatives to arrest the dividing cells in mitosis. Such a combination is not always practicable *in vivo* for a prolonged period and is ideally suited for application in tissue cultures. It has already been emphasized that the total duration of the cell cycle is obtainable by a continuous labeling in tumors provided that all the tumor cells are proliferating. This condition is seldom satisfied in most tumor cell populations. However, when this technique is combined with the labeled mitosis technique, valuable information is available regarding the proliferating fraction as well as the mode of cell loss.

Figure 7A,B,C represent the curves for labeling indices of tumor cells with time in a repeated ³H TdR-labeling experiment in three different zones of a tumor cord in a mouse mammary tumor (Tannock, 1968). The inner zone, which was nearest to the blood vessel, had the highest proliferative activity (all the cells appeared to be proliferating). The labeled mitosis curve for this zone has been presented in Fig. 5B, which indicates a 16-hour long cell cycle. However, this is the median cycle time, which showed a considerable spread in the distribution, as indicated in Fig. 6A. The maximum length of $G_2 + M + G_1$ was closer to 24 hours, as shown in the age distribution of cells in different phases (Fig. 6B). A 100% labeling is achieved during this interval (Fig. 7A) as expected, but it is quite clear from this illustration that no data about the mean or median length of $G_2 + M + G_1$ are obtainable from repeated labeling when variations in these phases are considerable. The median length of $G_2 + M + G_1$ measured from the labeled mitosis curve (Fig. 5B) was approximately 5.3 hours. Repeated labeling curves for the middle (Fig. 7B) and outer zones (Fig. 7C), which showed a cell cycle time fairly similar to that for the inner zone with the labeled mitosis technique, do not show 100% labeling during a 24-hour interval, indicating the presence of nonproliferating cells.

4. Double-Labeling Technique

Double labeling of a cell population with ³H-thymidine and ¹⁴C-thymidine has been widely used to estimate the duration of DNA

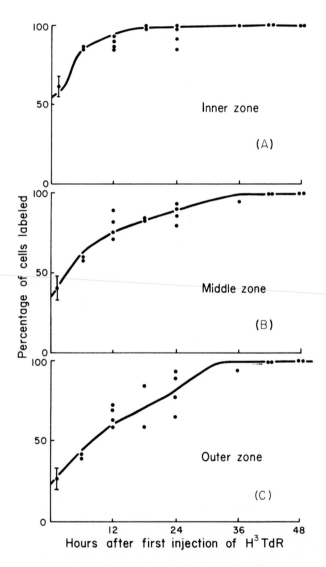

FIG. 7. Percentages of labeled tumor cells in three different zones (A, B, and C) of the tumor cords in a mouse mammary tumor observed after repeated labeling with ³H-thymidine (TdR). The zones represent regions in order of increasing distance from the vascular supply. Points represent experimental data and the plotted curves are predicted by assuming 100% proliferation (inner zone), 80% proliferation (middle zone), and 50% proliferation (outer zone). (Reproduced from Tannock, 1968, courtesy of the author and the *British Journal of Cancer*.)

synthesis (Pilgrim and Maurer, 1962, 1965; Wimber and Quastler, 1963; Baserga and Lisco, 1963; Lala *et al.*, 1965; Lala, 1968a; Kesse-Elias *et al.*, 1967; Ohkita, 1967; Vincent *et al.*, 1969). A long-term double labeling may also be used to estimate all the cycle phases (Wimber and Quastler, 1963), but such a study would offer little advantage or precision over the labeled mitosis technique. The discussion here will be limited to the application in the measurement of t_S of the commonly used technique of labeling cells with ^{3}H TdR followed at short intervals by ^{14}C TdR.

The use of this technique depends on the differential energy ranges of the β-particles emitted by ^{14}C and ^{3}H. The average energy of tritium β-particles is 5.5 keV and the average traveling distance is 0.5μ (Baserga, 1967); hence, silver grains produced by ^{3}H are localized over the nucleus on a plane immediately superficial to the nucleus. β-rays from ^{14}C have an average energy of 15 keV and an average traveling distance of 10μ, producing tracks beyond the nuclear boundary, and the grains are localized at various planes over the nucleus in a radioautogram having a sufficiently thick emulsion. These features permit the differentiation of cells labeled with ^{3}H only from the cells labeled with ^{14}C or ^{14}C $+$ ^{3}H (see Fig. 8). The latter two groups are not easily distinguished in most preparations, and for practical purposes are combined into one group, i.e., cells containing ^{14}C.

Of the several double-labeling experiments for measuring the S period, a method suitable for some tumor materials is illustrated here. This is a combined *in vivo–in vitro* technique that measures cell fluxes through DNA synthesis *in vivo*, and thus the DNA-synthesis time in a cell population labeled with ^{3}H TdR *in vivo* and at short intervals later with ^{14}C TdR *in vitro*. Initially this was applied to canine and human bone marrow cells (Lala *et al.*, 1965) and later extended to ascites tumor cells (Lala, 1968a). In brief, samples of cell population obtained at short intervals following an *in vivo* pulse-labeling with ^{3}H TdR are given a pulse exposure (10–15 minutes) to ^{14}C TdR *in vitro* in a suitable medium at 37°C. Under proper experimental conditions, with viability of cells well preserved, the *in vitro* flash-labeling index of cells shortly after sampling agrees well with the *in vivo* flash-labeling index, although the rate of synthesis *in vitro* may be appreciably altered (Lala *et al.*, 1965; Lala and Patt, 1966; Lala, 1968a). Thus cells labeled with ^{3}H only in the doubly labeled population at short intervals ($\leqslant t_{G_2 + M}$) following the ^{3}H TdR injection give a measure of the flux out of DNA synthesis, whereas the difference between the overall labeling indices *in vivo* and *in vitro* indicates the flux into DNA synthesis. In a steady-state system (with a rectangular type of age distribution of cells along the cycle), the fraction of the cohort in S that has moved out of DNA synthesis during an interval is given by

$$F_O = N_{^3\text{H}}/N_{^{14}\text{C}} \tag{21}$$

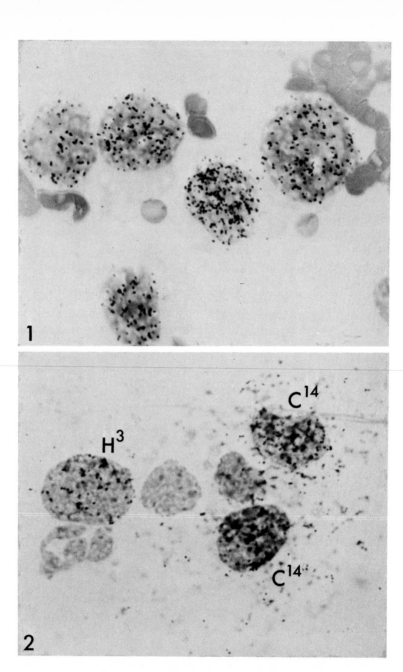

Fig. 8. (1) Radioautogram of Ehrlich ascites tumor cell nuclei labeled with ³H TdR, stained with Giemsa. (Magnification: ×1500.) (2) Radioautogram of a smear of bone marrow from a chronic myeloid leukemia patient showing double labeling. Marrow was aspirated 0.5 hour following intravenous injection of ³H TdR and incubated *in vitro* with ¹⁴C TdR for 15 minutes. Two myelocyte nuclei (right) are labeled with ¹⁴C (or ¹⁴C and ³H) and one myelocyte nucleus (left) is labeled with ³H only. The latter must have moved out of DNA synthesis during the interval between labeling *in vivo* and labeling *in vitro*. Stained with Giemsa. (Magnification: ×1500.)

where N_{3H} = number of cells labeled with ^{3}H alone after *in vitro* incubation with ^{14}C TdR and N_{14C} = number of cells labeled with ^{14}C or ^{14}C + ^{3}H in the same radioautogram. Similarly the fraction that moved into DNA synthesis during an interval is given by

$$F_I = \frac{I_L \ (vitro) - I_L \ (vivo)}{I_L \ (vivo)} \qquad (22)$$

where $I_L \ (vitro)$ = the overall labeling index postincubation with ^{14}C, and $I_L \ (vivo)$ = the labeling index preincubation with ^{14}C.

A plot of F_O and F_I with time after ^{3}H TdR injection provides the rates of movement out of DNA synthesis (k_O) or into synthesis (k_I), expressed as fraction of the S cohort per unit time. In a steady state, the DNA-synthesis time is then given by (Lala *et al.*, 1965)

$$t_S = 1/k_O = 1/k_I \qquad (23)$$

In a slowly growing tumor, where the age distribution along the cycle may be close to a steady state rather than an exponential, information from the doubly labeled population may only be used [Eq. (21)] to measure the S period. However, several samplings at more than one interval ($\leqslant t_{G_2 + M}$) after ^{3}H TdR injection should provide more precise information than would be obtainable from a single sample by averaging the variations in the cell fluxes through S.

In fast growing tumors, where steady-state equations are not applicable, appropriate corrections are needed. Since there are more young cells than old along the cycle in a growing population, influx into S is greater than efflux from S; thus a measurement of t_S is underestimated by the influx and overestimated by the efflux. A graphic solution for t_S was derived for growing populations from the knowledge of labeling indices in samples before and after incubation with ^{14}C TdR (Lala, 1968a). A corrected flux through DNA synthesis (F_C) was derived from such data, given by the equation:

$$F_C = \frac{N_O + N_I}{N_S + N_{S'}} \qquad (24)$$

where N_S = ^{3}H index preincubation with ^{14}C; N_O = ^{3}H index postincubation with ^{14}C; $N_{S'}$ = ^{14}C index (having ^{14}C or ^{14}C + ^{3}H) postincubation to ^{14}C; and N_I = $N_{S'} + N_O - N_S$.

Equation (24) is valid for any asynchronously growing cell population irrespective of its rate of growth, having growth characteristics anywhere between an exponential and a steady state. Figure 9 illustrates a plot of F_C with time in an Ehrlich ascites tumor in mouse at two different stages of growth. The duration of DNA synthesis (inverse of the slope) was 5.8 hours for the 1-day tumor and 20.4 hours for the 7-day

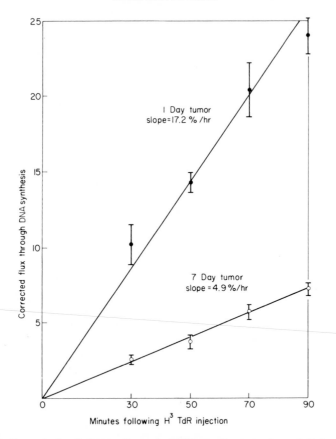

FIG. 9. Corrected cell fluxes through DNA synthesis in 1- and 7-day ascites tumors obtained with intraperitoneal inoculation of 10^6 cells in mice, computed from double labeling with ³H-thymidine (TdR) *in vivo* and ¹⁴C TdR *in vitro*. (Reproduced from Lala, 1968a, by permission of Academic Press, Inc., New York.)

tumor. These estimates were close to previously derived values of 6 and 18 hours, respectively, by using the labeled mitosis technique.

This technique may be of potential use in human tumors, where the information on the DNA synthetic index (I_S), DNA-synthesis time (t_S), and birth rate (k_B) are all obtainable from a single experiment requiring one injection of ³H TdR followed by one or several biopsies. All the information needed for Eq. (24) might be obtained from a single radioautogram of the sample postincubation with ¹⁴C TdR, if one could distinguish with precision the cells with ¹⁴C only from the cells with ¹⁴C + ³H, in addition to the cells with ³H only. Although techniques for making such distinctions have been described (Baserga and Lisco,

1963; Baserga, 1967), it has not been possible to apply them with confidence, and the author does not recommend them to beginners. To differentiate cells with ^{3}H only from those with ^{14}C $+$ ^{3}H, on the other hand, is easy enough to be handled by a beginner after a moderate amount of blind practice with control slides having ^{3}H only, ^{14}C only, or both ^{3}H and ^{14}C.

5. Stathmokinetic Technique

a. Estimation of Mitotic Time and Mitotic Rate. The use of agents to arrest mitosis for a determination of mitotic time and rate is one of the very old tools in kinetic studies. This technique has been reviewed by Dustin (1959) and is only infrequently employed now because more quantitation is possible with labeled thymidine. Practical difficulties in the use of mitotic arresting agents *in vivo* have been pointed out by Tannock (1967).

In a steady state, the mitotic index (I_M) at any interval following the application of a mitosis-arresting agent, such as Colcemid, is the result of accumulation of cells in mitosis during this interval. This is given by the following equation (where mitosis excludes anaphase and telophase):

$$I_M(t) = I_M(0) \left[1 + t/t_M \right] \qquad (25)$$

where $I_M(t) =$ mitotic index at time t after a complete mitotic blocking; $I_M(0) =$ initial mitotic index; and $t_M =$ mitotic time.

Mitotic time, calculated from the above equation is given by

$$t_M = I_M(0) \cdot t/[I_M(t) - I_M(0)] \qquad (26)$$

During exponential growth, this equation becomes

$$t_M = I_M(0) \cdot t/\ln 2\,[I_M(t) - I_M(0)] \qquad (27)$$

A knowledge of the mitotic index (I_M) and mitotic time (t_M) in any tissue permits the calculation of the birth rate, given by $k_B = I_M/t_M$, as already indicated in Eqs. (3) and (6).

b. Combination of ^{3}H TdR Labeling with Mitotic Arrest for Estimation of Cell Cycle Components. Continuous labeling in the presence of Colcemid has been employed in tissue cultures to estimate the duration of cell cycle phases from an analysis of the rates of accumulation of labeled and unlabeled cells in mitosis (Puck and Steffen, 1963; Puck *et al.*, 1964). This technique is most suited for application to ascitic tumors. Methods of analyses using this technique have been elegantly reviewed by Cleaver (1967) and will not be discussed here. An identical technique has been used *in vivo* by Maekawa and Tsuchiya (1968) for a direct estimation of G_1, G_2, and S phase. Assuming that Colcemid does not

influence cellular kinetics except for blocking in metaphase, this technique appears to possess the elegance of being able to distinguish between a long G_1 and the G_0 phase. An essentially similar technique was
employed by Lala (1968b), when a double-labeling was considered more
useful than a repeated labeling, combined with a mitotic block. Maekawa
and Tsuchiya (1968) employed repeated injections of ^{3}H TdR to imitate
a continuous labeling along with repeated injections of Colcemid at
proper intervals to maintain a long-term mitotic block. Colcemid
prevents an influx of cells into G_1, except for the short duration of
anaphase–telophase, but an outflow of cells from G_1 into S is not prevented. Such flow would result in the decline of the fraction of unlabeled cells in the population. When all the G_1 cells have moved into S,
no further decline would be observed, and a plateau should be attained.
Thus, the span of the decline should equal the G_1 interval. During the
plateau phase, the fraction of unlabeled population should represent the
cells initially present in G_2 + metaphase, if all the cells are proliferating.
Then, if the plateau is followed for a sufficiently long interval, all the
unlabeled cells should be in metaphase and no unlabeled interphase cells
should be seen. On the other hand, if unlabeled interphase cells are seen,
their fraction in the population should give a measure of the nonproliferating fraction. Another feature which was not pointed out is the
fact that a population having a distinct fraction of cells in a prolonged
G_1 rather than G_0 should show this by a slowly declining plateau rather
than a true plateau in the absence of a preferential cell loss from the G_0
stage. It should be emphasized that validity of all these computations
depends on two assumptions: (1) that the mitotic block is complete and
(2) that there is no loss of arrested metaphases by degeneration. The
latter may not always be true *in vivo*.

For measuring the durations of S and G_2, Maekawa and Tsuchiya
(1968) employed a single pulse of ^{3}H TdR and repeated injections of
Colcemid. The ratio of labeled to unlabeled *interphase* cells was plotted
against time. With the movement of cells in G_2 phase into M, this ratio
should rise for a time equal to the G_2 period and then decline because of
a progressive shortening of the sector in interphase that represented S.
The rate of this decline represents the rate of progress of S cohort into
the mitotic phase and, hence, the inverse of the slope of this decline
should estimate the S period.

A technique combining pulse-labeling with ^{3}H TdR and mitotic
blocking with Colcemid has also been reported by Kollmorgen *et al.*
(1967) for cell cycle analysis in cultured Chinese hamster cells. They
combined several series of cultures, in which the thymidine pulse and
the mitotic block were separated by varying intervals. For details of the
analysis, interested readers are referred to the original report.

6. Cellular DNA Measurements for Identification of Cells in Various Cycle Stages

Microspectrophotometric estimates of DNA in the nuclei of individual cells permit a placement of the cells in various cycle stages:

a. Cells with Postmitotic DNA Content (2n). This DNA value is shown by proliferating cells in G_1 or by postmitotic nonproliferating cells. The latter cells may either be sterile or may contain cells in a state of proliferative rest (G_0). Additional tools are needed to distinguish various classes of cells in this category.

b. Cells with DNA Values between Postmitotic and Premitotic Modes $(> 2n < 4n)$. These are cells in DNA synthesis. When ^{3}H TdR-labeling is combined with DNA measurement to identify the cells synthesizing DNA, one can examine the possibility of an arrest of DNA synthesis in cells. An arrest of this type has been reported for megaloblasts in pernicious anemia (Yoshida et al., 1968), but has not been observed in a few studies on tumors (Cooper et al., 1966; Lala and Patt, 1968).

c. Cells with Premitotic DNA Content (4n). Proliferating cells in G_2, cells arrested in G_2 phase (Gelfant, 1966), or mitotic cells before chromosomal segregation have such DNA values. To distinguish between the cycling G_2 cells and the cells in arrested G_2, one needs to combine appropriately prolonged ^{3}H TdR-labeling and a stimulus for mitosis in the arrested cells. A flow from the unlabeled G_2 population entering mitosis under stimulus should lower the labeling index of the mitotic figures. In one line of Ehrlich ascites tumors, a suppression of host immune apparatus with antilymphocyte serum seemed to provide a stimulus for the movement of resting G_2 cells into mitosis (De Cosse and Gelfant, 1968).

Problems peculiar to tumor cells are often encountered in the interpretation of DNA measurements owing to the presence of aneuploidy or polyploidy. Since the diploid DNA content of normal cells can not be used in such cases as a reference for the G_1 DNA value of tumor cells, the G_1 mode has to be established from DNA measurements in the single pole of anaphases and telophases. Similarly, the G_2 mode can be obtained from measurements in prophases and metaphases. Cells with multiple ploidy, however, are difficult to assign to one category or the other. For example, a tetraploid cell in G_1 cannot be distinguished from a diploid cell in G_2. Fortunately, the proportion of polyploid cells is usually low in most tumors.

In a population where all the cells are proliferating, a flash-labeling with ^{3}H TdR combined with DNA measurement in unlabeled nuclei might be useful in measuring the cell cycle phases if one could measure the duration of at least one cycle phase, such as S, independently. Then, one would simply use the age distribution diagram (Fig. 2) to place the relative cell number in appropriate stages and derive the duration of the cycle phases from the abscissa. As an alternative, one could also use the graphic technique described by Okada (1967). In tumors containing nonproliferating cells, an independent measurement of the cell cycle phases, for example, by labeled mitosis technique along with DNA estimates would provide valuable information on the DNA content of nonproliferative cells, when a knowledge of the growth fraction is available (Lala and Patt, 1968; Frindel et al., 1969). As will be discussed later, the growth fraction is measurable from the data obtained with a labeled mitosis experiment, and thus does not require any additional study.

Figure 10 illustrates the distribution of DNA content in a population of Ehrlich ascites tumor cells on the seventh day of ascitic growth following inoculation of 10^6 cells. Duration of cycle phases as well as the growth fraction had already been measured in this tumor, and this permitted the placement of noncycling cells in the proper DNA category. It was found that the noncycling cells had a G_1 DNA value. These cells were found to be in a resting state and under proper stimulation, re-entered the cycle by moving into DNA synthesis (Lala and Patt, 1968).

Deoxyribonucleic acid measurements seem to offer a promising area in human tumors. Although an estimate of the duration of cell cycle stages is not possible with this technique, information about the frequency of cells in various cycle stages may be valuable in formulating a therapeutic rationale with stage-specific antimetabolites. Cooper and his colleagues have performed studies on a number of human tumors, such as lymphomas, leukemia, Burkitt's tumor, and bladder carcinoma (Cooper et al., 1966, 1968; Foadi et al., 1967; Levi et al., 1969). Studies on DNA content have also been performed to understand the cell kinetics during carcinogenesis (Simard et al., 1968).

B. Measurement of Growth Fraction

Growth fraction or the proliferative index (I_P) of a tumor cell population was first measured by Mendelsohn (1962a). Any measurement of growth fraction assumes two compartments in the population under study—proliferating and nonproliferating cells. Such clear separation is only possible if the proliferating cells have a fairly uniform cell cycle time. If, on the other hand, the population contains some cells with very long cycle times that cannot be measured with conventional techniques, they are apt to be classified as nonproliferating. Thus, estimates of growth fraction by any of the techniques to be discussed below may, in some circumstances, represent the proportion of relatively fast cycling cells in the population rather than all the cycling cells. Despite the

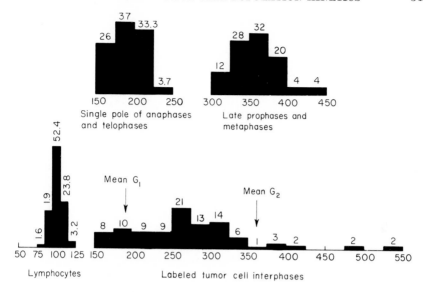

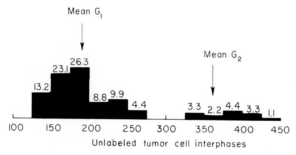

FIG. 10. Deoxyribonucleic acid (DNA) contents (abscissa) of cells in a 7-day ascites tumor obtained with an inoculum of 10^6 cells. The units are arbitrary with lymphocyte mean normalized to 100. Numbers on the top of histograms indicate the frequency in percent of the cell class under consideration. The tumor cells were collected 0.5 hour after an injection of ^{3}H-thymidine. Following DNA measurement in the Feulgen-stained nuclei with a two-wavelength technique, the smears were processed for radioautography to identify the cells synthesizing DNA. (Reproduced from Lala and Patt, 1968, by permission of Blackwell Scientific Publications, Oxford.)

limitations of such a "two-compartment" model, the growth fraction concept has been valuable in recognizing the presence of nonproliferating or slowly proliferating cells in a tumor (Lamerton and Steel, 1968).

Growth fraction may be represented as the ratio of the number of cycling cells (N_C) to the total cell number (N):

$$I_P = N_C/N \qquad (28)$$

This equation may be rewritten

$$I_P = (N_S/N)/(N_S/N_C) \qquad (29)$$

where N_S/N is the proportion of DNA-synthesizing cells in the population given by the flash ^{3}H TdR-labeling index; N_S/N_C indicates the fraction of the cycling cells in DNA synthesis. This value may either be determined experimentally from the labeled mitosis technique (Mendelsohn, 1962a) or from the knowledge of the cell cycle time (t_C), DNA-synthesis time (t_S), and age distribution of cells within the cycle as indicated in Fig. 2 (Lala and Patt, 1966). As an alternative, the value of N_C/N [Eq. (28)] may be directly measured by a repeated labeling technique (Mendelsohn, 1962b, 1965). Methods of estimating growth fraction are presented below.

1. Labeled Mitosis Technique

As indicated in Fig. 5b, successive waves of percentage of labeled mitoses after ^{3}H TdR injection damp out because of a variation in the duration of the cell cycle stages. Eventually, the percentage of labeled mitoses reaches an equilibrium value when the periodicity is completely lost due to a desynchronization of the labeled cohort. Such an equilibrium value would then give a measure of N_S/N_C [see Eq. (29)] since mitosis is an attribute of the cycling population only. On the other hand, N_S/N is given by the labeling index of the whole population, so that growth fraction can now be estimated from Eq. (29). Since measurements are made at an interval sufficiently long for the loss of synchrony of labeled cohort, Mendelsohn (1962a) introduced a correction to compensate for the growth of the population during the interval. If the measured I_P at an interval t following ^{3}H TdR injection is represented by $I_P(t)$, it was shown that, for an exponentially growing population, a semilogarithmic plot of $1 - I_P(t)$ against t gave a straight line. The I_P at time zero was then measured from an extrapolation of the straight line to time zero.

The advantage of this technique is that the cell cycle stages as well as the growth fraction can be measured from the same experiment. However, there are two limitations, besides the ones discussed at the beginning, which may result from the "waiting period" needed for the estimate. One is the possibility of label-dilution below threshold due to cell division, leading to some false negatives in the radioautograms; the second limitation might result from a possible reutilization of the label, which may occur to a significant extent in tumors at later intervals (Steel, 1966).

2. Technique of Computation from the Knowledge of Cell Cycle Stages

The ratio N_S/N_C can be computed in a population if the measurements on t_C and t_S are available, for example, from the labeled mitosis technique. For a steady-state population, where the age distribution of cells along the cycle is rectangular, this ratio is given by t_S/t_C. For an exponentially growing population, where duration of all the components of the cycle are known, N_S/N_C may simply be determined graphically from Fig. 2, given by the ratio of the area representing S to the area representing the total cycle (Lala and Patt, 1966). As an alternative, this can also be computed from the relationship presented in Eq. (5):

$$N_S/N_C = \{\exp(t_S \ln 2/t_C) - 1\} \exp(t_{G_2 + M} \ln 2/t_C)$$

The ratio N_S/N is given by the flash ^{3}H TdR-labeling index and, thus, I_P can be estimated from Eq. (29).

Major limitations of this technique are the general limitations discussed at the beginning. Since a choice of the type of age distribution of cells in the cycle influences the estimate of I_P, one can calculate the maximum possible error by comparing the estimates from a steady-state and an exponential distribution; the true value of I_P must be limited by these estimates (Lala and Patt, 1966).

3. Repeated Labeling Technique

A continuous or repeated labeling procedure with ^{3}H TdR to label all the cells passing through the S phase may be used to estimate I_P if some knowledge of the cell cycle is available. Ideally, such a labeling procedure should label all the cycling cells in a time equal to the maximum duration of $G_2 + M + G_1$. The fraction of labeled cells (I_L) at this interval should give a measure of the growth fraction. Although a measurement of the median duration of $G_2 + M + G_1$ is available from the labeled mitosis technique, the maximum duration cannot be measured with precision. For this reason, growth fraction is often measured as the labeling index obtained at the end of a "prolonged" labeling period (Clarkson et al., 1965), longer than the average duration of the cell cycle.

Besides the general limitations common to all techniques, there is an additional drawback. In a cell population where there is a continuous transition from the dividing to a nondividing state, a fraction of the nondividing population will also be labeled, the extent depending on two factors—the duration of labeling procedure and the life-span of the nonproliferating cells. With prolonged labeling, all the cells in the population may eventually be labeled whether in or out of cycle if nonproliferating cells are lost by some aging process. Thus this technique is very prone to overestimate the growth fraction. When the cell cycle components have been measured by an independent method, the repeated labeling should provide some insight into the mode of cell loss in a tumor (Steel et al., 1966).

Data on repeated labeling in Fig. 7A,B,C may again be examined in the light of the above discussion. The maximum duration of $G_2 + M + G_1$ for cells in the inner zone of the tumor cords is about 24 hours, as indicated in Fig. 6B by the age distribution diagram of cells in cycle. Nearly 100% labeling is achieved during this time, indicating an upper limit of the growth fraction. As the cell cycle components were not appreciably different in the middle and the outer zones of tumor cords, an upper limit for I_P may be calculated as 0.9 in the middle zone (Fig. 7B) and 0.8 in the outer zone (Fig. 7C) from repeated labeling data. However, calculations from the data reported on this tumor (Tannock, 1968) using technique 2 (above) give approximate values of 0.7 and 0.5, respectively, in these zones. Labeling of the outer zone of the tumor was complicated by the fact that there was some migration of nonproliferating cells from the middle to the outer zone. By taking this additional factor into consideration, Tannock (1968) approximated I_P for the middle and the outer zones as 0.8 and 0.5, respectively.

IX. Measurement of Rates and Related Parameters

A. GROWTH RATE

Practical difficulty in measuring the growth rate of a tumor arises from the fact that the growth rate varies with tumor age. However, as an approximation, one may assume an exponential growth for a brief period, and growth rate at any instant is then given by the slope of the tangent drawn to the growth curve. Alternatively an exponential growth could be assumed for one doubling time (t_D) of the tumor and growth rate during the interval may be expressed as

$$k_G = \ln 2/t_D \tag{30}$$

It will be seen later that in calculation of other rates, such as rate of birth and rate of cell loss, a similar assumption of exponential growth is frequently made as an approximation.

B. BIRTH RATE

Methods for computation of the birth rate for a proliferating population of cells have already been discussed in Section IV, D. For a mixed population containing nonproliferating cells, a knowledge of the growth fraction (I_P) would also be necessary to calculate the birth rate from cell cycle time. In a steady-state condition the birth rate is given by

$$k_B = I_P/t_C \tag{31}$$

For an exponential growth (without cell loss or a random cell loss), this is given by

$$k_B = \ln (1 + I_P)/t_C \tag{32}$$

When mitotic index (I_M) and mitotic time (t_M) or flash ^{3}H TdR-labeling index (I_S) and DNA-synthesis time (t_S) are known, the same equations as deduced in Section IV would hold, as the indices are now measured for the whole population. Thus, for a steady state,

$$k_B = I_M/t_M = I_S/t_S$$

as given in Eq. (3), and for an exponential growth [see Eq. (6)],

$$k_B = I_M/t_M$$

The potential doubling time (t_{PD}) indicates the growth potential of a tumor in the absence of cell loss and is given by [Eq. (9), Section IV]

$$t_{PD} = \ln 2/k_B$$

This should equal the observed doubling time (t_D) only when there is no cell loss from the tumor.

C. Rate of Cell Loss

This is measured from the discrepancy between the birth rate and the observed growth rate in a tumor (Lala and Patt, 1966; Steel, 1967, 1968). Assuming an exponential growth for a brief observed interval, the rate of cell loss expressed as the fraction lost per unit time is given by

$$k_L = k_B - k_G \tag{33}$$

When t_C, I_P, and t_D are known, replacing k_B and k_G from Eqs. (32) and (30),

$$k_L = \ln (1 + I_P)/t_C - \ln 2/t_D \tag{34}$$

This equation was used by Lala and Patt (1966) and Lala (1968b) for measuring cell loss in an ascitic tumor at different stages of growth. The rate did not change appreciably except during the terminal stage of tumor growth.

As an alternative, Eq. (6) may be used to measure k_B and, subsequently, k_L from the knowledge of I_M and t_M. Birth rate is also measurable from the rate of inflow of cells into mitosis following the use of mitotic arresting agents. With this technique, cell loss was calculated in several human tumors (Refsum and Berdal, 1967; Iversen, 1967).

Steel (1967, 1968) developed some equations to measure the birth rate from the knowledge of I_S and t_S and, subsequently, the rate of cell loss as in Eq. (33). In a growing cell population, the steady-state equation (3) cannot be used as such for a computation of the birth rate from the knowledge of I_S and t_S. For a precise estimate, one needs a correction factor that depends on the position of S phase within the cycle as well as the growth fraction. Considering these facts, Steel deduced a relationship that may be applied to approximate the degree of cell loss from tumors. For details the readers are referred to the original papers, and the principles are summarized here.

Equation (33) may be rewritten

$$k_L = \ln 2/t_{PD} - \ln 2/t_D \qquad (35)$$

where t_{PD} is the potential doubling time and t_D is the observed doubling time.

The potential doubling time may be deduced from the relationship:

$$t_{PD} = \lambda t_S/I_S \qquad (36)$$

where λ is a correction factor, the precise value of which depends on the knowledge of I_P and the position of S phase in the cycle. Theoretically λ may range from $\ln 2$ to twice $\ln 2$, i.e., from 0.693 to 1.386. In practical situations, where the duration of $G_2 + M$ is relatively short compared to other phases in the cycle and growth fraction is low, the value is closer to 0.693.

The "cell loss factor" was defined as the ratio of the rate of cell loss to birth rate:

$$\phi = k_L/k_B$$

(Steel, 1968) as given in Eq. (10). This may also be expressed in terms of t_D and t_{PD} by substituting k_L and k_B from Eqs. (35) and (9):

$$\phi = 1 - t_{PD}/t_D \qquad (37)$$

The advantage of this expression is that the time parameters (potential and true doubling times) are conceptually easier to follow than the rate parameters in a tumor. Expression of cell loss as a fraction of cell production possesses the elegance of indicating the degree of loss of growth potential by the tumor. A high cell loss factor is found both in experimental as well as in human tumors (Steel, 1967, 1968; Refsum and Berdal, 1967; Iversen, 1967).

Cell loss, as measurable from the above-mentioned relationships, does not provide any information about the mode of loss. In the anatomical sense, cell loss may be represented by cell death, removal by exfoliation, or migration by metastasis. In most tumors, cell death seems to represent the major pathway. In the kinetic sense, a loss could take place in various ways—at random or by some age-specific or other means from different compartments in the population. Repeated labeling technique seems to be the only promising way of obtaining some insight into these modes of loss when combined with the information on the duration of cell cycle stages, growth fraction, and the rate of cell loss. Such data may be used to obtain a best fit for labeling indices expected from the assumption of different modes of loss, such as (a) by an age-specific process from the nonproliferating population, (b) by loss at mitosis, and (c) by a random process from anywhere in the population (Steel et al., 1966). In addition to measurement of the overall labeling indices with the repeated labeling procedure, estimates of the labeling indices for pyknotic tumor cell nuclei may provide additional information about the nature of loss. Such estimates in the Ehrlich ascites tumor suggested some mitotic death in addition to death from the nondividing compartment (Lala, 1970a).

X. Illustration of Kinetic Studies

A large number of studies on tumor cell population kinetics has been performed to obtain information on one or more kinetic parameters with various objectives in view.

A. UNDERSTANDING THE CONTROL MECHANISMS IN TUMOR GROWTH

This is the broadest defined objective in studies of tumor cell kinetics. Although in reality, any kinetic study is relevant to an understanding of the process of tumor growth, studies on transplanted tumors are most appropriate toward achieving this objective, because only in transplanted tumor can the experimental conditions be controlled as well as manipulated.

The significance of the measurement of various kinetic parameters in a tumor with the available techniques mentioned in this chapter may be best illustrated by describing in brief some pertinent experiments performed on a single tumor. Several relatively complete studies on transplanted tumors are available now, and the one chosen for illustration here was performed in the author's laboratory (Lala and Patt, 1966, 1968; Lala, 1968a,b, 1969, 1970a,b).

The Ehrlich ascites tumor in mice was studied as a model system to elucidate the cytokinetic mechanisms controlling growth of tumor cell populations. This tumor line had a near-tetraploid DNA mode in the post mitotic cells, and the modal chromosome number of metaphases was 68; two large metacentric markers were found. The tumor was maintained by a weekly passage of 10^6 cells into the peritoneal space of Swiss albino female mice weighing about 25 gm. Studies in this tumor may be conveniently outlined by posing a number of specific questions and discussing in brief the attempts to answer them.

1. What Are the Reasons for a Retardation in the Growth Rate with an Increase in Tumor Mass?

There are three notable features in the growth dynamics as observed from the growth curves (Figs. 3 and 11): (a) Growth starts without any lag. (b) The initial rapid phase, which may be fitted to an exponential growth, is followed by a continuing decline in the growth rate. Within the limits of the standard errors, the growth may be fitted equally well to a Gompertz function. (c) Growth rate at any instant is dictated by the population size, irrespective of tumor age. For instance, inocula of 10^6, 20×10^6, and 50×10^6 cells (Fig. 11) resulted in initial tumor-doubling times (t_D) of 10.5, 16, and 18 hours.

A deceleration in the growth rate associated with an increase in tumor mass (attributable either to an increase in age or an increase in the inoculum size) may result from one or more of the three possibilities:

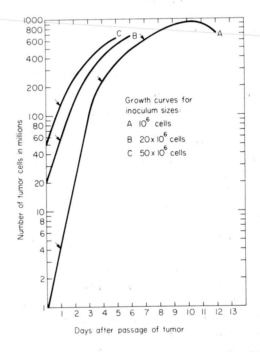

Growth curves for inoculum sizes:

A 10^6 cells

B 20×10^6 cells

C 50×10^6 cells

Number of tumor cells in millions

Days after passage of tumor

FIG. 11. Growth curves for Ehrlich ascites tumor in mice obtained with three different inoculum sizes. Arrows indicate the stages chosen for measurement of kinetic parameters. (Reproduced from Lala, 1968b, by the courtesy of IAEA, Vienna.)

(a) a prolongation of the cell cycle time (t_C), (b) a decline in the growth fraction (I_P), and (c) an increase in the rate of cell loss (k_L) from the tumor. These possibilities were evaluated by measurement of t_C, I_P, and k_L at different stages of tumor growth (indicated by arrows in Fig. 11).

The duration of the cell cycle and its component stages was measured by the labeled mitosis technique. Curves for percent labeled metaphases and anaphases following injection of ^{3}H TdR are presented in Fig. 12 for tumors of three different ages obtained with a standard

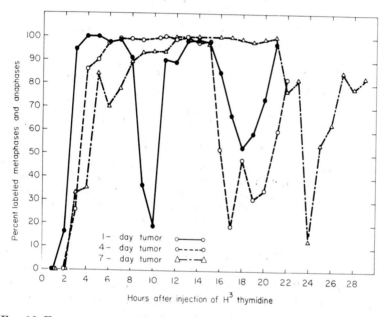

FIG. 12. Frequency of labeled metaphases and anaphases as a function of time after ^{3}H-thymidine injection into ascites tumors of three different ages, derived from an inoculum of 10^6 cells. Each point is an average of data from three animals at sacrifice. (From Lala, 1968b, courtesy of IAEA, Vienna.)

inoculum of 10^6 cells, and in Fig. 13 for tumors of the same age (1 day) obtained with three different inoculum sizes: 10^6, 20×10^6, and 50×10^6. Median durations of the cell cycle and its components computed from these curves show a prolongation with an increase in the tumor size (see Table I). The cell cycle showed no measurable G_1 at any stage of growth, and a prolongation of S period was fairly proportional to the prolongation of the total cycle. An increase in the duration of S was also confirmed by the double-labeling technique (Lala, 1968a; see also Fig. 9).

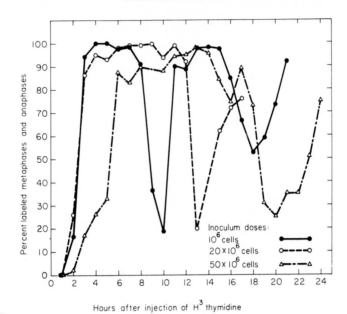

Hours after injection of H^3 thymidine

Fig. 13. Frequency of labeled metaphases and anaphases at different times after ³H-thymidine injection into 1-day-old ascites tumors obtained with three different doses of inoculum. Each point is an average of data from 3 animals at sacrifice in the case of 10^6 and 20×10^6 cells, and 2 animals in the case of 50×10^6 cells. (From Lala, 1968b, courtesy of IAEA, Vienna.)

Values for I_P at all these stages of growth were measured from the knowledge of the durations of cell cycle stages assuming an exponential distribution of cells within the cycle (Section VIII, B, 2) and are presented in Table I. These values were in some instances verified by repeated labeling for a period equal to the maximum duration of $G_2 + M + G_1$. The latter technique gave slightly higher values possibly because of some transition of labeled cells from the proliferative to the nonproliferative state. The growth fraction declined with an increase in tumor size (see Table I). Because of a proportionate lengthening of S period compared to the cell cycle time, the decline in growth fraction with tumor age paralleled the decline in the flash ³H TdR-labeling index (Fig. 14).

The rate of cell loss was measured at different stages from the discrepancy between the expected growth rate (computed from the cell cycle time and the growth fraction) and the observed growth rate (computed from the growth curve) from Eq. (34). The values are presented in Table I. There was no appreciable change in the overall rate of loss

TABLE I

KINETIC PARAMETERS AT DIFFERENT STAGES OF ASCITES TUMOR
DEVELOPMENT[a]

Parameter	Following inoculation of 10^6 cells			One-day tumors obtained with inocula of	
	1-day tumor	4-day tumor	7-day tumor	20×10^6 cells	50×10^6 cells
Cell population size (millions)	4.2	200	600	56	130
Doubling time (hours)	11	40	120	18	28
Duration (hrs) of cell cycle and components					
C	8	17	22	12	17.7
G_1	b	b	b	b	b
S	6	13	18	10	13.2
$G_2 + M$	2	4	4	2	4.5
Growth fraction[c]	0.82 ± 0.02	0.67 ± 0.02	0.53 ± 0.02	0.75 ± 0.03	0.71 ± 0.03
Rate of cell loss (hr^{-1})	0.012	0.013	0.014	0.008	0.006
Cell loss factor	0.16	0.43	0.72	0.18	0.20

[a] From Lala (1968b).
[b] Inappreciable.
[c] Mean ± 1 standard error.

with increasing age up to 7 days. However, during the terminal period
of growth (days 12–15, not shown in the table), there was a significant
increase in this rate, mostly due to cell death, which on occasions
exceeded the rate of production, resulting in a negative slope in the
growth curve. Further attempts to characterize the mode of loss from
repeated labeling experiments in older tumors indicate two important
pathways for cell loss: (a) mitotic death—represented morphologically
by fragmented pyknotic nuclei, which show a labeling pattern fairly
similar to that in mitotic cells, and (b) age-specific loss of nondividing
cells. The latter appeared to be the major pathway for cell death in this
tumor.

It may be concluded from the above experiments that a retardation
in the growth rate with increasing tumor mass essentially results from a
progressive lengthening of the mitotic cell cycle as well as from a
decline in the growth fraction; an increase in the rate of cell loss
becomes contributory only in the terminal stage.

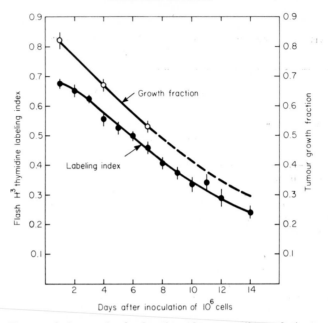

Fig. 14. Temporal changes in the fraction of tumor cell population engaged in DNA synthesis in the Ehrlich ascites tumors obtained with inoculation of 10^6 cells. Changes in the growth fraction follow a parallel course. (From Lala, 1968b, courtesy of IAEA, Vienna.)

2. What Is the Status of Noncycling Cells? Are They Sterile or in a State of Proliferative Rest?

It has been observed that the noncycling cells can be induced to cycle again under appropriate stimuli such as retransplantation into new hosts or aspiration of a significant fraction of the tumor. Both these procedures lead to a prompt rise in the growth fraction. It rises to near unity in transplants obtained with smaller inocula (1–20 × 10^6 cells), whereas the growth curve extrapolates back to the inoculum size, indicative of a recycling of most of the nonproliferating cells. Thus the noncycling cells seem to remain in a state of proliferative rest (G_0).

3. At What Stages Do Cells Decycle or Recycle?

It was found that both the decycling as well as recycling occurred only after completion of mitosis and before DNA synthesis, i.e., in a G_1-like state. This conclusion was reached from three studies—recycling was initiated in the first two studies to identify the stages for reentry into the cycle, and the third study attempted an identification of the stages for decycling as outlined below.

a. Retransplantation of a fraction of old tumor into new hosts led to a prompt rise in the fraction of the population in mitosis as well as in DNA synthesis. The rise in mitotic index may be explained either by flow into mitosis of some cells resting in G_2 or by a relative lag of the mitotic process compared to the other cell cycle stages during an initial shortening of the cell cycle induced by transplantation. The former possibility was excluded by experiment (b) described below. Since the cycling cells had no appreciable G_1, a rise in the labeling index in the transplants could be explained by either a movement of G_0 cells (arrested in G_1) into S or a resumption of DNA synthesis in some cells blocked in S. The latter possibility was excluded by micro-spectrophotometric estimation of DNA as indicated below in experiment (c.)

b. All the cycling cells were labeled by a repeated injection of [3]H TdR in the older tumor, still leaving unlabeled a considerable fraction of the population which represented nonproliferating cells. Retransplantation of a fraction of the prelabeled tumor was done to initiate the cycle in the resting cells. If some resting cells were arrested in G_2 they should now enter mitosis and cause a prompt decline in the fraction of labeled mitoses. Inasmuch as no such decline was observed, any significant G_2–G_0 transition was excluded.

c. Microspectrophotometric estimation of DNA was made in cells from young as well as old tumors for a placement of the cells in appropriate DNA categories related to the cell cycle stages. Same cell populations were flash-labeled *in vivo* with [3]H TdR to identify cells synthesizing DNA. Figure 10 illustrates the distribution of DNA content in labeled and unlabeled cells from a 7-day ascites tumor. A comparison of the expected distribution of cells in various cycle stages and the observed distribution as given by the DNA content suggested that no appreciable decycling occurred in S or G_2 and that the G_0 cells had a postmitotic (G_1) DNA content.

4. Is the G_0 Stage Distinguishable from a Prolonged G_1?

A combined technique of mitotic arrest with Colcemid and double labeling with [14]C TdR followed at intervals by [3]H TdR was used to measure the flux into DNA synthesis. As cycling cells showed no measurable G_1 by the labeled mitosis technique, any appreciable entry from a long G_1 into S should be detectable by the presence of an increasing number of cells with ^{3}H only. The absence of a detectable influx suggested that the cells branded as G_0 were possibly in a truly resting state rather than in a prolonged G_1.

Control mechanisms regulating growth in this tumor can be summarized. A deceleration in growth rate observed with increasing tumor mass is caused in part by a gradual prolongation of the mitotic cell cycle and

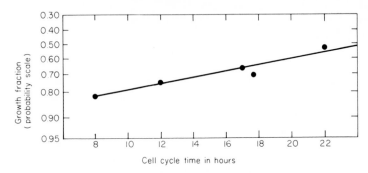

FIG. 15. Probability of decycling with prolongation of the cell cycle in the Ehrlich ascites tumor. (From Lala, 1968b, courtesy of IAEA, Vienna.)

its component stages in the proliferating cells and, in part, by a progressive transition of these cells to a resting state following mitosis. Although it is not known whether the latter is an effect of the former, the probability of recycling appears to decline with an increase in the cell cycle time (Fig. 15). Both these changes are reversible under favorable conditions. Molecular mechanisms responsible for an alteration in the kinetic parameters remain to be understood. In some recent searches for stage-specific biochemical parameters in the cell cycle, which might be related to cellular radiosensitivity (Harris and Patt, 1969; Harris, 1969; Harris *et al.*, 1969), it was found that the decycling process was associated with a decline in the cellular, nonprotein sulfhydryl (NPSH) content, which promptly increased again along with cell cycle initiation. However, this parameter did not explain the differential radiosensitivity of the cell in various cycle stages. A kinetic model for this tumor is represented in Fig. 16.

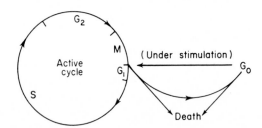

FIG. 16. A kinetic model for the Ehrlich ascites tumor studied by the author. The postmitotic G_1 phase is immeasurably short in the cycling cells. From this phase cells may recycle or move into a state of proliferative rest (G_0) which is reversible into active cell cycle under appropriate stimuli. Although the degree of cell loss from the individual compartments is not precisely known, some mitotic death, as well as substantial death from the G_0 compartment by aging, have been identified.

Findings on this particular ascites tumor may now be compared to the data available from other ascites tumors. Although studies on cell cycle have been reported for a considerable number of tumors growing in ascitic form (Hornsey and Howard, 1956; Edwards et al., 1960; Kim and Evans, 1964; Clarkson et al., 1965; Tolani 1965; Bertalanffy et al., 1965; Wheeler et al., 1967), a comparison is possible with only a few ascites tumors that have been studied at different stages of growth (Baserga, 1963; Wiebel and Baserga, 1968; Yankee et al., 1967; Frindel et al., 1969; Tannock, 1969). Table II summarizes data obtained from the latter reports (excluding Baserga, 1963). An examination of the data presented in Table II permits one to make some general conclusions about the reasons for a deceleration of growth rate in these tumors with an increase in age: (1) There is a progressive increase in the duration of the cell cycle, contributed by a prolongation of various cycle stages; in order of degree, they are G_1, S, and $G_2 + M$. (2) A decline in growth fraction seems to play a variable role; in some instances there is no decline, and in others a decline in the fraction of proliferating cells seems to contribute to a lesser extent than cell cycle prolongation. (3) An increase in the rate of cell loss from the population seems to play only a minor role. Several studies have also confirmed that changes in kinetic parameters are reversible under favorable conditions, such as ascites aspiration or retransplantation (Burns, 1968; Wiebel and Baserga, 1968).

In summary, it may be concluded that all ascites tumors exhibit a prolongation of the cell cycle with an increase in tumor mass and that the growth potential of cells seems to be retained in older tumors. A retention of such potential is achieved either by a substantial prolongation of G_1 or by a suspension of the cycle in the G_1 phase.

The model for ascites tumor growth may not be applicable to solid tumors. On the other hand, applicability of the model to acute human leukemia needs to be tested. In the latter, there seems to exist a morphological transition of cells from a rapidly proliferating to a slowly proliferating to a presumably nonproliferating state (Gavosto et al., 1964). The relative contribution of a possible cell cycle prolongation and decline in growth fraction remains to be determined. The nonproliferating cells exhibit a postmitotic (G_1) DNA content (Foadi et al., 1967). Although such cells are often assumed to be sterile, no direct evidence exists in favor of this assumption. An increase in the fraction of proliferating cells sometimes observed during a relapse following cessation of therapy (Foadi et al., 1967; Chan et al., 1969) may be explained by a resumption of cell cycle by the noncycling cells rather than a preferential killing of such cells. Recently, [3]H TdR-labeling studies have prompted Saunders and Mauer (1969) to suggest that these cells may

TABLE II

Kinetic Parameters at Different Stages of Growth in a Number of Ascites Tumors[a]

Tumor	Inoculum size (cells in millions)	Stage of growth (days)	I_S	t_C (hr)	t_S (hr)	t_{G_2+M} (hr)	t_{G_1} (hr)	I_P	t_D (hr)	k_G (hr⁻¹)	k_B (hr⁻¹)	k_L (hr⁻¹)	ϕ	Ref.
L 1210	2–3	6	0.62	11.8	8.9	2[b]	0.9[b]	1.0	14.5	0.047[b]	0.059[b]	0.012[b]	0.20[b]	Yankee et al. (1967)
	2–3	7	0.53	21.0	10.7	3[b]	7.3[b]	1.0[b]	36[b]	0.019[b]	0.033[b]	0.014[b]	0.42[b]	
Ehrlich	120	0	0.62	21.5	16.0	5.0	0.5	1.0	—	—	—	—	—	Wiebel and Baserga (1968)
	10–14	5	0.55	47.0	26.5	6.5	14.0	1.0	—	—	—	—	—	
NCTC	1.0	2	0.57	13.0	9.0	1.6	2.5	0.84	19.2	0.036[b]	0.041[b]	0.005[b]	0.14[b]	Frindel et al. (1969)
	1.0	4	0.46	17.0	9.0	1.6	6.0	0.99	125	0.006[b]	0.013	0.007[b]	0.54[b]	
	1.0	12	0.39	40.0	21.0	4.5	15.0	0.75	—	—	—	—	—	
	1.0	18	0.20	—	—	8.8	—	0.62	—	—	—	—	—	
Ehrlich	1.7	2	0.69	12.0	9.2	2.5[b]	1.7	0.9–1.0	12	—	—	—	0	Tannock (1969)
	1.7	6	0.42	44.0	22.0	6.5[b]	18.0	0.9–1.0	60	—	—	—	0.25	
	1.7	10	0.25	83.0[c]	48.0	7.5[b]	40.0[c]	0.6–1.0	144	—	—	—	0.2–0.4	

[a] For definition of symbols, see Section I.
[b] Calculated by the present author.
[c] Crude estimates.

serve as a "stem" compartment in a state of proliferative rest (G_0), slowly recruited into the rapidly proliferating compartment. A further testing of this hypothesis should be useful. It may be possible to test whether a decline in the number of cells in the rapidly proliferating pool after therapy acts as a feedback mechanism for an enhanced recruitment of G_0 cells into the cycle.

Studies on ascites tumor cells grown subcutaneously as solid tumors, or vice versa, in identical strains of mice have provided valuable information. Bertalanffy et al. (1965) observed a slower mitotic rate in the solid tumor. Frindel et al. (1967) reported the cycle characteristics in subcutaneously grown tumors with NCTC fibrosarcoma cells at different stages of tumor growth. Subsequently, to perform kinetic studies, they grew these cells in ascites form by repeated passage in mice (Frindel et al., 1969). Data on the ascites form are presented in Table II. The solid tumors studied at three different ages, 3, 7, and 20 days, having doubling times of 24, 38, and 110 hours, respectively, showed a fairly unaltered cell cycle time (about 17 hours). An appreciable decline in growth fraction occurred in the 20-day tumor, and there was a progressive increase in the rate of cell loss. Tannock (1969) studied Ehrlich ascites tumor cells grown in ascitic form (data presented in Table II) as well as in solid form. He did not perform age-specific studies on solid tumors; tumors ranging from 0.4 to 1.8 gm (showing a fairly unchanged doubling time of 10 days) were pooled for the study. He found a 17-hour cell cycle time, a high growth fraction, and an appreciable degree of cell loss in these tumors. Lala (1970b) studied Ehrlich ascites tumor cells grown as solid tumors at two different ages—6 days (average doubling time = 2.4 days) and 14 days (average doubling time = 6.5 days). A growth curve for these tumors has already been presented in Fig. 4, and the data on the ascitic form are presented in Table I. Interestingly, an almost identical cell cycle time (16–18 hours) was also observed in these tumors. In addition, there was some decline in the growth fraction as well as an appreciable increase in the rate of cell loss with increase in age, in accordance with the findings of Frindel et al. (1967). Thus, in solid tumors, a fairly abrupt transition seems to occur between the cycling and the noncycling state, rather than a gradual transition from a fast cycle to a slow cycle to no cycle as observed in the ascitic state.

Cell cycle time has been measured in a number of transplanted solid tumors with or without reference to growth rate (Goldfeder, 1965; Steel et al., 1966; Hermens and Barendsen, 1967; DeneKamp et al., 1968; Tannock, 1968; Simpson-Herren et al., 1968). Such measurement may be very useful, if cycle time is considered rather invariant in a particular tumor. Simpson-Herren et al. (1968), in their studies on a subcutaneously transplanted mouse sarcoma, used a wide range of tumor weights (presumably having different growth rates) for construction of the labeled mitosis curve and obtained reproducible curves at different generations of transplant. This suggested a stability of the cell cycle time in the tumor in general agreement with the findings discussed above. Although no age-specific studies are available on spontaneous solid tumors, studies on C3H mouse mammary tumors, having a fairly wide weight range and showing a wide spectrum of growth rate, also suggested a fairly stable cell cycle time (Mendelsohn, 1965).

Variation in proliferation rates among different sites within the same tumor is a common observation in many solid tumors and is found to increase with an increase in size or age. Although it may not be improbable for a minority of cell population to possess a prolonged cycle in a poorly proliferating zone, variations in growth fraction seem to be more important in resulting in such differences within the same tumor (Hermens and Barendsen, 1967; Frindel et al., 1967; Tannock, 1968; Lala, 1969).

In summary, growth of a solid tumor is characterized by changes in the growth fraction, whereas changes in the cell cycle time seem to characterize ascites tumor growth.

In a solid tumor, the growth fraction seems to be related to the availability of oxygen supply which, in turn, depends on the distance of a cell from the nearest vascular supply, as suggested by elegant kinetic studies (Tannock, 1968) in a transplantable mouse mammary tumor. Histologically it showed cordlike structures containing viable tissue arranged cylindrically around blood vessels. Studies on the different zones, in order of increasing distance from the vessels, indicated a fairly constant cell cycle time but a progressive decline in the growth fraction. Some points made in this study are illustrated in Figs. 5B and 7A, B, C. An induction of hypoxia in the tumor-bearing animals caused a reduction in the growth fraction in all the zones as well as a reduction in the cord size.*

Although some speculations have been made (Tannock, 1969) to explain the differences in the kinetic behavior of ascitic and solid tumors, further work needs to be done to understand the mechanisms leading to these differences.

B. Understanding the Evolution of the Neoplastic Process

Two distinct categories of studies have been useful toward understanding the evolution of the neoplastic process: (1) studies performed during carcinogenesis by induction and (2) studies permitting a comparison of spontaneous tumors with normal tissues.

---

* Studies of ascites tumor indicate hypoxia can induce decline in growth fraction without change in cell cycle time (Harris et al., 1970).

Many kinetic studies have been performed on mammalian tissues following exposure to various carcinogenic agents with the hope of obtaining some insight into the process of carcinogen-induced hyperplasia or neoplasia.

McCarter and Quastler (1962) showed that the rate of DNA synthesis in mouse hair follicle was reduced by application of dimethylbenzanthracene (DMBA). Variations in the duration of DNA synthesis and mitosis were observed during carcinogenesis in mouse epidermis by Evensen (1962a,b), and the degree of cell killing was measured by Iversen (1964). Frei and Ritchie (1964) showed that susceptibility of mouse epidermis to carcinogen might be related to DNA synthesis. Effects of chemical carcinogens on mitosis in this tissue have been extensively investigated (Iversen and Evensen, 1962; Skaeggestad, 1964; Elgjo, 1968a,b). Application of carcinogen, even as a single moderate dose, was found to cause marked cellular destruction followed by regeneration. Although the cellular proliferation rate was accelerated during regeneration, a concomitant prolongation of the mitotic duration seemed to present a paradox. Studies by Dörmer et al. (1964) on the effects of chemical carcinogen applied to mouse skin are also indicative of a progressive increase in the proliferation rate with the evolution of hyperplasia and neoplasia. Normal skin and skin papillomas induced by virus or chemicals in rabbits were studied by Rashad and Evans (1968). Tumors showed a higher proliferation rate, and, in the case of virus-induced tumors, this was at least in part due to an extension of the proliferating zone. Won Song and Tabachnick (1969) also found an extension of the proliferating zone in radiation-induced hyperplasia of guinea pig skin, but no alteration in the DNA-synthesis time was detected

Elegant studies have been performed on hamster cheek pouch with the hope of understanding the process of tumorogenesis as well as finding some biological basis for therapy (Reiskin and Mendelsohn, 1964; Reiskin and Berry, 1968; Brown and Berry, 1968b). Cheek pouch offers an immunologically privileged site, is rich in blood vessels, and the contralateral pouch in the same animal serves as an excellent control. The duration of DNA synthesis was found to be shorter in the tumors than in the controls. No acceleration of DNA synthesis, however, was found in the DMBA-induced hyperplastic epithelium. The shortening of DNA-synthesis time did not appear to be specific in relation to carcinogenesis, since such shortening was also observed in the neonatal as well as in regenerating epithelia. Some useful information may be derived from a comparison of data obtained with normal, hyperplastic and neoplastic tissues in this system. Table III summarizes the kinetic parameters obtained from the data reported by Reiskin and Berry (1968). Values for the growth fraction presented in this

PEEYUSH K. LALA

TABLE III

KINETIC PARAMETERS IN NORMAL, HYPERPLASTIC, AND NEOPLASTIC
CELLS OF CHEEK POUCH IN DIFFERENT HAMSTER STRAINS[a]

Parameter[b]	DEA normal adult[c]	DEA normal newborn[c]	Golden normal adult[c]	DEA hyper-plastic	Tumor		
					DEA	Golden	Cream
I_S	0.06	0.23	0.07	0.16	0.25	0.31	0.23
t_C	140[d]	29.2	141	61	11	16	16
t_S	9.3	6.7	9.9	10.4	6.5	7.9	7.4
t_{G2+M}	3.3	1.8	4.2	3.2	2.5	2.4	2.4
t_{G1}	127.4	20.7	126.9	47.4	2.0	5.7	6.2
I_P	1.0	1.0	1.0	1.0	0.38[e]	0.57[e]	0.55[e]
t_D	—	—	—	—	113	295	223
k_G	0	—	0	—	0.0061	0.0027	0.0036
k_B	0.006	0.034	0.007	0.015	0.0286	0.0172	0.0171
$k_L{}^f$	0.006	—	0.007	—	0.0225	0.0145	0.0135
ϕ^f	—	—	—	—	0.78	0.84	0.79

[a] From data of Reiskin and Berry (1968).
[b] All the times are expressed in hours and the rates in fraction per hour; for a description of the symbols, see Section I.
[c] Basal epithelium only, representing the proliferating zone.
[d] Measured by Brown and Berry (1968b).
[e] Calculated by the present author using technique of Section VIII, B, 2.
[f] Calculated by the present author.

table are estimates by this author using the procedure of Section VIII, B, 2, and are different from those presented in their paper, where the possibility of cell loss was not considered. It may be inferred from this table that with an evolution from normal proliferation to hyperplasia to neoplasia, there is an increase in the rate of cell production primarily due to a reduction in the cell cycle time. The increase in the rate of cell production would have been more obvious if in the normal pouch the total epithelial population were taken into account for a computation of birth rate rather than the basal zone, which only represents the proliferating part. For the same reason, the finding of an appreciable fraction of the neoplastic population in a nonproliferative state might not be indicative of a reduction in growth fraction in the tumor. For a true comparison of this parameter, the growth fraction of the total population in the normal tissue ought to be measured (Bresciani, 1968). Table III also indicates that, in spite of a high cell proliferation rate in the tumor, growth resulted only from the retention of 20% of the production; about 80% of the production was lost from the tumor.

Changes in proliferation kinetics during hepatic carcinogenesis have been subjected to studies by Rubin et al. (1964), Daoust and Molnar (1964), Banerjee (1965), Simard and Daoust (1966), Rajewsky (1967), and Simard et al., (1968). In the last study, an evolution of neoplasia from normal tissue exhibited the following events: Normal hepatocytes showed a strong G_1 block but a weak G_2 block, so that cells were prevented from entering S; but once in S, they proceeded to mitosis. In preoplastic nodules, the G_1 block was weaker but the G_2 block was strengthened. In neoplastic transformation or fully evolved tumors, both these blocks were weakened resulting in greater proliferation. Post and Hoffman (1964), on the other hand, suggested that the generation time of chemically induced hepatomas was longer than that for hepatocytes in growing rats (Post et al., 1963). However, a reinterpretation of their data by Bresciani (1968) reverses this conclusion.

Hoffman and Post (1965, 1966) measured the cell cycle parameters in DMBA-induced rat mammary carcinoma (Huggins mammary tumor) and compared them with the estimates in ilial epithelia. Mammary tumor cells exhibited a considerably longer t_C as well as t_S (45 and 10 hours) than those for ilial cells (12 and 6 hours). They also reviewed the existing data on a variety of tumors as well as normal fast renewing tissues to suggest that tumor cells may replicate less rapidly than normal rapidly proliferating cells, and thus may suffer less damage by cycle-specific antimetabolites than normal cells during conventional chemotherapy.

The second group of studies aimed at understanding the evolution of neoplasia was concerned with spontaneous tissue-specific tumors as well as their "normal" or "preoplastic" tissue counterparts with the hope of unveiling some specific differences in kinetic characteristics.

Because of obvious difficulties in finding suitable experimental materials, the number of significant studies in this category is limited. A notable exception is, however, provided by a fair number of detailed studies on human leukemias and their normal counterparts—hematopoietic tissues. These have been recently reviewed (Cronkite, 1968; Killmann, 1968b; Schiffer, 1968; Chervenick and Boggs, 1968) and have produced a wealth of information toward our understanding of human leukemias. Illustrations here will be confined to conventional tumors and related tissues.

Alveolar epithelium in mouse mammary gland provides a good example if a comparison of the kinetic parameters of the normal tissue and the tissue-specific lesions is possible. Normal and hormone-stimulated alveoli as well as hyperplastic and neoplastic lesions of mammary alveoli of C3H mouse have been studied in detail by Bresciani (1964, 1965a,b, 1968). Mendelsohn and associates have extensively studied the spontaneous mammary carcinoma in this species (Mendelsohn *et al.*, 1960; Mendelsohn, 1960b, 1962a, 1965). A comparison of the kinetic parameters (Bresciani, 1968) revealed a progressive shortening of the mitotic cycle and its components, as well as an increase in growth fraction from normal epithelium to nodular hyperplasia to mammary carcinoma. However, the reduction in the cycle time in tumor was less than that observed with hormonal stimulation of normal cells. Banerjee and Walker (1967a,b) studied, in a different strain of mice, normal mammary alveoli in different hormonal environments as well as hyperplastic alveolar nodules transferred from old females into the mammary fat pad of virgin young females. In agreement with the above findings, they found that the *S* period in transplants of hyperplastic nodules had values intermediate between those for normal alveoli in virgin mice and those for the hormone-induced prelactating alveoli. These findings indicate an altered hormonal sensitivity of the hyperplastic or neoplastic cells and also suggest that a shortening of the duration of cell cycle phases is not specific to tumorogenesis.

Cell cycle parameters in the normal thymus and spontaneous thymic lymphoma of the AKR mouse were estimated by Metcalf and Wiadrowski (1966). Normal large and medium thymic lymphocytes had cycle times of 6.8 and 8.2 hours compared to the values of 7.6 and 20.2 hours in lymphoma counterparts. Small lymphocytes that were nondividing in both these groups turned over faster in the lymphoma (in less than 2 days) than in the normal thymus (every 3.2 days).

Studies in man in most instances do not permit a comparison of the cell cycle characteristics of a tissue-specific lesion with those of normal tissue counterparts. For this reason, studies from various sources need to be combined and available data on rapidly renewing human tissues have to be used for a comparison. Such a comparison, although not always useful for understanding the process of neoplasia, is of paramount importance in formulating a biological basis for therapy. Considering the obvious difficulties in human experimentation, significant data on human tumors will be summarized here despite the incomplete nature of many studies.

Bresciani (1968) pooled data from different sources for a comparison of the kinetic parameters in the tumors with normal tissues in man. In general, tumors exhibited a higher [3]H TdR-labeling index than that for the normal rapidly renewing tissues. This finding, considered as a whole, was explained by a higher growth fraction in tumors.

Studies on 5 cases of human skin carcinoma by Frindel *et al.* (1968) showed a cell cycle time of 1 to 4 days, a DNA-synthesis time of 7 to 19 hours, and a growth fraction of 0.3 to 0.8. Although no data on normal human epidermis exist, comparatively long cell cycle times observed in the epidermis of other mammals would suggest that cycle times found in these tumors may not be really longer than that for the normal epidermal cells. Clarkson *et al.* (1965) found considerably longer times ($t_C = 3 - 5$ days and $t_S = 17$–60 hours) for free cancer cells in neoplastic effusions from various malignant conditions in 6 patients. These times are considerably longer than the times observed in rapidly renewing human tissues. For example, in the intestinal crypt cells the cycle time is 24 hours, and the duration of DNA synthesis ranges from 11 to 15 hours (Lipkin *et al.*, 1963a,b).

Feit and Stanicek (1967) measured *in vitro* flash-labeling indices with ^{3}H TdR in biopsy specimens from uterine cervix which were histologically graded into four groups: normal, abnormal, and atypical epithelia, and preinvasive carcinoma. Labeling indices increased in successive grades, and would indicate a progressive increase in the rate of proliferation in the absence of a proportionate lengthening of S phase. There was an associated extension of labeling zones toward the surface in the succeeding grades, highly indicative of an increase in growth fraction. An extension of labeling zone in cervical carcinoma *in situ* has also been observed by others (Iliya and Azar, 1967; Bennington, 1969). A similar finding has also been reported for rectal mucosa in multiple polyposis, a precancerous lesion in man, by Deschner *et al.* (1962, 1963). Bennington (1969) measured the cell cycle time and the growth fraction for the invasive carcinoma of cervix in two patients. Values for t_C were 14.3–15.5 hours, t_S 9–11.8 hours, and I_P 0.41–0.53. Although no comparable estimates on cell cycle are available for normal cervical epithelium, these times were not too different from those observed in rapidly renewing epithelia such as intestinal crypts (Lipkin *et al.*, 1962, 1963a,b; Lipkin, 1965).

Table IV summarizes the data on kinetic parameters obtained from some of the studies mentioned above (Clarkson *et al.*, 1965; Frindel *et al.*, 1968; Bennington, 1969). This table illustrates the strikingly wide range of values obtained for different tumors. For the skin carcinoma, the extent of cell loss was computed and reported in a later publication (Tubiana *et al.*, 1968). This amounted to 90 to 97% of the production. It is interesting to note that in the tumor showing the highest proliferation rate (cervical cancer), differences in the proliferation rates in different zones of the same tumor were attributable to an alteration in the growth fraction rather than the cell cycle time. This is in agreement with the observation in transplanted solid tumors in animals (Hermens and Barendsen, 1967; Tannock, 1968; Lala, 1969).

Hoffman and Post (1967) attempted a comparison of the proliferation kinetics of cancerous tissues with their normal counterparts in 7 patients with carcinoma of digestive tract, parotid, and ovary from a

TABLE IV

KINETIC PARAMETERS IN SOME HUMAN TUMORS[a]

Type of tumor	No. of patients	I_S	t_C (hr)	t_S (hr)	t_{G_2+M} (hr)	t_{G_1} (hr)	I_P	k_B (hr^{-1})[b]	Ref.
Neoplastic effusions (from various malignancies)	6	0.045–0.28	72–120[c]	17–60	3–9	48–84	0.13–0.95[d]	0.0017–0.013	Clarkson et al. (1965)
Skin carcinoma	5	0.05–0.17	25–97[e]	11–21	5–16	9–62	0.3–0.8	0.0026–0.016	Frindel et al. (1968)
Cervical cancer { basal cells	2	0.26–0.40	14.3–15.5	9.3–11.8	2.6–3.6	1.1–1.5	0.41–0.53	0.028–0.034	Bennington (1969)
interior cells		0.13	14.3–15.5	—	—	—	0.17–0.20	—	

[a] For definition of symbols, see Section I.
[b] Calculated by the present author.
[c] Indicates upper limit; mostly derived from grain count halving.
[d] Derived mostly from chronic ^{3}HTdR infusion.
[e] Excluding one case, where a calculated value of 241 hours was considered questionable.

single sampling of tissues following [3]H TdR injection. A lower grain count in the labeled tumor cells, in general, was taken as an indication of slower rate of DNA synthesis or longer DNA-synthesis time compared to normal tissues. Similarly, a lower labeling or mitotic index in tumor cells was considered indicative of a lower proliferation rate. These analyses, however, are not free from pitfalls, difficult to cope with in human studies, as pointed out in detail by Bresciani (1968). For example, a lower grain count could reflect a higher thymidine pool in tumor cells; similarly, if the labeling and mitotic indices for normal cells reported by Hoffman and Post (1967) were pertinent to the proliferating zones only, then their data might suggest that tumors may proliferate less rapidly than the proliferating population in normal tissues rather than normal tissues as a whole. No comparison can be made of the cell cycle times from these data.

Numerous studies, other than those mentioned above, have been performed on human tumor materials to obtain qualitative information about cellular proliferation. A commonly employed parameter is the thymidine-labeling index *in vivo* or *in vitro*. In the former, tissues were sampled at a short interval following administration of the [3]H TdR, and, in the latter, thin tumor slices from biopsy specimens were given a short exposure to [3]H TdR *in vitro*. Although DNA synthetic rates may drastically alter *in vitro*, the labeling index *in vitro* may be fairly representative of the fraction in DNA synthesis in the superficial parts of the specimens. The use of 95% oxygen (Deschner *et al.*, 1963; Kury and Carter, 1965; Lieb and Lisco, 1966; Meyer and Donaldson, 1969) or high-pressure oxygen (Steel and Bensted, 1965) appears to improve penetration of label. Estimates of labeling index (I_S) in conjunction with DNA-synthesis time (t_S) are useful in measuring the birth rate and the potential doubling time (t_{PD}). Lamerton and Steel (1968) summarized the existing data on I_S in a variety of human tumors and calculated the values for t_{PD} using a value of 15 hours for t_S. In most instances, values for I_S were low (0.01-0.07) and the estimates for t_{PD} ranged from 7 to 43 days. These values were different in respiratory carcinoma $(I_S = 0.15, t_{PD} = 3$ days) and lympho-sarcoma $(I_S = 0.32, t_{PD} = 1.5$ days). Observed volume doubling times in human tumors were much longer than the crude estimates of potential doubling times and the discrepancy was accounted for by a high degree of cell loss (Steel, 1967).

The birth rate is also measurable from estimates of mitotic indices following the use of mitotic arresting agents. By using colchicine *in vivo*, Refsum and Berdal (1967) and Iversen (1967) supported the existence of a high cell loss factor in human tumors. More recently, the stathmo-kinetic effect of vinblastine was used by Meyer and Donaldson (1969) during therapy of squamous cell carcinoma in man to measure the influx into mitosis. From this, they measured the "generation times," which in reality, are potential doubling times. These times ranged from 6 to 9 days except one doubtful case, where the value was 24 days. Mitotic times were estimated as 17–92 minutes. *In vitro* ^{3}H TdR-labeling indices measured in 2 cases ranged from 0.024 to 0.177. Assuming a direct relationship between I_S and t_S (steady-state equation) the t_S was estimated as 4.6 and 39 hours. Observed doubling times (t_D) for metastatic squamous cell carcinoma in lung (Schwartz, 1961; Collins *et al.*, 1956; Spratt and Spratt, 1964) mostly ranged from 37 to 46 days and may be as long as 143 days. If these times were also representative of a primary squamous cell carcinoma, the discrepancy between the t_D and t_{PD} must be explained by a substantial degree of cell loss in these tumors.

Cooper and his associates have attempted to gather valuable kinetic information on human tumors by combining ^{3}H TdR-labeling *in vitro* and measurements of DNA content in cells to locate them relative to the cell cycle stages. Studies on Burkitt's lymphomas (Cooper *et al.*, 1966) indicated a very high proliferative activity compared to any other human tumors. No arrest of tumor cells in S phase was observed. The difference between the calculated t_{PD} (1–2 days) and t_D (>7 days) was accounted for by a high death rate and supported by the finding of histiophagocytosis of pyknotic cells. Studies on lymph node materials from a variety of malignant lymphomas (Cooper *et al.*, 1968) showed considerable variation in proliferative behavior within the same histological category, partly explained by a variation in the growth fraction. Considerable cell loss was also suggested for the tumors with high proliferative activity. Extension of similar studies (Levi *et al.*, 1969) to transitional cell carcinoma (31 bladder and 5 ureteric tumors) showed a low proliferative activity in most tumors, and no correlation between histological type and thymidine labeling. In spite of the fact that normal bladder epithelium was polyploid, bladder tumors were found to arise as diploid and progress to hypotetraploid and finally grossly aneuploid populations; ploidy bore no relation to nuclear size.

Kinetic studies directed to the understanding of the evolution of neoplasia permit several conclusions. Studies that allow an examination of the transition from normal proliferation to hyperplasia to neoplasia, indicate the following. (*1*) There is a gradual reduction in the duration of cell cycle and its components during this transition. However, such a reduction may not be a specific mechanism in carcinogenesis. Normal tissues during rapid growth or under stimulus (such as hormones) may exhibit even shorter cycle times. (*2*) There is an increase in the growth fraction, if the whole cell population in a tissue is taken into account. This could indicate that, on the average, a cancer cell must be able to go through a larger number of multiplicative divisions in its life time than its normal proliferating counterpart. Bresciani (1968) tested various models of cell proliferation that could lead to "unlimited growth characteristics" of cancer. He concluded that such an unlimited growth can only be generated when the number of postmitotic cells recycling exceeded those decycling. The ratio between these numbers is 1 in steady state and >1 in growth. When other kinetic parameters are unaltered, this ratio maintains a direct relationship with the growth fraction. Thus, in theory, the growth fraction in cancer should always be higher than its normal, whole-tissue counterpart if other kinetic parameters are undisturbed. This was, in general, found to be true in most experimental tumors.

Other studies, especially in man, which permit a general comparison between normal cell renewal systems and tumors reveal two important features: (1) Cancer cells may not always proliferate faster than the rapidly renewing tissues in the body. This finding calls for a re-evaluation of the therapeutic measures directed against dividing cells and a continued search for agents with preferential toxicity to tumor cells. (2) A tumor in many respects resembles a growing cell renewal system rather than pure growth. A very high cell loss factor seems to be one of the characteristics of most human tumors.

C. Searches for a Biological Basis in Tumor Therapy

All the studies illustrated before should be of considerable use in formulating a therapeutic rationale. A large number of studies have been performed to identify the effects of various therapeutic agents, such as radiation or radiomimetic chemicals and antimetabolites, on the survival of malignant cell lines *in vitro*, primarily to detect a possible differential sensitivity of cells in various stages of cell cycle. A discussion of these studies are beyond the scope of this chapter. A few *in vivo* studies on tumors that were primarily designed for guidance in therapy will be mentioned here.

The spleen colony technique has been very fruitfully employed to study the relative sensitivity of clonogenic tumor cells and hematopoietic colony-forming cells in mice to various cytotoxic agents (Bruce et al., 1966, 1969; Valeriote and Bruce, 1967; Wodinsky et al., 1967; Bruce and Valeriote, 1968; Bruce and Bergsagel, 1967). Several murine tumors, such as lymphomas and L1210 leukemia, have been studied with this technique. Bruce and Valeriote (1968) classified anticancer agents into three classes based on their actions on proliferating and nonproliferating cells: (a) nonspecific, (b) phase-specific, and (c) cycle-specific. A number of cytotoxic chemicals in classes (b) and (c) were found to have a selective toxicity on lymphoma cells compared to the normal hematopoietic stem cells. This was explained by possible differences in the distribution of cells in active cycle and proliferative rest. Their findings also suggested that a repeated cyclic therapy with these agents might be a useful part of a therapy regime (Bruce et al., 1969). For these findings to be fruitfully exploited in the therapy of human tumors and leukemias, much has to be learned about the action of cytotoxic agents at the cellular level.

Skipper and his colleagues (Skipper, 1967, 1968a; Schabel, 1968) have extensively studied L1210 leukemia as a model experimental system for therapeutic planning in leukemia. These tumor cells grow exponentially in mice with a growth fraction of near unity for a large part of the growth period. The inoculum size, as well as the tumor cell population size at any instant, seems to bear a direct relationship to the host survival time and such a relationship may be used to assay the survival fraction of tumor cells following exposure to therapeutic agents (see Section VII, C). These workers found that cellular survival followed first-order kinetics (i.e., a constant per cent kill with an effective dose of the agent, irrespective of population size) and were able to result in "cures" with proper therapeutic planning. Although these studies have contributed a great deal to our understanding of the therapeutic planning, it is difficult at this moment to extrapolate this model to human leukemia, which may be quite removed from a simple proliferative model.

Information on cellular kinetic parameters in tumors as well as in host tissues and possible changes in these parameters following therapy is of considerable importance in therapeutic planning. Although effects of therapy on various proliferation parameters of tumors have been investigated in a large number of studies (Layde and Baserga, 1964; Palme and Liss, 1965; Révész and Lindfors, 1967; Chernozemski, 1968; Basrur et al., 1968; Farber and Baserga, 1969), a relatively complete measurement of cell cycle characteristics has been possible only in a few studies. Ball et al. (1967) compared the effects of treatment with L-phenylalanine mustard (Melphalan) on two rat sarcomas in ascitic form—one sensitive and the other resistant to the drug. Following treatment the two tumor lines did not exhibit any marked difference in the progress of DNA-synthesizing cells through mitosis. The differences in sensitivity seemed to stem from differences in cellular repair mechanisms, rather than differences in cellular proliferation kinetics. Schmeer (1968b) studied the effects of Mercenene clam extract that was cytotoxic to Krebs-2 solid carcinoma in mice and found that the effect was exerted primarily by blocking G_1 cells from entering DNA synthesis. Brown and Berry (1968b) made a detailed kinetic study of the effects of X-irradiation on cell proliferation in normal epithelium and tumors of the hamster cheek pouch. They used a single ^{3}H TdR pulse as well as continuous labeling with ^{3}H TdR to study cellular kinetics before and after local irradiation of the cheek pouches. After a dose-dependent delay in their first postirradiation division, cells of normal cheek pouch epithelium showed a small reduction in the cell cycle time. In contrast, the cell cycle time in tumors was slightly prolonged. Comparative studies of the effects of irradiation on cellular kinetics in bone marrow cells and ascites tumor cells in mice by Tubiana et al. (1968) resulted in qualitatively similar findings. Following the recovery from the initial G_2 block, the cell cycle time in the bone marrow cells of the irradiated animals was comparable to that in the control animals. On the other hand, tumor cells following irradiation showed a considerable prolongation of the cell cycle mainly due to a retardation in G_1 phase. Differential effects of irradiation on the cell cycle of tumor cells and the normal cells in the tumor-bearing host are of considerable significance in radiotherapy, especially in the dose-fractionation procedure.

The degree of oxygenation of a cell is an important parameter influencing cellular kinetics following radiotherapy. Van Putten (1968) attempted a correlation between this parameter and a temporal change in the number of clonogenic cells in a tumor following radiotherapy. An in vivo labeling procedure with ^{125}I-labeled IUDR was used to estimate the total cell number in a tumor. This procedure combined with the TD_{50} technique permitted a quantitation of the total number of clonogenic cells in the tumor. Studies on a transplantable osteosarcoma in mice suggested a considerable loss of clonogenic cells 2–4 days following irradiation with 1000 rads. When blood vessels were clamped in such tumors to produce anoxia, no appreciable loss took place. As an explanation, it was suggested that in the tumors with an intact circulation, the surviving cells were primarily located in the anoxic rim of the tumor where they might die of anoxia during a resumption of growth. In the other group where circulation was blocked during irradiation, anoxic surviving cells were randomly distributed, so that a loss in the anoxic rim was made up by proliferation in the center during a resumption of growth. These findings suggest that the presence of natural cell death in the anoxic part of the tumor may be exploited in a radiotherapeutic scheme.

Several interesting papers have been published to consider the implications of cell proliferation kinetics for radiotherapy (Mendelsohn, 1966; Suit and Wette, 1966; Suit and Batten, 1968) and chemotherapy (Skipper, 1968b) in solid tumors. The number of variables that remains to be measured before constructing a scientific model for therapy indicates that empirical experiments should still be fruitful in therapeutic guidance (Mendelsohn, 1966). On the other hand, further studies on cell kinetics before and after therapy in normal and tumor tissue and a continued search for agents having selective effects on tumor cells should be fruitful areas of investigation. For the latter, use of *in vitro* colony techniques for hematopoietic cells (Pluznic and Sachs, 1965; Robinson *et al.*, 1967) and tumor cells (Pearson, 1964; Himmelfarb *et al.*, 1967) may be of additional use in screening therapeutic agents.

D. STUDY OF EFFECTS OF TUMORS ON THE HOST

Only a few kinetic studies have been performed on normal cell renewal systems to evaluate the effects of tumors on the host. They reveal no appreciable change in the kinetic parameters of the renewing tissue of the animals bearing tumors compared to that in controls. Betts *et al.* (1966) found that the mean cell cycle time and the duration of DNA synthesis was 13 and 6.7 hours, respectively, in the normal hamster jejunum. These times were 12 and 6.1 hours in the jejunum of animals bearing fibrosarcomas in the axillary regions. Although the data were interpreted as indicative of shortening of the cycle in tumor-bearing animals, these differences do not seem to be highly significant. Schmeer (1967, 1968a) measured the cell cycle phases in the duodenal crypts of mice bearing solid tumors obtained with subcutaneous implantation of Krebs-2 ascites tumor cells. The cell cycle time was 19 hours and the S period 7.5 hours in the tumor-bearing animals, compared to the respective values of 20 and 7.5 hours in the control animals.

XI. General Remarks

The words "tumor" and "cancer" have been used synonymously in this chapter to imply malignant neoplasm rather than benign growth, although a few studies on the latter have also been illustrated in the preceding section. A number of features have emerged out of the wide range of kinetic studies. Some of these are acceptable facts and some are suggestions that need further testing. Further exploration is needed in many areas, and a number of questions remain to be answered.

The picture of cancer as was visualized by a clinician a decade ago has considerably changed. A tumor does not necessarily represent a pure all-out growth. As a cell population, it may very well be comparable to a growing cell renewal system. A solid tumor is usually composed of both proliferating and nonproliferating cells, and growth results from a higher rate of cell production than cell death. Cell death may represent a major feature in most human tumors.

The duration of the cell cycle and its components in a tumor is, in general, shorter than that in its normal tissue counterpart. Such shortening, on the other hand, is not a specific attribute of neoplastic transformation. Cell cycle time in the tumor could be considerably longer than the minimum cycle time of normal tissues observed under various physiological conditions such as normal growth or functional hyperplasia induced by hormones. The growth fraction, on the other hand, is generally higher in a tumor when compared to the total cell population of a normal tissue. This finding is consistent with the concept that malignant transformation is associated with an impairment or loss of cellular differentiation, resulting in an amplification of the proliferating compartment, which, in turn, is primarily responsible for an increased rate of cell production.

Studies on experimental solid tumors are indicative of a fairly stable cell cycle duration for the majority of cycling cells contributing to growth. If this finding holds true for human tumors, then a single estimate of the cell cycle in a human tumor should be useful for an understanding of the tumor life history. The growth fraction, on the other hand, appears to be a more variable parameter in the solid tumor, declining with tumor age or an increasing distance from the vascular supply. Tests are needed to determine whether the proportion of non-proliferating cells can be equated with the proportion of anoxic cells in a tumor. Although one may not anticipate such an oversimplified biological relationship, such a test should be of considerable value in radiotherapeutic planning.

Although an extrapolation of findings from an experimental tumor to a human tumor may not always be justified, tumor models in the experimental situation may be of considerable use in the human situation, not only in planning therapy, but also in the understanding of tumor cell biology. For example, experimental ascites tumors may provide a close model for acute leukemia in man—a suggestion that needs to be tested. In ascites tumors, most tumor cells retain their proliferative potential during tumor growth by a retardation of the cell cycle and sometimes by a transition into a state of proliferative rest at the postmitotic stage. Proper stimuli, such as partial removal of the tumor or transfer into a new host, promptly accelerate the cell cycle or initiate the cell cycle in the resting cells. Suggestive evidence is accumulating for the possibility that the nonproliferating "small blast" cells in human acute leukemia, which constitute the majority of the leukemic blast cell population, may not represent an end stage. Further tests are needed to examine the possibility that therapeutic destruction of cycling cells may provide a stimulus for recruitment of these cells into the cycle. "Blast crisis" in subacute or chronic leukemias may also represent the proliferative response of a clone of resting cells to some unknown stimuli.

Planning for tumor therapy should continue to benefit from kinetic studies. Awareness of the fact that tumors may proliferate less rapidly than the rapidly renewing tissues cautions against indiscriminate use of cycle-specific antimetabolites; on the other hand, screening procedures, such as the spleen colony technique, should be of continued use in selecting agents having preferential toxicity to tumor cells.

Tumor–host barriers, such as host immune mechanisms directed against tumors, are known to play a considerable role in influencing the survival of the tumor cells in the host environment. Few kinetic studies have been performed to understand the adaptive mechanisms in tumor cells in response to the host immune processes. One such study mentioned before (De Cosse and Gelfant, 1968) suggested that an arrest of cells in G_2 in an ascites tumor may represent such a defense mechanism. This area needs further exploration by kinetic studies in tumors.

If a loss of control in cellular differentiation represents the primary defect in neoplasia, as suggested by the kinetic studies, an understanding of cancer requires the knowledge of normal control mechanisms in cellular differentiation. Such mechanisms are poorly understood at present. Existing evidence indicates that the process of differentiation of a cell toward a functional state is associated with a decline in the proliferative ability, so that differentiation eventually proceeds without division. The decycling process may represent a critical step in the differentiation pathway. Since recycling is represented by an initiation of DNA synthesis in the G_1 phase, decycling must be achieved by an inhibition of this initiation process. A number of inhibitory mechanisms for cellular proliferation have been suggested for normal cell populations, such as cell–cell interactions (Simonovitch and Axelrad, 1963), contact control (Sauer, 1963; Marques-Pereira and Leblond, 1965), and chemical microenvironment (Bullough, 1965; Bullough and Lawrence, 1966; Bullough et al., 1967). The last named workers have succeeded in extracting a factor from epidermal tissue, termed "chalone" which inhibits cell division in epidermis in a wide range of vertebrates. Diurnal variations of the mitotic index is a fairly general observation in many normal tissues. Such fluctuations have also been reported for the DNA synthetic index. Curiously enough, studies on some tumors indicate the absence of a diurnal variation in the mitotic index (Bertalanffy et al., 1965; Brown and Berry, 1968a) as well as in the DNA synthetic index (Brown and Berry, 1968a). This area needs further exploration to throw some light on the biology of tumor cells. A diurnal variation of the mitotic index in normal tissues is considered to be brought about by a fluctuation of the humoral level of adrenal hormones operating through a chalone-type mechanism on the mitotic process itself (Bullough, 1962; Bullough and Lawrence, 1966, 1968). Several studies indicate a parallel diurnal fluctuation in the fraction of the cell population synthesizing DNA (Pilgrim et al., 1963; Scheving and Chiakulas, 1965; Scheving and Pauly, 1967; Brown and Berry, 1968a). Studies by the last named authors indicate that a parallel relationship between the two indices was primarily due to a partial synchrony of cells in DNA synthesis. Although a dual regulation of cell fluxes through mitoses and DNA synthesis is possible, the postulate of a common mechanism operating on the process of initiation of DNA synthesis appears to be more appealing. Frankfurt (1968) observed that in the normal tissue, a cell in the later part of G_1 went through a critical transition leading to an inevitable initiation of DNA synthesis. Hydrocortisone inhibited the progression of cells from G_1 to S only when applied before this transition, and this transition was believed to be associated with the synthesis of specific RNA molecules. Diurnal fluctuations in the DNA synthetic index was explained by the diurnal fluctuations in the humoral glucocorticoid level on the basis of these observations. The hydrocortisone effect appeared to be less pronounced on the carcinogen induced hyperplastic epithelium, and absent on the papillomas of mouse forestomach. Further studies on tumor cell populations are needed to examine whether the tumor cells are refractory to these regulatory mechanisms proposed for normal cells. Much more needs to be learned about the regulatory mechanisms in cellular proliferations as well as differentiation to understand the biology of cancer.

A number of practical questions raised by the current kinetic studies in tumor needs to be answered by future experimenters, although a quick answer may not be coming forth to all of them.

1. How valid is the "two-compartment" model for tumor cell proliferation?

Techniques available at present permit a distinction of the relatively fast cycling cells from the rest of the population, i.e., noncycling or slowly cycling. No study in solid tumors is known to have attempted a separation between the last two groups. The two-compartment model may still be a practical one in solid tumors, since in solid tumors, factors that cause a decline in the growth fraction do not appear to result in a prolongation of the cell cycle in the majority of the cycling cells. The noncycling cells in this case would constitute truly nondividing cells and/or cells with very long cycles. A distinction between cells possessing very long cycles and cells in G_0 phase may not be essential; what is needed, is a distinction between sterile cells and cells retaining proliferative potential. This is indicated in the next question.

2. What is the status of "nonproliferating" cells in a solid tumor? Is the growth potential completely lost or retained in these cells?

An answer to this question has important implications for therapy. Finding an answer, although difficult, may not be impossible in an experimental solid tumor. One needs to find a presumptive stimulus (such as resection of most part of the tumor) for proliferation in the nonproliferating cells. Since there is considerable evidence that these cells remain in a postmitotic (G_1) state, proliferation in these cells would be indicated by an increase in the fraction of the total cell population synthesizing DNA.

3. What is the proportion of stem cells in the proliferating tumor cell population?

Although some transplanted tumors are reproducible by a single cell, all the proliferating cells in any tumor may not be capable of extensive proliferation. It is possible for such cells to have various grades of proliferative potential. A therapist is interested in the cells capable of reproducing the tumor rather than any proliferating cell. If the fraction of clonogenic cells in a tumor represents only a small minority and these have cycle characteristics very different from most proliferating cells, then a conventional measurement of the cell cycle will not show these characteristics and, consequently, would be of little use in therapeutic planning. The spleen colony technique has proved very useful only in some transplantable murine tumors, but, unfortunately, no general technique exists at present for a measurement of the clonogenic fraction in any tumor. Since any *in vivo* assay is complicated by various factors constituting the tumor–host barrier, such as immunological differences between the tumor and the host, further searches for some standard *in vitro* assay system may be fruitful in evaluating the colony-forming ability of tumor cells.

4. What is the relationship between the G_0 state and the stem cell?

Although retention of a growth potential by transition into a G_0 state may be suggestive of "stem cell potential" in a tumor, such a relationship remains to be established. This question may be answered by a comparative assay of the clonogenic fractions in the total cell population before and after initiation of cell cycle in the G_0 fraction. Since the clonogenic potential in the former case represents the potential of the cycling cells in the population, a knowledge of the proportions of cycling and G_0 cells in the population would permit an estimation of the clonogenic potential of the G_0 cells from such a comparison. As an alternative, agents employed for a preferential killing of cycling cells (such as the use of high dose–high specific activity [3]H TdR or methotrexate) may be useful for a separation of the G_0 cells. Following an initiation of cell cycle in such cells, a direct assay of their clonogenic potential could be undertaken.

ACKNOWLEDGEMENTS

Studies reported in this chapter were supported in various phases by U.S. Atomic Energy Commission, Atomic Energy of Canada Ltd., National Cancer Institute of Canada, and Medical Research Council of Canada. They were carried out at various places—Argonne National Laboratory, Illinois; Laboratory of Radiobiology, University of California, San Francisco; Chalk River Nuclear Laboratories, Ontario; and the Department of Anatomy, McGill University, Montreal.

Addendum

Several important publications, including symposium volumes pertinent to this chapter, have recently appeared or have been submitted to the press, indicating a rapidly growing interest in the field of tumor cell population kinetics. Those considered to be of immediate relevance are cited here: Human tumor cell kinetics, *Nat. Cancer Inst. Monogr.* **30** (S. Perry, ed.), U.S. Department of Health, Education and Welfare, Public Health Service, National Cancer Institute, Bethesda, Maryland, 1969; "Normal and Malignant Cell Growth" (for a complete ref. see Patt, 1969); "The Cell Cycle and Cancer" (R. Baserga, ed.), Marcel Dekker, New York, 1970, in press.

A closed symposium, "Solid Tumor Kinetics," was held in February, 1970 at Williamsburg, Virginia under the chairmanship of Dr. M. L. Mendelsohn and the sponsorship of the National Cancer Institute, Bethesda, Maryland. Since the proceedings are not to be published, and presentations in some areas based on either unpublished or recently published materials appear to supplement Section X of this chapter, these will be briefly discussed here.* Labeled mitosis curves compiled by G. G. Steel for several well established transplanted solid tumors in mouse were remarkably identical and had definite second peaks. These might reflect the fastest possible tumor cell cycle in this host. In contrast, in spontaneous tumors of several mammalian species including man, a second peak in the labeled mitosis curve is either inconspicuous or absent, suggesting a very wide distribution of cell cycle times [see also Owen, L. N., and Steel, G. G. (1969) *Brit. J. Cancer* **23**, 493]. Despite a wide variance of cycle times in a single human tumor, it is possible that the same histopathological type of tumor in different individuals may possess similar cell cycle characteristics. Although a generalization seems premature at this moment, this similarity was suggested by a remarkable similarity in labeled mitosis curves for human melanoma presented from two different laboratories. Studies from the M. D. Anderson Hospital and Tumor Institute at Houston,

---

* Although permission of the chairman was obtained for a brief reproduction of its contents, I assume full responsibility for the authenticity and the interpretation of data.

Texas were presented by Tannock [Shirakawa, S., Luce, J. K., Tannock, I. F., and Frei III, E. (1970). *J. Clin. Invest.* in press]. Labeled mitosis curves constructed from serial biopsies of the metastic skin nodules in two patients indicated a median cell cycle time of 3 days (with a wide distribution) and a median S period of 21 hours. The growth fraction was calculated as 0.2–0.3. Studies on three malignant melanoma patients performed at the Solid Tumor Service, Medicine Branch, National Cancer Institute, Bethesda, Maryland were presented by R. T. Young and V. T. DeVita who used an ingenious technique of labeling the skin nodules by topical injection of ^{3}H TdR at the beginning of the experiment, followed by serial biopsies of different nodules to construct the labeled mitosis curves. The median DNA synthesis time was found to be 22–24 hours and the cell cycle duration could not be calculated in the absence of a distinct second wave. Although the growth fraction was not measurable in these cases, the tumor nodules showed appreciably higher labeling indices with this technique than those reported by Tannock using intravenous injection of the label. Similar studies by Young and DeVita on skin nodules in three patients with breast carcinoma gave a median S period of 19–24 hours. In an attempt to correlate various kinetic parameters in tumors with widely different growth rates, J. DeneKamp pooled data from her own as well as other laboratories [see also DeneKamp, J. (1970) *Cancer Res.* **30**, 393]. The cell cycle time appeared to increase with an increase in the volume double time in sarcomas, but no such correlation was found in carcinomas. The latter exhibited a fairly stable cell cycle time. Carcinomas, in general, had shorter cell cycle times and higher cell loss factors than sarcomas. Variation in growth rate among carcinomas could be primarily explained by differences in the extent of cell loss. Although studies pertaining to the effects of irradiation on the cell cycle parameters in solid tumors were discussed in this symposium, no general conclusion can be drawn about the changes in these parameters during the period of postirradiation regrowth of a tumor. The cell cycle was either accelerated (A. F. Hermans), or retarded (M. Brown), or fairly unchanged (J. DeneKamp; E. Frindel and M. Tubiana). Variables such as the dose of irradiation and interval between irradiation and observation may explain the differences. However, in most of these studies there was an indication of an increase in the growth fraction during the period of regeneration; this would suggest that nonproliferating cells in the solid tumor may be recruited into proliferation following a partial destruction of the tumor. Out of these studies, the most detailed one (A. F. Hermans) was performed with a rhabdomyosarcoma in rats at 4 to 14 days following X-irradiation with a dose of 2000 rads. At all these intervals there was an acceleration of the cell cycle both in the central (slowly growing) as well as the peripheral (rapidly growing) part of the tumor. A marked increase in the growth fraction was noticeable at the central part at 8 days following irradiation. Part of these findings has recently been published [Hermans, A. F., and Berendsen, G. W. (1969) *Eur. J. Cancer* **5**, 173].

REFERENCES

Agnish, N. D., and Federoff, S. (1968). *Can. J. Genet. Cytol.* **10**, 723.

Alexander, P. (1962). *Trans. N.Y. Acad. Sci.* **24**, 966.

Allen, E., Smith, G. M., and Gardner, W. U. (1937). *Amer. J. Anat.* **61**, 321.

Alpen, E. L., and Johnston, M. E. (1967). *Exp. Cell Res.* **47**, 177.

Bader, S., Miller, O. J., and Mukherjee, B. B. (1963). *Exp. Cell Res.* **31**, 100.

Bagshawe, K. D. (1968). *Brit. J. Cancer* **22**, 698.

Ball, C. R., Connors, T. A., Cooper, E. H., and Topping, N. E. (1967). *Neoplasma* **14**, 253.

Banerjee, M. R. (1965). *J. Nat. Cancer Inst.* **35**, 585.

Banerjee, M. R., and Walker, R. J. (1967a). *J. Cell Physiol.* **69**, 133.

Banerjee, M. R., and Walker, R. J. (1967b). *J. Nat. Cancer Inst.* **39**, 551.

Barnes, D. W. H., and Loutit, J. F. (1968). *Proc. Symp. Eff. Radiat. Cell. Proliferation Differentiation, Monaco.* Int. At. Energy Ag., Vienna. (Abstr.)

Barrett, J. C. (1966). *J. Nat. Cancer Inst.* **37**, 443.

Baserga, R. (1963). *AMA Arch. Pathol.* **75**, 58.

Baserga, R. (1965). *Cancer Res.* **25**, 581.

Baserga, R. (1967). *Methods Cancer Res.* **1**, 45.

Baserga, R. (1968). *Cell Tissue Kinet.* **1**, 167.

Baserga, R., and Kisieleski, W. E. (1963). *Acch. Ital. Patol. Clin. Tumori* **6**, 3.

Baserga, R., and Lisco, E. (1963). *J. Nat. Cancer Inst.* **31**, 1559.

Basrur, P. K., Swierenga, S. H., and Townsend, G. F. (1968). *Cancer* **21**, 888.

Bennington, J. L. (1969). *Cancer Res.* **29**, 1082.

Bergsagel, D. E., and Valeriote, F. A. (1968). *Cancer Res.* **28**, 2187.

Bertalanffy, F. D., Schacter, R., Ali, J., and Ingimundson, J. C. (1965). *Cancer Res.* **25**, 685.

Betts, A., Sewall, E. J., and Tanguay, R. (1966). *Cancer Res.* **26**, 898.

Biczowa, B., Kieler, J., and Moore, J. (1968). *Eur. J. Cancer* **4**, 67.

Boyd, G. A. (1955). "Autoradiography In Biology and Medicine." Academic Press, New York.

Bresciani, F. (1964). *Science* **146**, 653.

Bresciani, F. (1965a). *Exp. Cell Res.* **38**, 13.

Bresciani, F. (1965b). *In* "Cellular Radiation Biology" (The Univ. Texas M. D. Anderson Hosp. Tumor Inst. ed.), p. 547. Williams & Wilkins, Baltimore, Maryland.

Bresciani, F. (1968). *Eur. J. Cancer* **4**, 343.

Bronk, B. V. (1969). *J. Theor. Biol.* **22**, 468.

Bronk, B. V., Diens, G. J., and Paskin, A. (1968). *Biophys. J.* **8**, 1353.

Brown, J. M. (1968). *Exp. Cell Res.* **52**, 565.

Brown, J. M., and Berry, R. J. (1968a). *Cell Tissue Kinet.* **1**, 23.

Brown, J. M., and Berry, R. J. (1968b). *Proc. Symp. Eff. Radiat. Cell. Proliferation Differentiation, Monaco* p. 475. Int. At. Energy Ag., Vienna.

Bruce, W. R. (1967). *J. Nat. Cancer Inst.* **38**, 401.

Bruce, W. R., and Bergsagel, D. E. (1967). *Cancer Res.* **27**, 2646.

Bruce, W. R., and Meeker, B. E. (1965). *J. Nat. Cancer Inst.* **34**, 849.

Bruce, W. R., and Valeriote, F. A. (1968). *In* "The Proliferation and Spread of Neoplastic Cells" (The Univ. Texas M. D. Anderson Hosp. Tumor Inst. ed.), p. 409. Williams & Wilkins, Baltimore, Maryland.

Bruce, W. R., and Vander Gaag, H. A. (1963). *Nature (London)* **199**, 79.

Bruce, W. R., Meeker, B. E., and Valeriote, F. A. (1966). *J. Nat. Cancer Inst.* **37**-233.

Bruce, W. R., Meeker, B. E., Powers, W. E., and Valeriote, F. A. (1969). *J. Nat. Cancer Inst.* **42**, 1015.

Brues, A. M., Wiener, A. E., and Andervont, H. B. (1939). *Proc. Soc. Exp. Biol. Med.* **42**, 374.

Bryant, B. J. (1962). *Exp. Cell Res.* **27**, 70.

Bryant, B. J. (1965). *Exp. Cell Res.* **37**, 490.

Bullough, W. S. (1962). *Biol. Rev. Cambridge Phil. Soc.* **37**, 307.

Bullough, W. S. (1965). *Cancer Res.* **25**, 1683.

Bullough, W. S., and Lawrence, E. B. (1966). *Advan. Biol. Skin* **7**, 1.

Bullough, W. S., and Lawrence, E. B. (1968). *Cell Tissue Kinet.* **1**, 5.

Bullough, W. S., Lawrence, E. B., Iversen, O. H., and Elgjo, K. (1967). *Nature (London)* **214**, 578.

Burns, E. R. (1968). *Cancer Res.* **28**, 1191.

Bush, R. S., and Bruce, W. R. (1964). *Radiat. Res.* **21**, 612.

Carney, P. C., and Malmgren, R. A. (1967). *Transplantation* **5**, 455.

Chan, B. W. B., Hayhoe, F. G. J., and Bullimore, J. A. (1969). *Nature (London)* **221**, 972.

Chang, L. O., and Looney, W. B. (1965). *Cancer Res.* **25**, 1815.

Chernozemski, I. N. (1968). *Cancer Res.* **28**, 992.

Chervenick, P. A., and Boggs, D. R. (1968). *Ser. Haematol.* **1**(3), 24.

Choi, Y. C., Smetana, K., and Busch, H. (1968). *Exp. Cell Res.* **53**, 582–602.

Clarkson, B., Ota, K., Ohkita, T., and O'Connor, A. (1965). *Cancer* **18**, 1189.

Cleaver, J. E. (1964). Ph.D. Thesis, Univ. of Cambridge, Cambridge, England.

Cleaver, J. E. (1965). *Exp. Cell Res.* **39**, 697.

Cleaver, J. E. (1967). "Thymidine Metabolism and Cell Kinetics." North-Holland Publ., Amsterdam.

Collins, V. P. (1962). *Cancer* **15**, 387.

Collins, V. P., Loeffler, R. K., and Tivey, H. (1956). *Amer. J. Roentgenol. Radium Ther. Nucl. Med.* **76**, 988.

Cook, J. R., and James, T. W. (1964). *In* "Synchrony of Cell Division and Growth" (E. Zeuthen, ed.), pp. 485–489. Wiley (Interscience), New York.

Cooper, E. H., Frank, G. L., and Wright, D. H. (1966). *Eur. J. Cancer* **2**, 377.

Cooper, E. H., Peckham, M. J., Millerd, R. E., Hamlin, I. M. E., and Gerard-Merchant, R. (1968). *Eur. J. Cancer* **4**, 286.

Cronkite, E. P. (1967). *Semin. Hematol.* **4**, 415.

Cronkite, E. P. (1968). *In* "Perspectives in Leukemia" (W. Dameshek and R. M. Dutcher, eds.), pp. 158–186. Grune & Stratton, New York.

Cronkite, E. P., Bond, V. P., Fliedner, T. M., and Killmann, S. A. (1960). *In* "Haemopoiesis" (G. W. W. Wolstenholme and M. O. Conner, eds.), p. 70. Churchill, London.

Currie, A. R. (1967). *In* "Endogenous Factors Influencing Host-Tumor Balance" (R. W. Wissler, T. L. Dao, and S. Wood, eds.). Univ. of Chicago Press, Chicago, Illinois.

Dao, T. L. (1967). *In* "Endogenous Factors Influencing Host-Tumor Balance" (R. W. Wissler, T. L. Dao, and S. Wood, eds.). Univ. of Chicago Press, Chicago, Illinois.

Daoust, R., and Molnar, F. (1964). *Cancer Res.* **24**, 1898.

Dawson, K. B., and Field, E. O. (1964). *Exp. Cell Res.* **34**, 507.

De Cosse, J. J., and Gelfant, S. (1968). *Science* **162**, 698.

DeneKamp, J., Thomlinson, R. H., and Fowler, J. H. (1968). *Abstr. Papers 16th Annu. Meet. Radiat. Res. Soc. Houston, Texas*, p. 6.

Deschner, E. D., Lewis, C. M., and Lipkin, M. (1962). *Clin. Res.* **10**(4), 393.

Deschner, E. D., Lewis, C. M., and Lipkin, M. (1963). *J. Clin. Invest.* **42**, 1922.

Dethlefsen, L. A., Prewitt, J. M. S., and Mendelsohn, M. L. (1968). *J. Nat. Cancer Inst.* **40**, 389.

Dörmer, P., Tulinius, H., and Oehlert, W. (1964). *Z. Krebsforsch.* **66**, 11.

Donnelly, G. M., and Sisken, J. E. (1967). *Exp. Cell Res.* **46**, 93.

Dubin, P. W., Jeung, N., Williams, M. H., and Arnold, J. S. (1967). *Cancer Res.* **27**, 1341.

Dustin, A. P. (1943). *Arch. Biol.* **54**, 111.

Dustin, P., Jr. (1959). *In* "Kinetics of Cellular Proliferation" (F. Stohlman, ed.), p. 50. Grune & Stratton, New York.

Edwards, J. L., Koch, A. L., Youcis, P., Freeze, H. L., Laite, M. B., and Donaldson, J. T. (1960). *J. Biophys. Biochem. Cytol.* **7**, 273.

Eichten, J. G., and Maruyama, Y. (1968). *Growth* **32**, 211.

Eigsti, O. J., and Dustin, P., Jr. (1955). "Colchicine—In Agriculture, Medicine, Biology and Chemistry." Iowa State.College Press, Ames, Iowa.

Elgjo, K. (1968a). *Eur. J. Cancer* **3**, 519.

Elgjo, K. (1968b). *Eur. J. Cancer* **4**, 183.

Epifanova, E., and Terskikh, V. V. (1969). *Cell Tissue Kinet.* **2**, 75.

Evensen, A. (1962a). *Nature (London)* **195**, 718.

Evensen, A. (1962b). *Acta Pathol. Microbiol. Scand. Suppl.* **156**, Pt. II, 95.

Farber, E., and Baserga, R. (1969). *Cancer Res.* **29**, 136.

Feinendegen, L. E. (1967). "Tritium-Labeled Molecules in Biology and Medicine." Academic Press, New York.

Feit, J., and Stanicek, J. (1967). *Neoplasma* **14**, 499.

Foadi, M. D., Cooper, E. H., and Hardisty, R. M. (1967). *Nature (London)* **216**, 134.

Fortner, J. G., Mahy, A. G., and Cotran, R. S. (1961). *Cancer Res.* **21**, 199.

Frankfurt, O. S. (1968). *Exp. Cell Res.* **52**, 220.

Frei, J. V., and Ritchie, A. C. (1964). *J. Nat. Cancer Inst.* **32**, 1213.

Fried, J. (1968). *Biophys. J.* **8**, 710.

Fried, J. (1969). *J. Theor. Biol.* **24**, 108.

Frindel, E., Malaise, E., Alpen, E., and Tubiana, M. (1967). *Cancer Res.* **27**, 1122.

Frindel, E., Malaise, E., and Tubiana, M. (1968). *Cancer* **22**, 611.

Frindel, E., Valleron, A. J., Vassort, F., and Tubiana, M. (1969). *Cell Tissue Kinet.* **2**, 51.

Furth, J., and Kahn, M. C. (1937). *Amer. J. Cancer* **31**, 276.

Garland, L. H., Coulson, W., and Wollin, E. (1963). *Cancer* **16**, 694.

Gavosto, F., Pileri, A., Bachi, C., and Pegoraro, L. (1964). *Nature (London)* **203**, 92.

Gelfant, S. (1962). *Exp. Cell Res.* **26**, 395.

Gelfant, S. (1963). *Exp. Cell Res.* **32**, 521.

Gelfant, S. (1966). *Methods Cell Physiol.* **2**, 359–395.

German, J. L. (1964). *J. Cell Biol.* **20**(1), 37.

German, J. L., and Bearn, A. G. (1961). *J. Clin. Invest.* **40**, 1041.

Gilbert, C. W., and Lajtha, L. G. (1965). *In* "Cellular Radiation Biology" (The Univ. Texas M. D. Anderson Hosp. Tumor Inst. ed.), p. 474. Williams & Wilkins, Baltimore, Maryland.

Gilbert, C. W., Muldal, S., and Lajtha, L. G. (1962). *Nature (London)* **195**, 869.

Goldfeder, A. (1965). *Nature (London)* **207**, 612.

Haddow, A. (1938). *J. Pathol. Bacteriol.* **47**, 553.

Hamilton, I. A. (1969). *Science* **164**, 952.

Harris, J. W. (1969). *Exp. Cell Res.* **56**, 134.

Harris, J. W., and Patt, H. M. (1969). *Exp., Cell. Res.* **56**, 134.

Harris, J. W., Painter, R. B., and Hahn, G. M. (1969). *Int. J. Radiat. Biol.* **15**, 289.

Harris, J. W., Meyskens, F., and Patt, H. M. (1970). *Cancer Res.* **30**, 1937.

Hellström, K. E., and Hellström, I. (1967). *In* "Endogenous Factors Influencing Host-Tumor Balance" (R. W. Wissler, T. L. Dao, and S. Wood, Jr., eds.). Univ. of Chicago Press, Chicago, Illinois.

Hermens, A. F., and Barendsen, G. W. (1967). *Eur. J. Cancer* **3**, 361.

Hewitt, H. B. (1953a). *Brit. J. Cancer* **7**, 367.

Hewitt, H. B. (1953b). *Brit. J. Cancer* **7**, 384.

Hewitt, H. B., and Wilson, C. W. (1959). *Brit. J. Cancer* **13**, 769.

Hewitt, H. B., and Wilson, C. W. (1961). *Ann. N.Y. Acad. Sci,* **95**, 818.

Hill, M. (1962). *Exp. Cell Res.* **28**, 21.

Himmelfarb, P., Thayer, P., and Martin, H. (1967). *Cancer Chemother. Rep.* **51**, (7), 451.

Hoffman, J., and Post, J. (1965). *J. Clin. Invest.* **44**, 1060.

Hoffman, J., and Post, J. (1966). *Cancer Res.* **26**, 1313.

Hoffman, J., and Post, J. (1967). *Cancer Res.* **27**, 898.

Hornsey, S., and Howard, A. (1956). *Ann. N.Y. Acad. Sci.* **63**, 915.

Hornsey, S., and Silini, J. (1961a). *Int. J. Radiat. Biol.* **4**, 127.

Hornsey, S., and Silini, J. (1961b). *Int. J. Radiat. Biol.* **4**, 135.

Hornsey, S., and Silini, J. (1962). *Int. J. Radiat. Biol.* **5**, 147.

Howard, A., and Pelc, S. R. (1951). *In* "Isotopes in Biochemistry" (G. E. W. Wolstenholme, ed.), p. 138. Churchill, London.

Howard, A., and Pelc, S. R. (1953). *Heredity* **6**, Suppl. 261.

Huggins, C. (1967). *Cancer Res.* **27**, 1925.

Hughes, W. L., Bond, V. P., Brecher, G., Cronkite, E. P., Painter, R. B., Quastler, H., and Sherman, F. G. (1958). *Proc. Nat. Acad. Sci. U.S.* **44**, 476.

Hunter, J. C. (1955). *J. Nat. Cancer Inst.* **16**, 405.

Iliya, F. A., and Azar, H. A. (1967). *Amer. J. Obstet. Gynecol.* **99**, 515.

Ingleby, H., Moore, L., and Gershon-Cohen, J. (1960). "Comparative Anatomy, Pathology and Roentgenology of the Breast." Univ. of Pennsylvania Press, Philadelphia, Pennsylvania.

Iversen, O. H. (1964). *Progr. Exp. Tumor Res.* **4**, 169.

Iversen, O. H. (1967). *Eur. J. Cancer* **3**, 389.

Iversen, O. H., and Evensen, A. (1962). *Acta Pathol. Microbiol. Scand. Suppl.* **156**.

Jensen, E. V. (1967). *In* "Endogenous Factors Influencing Host-Tumor Balance" (R. W. Wissler, T. L. Dao, and S. Wood, eds.). Univ. of Chicago Press Chicago, Illinois.

Johnson, H. A. (1961). *Cytologia* **26**, 32.

Kallman, R. F. (1968). *Methods Cancer Res.* **4**, 309.

Kallman, R. F., Silini, G., and Van Putten, L. M. (1967). *J. Nat. Cancer Inst.* **39**, 539.

Kay, H. E. M. (1965). *Lancet* ii, 418.

Kesse-Elias, M., Harris, E. B., and Gyftaki, E. (1967). *Acta Haematol.* **38**, 170.

Killmann, S. A. (1968a). *Ser. Haematol.* 1(3), 103.

Killmann, S. A. (1968b). *Ser. Haematol.* 1(3), 38.

Killmann, S. A., Cronkite, E. P., Robertson, J. S., Fliedner, T. M., and Bond, V. P. (1963). *Lab. Invest.* **12**, 671.

Kim, J. H., and Evans, T. C. (1964). *Radiat. Res.* **21**, 129.

Klein, G. (1968). *Cancer Res.* **28**, 625.

Klein, G., and Révész, L. (1953). *J. Nat. Cancer Inst.* **14**, 229.

Kollmorgen, G. M., Trucco, E., and Sacher, G. A. (1967). *Exp. Cell Res.* **47**, 49.

Kubitschek, H. E. (1962). *Exp. Cell Res.* **26**, 439.

Kubitschek, H. E. (1966). *Nature (London)* **209**, 1039.

Kury, G., and Carter, H. W. (1965). *AMA Arch. Pathol.* **80**, 38.

Laird, A. K. (1964). *Brit. J. Cancer* **18**, 490.

Laird, A. K. (1965). *Brit. J. Cancer* **19**, 278.

Lajtha, L. G. (1963). *J. Cell. Comp. Physiol.* **60**, Suppl. 1, 143.

Lajtha, L. G., Oliver, R., and Ellis, F. (1954). *Brit. J. Cancer* **8**, 367.

Lajtha, L. G., Oliver, R., and Gurney, C. W. (1962). *Brit. J. Haematol.* **8**, 442.

Lala, P. K. (1968a). *Exp. Cell. Res.* **50**, 459.

Lala, P. K. (1968b). *Proc. Symp. Eff. Radiat. Cell. Proliferation Differentiation, Monaco* p. 463. Int. At. Energy Ag., Vienna.

Lala, P. K. (1969). Unpublished observations.

Lala, P. K. (1970a). *Proc. 10th Int. Cancer Congr., Houston,* p. 368 (Abstr.).

Lala, P. K. (1970b). *Abstr. Papers 13th Annu. Meet. Can. Fed. Biol. Soc. Montreal, Quebec,* p. 6.

Lala, P. K., and Patt, H. M. (1966). *Proc. Nat. Acad. Sci. U.S.* **56**, 1735.

Lala, P. K., and Patt, H. M. (1968). *Cell Tissue Kinet.* **1**, 137.

Lala, P. K., Maloney, M. A., and Patt, H. M. (1964). *Acta Haematol.* **31**. 1.

Lala, P. K., Maloney, M. A., and Patt, H. M. (1965). *Exp. Cell Res.* **38**, 626.

Lamerton, L. F., and Fry, R. J. M., eds. (1963). "Cell Proliferation." Blackwell, Oxford.

Lamerton, L. F., and Steel, G. G. (1968). *Progr. Biophys. Mol. Biol.* **18**, 245–283.

Layde, J. P., and Baserga, R. (1964). *Brit. J. Cancer* **18**, 150.

Leblond, C. P., and Allen, E. (1937). *Endocrinology* **21**, 455.

Leblond, C. P., and Stevens, C. E. (1948). *Anat. Rec.* **100**, 357.

Leblond, C. P., and Walker, B. E. (1956). *Physiol. Rev.* **36**, 255.

Leblond, C. P., Messier, B., and Kopriwa, B. (1959). *Lab. Invest.* **8**, 296.

Levi, E. L., Cooper, E. H., Anderson, C. K., and Williams, R. E. (1969). *Cancer* **23**, 1074.

Lieb, L. M., and Lisco, H. (1966). *Cancer Res.* **26**, 73.

Liebelt, A. G., and Liebelt, R. (1967). *Methods Cancer Res.* **1**, 143.

Lima-de-faria, A. (1964). *In* "Mammalian Cytogenetics and Related Problems in Radiobiology" (C. Pavan, C. Chagas, O. Freta-Pessoa, and L. R. Caldas, eds.), p. 31. Macmillan (Pergamon), New York.

Lipkin, M. (1965). *Gastroenterology* **48**, 616.

Lipkin, M., Sherlock, P., and Bell, B. (1962). *Nature (London)* **195**, 175.

Lipkin, M., Bell, B., and Sherlock, P. (1963a). *J. Clin. Invest.* **42**, 767.

Lipkin, M., Sherlock. P., and Bell, B. (1963b). *Gastroenterology* **45**, 721.

Lord, B. I. (1968). *Proc. Symp. Eff. Radiat. Cell. Proliferation Differentiation, Monaco* p. 247. Int. At. Energy Ag., Vienna.

McCarter, J. A., and Quastler, H. (1962). *Nature (London)* **194**, 873.

McCredie, J. A., Inch, W. R., Kruuv, J., and Watson, T. A. (1965). *Growth* **29**, 331.

Maekawa, T., and Tsuchiya, J. (1968). *Exp. Cell Res.* **53**, 55.

Maloney, M. A., Patt, H. M., and Weber, C. L. (1962). *Nature (London)* **193**, 134.

Marques-Pereira, J. P., and Leblond, C. P. (1965). *Amer. J. Anat.* **117**, 73.

Maruyama, Y. (1964). *Nature (London)* **201**, 93.

Maruyama, Y., and Brown, B. W., Jr. (1964). *Int. J. Radiat. Biol.* **8**, 59.

Maruyama, Y., and Knuth, P. (1966). *Growth* **30**, 453.

Mayneord, W. V. (1932). *Amer. J. Cancer* **16**, 841.

Mendelsohn, M. L. (1960a). *Science* **132**, 1496.

Mendelsohn, M. L. (1960b). *J. Nat. Cancer Inst.* **25**, 485.

Mendelsohn, M. L. (1962a). *J. Nat. Cancer Inst.* **28**, 1015.

Mendelsohn, M. L. (1962b). *Science* **135**, 213.

Mendelsohn, M. L. (1963). *In* "Cell Proliferation" (L. F. Lamerton and R. J. M. Fry, eds.), pp. 190–212. Blackwell, Oxford.

Mendelsohn, M. L. (1965). *In* "Cellular Radiation Biology" (The Univ. Texas M. D. Anderson Hosp. Tumor Inst. ed.), p. 498. Williams & Wilkins, Baltimore, Maryland.

Mendelsohn, M. L. (1966). *In* "Radiation Research" (G. Silini, ed.). p. 659–675 North-Holland Publ., Amsterdam.

Mendelsohn, M. L., and Dethlefsen, L. A. (1968). *In* "The Proliferation and Spread of Neoplastic Cells" (The Univ. Texas M. D. Anderson Hosp. Tumor Inst. ed.), p. 197. Williams & Wilkins, Baltimore, Maryland.

Mendelsohn, M. L., Dohan, C. F., Jr., and Moore, H. A. (1960). *J. Nat. Cancer Inst.* **25**, 477.

Merchant, D. J., Kahn, R. H., and Murphy, W. H., Jr. (1964). "Handbook of Cell and Organ Culture," p. 29. Burgess, Minneapolis, Minnesota.

Metcalf, D., and Wiadrowski, M. (1966). *Cancer Res.* **26**, 483.

Meyer, J. S., and Donaldson, R. C. (1969). *AMA Arch. Pathol.* **87**, 479.

Morishima, A., Grumbach, M. M., and Taylor. J. H. (1962). *Proc. Nat. Acad. Sci. U.S.* **48**, 756.

Mottram, J. C. (1935). *J. Pathol. Bacteriol.* **40**, 407.

Mukherjee, B. B., and Sinha, A. K. (1963). *Can. J. Genet. Cytol.* **5**, 490.

Mukherjee, B. B., and Sinha, A. K. (1964). *Proc. Nat. Acad. Sci U.S.* **51**, 252.

Mukherjee, B. B., and Sinha, A. K. (1965). *J. Med. Genet.* **2**, 192.

Ohkita, T. (1967). *Nippon Ketsueki Gakkai Zasshi* **30**, 507.

Okada, S. (1967). *J. Cell Biol.* **34**, 915.

Painter, R. B., Jermany, D. A., and Rasmussen, R. E. (1966). *J. Mol. Biol.* **17**, 47.

Palme, G., and Liss, E. (1965). *Eur. J. Cancer* **1**, 245.

Patt, H. M. (1963). *Amer. J. Roentgenol. Radium Ther. Nucl. Med.* **90**, 928.

Patt, H. M. (1969). *In* "Normal and Malignant Cell Growth" (R. J. M. Fry, M. L. Griem, and W. H. Kirsten, eds.), p. 218. Springer-Verlag, New York.

Patt, H. M., and Blackford, M. E. (1954). *Cancer Res.* **14**, 391.

Patt, H. M., and Quastler, H. (1963). *Physiol. Rev.* **43**, 357.

Patt, H. M., and Straube, R. L. (1956). *Ann. N.Y. Acad. Sci.* **63**, 728.

Patt, H. M., Blackford, M. E., and Drallmeier, J. L. (1953). *Proc. Soc. Exp. Biol. Med.* **83**, 520.

Pearson, H. E. (1964). *Nature (London)* **204**, 198.

Pelc, S. R. (1963). *In* "Cell Proliferation" (L. F. Lamerton and R. J. M. Fry, eds.), p. 94. Blackwell, Oxford.

Pelc, S. R. (1964). *J. Cell Biol.* **22**, 21.

Pilgrim, C., and Maurer, W. (1962). *Naturwissenschaften* **49**, 544.

Pilgrim, C. and Maurer, W. (1965). *Exp. Cell Res.* **37**, 183.

Pilgrim, C., Erb, W., and Maurer, W. (1963). *Nature (London)* **199**, 863.

Pluznic, D. H., and Sachs, L. J. (1965). *J. Cell. Physiol.* **66**, 319.

Post, J., and Hoffman, J. (1964). *J. Cell Biol.* **22**, 341.

Post, J., and Hoffman, J. (1965). *Radiat. Res.* **26**, 422.

Post, J., and Hoffman, J. (1967). *Radiat. Res.* **30**, 748.

Post, J., Huang, C., and Hoffman, J. (1963). *J. Cell. Biol.* **18**, 1.

Powell, E. O. (1956). *J. Gen. Microbiol.* **15**, 492.

Prescott, D. M. (1968). *Cancer Res.* **28**, 1815.

Puck, T. T., and Steffen, J. (1963). *Biophys. J.* **3**, 379.

Puck, T. T., Saunders, P., and Petersen, D. (1964). *Biophys. J.* **4**, 441.

Quastler, H. (1963). *In* "Cell Proliferation" (L. F. Lamerton and R. J. M. Fry, eds.), pp. 18–34. Blackwell, Oxford.

Quastler, H., and Sherman, F. G. (1959). *Exp. Cell Res.* **17**, 420.

Rajewsky, M. F. (1967). *Eur. J. Cancer* **3**, 335.

Rashad, A. L., and Evans, C. A. (1968). *J. Nat. Cancer Inst.* **41**, 845.

Refsum, S. B., and Berdal, P. (1967). *Eur. J. Cancer* **3**, 235.

Reinhold, H. S. (1965). *Eur. J. Cancer* **1**, 67.

Reiskin, A. B., and Berry, R. J. (1968). *Cancer Res.* **28**, 898.

Reiskin, A. B., and Mendelsohn, M. L. (1964). *Cancer Res.* **24**, 1131.

Révész, L., and Lindfors, P. (1967). *Eur. J. Cancer* **3**, 329.

Rieke, W. O. (1962). *J. Cell Biol.* **13**, 205.

Robbins, E., and Borun, T. W. (1967). *Proc. Nat. Acad. Sci. U.S.* **57**, 409.

Robinson, W., Metcalf, D., and Bradley, T. R. (1967). *J. Cell. Physiol.* **69**, 83.

Rogers, A. W. (1967). "Techniques of Autoradiography." Elsevier, Amsterdam.

Rubin, E., Masuko, K., Goldfarb, S., and Zak, R. G. (1964). *Proc. Soc. Exp. Biol. Med.* **115**, 381.

Rubini, J. R., Cronkite, E. P., Bond, V. P., and Fliedner, T. M. (1960). *J. Clin. Invest.* **39**, 909.

Sauer, F. C. (1963). *J. Morphol.* **60**, 1.

Saunders, E. F., and Mauer, A. M. (1969). *J. Clin. Invest.* **48**, 1299.

Schabel, F. M., Jr. (1968). *In* "The Proliferation and Spread of Neoplastic Cells," (The Univ. Texas M. D. Anderson Hosp. Tumor Inst. ed.), p. 379. Williams & Wilkins, Baltimore, Maryland.

Scheving, L. E., and Chiakulas, J. J. (1965). *Exp. Cell Res.* **39**, 161.

Scheving, L. E., and Pauly, J. E. (1967). *J. Cell Biol.* **32**, 677.

Schiffer, L. M. (1968). *Ser. Haemotol.* **1** (3), 3.

Schmeer, R. [A. C.] (1967). *Biol. Bull.* **133**, 483.

Schmeer, A. C. (1968a). *Int. J. Cancer* **3**, 829.

Schmeer, A. C. (1968b). *Biol. Bull.* **135**, 434.

Schrek, R. (1935). *Amer. J. Cancer.* **24**, 807.

Schrek, R. (1936). *Amer. J. Cancer* **28**, 345.

Schwartz. M. (1961). *Cancer* **14**, 1272.

Simard, A., and Daoust, R. (1966). *Cancer Res.* **26**, 1966.

Simard, A., Cousineau, G., and Daoust, R. (1968). *J. Nat. Cancer Inst.* **41**, 1257.

Siminovitch, L., and Axelrad, A. A. (1963). *Proc. Can. Cancer Res. Conf.* **5**, 149.

Simpson-Herren, L., Blow, J. G., and Brown, P. H. (1968). *Cancer Res.* **28**, 724.

Sisken, J. E., and Morasca, L. (1965). *J. Cell Biol.* **25**, 179.

Skaeggestad, O. (1964). *Acta Pathol. Microbiol. Scand. Suppl.* **169**.

Skipper, H. E. (1967). *Cancer Res.* **27**, 2636.

Skipper, H. E. (1968a). *In* "Perspectives in Leukemia" (W. Dameshek and R. M. Dutcher, eds.), p. 187. Grune & Stratton, New York.

Skipper, H. E. (1968b). *In* "The Proliferation and Spread of Neoplastic Cells" (The Univ. Texas M.D. Anderson Hosp. Tumor Inst. ed.), p. 213. Williams & Wilkins, Baltimore, Maryland.

Skipper, H. E., Schabel, F. M., Jr., and Wilcox, W. S. (1964). *Cancer Chemother. Rep.* **35**, 3.

Smith, C. L., and Dendy, P. P. (1962). *Nature (London)* **193**, 555.

Southam, C. M. (1967). *In* "Endogenous Factors Influencing Host-Tumor Balance" (R. W. Wissler, T. L. Dao, and S. Wood, eds.). Univ. of Chicago Press, Chicago, Illinois.

Spratt, J. S. (1965). *Cancer* **18**, 14.

Spratt, J. S., Jr., and Spratt, T. L. (1964). *Ann. Surg.* **159**, 161.

Spratt, J. S., Ter-Pogossian, M., and Long, R. T. L. (1963). *Arch. Surg. (Chicago)* **86**, 283.

Staroscik, R. N., Jenkins, W. H., and Mendelsohn, M. L. (1964). *Nature (London)* **202**, 456.

Steel, G. G. (1966). *Nature (London)* **210**, 806.

Steel, G. G. (1967). *Eur. J. Cancer* **3**, 381.

Steel, G. G. (1968). *Cell Tissue Kinet.* **1**, 193.

Steel, G. G., and Bensted, J. P. M. (1965). *Eur. J. Cancer* **1**, 275.

Steel, G. G., and Lamerton, L. F. (1966). *Brit. J. Cancer* **20**, 74.

Steel, G. G., Adams, K., and Barrett, J. C. (1966). *Brit. J. Cancer* **20**, 784.

Stohlman, F., Jr., ed. (1959). "The Kinetics of Cellular Proliferation." Grune & Stratton, New York.

Stryckmans, P., Cronkite, E. P., Fache, J., Fliedner, T. M., and Ramos, J. (1966). *Nature (London)* **211**, 717.

Stubblefield, E. (1965). *J. Cell Biol.* **25**, 137.

Suit, H. D., and Batten, G. W. (1968). *In* "The Proliferation and Spread of Neoplastic Cells," (The Univ. Texas M. D. Anderson Hosp. Tumor Inst. ed.), p. 423. Williams & Wilkins, Baltimore, Maryland.

Suit, H. D., and Wette, R. (1966). *Radiat. Res.* **29**, 267.

Takahashi, M. (1966) *J. Theor. Biol.* **13**, 202.

Tannock, I. F. (1967). *Exp. Cell. Res* **47**, 345.

Tannock, I. F. (1968). *Brit. J. Cancer* **22**, 258.

Tannock, I. F. (1969). *Cancer Res.* **29**, 1527.

Taylor, J. H. (1960). *J. Biophys. Biochem. Cytol.* **7**, 455.

Taylor, J. H., Woods, P. S., and Hughes, W. L. (1957). *Proc. Nat. Acad. Sci. U.S.* **43**, 122.

Till, J. E., and McCulloch, E. A. (1961). *Radiat. Res.* **14**, 213.

Tolani, S. (1965). *Lab. Invest.* **14**, 701.

Trucco, E., and Brockwell, P. J. (1968). *J. Theor. Biol.* **20**, 321.

Tubiana, M., Frindel, E., and Malaise, E. (1968). *Proc. Symp. Eff. Radiat. Cell. Proliferation Differentiation, Monaco* p. 423. Int. At. Energy Ag., Vienna.

Valeriote, F. A., and Bruce, W. R. (1967). *J. Nat. Cancer Inst.* **38**, 393.

Van Putten, L. M. (1968). *Proc. Symp. Eff. Radiat. Cell. Proliferation Differentiation, Monaco* p. 493. Int. At. Energy Ag., Vienna.

Verly, W. G., Firket, H., and Hunebelle, C. (1958). *Proc. 2nd U.N. Int. Conf. Peaceful Uses At. Energy, Geneva*, pp. 181–185.

Vincent, P. C., and Nicholls, A. (1967). *Cancer Res.* **27**, 1058.

Vincent, P. C., Cronkite, E. P., Greenberg, M. L., Kirstent, C., Schiffer, L. M., and Stryckmans, P. A. (1969). *Blood* **33**, 843.

Walker, P. M. B., and Yates, H. B. (1952). *Proc. Roy. Soc., Ser. B* **140**, 274.

Welin, S., Yonker, J., and Spratt, J. S. (1963). *Amer. J. Roentgenol. Radium Ther. Nucl. Med.* **90**, 673.

Wheeler, G. P., Bowden, B. J., Wilkoff, L. J., and Dulmadge, E. A. (1967). *Proc. Soc. Exp. Biol. Med.* **126**, 903.

White, A. (1967). *In* "Endogenous Factors Influencing Host-Tumor Balance" (R. W. Wissler, T. L. Dao, and S. Wood, eds.). Univ. of Chicago Press, Chicago, Illinois.

Wiebel, F., and Baserga, R. (1968). *Cell Tissue Kinet.* **1**, 273.

Wilkoff, L. J., Wilcox, W. S., Burdeshaw, J. A., Dixon, G. J., and Dulmadge, E. A. (1967). *J. Nat. Cancer Inst.* **39**, 965.

Wilkoff, L. J., Dulmadge, E. A., and Dixon, G. J. (1968a). *Proc. Soc. Exp. Biol. Med.* **127**, 472.

Wilkoff, L. J., Dulmadge, E. A., and Dixon, G. J. (1968b). *Cancer Chemother. Rep.* **52**(7), 725.

Williams-Ashman, H. G. (1967). *In* "Endogenous Factors Influencing Host-Tumor Balance" (R. W. Wissler, T. L. Dao, and S. Wood, eds.). Univ. of Chicago Press, Chicago, Illinois.

Wimber, D. E., and Quastler, H. (1963). *Exp. Cell Res.* **30**, 8.

Wodinsky, I., Swinarski, J., and Kensler, C. J. (1967). *Cancer Chemother. Rep.* **51**(7), 415.

Wolfsberg, M. F. (1964). *Exp. Cell Res.* **35**, 119.

Won Song, C., and Tabachnick, J. (1969). *Int. J. Radiat. Biol.* **15**, 171.

Yamada, M. and Puck, T. T. (1961). *Proc. Nat. Nat. Acad. Sci. U.S.* **47**, 1181.

Yankee, R. A., De Vita, V. T., and Perry, S. (1967). *Cancer Res.* **27**, 2381.

Yoshida, Y., Todo, A., Shirakawa, S., Wakisaka, G., and Uchino, H. (1968). *Blood* **31**, 292.

CHAPTER II

COMPARATIVE STUDIES OF ASCITES HEPATOMAS

TOMIZO YOSHIDA

I. Introduction

The life of somatic cells constituting the animal body is separable from that of the whole animal as demonstrated by the *in vitro* cell culture technique. Cancer cells of somatic origin also demonstrate this relationship, i.e., the growth of cancer in the host follows its own regulatory systems which are independent of that of the host. This relation is illustrated by the technique of transplantation of animal cancers. As long as the transplantation is continued, the life of cancer cells continues beyond the life-span of individual host animals.

However, as the transplantation technique is usually unavailable for most human cancers, they terminate together with the death of the host in which they originated. In other words, experiences in human cancer are usually not reproducible and this places a limitation on the research using human cancer material. Studies of transplantation of animal tumors are expected to overcome this restriction, but studies in this line have adhered too long to mere prolongation of given animal tumors by establishing transplantable strains and studying this particular tumor strain.

One point which should be emphasized in cancer research is that the cancer cell originates by the cancerization of normal somatic cells. Apart from the question of the causes and mechanisms of oncogenesis, it was recognized from pathological studies over a hundred years ago that a cancer cell is produced by transformation of a normal somatic cell through a series of events taking place in it. Consequently, cancer is characterized by the fact that the elementary agent of the harmful growth in the body of a patient originates from the somatic cell which is a structural as well as functional constituent of the body.

Therefore, the most important field of cancer research involves comparative studies on cancerized cells and normal somatic cells. Such studies extend to comparative studies among cancerized or established cancer cells. All these comparative studies in cancer distinguish the research of cancer disease from that of infectious diseases. In the latter, the pathogen for a certain disease is empirically anticipated to be a single entity, whereas in the former the pathogen, the cancer cell, is as multiple as the multiplicity of the mother (somatic) cells and the multiplicity of causative factors.

The discovery of chemical carcinogens, such as polycyclic aromatic hydrocarbons of coal tar as well as the aminoazo compounds, opened the way to optional production of cancer in animals. These chemically induced cancers are reproducible, being derived from normal cells of the same type, and thus the scope of comparative studies was expanded.

However, as long as pathological studies were carried on with "solid tumors," these comparative studies did not show a significant advance. As a matter of fact, solid tumors, especially those induced by the same chemical agents, do not necessarily present significant difference either in their gross or histological appearance. Moreover, comparative studies by morphological means are technically restricted. As a result, comparative studies in other fields, such as biology or biochemistry of cancer, have not developed either. These situations seem to be the main reasons why comparative studies in cancer research have remained behind. This technical problem involved in studies with solid tumors is not limited to primary tumors but also holds true for transplanted tumors.

Studies on the ascites tumor are said to have opened a new field of "quantitative oncology" (Hauschka, 1956). If so, the ascites tumor must have opened, at the same time, a new field of comparative studies in cancer, because quantity is the basis of comparison. This point may be regarded as the main contribution of the ascites tumor to cancer research.

In this regard, the "ascites hepatomas," which I and my associates initiated and have worked with for the past 20 years, seem to have added a method for further cancer research. As a matter of fact, our studies with ascites hepatomas resulted in presenting remarkable differences which had been either masked or difficult to see in studies with solid tumors but had actually existed among tumors induced by the same chemical agents.

II. Ascites Tumor

The type of malignant growth which is called at present "ascites tumor" was first produced in Germany. The "Ehrlich ascites tumor" which is now internationally used was produced in 1932 (Löwenthal and Jahn, 1932) and used to be called simply "Aszites-Krebs." The English terms "ascites cancer" or "ascites carcinoma" seem to correspond to this German term but neither is in common use. Goldie (Goldie and Felix, 1951), one of the early workers in this field, proposed the term "free-cell tumor (cancer)." He emphasized with this term that the (individually isolated) free-cell type of malignant growth is not limited to that of "ascites" growth, but it can occur or be experimentally produced in other parts of the body such as the pleural or cerebrospinal fluid. In 1944 the author and co-workers published the initial work on the so-called Yoshida sarcoma and later proposed the term "fluid tumor (cancer)" in contrast to "solid tumor"; this term was proposed (Yoshida, 1949a,b) for instructive purposes. At that time, the concept that malignant growth or neoplasm should primarily be in solid form was still prevalent. For instance, it was discussed among pathologists in Japan whether leukemia could be accepted as a type of neoplasm, and one of those who opposed the acceptance pointed out, among other reasons, the fact that leukemia does not form any evident primary focus or solid tumor at all. This seemed to me to have reflected an unspoken general tendency at that time. Actually, after the publication of studies on Yoshida sarcoma, it was often necessary to explain and emphasize that the growth of malignant neoplasm is not necessarily limited to the formation of a solid tumor. The author stressed the importance of the intercellular substance which determines the physical states of various tissues not only in malignant growth but also in normal tissues, comparing the blood as a tissue with the bone or cartilage.

In 1952, eight transplant strains of ascites tumors were listed from reports of different laboratories (Table I). The number has increased tremendously since that time. As seen in Table I, all the tumors listed, except Yoshida sarcoma, are ones that were converted

TABLE I

ASCITES TUMORS KNOWN BEFORE 1952

Ascites tumor	Original tumor	Originated in	Animal	Reported	
				In	By
Flexner-Jobling carcinoma	"Gemishtzel-linges" Sarkom (Karzinom?)	1906	Rat	1927	Hesse
Ehrlich ascites tumor	Mammary carcinoma	—	Mouse	1932	Löwenthal Jahn
Yoshida sarcoma	Reticuloendo-thelial cell (?) sarcoma	1943	Rat	1947	Yoshida
S37	Carcinoma	1906	Mouse	1951	Goldie
Lympho-sarcoma 6C3HED	Lymphosarcoma	1941	Mouse (C3H)	1953	Klein
MCIA	Leiomyosarcoma	1945	Mouse (C3H)	1953	Klein
Krebs 2	Carcinoma simplex	1933	Mouse	1953	Klein
S-180 (Crocker)	Polymorph-cell sarcoma	1914	Mouse (C)	1952	Goldie

into the ascites form from transplanted solid tumors. Tumors such as S-180 and S-37 had been kept in solid form throughout the transplantation for almost 40 years after their origination and then converted into ascites form. For the Ehrlich ascites tumor, the information about the period of solid tumor is not certain, but it is assumed to be not much less (or more) than the above cases. On the other hand, their present features are quite different from their original features. The Ehrlich ascites tumor was originally a carcinoma, but it does not show at present any sign of the epithelial tumor at all. Also, S-37 was designated primarily a carcinoma, but now it is called a sarcoma. From the point of view of pathology this kind of change is a significant event worthy of study, but with materials available at present there is no means to trace when and under what conditions these changes took place.

Yoshida sarcoma is an exceptional case since the transplant strain of this ascites tumor was established by transplantation of tumor ascites which were found in the peritoneal cavity of the primary tumor animal. However, it cannot easily be concluded that this tumor had originated in the ascites form, because tumors growing in the solid form were found at the same time in the primary animal; it may rather be natural to consider that the tumor originated in a solid form from which the ascitic growth developed secondarily.

Ascites tumor does not mean a tumor growth in which tumor cells involved proliferate exclusively in the ascites fluid. Although it is characterized by production of abundant ascites fluid with tumor cells proliferating in it, formation of tumor nodules over the peritoneum, infiltration of tumor cells into the surrounding tissues of the abdomen, and metastasis (in solid type) in distant parts are evident as well.

The borderline between the ascitic and solid tumor growth can never be a clear-cut one, i.e., there are many intermediate types. The characteristics of ascites tumors will be found only if the successive transplantation of the tumor is continued exclusively with the ascites tumors.

One more fact of interest is that only a limited number of all transplantable tumors can be converted into ascites tumor. Presumably, the percentage of this convertibility does not surpass 20%. This will be discussed in the next section based on results of our studies on ascitic conversion of azo dye-induced hepatoma.

FROM YOSHIDA SARCOMA TO ASCITES HEPATOMA

Interest in ascites tumor originated from the author's studies on the histological structure of malignant growth, especially on the so-called stroma—interstitial supporting tissues—of the tumor. The role of the stroma, especially that of the vascular system involved in the tumor formation was studied to obtain information about interrelations between the vascular system and growth—numerical increase—of neoplastic cells.

The results of related studies carried out in the beginning of the 1940's (Yoshida and Kim, 1943; Yoshida and Tsurusaki, 1943; Yoshida et al., 1943; Yoshida, 1949a) using transplantable (solid) tumors of mice and rats, as well as rabbits, may be summarized as follows.

First, in transplantation of tumor tissue, all of the stromal tissues involved in the graft undergo necrosis without showing any sign of further proliferation at all. The majority of the tumor cells die, too, except that a few individually separated cells survive in the very peripheral zone of the necrotic graft. New growth of the transplanted tumor in the new host starts with multiplication of these surviving cells. Therefore, the grafting of a piece of tumor tissue is the same, in the end, as that of inoculation of a few individually isolated cells. This was first observed by Rössle (1936) and was confirmed by Satomi (1941) of our institute.

Second, blood vessels of normal structure involved in transplanted tumors are not newly formed there accompanying the development of tumors, but they accidentally preexisted there and belong to the vascular system of the host organization. The same relation as this was observed during the course of development of experimentally induced Thorotrast sarcoma of the rat (Yoshida and Tsurusaki, 1943).

Third, blood capillaries in the tumor tissue do not show the regular network formation of the normal tissue and they terminate, openly dispersing into the intercellular space where the tissue fluid, containing blood cells, is more or less accumulated. This tissue fluid seems to flow through the intercellular space presenting a peculiar pathway looking like blood capillary, but the lining of this stream is not made of any kind of special cells, and the tumor cells are in immediate contact with the streaming fluid. Tumor tissue, therefore, is not a tissue that is provided with its own circuit of blood circulation like normal tissue (Yoshida et al., 1943).

Fourth, malignant growths vary in both origin and structure so that classification such as carcinoma and sarcoma is required, but malignant cells growing within these formations are, in the end, individually separated and suspended in the tissue fluid. Therefore, on the cellular level and from the point of view of condition of the life and growth of malignant cells, the structures of tumors are not a fundamental problem and the cells are suspended in the tissue fluid.

Around 1942, our research group initiated preliminary experiments on ascitic conversion of transplantable solid tumors. At first, it was anticipated that every transplantable tumor could be tranformed into an ascites tumor, either at once or after repetition of intraperitoneal inoculation of mashed tumor tissue, but all the preliminary experiments were unsuccessful. Animals inoculated with such material died of solid tumors without showing sufficient accumulation of the ascites.

During the course of these experiments, the primary tumor of the Yoshida sarcoma originated in 1 of 10 rats which had been fed o-aminoazotoluene (4'-amino-2,3'-dimethylazobenzene) for a period of 3 months and then, after stopping the feeding, painted on the skin of the back with KAs_2O_3 solution. This experiment was one of a series carried out in our institute during the period of 1941 to 1943. The purpose of the experiments was to examine whether an initial short-term feeding of aminoazo compound insufficient for inducing hepatomas could produce a preneoplastic state in the liver which might respond with hepatoma development (in a sense of "cellular predisposition") to the action of carcinogenic substances such as coal tar, benzopyrene, as well as a very weakly carcinogenic arsenic compound. These substances were administered through the skin by painting them on the back of the animals. Hepatoma development in normal rats by painting these substances has still not been reported. However, in animals pretreated with the aforementioned feeding, paintings with these substances resulted in successful induction of hepatoma in every series of experiment. In fact, the percentage of hepatomas developed was similar to that obtained by continuous feeding with aminoazo compounds for sufficient periods (Muta, 1943).

In an animal of this experimental series (KAs_2O_3), after about 4 months of painting, a remarkable expansion of the abdomen occurred along with solid enlargement of the scrotum. The animal was killed and autopsy confirmed that the abdominal enlargement was due to accumulation of a large amount of milky white ascitic fluid; this was successfully transplanted into the peritoneal cavity of 1 of 2 animals, giving rise to the same ascitic growth as the primary one. It was thus demonstrated that the ascitic fluid of the primary animal was "ascitic tumor." Serial transplantation with this ascitic fluid has been continued up to the present (about 27 years) through almost 2000 generations of intraperitoneal transplantation.

If experiments had not been proceeding on ascitic conversion of tumors at that time, it is very likely that transplantation of the milky white ascites present would not have been carried out.

At a time during World War II when almost all the transplantable animal tumors for cancer research had been lost, this easily transplantable and rapidly growing ascites tumor was welcomed by oncologists in Japan and was distributed over the country. In 1947, the name "Yoshida sarcoma" was given to this tumor at the general assembly of the Japanese Cancer Association.

From the beginning the origin of the tumor was not apparent. At autopsy of the primary tumor animal, rather small hepatoma nodules were observed in the liver; regrettably, their histology was not defined. The enlargement of the scrotum was due to intensive infiltration of tumor cells. Subcutaneous grafting of tumor pieces from this infiltrative growth was tried together with the aforementioned intraperitoneal inoculation of the tumor ascites. The transplantation was also successful in giving rise to solid tumors at the graft site. It was found later that intraperitoneal inoculation of tumor pieces from the subcutaneous tumor resulted in ascitic growth which was not distinguishable from the ascites tumor established with the primary ascitic growth. Conversely, subcutaneous inoculation of tumor ascites produced solid tumor growth at the site. It was then decided to keep the tumor strain only in the ascitic form.

Both histological and cytological examinations of the solid growth and cytological examination of smear preparations of the ascitic growth led to the assumption that this particular tumor might have originated from the reticuloendothelial system (Yoshida, 1952).

Although the mother cell of the tumor was assumed to be a reticuloendothelial cell, there was no way to define which reticuloendothelial cells of which organ had served as its source. In carcinoma, each step of the histological process of development from normal epithelial tissue has been traced from early stages of cell proliferation to carcinomatous change, but this is not the case in sarcomas, especially in reticuloendothelial cell sarcomas.

Questions about the origin of Yoshida sarcoma have remained unsolved for a long time, although exact information on the origin of the tumor is the prerequisite for any kind of experiment of its reproduction. About 1950, a histological finding in the liver of a rat fed with aminoazo compound seemed significant. Administration of these compounds to rats caused hyperplasia of Kupffer's stellate cells of the liver which resulted in a marked local proliferation of cells. As a matter of fact, these lesions have been found frequently (Yoshida, 1942), but it was not until that time that lesions with local cell proliferation that looked like leukemic infiltration suggested a connection with the Yoshida sarcoma.

Subsequent speculation was that the azo dye-induced hepatoma is constituted of two different kinds of cancerized cells—one derived from hepatic (epithelial) cells and the other from Kupffer cells—which are growing together. Microscopic evidence was sought that would demonstrate combined growth of the two types of malignant cells and, on the other hand, attempted ascitic conversion of azo dye-induced hepatomas in the hope that separation of the two cell lines would occur in the ascitic growth. If after separation the tumor cell lines derived from the Kupffer cell would overcome the other, the result would be establishment of ascites tumor strains of reticuloendothelial origin—the reproduction of Yoshida sarcoma.

In any event, repeated attempts on ascitic conversion of hepatoma, initiated by a misleading speculation, led us, in the end, to studies on ascites hepatoma.

III. Ascites Hepatoma in Rats

A. EXPERIMENTAL ANIMALS

From the beginning of studies on Yoshida sarcoma to those on ascites hepatoma, "pure" strains of rats were not used, partly because inbred rats were not available in Japan, especially in the period of 1940's and 1950's. Even if they were available, it was likely that commercial hybrid animals would have been preferred for this series of experiments.

During studies on azo dye-induced hepatomas attempts were made to transplant into wild brown sewer rats. At that time it seemed that pathological animal experiments, such as carcinogenesis or transplantation of tumors, should first be started with most common hybrid animals, because humans are too far removed from inbred animals and the primary aim of experiments employing laboratory animals is to assist the research of human cancer. Natural variations, such as individual differences in the rate of incidence as well as growth rates of azo dye-induced hepatomas, and differences in their transplantability were thought to be important in connection with pathological and clinical information on human cancer.

Among hybrid rats, only about 5% showed resistance to transplantation of the Yoshida sarcoma. Satoh (1955) tried inbreeding of these resistant animals and found that the number of resistant animals increased to 45% in F_3 colony. Partially resistant animals in which transplanted tumors grew more slowly, and which existed among untreated hybrid animals, also increased.

Around 1952, the Yoshida sarcoma was introduced into rats bred from a closed colony started from a pair of hybrid rats (Yoshida, 1958) called "Donryu," the place where the animals came from. Practically a 100% take of the Yoshida sarcoma occurred in rats of this colony despite the fact that the tumor had originated in 1943 in a rat entirely unrelated to the Donryu strain. This 100% take—continuing unchanged to the present—was useful.

In the first half of studies on the ascitic conversion of azo dye-induced hepatomas, there was chance that hepatomas induced in hybrid rats were transplanted into Donryu rats but, in the second half, both induction and transplantation were carried out with Donryus. Between the first and second half, to be described later, noteworthy differences have been observed in the results.

Gradually the Donryu rat became known, and it may be said that it is at present one of the most popular laboratory rats in Japan. However, it seems rather unnatural that resistance to the Yoshida sarcoma is not observed. Reluctance to employ genetically controlled animals in these studies is due partly to the fact that they were practically lacking in Japan and partly to conservative attitudes toward experimental animals. Irregular phenomena based on the individual conditions of animals induce problems. No doubt, the so-called "pure-strain" animals with minimal individual differences and fed on standardized diets are quite useful for accurate and detailed analysis of these problems and for approaches to their solution.

B. Techniques and Results of Ascitic Conversion

For induction of hepatoma in rats by feeding, three compounds were used: o-aminoazotoluene (o-AAT) (4'-amino-2,3'-dimethylazobenzene); 4-dimethylaminoazobenzene (DAB); and 3'-methyl-4-aminoazobenzene (3'-Me-DAB). In the early stage of the work ranging over 27 years, o-AAT was used; DAB and 3'-Me-DAB were introduced later. The capacity of inducing hepatomas, measured roughly by the time required for development of tumors sufficient for experimental use, is in the reverse order of the above list.

In an early stage, o-AAT was dissolved in olive oil and mixed with coarsely crushed rice grains and fed to animals with colored rice grains. After standardized mixed diet (cube diet) for rats was developed, the compounds were mixed in the cube diet in definite percentage as indicated in Table II. This percentage may be changed according to the experimental objective.

TABLE II

Components of Basic Cube Diet

Substance	gm/kg
Carbohydrate	510
Crude protein	240
Crude fat	35
Salt mixture	90
Vegetable fiber	45
Water	80

Experimental Diet[a]	
DAB[b]	0.060%
3'-Me-DAB[c]	0.050%

[a] Each substance of the Experimental Diet, in the above-indicated percentages, is mixed with the basic diet before it is made into cubes.
[b] 4-Dimethylaminoazobenzene.
[c] 3'-Methyl-4-aminoazobenzene.

The main difference between the standardized cube diet and the previous one is the high content of protein in the former. The influence of protein-rich diet on the development of hepatoma is not defined, but the hepatomas grew faster on protein-rich diets.

Animals generally weighed 100 gm at the beginning of experiments. On a protein-rich diet, they reach this body weight in 7 to 8 weeks after birth, whereas on the older diet it used to take about 10 weeks to reach this body weight.

The period needed for sufficient development of hepatoma for transplantation is variable; Table III shows the optimal times. It seems desirable to wait several weeks after stopping the azo dye feeding for "good" hepatomas to develop. This waiting time depends on the length of feeding time. The animals are usually killed by inhalation of ether.

TABLE III

RESULTS OF TRANSPLANTATION OF HEPATOMAS DEVELOPED IN
RATS FED WITH 3'-METHYL-4-AMINOAZOBENZENE FOR 3 TO 6 MONTHS

Months of feeding	No. of cases	Failed		Successful	
		No.	%	No.	%
3	13	6	46	7	54
4	18	6	33	12	66
5	25	7	28	18	72
6	27	6	22	21	78

1. Conversion of Hepatoma Nodules

A hepatoma nodule (eventually cut off *in situ* before removing the whole liver) is minced as finely as possible with scissors or with tissue press. Saline is added to make it easy for the cells to pass through a 16–19-gauge needle.

For the transplantation of this primary material, customarily 5 animals are used; empirically, this number is sufficient.

After about 1 week, test abdominal punctures are made for the ascites. For this purpose a fine glass capillary (22–25 gauge) is preferable. Even in case of successful conversion in the first trial, it is rare to have sufficient accumulation of the ascites in a week and it takes usually 2–3 weeks.

The overall results of the ascitic conversion carried out during 1956 to 1960 are summarized in Table IV. Out of 204 trials, ascitic conversion of hepatoma nodules was successful in 13 (6.4%) cases, whereas in the other 58 (29.4%) cases of successful transplantation, the conversion failed and the tumor took on solid form. Transplantability in total was 34.8% (71/204). Among these 71 transplantable hepatomas, 13, or 18.4% (13/71), were convertible into the ascitic form.

In experiments exclusively using Donryu rats, the incidence of both tumor induction and transplantation increased. Transplantability of the tumors almost doubled and convertibility of the transplantable hepatomas to ascites in Donryu series was 28.0% (16/57) against 18.4% in hybrids.

TABLE IV

RESULTS OF INTRAPERITONEAL TRANSPLANTATION OF
AZO DYE-INDUCED HEPATOMA "NODULES" (1956–1960)

No. of hepatomas	Successful transplantations		
	In solid form	In ascitic form	Total
204	58^a(29.4%)	13(6.4%)	71(34.8%)

^{a} Five of these transformed later into ascitic growth.

From all these results it may be said roughly that the azo dye-induced hepatoma was convertible into ascitic form in 20 to 30% of transplantable tumors.

2. Transplantation with Primary Tumor Ascites

It is not rare to find a considerable accumulation of tumor ascites in animals at the terminal stage of azo dye-induced hepatoma. The incidence is estimated to be in less than 30% of overall hepatoma animals. The amount of ascites fluid and the content of tumor cells suspended in it vary over a wide range. This ascites serves as a good source for establishing ascites hepatomas.

An example of such an experiment is as follows: A droplet of the ascites is taken on a glass slide and covered with 18 × 18-mm cover glass, and the number of tumor cells found within the whole visual field under the cover glass is counted. Every ascitic fluid from separate hepatoma animals, which contained more than two tumor cells within the visual field, was transplanted into the abdominal cavity of normal rats. In 31 out of 136 trials (22.8%), the transplantation was successful, and in 19 cases (14.0%) the tumor showed the ascitic growth, whereas in 12 cases (8.8%) it resulted in solid growth (Table V).

TABLE V

RESULTS OF INTRAPERITONEAL TRANSPLANTATION WITH
SPONTANEOUS TUMOR ASCITES IN PRIMARY AZO
DYE-INDUCED HEPATOMA ANIMALS (1956–1960)

No. of hepatoma animals	Successful transplantations		
	In ascitic form	In solid form	Total
136	19(14.0%)	12(8.8%)	31(22.8%)

Compared with the above results of experiments with hepatoma nodules (cf. Table IV), the ratio of ascitic and solid growths in the positively transplanted cases is reversed. In the former the solid growth surpassed by far the ascitic (58:13), whereas in the latter the ascitic surpassed the solid, although the difference was not as much as the former (19:12). However, it is noteworthy that the transplantation with the ascitic tumor material did not necessarily result in the formation of ascitic growth. The ratio between ascitic and solid takes was almost 3:2.

The overall transplantabilities of ascitic and solid tumors, although they showed difference of 22.8 to 34.8% (Tables IV and V), are not easy to compare, since the content of tumor cells in the ascitic materials varies largely.

In an experiment carried out in this regard during 1958 to 1960 (Table VI), the content of tumor cells in the ascitic fluid was counted by the microscopic method described above. It is quite evident that transplantability depends on the number of cells transplanted.

TABLE VI

RELATION BETWEEN SUCCESSFUL TRANSPLANTATION AND NUMBER
OF TUMOR CELLS IN PRIMARY ASCITES (1958–1960)

Amount of cells in ascites[a]	No. of tumor animals	Successful trans-plantations in ascites form
Very few	16	1 (6.3%)
Few (<10)	28	2 (7.2%)
Many (>10)	6	1 (16.7%)
Very many	7	3 (42.9%)

[a] A droplet of ascites on a slide glass is covered with cover glass; amount of cells in the visual field under the cover glass is examined.

3. Establishment of Transplant Strains

Transplant strains of ascites hepatoma were established by serial transplantation of tumor ascites developed in the successfully transplanted animals regardless of whether primary material of inoculation was solid or ascitic. During 1951 to 1962, fifty-nine transplant strains were established. These strains were marked with an AH sign to the number. Some of these strains showed unusual courses before being finally established (Yoshida et al., 1956, 1957, and 1958). Sometimes a significant accumulation of tumor ascites (a state of pure culture of tumor cells) which was present in the first recipient animal disappeared suddenly later, but the second transplantation that was made before the disappearance took so perfectly that the transplant strain was established from it.

Cases such as the following were not rare. Tumors took in the first generation in the solid form (irrespective of the form of the primary inoculum—nodular or ascitic) without producing significant ascites. Then transplantations (following the ascitic conversion technique) with tumor nodules developed on the peritoneal surface were tried again. After repeating the same procedure for several transplant generations the solid tumors changed into the ascitic form. This change may correspond to the "indirect conversion" of Klein and Klein (1956), but, in the case of hepatomas, it did not occur in such a way that the amount of ascitic fluid increased gradually generation by generation in order to overcome, at least, the solid tumor formation. Instead, the change occurred suddenly in every case in one transplantation after several repetitions. As an extreme case, this change was observed in the fourteenth transplant generation (Odasima, personal communication).

IV. Comparative Studies with Ascites Hepatomas

As mentioned above, during 1951 to 1962, fifty-nine transplant strains of ascites hepatoma were established in the author's laboratory. After that many strains were established for various purposes. A certain number of them were derived from separate hepatoma nodules developed in the same liver of the same animal. Some others were established as sublines of already established strains and were distinguished from the original strains by change of characteristics to be discussed below.

That two or more ascites hepatoma strains of evidently different characteristics have been established from separate hepatoma nodules developed in the same animal became an attractive research subject for our group, and Odashima (1964), Ishidate (1968), and others have carried out further studies in this line.

Starting with transplantation rate and survival time of tumor-bearing animals, results of comparative studies on these ascites hepatoma strains will be outlined below.

A. TRANSPLANTABILITY AND SURVIVAL TIME

The rate of transplantation and survival time of tumor-bearing animals of twenty-eight ascites hepatoma strains which were established in an earlier period are indicated in Table VII. As seen in the

II. COMPARATIVE STUDIES OF ASCITES HEPATOMAS   111

TABLE VII

Transplant Strains of Ascites Hepatomas (1951–1960)

Strain	Established in	Transplantation		Average survival in days (max.–min.)
		Generation	Rate	
AH-130	1951	400	96.5	12 (5–89)
AH-7974	1952	360	96.5	12 (5–76)
AH-601	1952	260	85.7	16 (6–133)
AH-602	1952	280	93.7	16 (6–120)
AH-66	1954	250	90.0	13 (5–156)
AH-63	1955	200	80.7	15 (6–126)
AH-149	1955	180	91.8	13 (5–139)
AH-39	1955	180	86.4	16 (5–150)
AH-49	1955	190	81.8	14 (6–101)
AH-99	1956	170	90.8	11 (6–83)
AH-66F	1956	181	87.7	10 (5–95)
AH-322	1957	150	81.0	12 (5–90)
AH-414	1957	130	74.9	15 (6–160)
AH-21	1957	150	89.3	8 (5–84)
AH-318	1957	160	91.0	8 (5–110)
AH-423	1957	151	63.7	17 (6–105)
AH-13	1957	172	94.7	8 (4–63)
AH-62	1957	120	92.2	13 (5–79)
AH-173	1958	110	79.5	13 (5–71)
AH-408	1958	100	82.9	13 (5–147)
AH-310	1958	80	77.8	15 (7–95)
AH-311	1958	90	72.9	13 (8–97)
AH-272	1958	110	96.4	9 (5–87)
AH-286	1958	70	76.2	17 (6–100)
AH-127	1958	50	93.6	18 (8–83)
AH-62F	1959	20	90.5	19 (11–58)
AH-44	1959	10	61.3	13 (7–39)
AH-34	1960	10	45.0	22 (20–86)

table, the transplantation rate differs even among tumor strains that have passed through more than 150 transplant generations, over the range of 63.7 to 96.5%, and the survival time over the range of 8 to 17 days.

As to the transplantation rate of malignant tumors in general, it is commonly accepted that the rate increases gradually generation by generation. Seemingly, there is no firm support to this acceptance. Selection of "more malignant" cells through animal passages used to be discussed. If this is true, every tumor strain should come close to 100% "malignancy" after continuation of a certain series of transplantation, but this is not so in reality. Some strains in Table VII have a low rate for a long time. In some strains, the transplantation rate and the survival time remain quite stable from the beginning. Figures 1 and 2 show examples of this relationship. In two strains, AH-7974 (Fig. 1) and AH-13 (Fig. 2), the two values have remained almost unchanged from the beginning to 400 and 200 transplant generations, respectively.

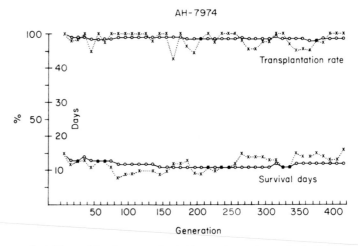

FIG. 1. Stability of both transplantation rate and survival time from the beginning (AH-7974). (---×---) Average value for every ten transplant generations; (○—○—○) average value of sum total calculated at every tenth generation.

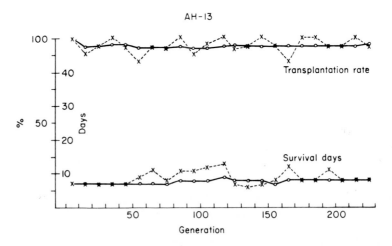

FIG. 2. Stability of both transplantation rate and survival time from the beginning (AH-13). (---×---) Average value for every ten transplant generations; (—○—○—) average value of sum total calculated at every tenth generation.

Odashima (1964) surveyed all the records relative to the transplantation rate and survival time, which have accumulated in our institute from the very beginning of studies on the ascitic conversion of the hepatoma. Many interesting figures, besides the afore indicated two, were prepared.

For hepatoma AH-272 (Fig. 3) a gradual increase in the transplantation rate and a gradual decrease in the survival time occurred, and then the two values became stationary at about the hundredth generation. This example agrees with the general expectation that in tumors of high transplantability the survival time should be short, since it is generally accepted that the rate of transplantation of a tumor is an indicator of its "malignancy."

However, there was a case, hepatoma AH-62F, which showed just the opposite relationship for the transplantability and survival time (Fig. 4). With the decrease in the transplantability, the survival time was prolonged. It is more common that the rate of transplantation increases, and the survival time decreases. Actually, from the point of view of "selection," it is difficult to expect other relations of the two variables because this implies selection of "less malignant" cells. As a matter of fact, the greater part of the hepatomas showed, with the

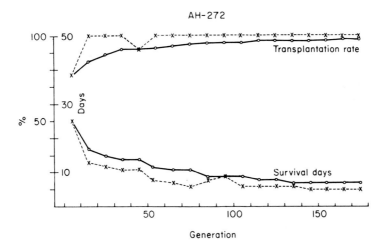

FIG. 3. Instability of both transplantation rate and survival time (AH-272). The transplantation rate increased gradually from initial rate of 80% to reach a constant rate of 100% at about the hundredth generation. The survival days shortened gradually, from the initial level of more than 20 days to the constant level of about 10 days. (In both the transplantability and the survival time the "grade of malignancy" has, according to expectation, gradually increased.) (---×---) Average value for every ten transplant generations; (—○—○—) average value of sum total calculated at every tenth generation.

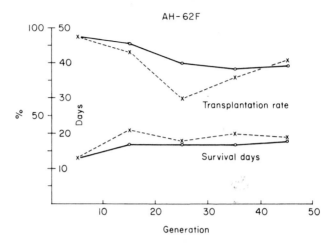

FIG. 4. Instability of both transplantation rate and survival time (AH-62F). An example of the opposite of Fig. 3. Along with decrease in the transplantation rate, the survival time was prolonged. (With the progress of serial transplantation, the "grade of malignancy" has decreased.) (--- ✕ ---) Average value for every ten transplant generations; (— ○— ○—) average value of sum total calculated at every tenth generation.

progress of serial transplantation, an increase in the transplantation rate and decrease in the survival time. Among different ascites hepatoma strains, however, there were cases, besides hepatoma AH-62F, which showed an unusual type of interrelation of the transplantation rate and survival time, e.g., Figs. 5 and 6. In each of these illustrations, the grade of "malignancy" of the tumor inferred from its transplantability is contradictory to that inferred from the survival time.

In summarizing the cases described above, it is obvious that both the rate of transplantation and the survival time can change in either direction—increase or decrease. On the other hand, it has also been demonstrated that these two characters of the transplanted tumor do not always have a definite interrelation and that they may be independent of one another.

For the two variables, there are five types of possibilities, as shown in Fig. 7. Each example in Figs. 1 to 6 belongs to one of the five types. Among thirty-seven strains examined, twenty-two belonged to Type II and ten to Type I. The remaining three types had either 2 cases or only 1, as indicated in Fig. 7.

The majority of cases were in Type II, indicating that, in the greater number of cases of transplantation, a tumor increases its transplantability, and together with this increased transplantability, it kills the host animal increasingly faster. This agrees with the general expectation

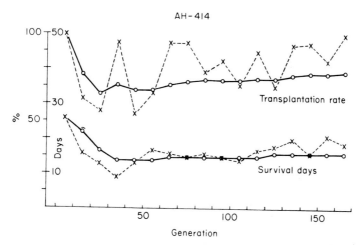

FIG. 5. An example of unusual contradiction between the transplantation rate and survival time (AH-414). Although the survival time shortened (the tumor became more malignant) the transplantability decreased (became less malignant). (———×———) Average value for every ten transplant generations; (— O— O—) average value of sum total calculated at every tenth generation.

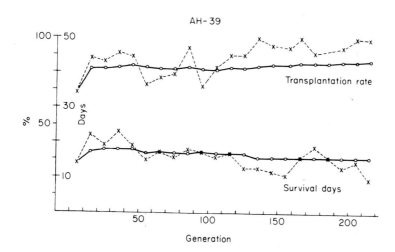

FIG. 6. An example (AH-39) of the opposite of Fig. 5. In the first fifty transplant generations, the transplantability increased (became more malignant) but, contrary to expectation, the survival time was prolonged (became less malignant). (———×———) Average value per every ten transplant generations; (— O— O—) average value of sum total calculated at every tenth generation.

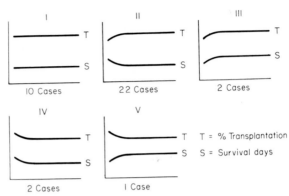

FIG. 7. Five patterns of possible interrelation between the transplantation rate and survival time.

that a tumor becomes more malignant in the course of transplantation through the process of selecting cells of greater malignancy.

On the other hand, attention should be paid to the fact that there are some cases in which the interrelation between the transplantability and survival time behaves differently. Although they are not great in number they should not be disregarded. In these cases, it is seen that, although the range of the takes of a tumor becomes broader, the time required for killing the host animal is prolonged and vice versa. This may indicate a discrepancy between the concept of malignancy and transplantability.

Multiple factors determining the transplantability of tumors and the survival time of inoculated animals are beyond analysis with present techniques, but, in an attempt to interpret the parallelism or discrepancy between the transplantability and survival time, assumption of two determining factors as explained in the following seems to be helpful to some extent.

1. Compatibility

The rate of transplantation of a given tumor is not always 100% in hybrid animals. This implies that a certain number of animals that are "incompatible" with that tumor exist naturally (Hauschka, 1953). The range of distribution of these incompatible animals (in the same species) is not uniform for every transplantable tumor, but every tumor has its own range of distribution of such animals.

2. Virulence

If the time required for killing the host is designated as virulence of a tumor, this virulence is also not uniform. Every tumor has its own virulence.

Compatibility and virulence as presumed above are helpful for interpretation of the cases presented in Figs. 4 and 5. Thus, one can argue that it is usual that tumors with broad compatibility have high virulence and vice versa, but there are tumors with high virulence despite narrowness of compatibility and vice versa.

The following experiments carried out by Satoh (Satoh, 1952 and 1953) are of interest. During the long course of transplantation of ascites hepatomas there was formed a colony by many animals which survived the transplantation; these were called simply "negative animals." Each had proved once to be incompatible with any one of the ascites hepatoma strains, but compatibility of each of them with any other strain was not known. Then, in 51 animals of this colony retransplantation with AH-99 was tried. The transplantability of AH-99 is as high as 90.8% (Table VII). The transplantation rate of AH-99 in the negative animals was reduced by more than half from the rate in normal animals. This result showed that a great number of animals of the negative colony were resistant again to AH-99, whereas a small number were compatible with this tumor.

Another experiment in the same line was carried out with another colony of negative animals (126 in number) which survived the transplantation of primary hepatoma, used for the purpose of ascitic conversion. The result was essentially the same. In this experiment more animals were compatible with AH-99.

The presumption of both compatibility and virulence was induced from the individuality concept of the malignant cell (Yoshida, 1957). This idea is also applicable to an interpretation for the earliest stage of cancer development, which is actually beyond the direct human observation, with the result that the origin of the whole malignant growth which develops in a host is traced ultimately to a single malignant cell (Yoshida, 1963). Under a certain cancerogenous circumstance of an organ or tissue, many cells may undergo cancerous change and acquire, respectively, their own individuality as a cancer cell, which is transferred unchanged to the descendant cells through their continuous multiplication. The result of multiplication of these numerous original cancer cells is a mosaic aggregation of numerous clonal colonies of cancer cells which differ more or less, and sometimes a great deal, from one another as to the respective original ancestor cells, especially in virulence and in compatibility with the host organism. This is the image of the earliest stage of cancer development depicted on the basis of the individuality concept.

As the growth of the tumor—actually, the growth of respective constituent clones—progresses, it is natural that there occurs a process of competition or selection, relating to virulence and compatibility, among the clones, and, consequently, the tumor as a whole acquires a "homogeneous state." When a tumor at last reaches this homogeneity, the origin of this tumor as a whole can be traced back to a single cancer cell. In some cases, of course, a state of coexistence of several clones may continue for a long time, presenting a tumor of "heterogeneous cell constitution."

If a heterogeneous tumor of this kind is taken as an inoculum for transplantation—not for subcutaneous grafting of solid tumor (cf. Section II) but for intraperitoneal transplantation with the objective of ascitic conversion—and it takes, competition and selection among the constituent clones must take place anew in the series of new hosts, because the counterbalance of compatibilities of respective clones becomes changed in the new hosts. The fluctuation of the transplantation rate and survival time which is observed in the series of continuing transplantations is regarded as the reflection of the competition among the clones in the inocula. This lability comes to an end after a certain series of animal passages which bring a gradual stabilization in the further serial transplantations.

On the other hand, when a tumor that has become homogeneous in its primary growth is taken as the original inoculum, both transplantability and survival time will be stable from the beginning. Tumors indicated in Figs. 1 and 2 will be regarded as representative of this kind of tumor.

As stated in the beginning of this Section, ascites hepatoma strains derived from separate hepatoma nodules developed in the same liver showed different characteristics from each other just as the strains derived from separate animals differed from each other.

This investigation of establishing ascites hepatoma strains from separate hepatoma nodules of the same liver was primarily initiated on the basis of the aforementioned mosaic concept of clones of cancer development, and the results obtained agreed with the expectation that multiple nodules would be variable. Recently, Ishidate (1968) established four strains from four nodules and demonstrated that all of them were evidently different from each other.

B. QUALITY OF ASCITIC FLUID

Although white milky fluid should be taken for the typical quality of tumor ascites, there are many kinds of modifications among different strains of ascites hepatomas. The most marked is the difference in the content of the red blood cell.

Hemorrhage in ascitic fluids is a frequent occurrence, especially in the terminal stage of tumor growth. In some strains, evident hemorrhage occurs regularly in 3 to 4 days after the transplantation and continues to the termination of the growth. In such cases, hemorrhage is regarded as very likely one of the original characteristics. In other strains, hemorrhage is not regularly associated.

The "thickness" of ascitic fluid or the proportion of the cell number to the fluid is also not uniform. In general, "thin" ascites with a large volume of fluid tend to accumulate in a large amount and to result in marked abdominal expansion. In such cases, abdominal puncture for the examination of the ascites is easy. In "thick" ascites with a large cell content, the amount of ascites is usually small. A strain difference in this condition of the ascites, thick and thin, is not evident.

In the terminal stage of ascitic tumor growth, there is a general tendency for the ascites to become abundant due to increased exudation. At this stage, the infiltrative growth of tumor cells in the abdominal tissues becomes evident, indicating a gradual transition of the place of cell growth from the peritoneal cavity into the tissue. Therefore, as a tool for cancer research ascites tumors should be more useful in the first half of their ascitic tumor growth.

C. Metastasis

The formation of metastasis is not a significant result in ascites hepatoma probably because there is too short a survival time of tumor-bearing animals. In animals that either survived unusually long or survived long after chemotherapeutic experiments, metastases are not very rare.

With respect to metastasis, a comparative study was made of the earliest time when tumor cells were found circulating in the bloodstream after intraperitoneal transplantation of various strains (Kurata, 1959). In humans, examinations for cancer cells in the bloodstream can only be made by examination of stained preparations of the blood. With ascites hepatomas (or ascites tumors in general), a kind of bioassay is available. If the blood of tumor animals to be examined contains a certain number of tumor cells, even in very small amounts, inoculation of that blood into the peritoneal cavity of normal animals results in tumor growth. It has been confirmed with ascites hepatoma AH-13 (and later with several other strains) that transplantation with a single cell was successful (Isaka et al., 1954).

In Table VIII, the results are summarized of studies of blood-borne dissemination of hepatoma cells by the bioassay system. It was confirmed in some strains that tumor cells were circulating in the bloodstream as early as 24 hours after inoculation. Successful confirmation of the same fact by the usual stained preparation of the blood smear was not made until 3 days after inoculation.

TABLE VIII

EARLIEST APPEARANCE OF TRANSPLANTED
ASCITES HEPATOMA CELLS IN BLOOD CIRCULATION[a]

Strain	Days		Strain	Days	
	In heart blood[b]	In smear preparation		In heart blood[b]	In smear preparation
AH-13	1	3	AH-63	7	13
AH-66F	1	5	AH-62	7	—
AH-130	3	6	AH-322	7	—
AH-21	3	7	AH-99	7–10	10
AH-7974	4	8	AH-602	7–10	—
AH-149	4	9	AH-601	7–10	—
AH-49	4	10	AH-414	7–10	—
AH-39	4	15	AH-423	10–15	—
AH-66	4	—	AH-364	10–15	9
AH-318	7	7			

[a] From Kurata, 1959.
[b] Tested by transplantation with the blood taken from the left heart chamber
every 24 hours after transplantation of ascites hepatoma.

Tumor cells found in the circulating blood by smear preparations
are either isolated individual cells or pairs (see Section IV,D). Larger-
sized cell conglomerates (islands; Section IV,D) have so far not been
found. From this fact it is considered that in those strains that are
rich in isolated free tumor cells, metastasis formation would be earlier
and more frequent.

However, the results did not necessarily agree with this expectation.
At autopsy of ascites hepatoma animals that died in due course of

TABLE IX

FREQUENCY OF LYMPH NODE METASTASIS AT AUTOPSY

Survival (days)	In lymph node in the mediastinum	
	Frequent (hepatoma strain)	Rare (hepatoma strain)
> 10	AH-13	AH-21, 272, 318
11–15	AH-44, 62, 49, 66, 66F, 130, 149, 173, 322, 414, 7974	AH-63, 99, 310, 311, 408
16 >	AH-62F, 127	AH-34, 39, 286, 423, 601, 602

respective strains, the metastasis formations (if any) are found predominantly in the lymph nodes of the chest cavity and the retroperitoneum. According to the frequency of these metastasis formations, the ascites hepatoma strains can be divided into two groups, as indicated in Table IX. What is seen from this table is that (*1*) metastasis is not always frequent in strains of longer survival time, and (*2*) frequency of metastasis does not necessarily parallel with abundance of isolated free cells in the ascites. The latter relation will become clear by comparison of Tables IX and X.

TABLE X

RATIO OF FREE CELLS AND ISLANDS IN ASCITES OF TUMORS
OF FREQUENT LYMPH NODE METASTASIS[a]

Strain	Free cells (%)	Smaller islands of less than 4 cells (%)	Larger islands of more than 5 cells (%)
AH-13	97.4	2.6	0
AH-66F	100.0	0	0
AH-414	96.8	2.8	0.4
AH-130	94.1	3.6	2.3
AH-66	39.8	26.0	34.2
AH-62	22.9	10.1	67.0
AH-7974	17.7	49.3	33.0
AH-173	16.3	14.8	68.9
AH-49	8.8	13.9	77.3
AH-44	7.3	20.8	71.9
AH-322	6.1	12.0	81.9
AH-149	5.3	14.4	80.3
AH-62F	98.6	0.9	0.5
AH-127	20.0	18.5	61.5

[a] Examined with 4-day-old tumors. Ratio of free cells and islands in 500 of their total is indicated. In every strain an average of 4 tumors.

D. PICTURES OF ASCITES

The epithelial nature of the hepatic cell involved in intercellular bonding is inherited in the hepatoma cells, so that they form cell clusters of various sizes and shapes by bonding of the cells. These formations are called "hepatoma islands." The microscopic picture of tumor ascites is defined by these islands (Plate I).

Extremely large islands, having a diameter of around 1 mm, can be recognized by the naked eye, but islands of that size are quite rare. In the majority of cases, innumerable islands of much smaller sizes are scattered under the microscope.

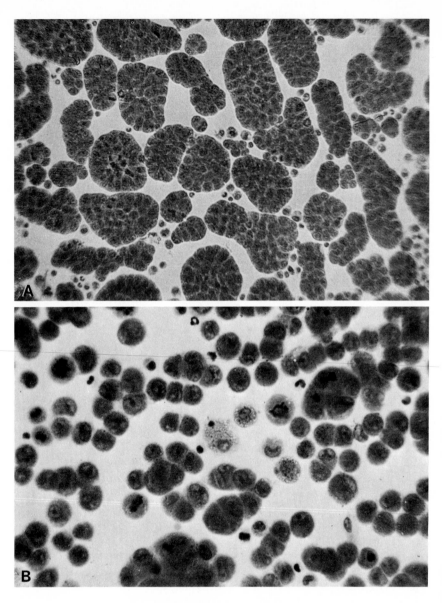

PLATE I. A: Uniformly medium-sized islands with a few free cells and smaller islands like doublets and triplets (AH-7974). B: Small islands—doublets, triplets, free cells Incompact appearance of island formation (AH-130).

The island is regularly a solid globe composed merely of hepatoma cells, but exceptionally it can be hollow like a blastula (Plate I,D). The strain AH-602 of all the ascites hepatoma strains was so far the only one that showed hollow islands. In all other strains, the island was always solid, and no strain contained a mixture of solid and hollow islands.

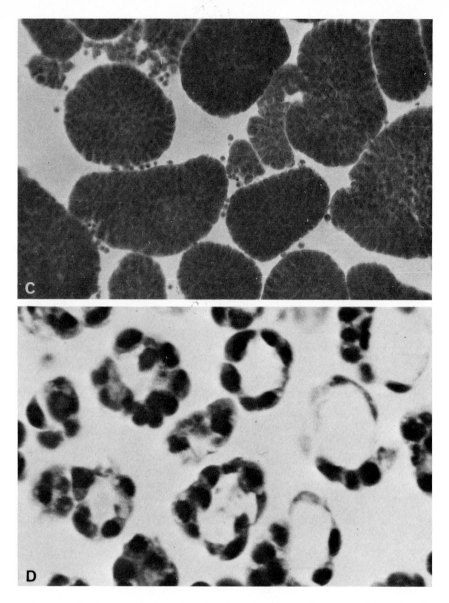

PLATE I. C: Large compact islands almost without free cells (AH-149). D: Hollow islands. (Centrifuged ascites fixed with formalin, embedded in paraffin, and sectioned.) (AH-602 only case of hollow islands examined so far.)

The shape of the island can be spherical, elongated, or irregular being quite variable in size. Among these islands, there are scattered many individually isolated cells and smaller islands, a bonding of two cells (pair or "doublet") or three cells (a "triplet"). The proportion of mixing of all these kinds of islands makes up the picture of the tumor ascites which is quite characteristic to each strain. It is not

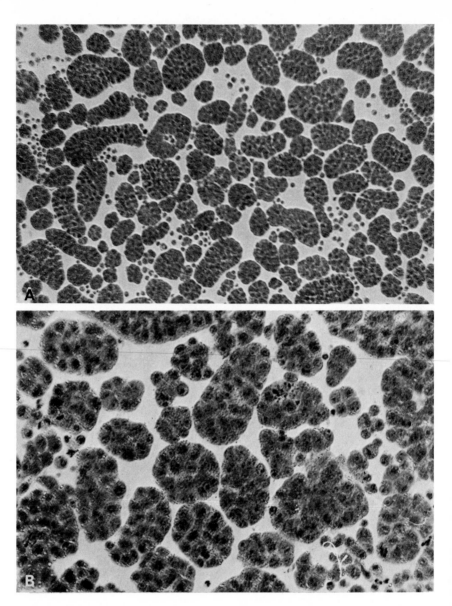

PLATE II. A and B: Ascites AH-7974 in 1953 (A) and 1958 (B). No changes noted.

only characteristic but constant, as a rule. For example, the picture of AH-7974, one of the oldest strains, has remained practically unchanged for more than 10 years (Plate II,A and B).

In Table XI, the variations in hepatoma island and free-cell distribution for twenty-eight strains are summarized. They are fairly strain-specific, and after a certain experience in studies with ascites hepatomas,

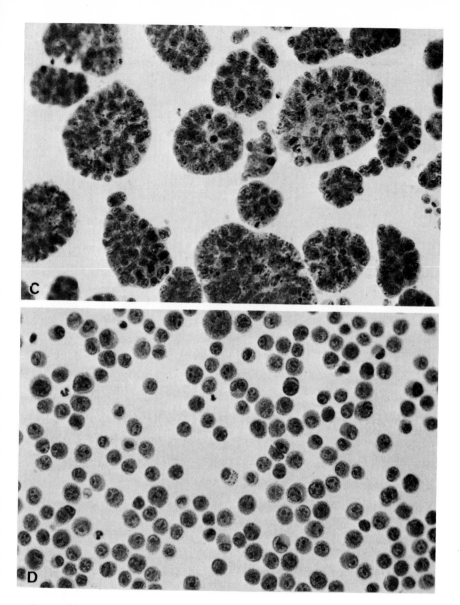

PLATE II. C and D: Island-type AH-62 (C) transformed to free-cell type AH-62F (D).

it is not very difficult, by looking at the ascitic picture, to distinguish the strain of origin. As a matter of fact, it was this strain specificity and stability of ascites pictures of hepatomas that first drew attention and brought about the idea of individuality of malignant growth.

However, in these ascites, a gradual change takes place which progresses very slowly through the course of years of serial transplantations.

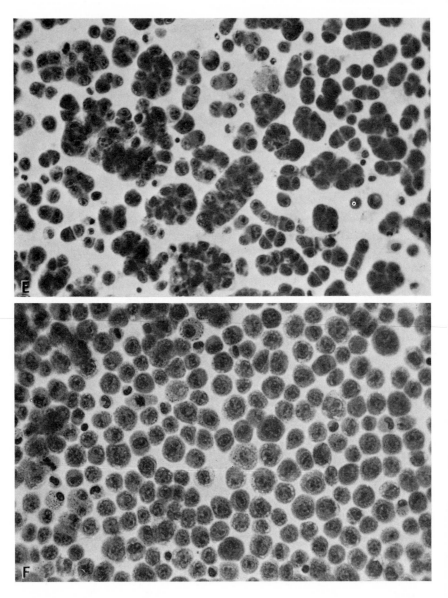

PLATE II. E and F: Island-type AH-66 (E) transformed to free-cell type AH-66F (F).

The picture of the AH-7974 have begun to show such a change in recent years. The islands have become generally smaller and now (1969), that is, after more than 800 transplant generations in 18 years since its origin, it is constituted of small islands and appears considerably different from that of the earlier stage. This kind of a change

TABLE XI

RATIO OF FREE CELLS AND ISLANDS IN
ASCITES HEPATOMAS (1951–1960)[a]

Strain	Free cells (%)	Hepatoma islands				
		"Doublets" (%)	"Triplets" (%)	Islands of 4 cells (%)	Islands of 5–10 cells (%)	Islands of more than 11 cells (%)
AH-66F	100.0	0	0	0	0	0
AH-62F	98.6	1.2	0	0.5	0.5	0
AH-13	97.4	2.5	0.1	0	0	0
AH-414	96.8	2.2	0.4	0.3	0.3	0.1
AH-39	96.1	3.4	0.3	0.1	0.1	0.1
AH-130	94.1	3.1	0.4	0.1	1.3	1.0
AH-21	90.1	7.7	0.9	0.5	0.6	0.4
AH-423	82.4	5.0	3.4	3.1	4.9	1.8
AH-272	72.5	9.2	3.3	1.9	6.1	7.0
AH-66	39.8	13.6	7.9	4.7	17.5	16.7
AH-63	29.8	25.7	11.7	8.0	17.1	7.6
AH-62	22.9	7.4	3.6	1.3	15.1	51.9
AH-34	21.8	15.5	8.8	5.9	20.5	26.3
AH-127	20.0	11.7	3.9	2.8	25.7	35.8
AH-7974	17.7	28.6	13.0	7.6	16.1	16.9
AH-173	16.3	8.3	3.8	2.8	7.0	61.9
AH-311	15.9	15.9	7.3	3.7	19.8	37.3
AH-310	13.2	13.9	5.4	2.1	12.7	52.5
AH-408	11.4	13.9	4.4	2.5	10.0	58.2
AH-49	8.8	8.4	3.6	1.9	16.9	60.4
AH-318	8.5	13.4	4.5	2.5	12.3	58.9
AH-44	7.3	9.9	6.0	4.7	37.9	34.2
AH-601	6.5	8.1	4.5	3.4	18.8	58.9
AH-602	6.5	3.1	1.2	0.9	12.3	75.9
AH-322	6.1	6.2	3.5	1.7	11.8	70.1
AH-149	5.3	7.5	3.5	3.5	32.1	48.2
AH-99	3.6	5.8	1.5	1.2	13.1	75.6
AH-286	1.8	1.8	0.6	0.6	3.6	93.1

[a] Examined with 4-day-old tumors. Ratio of free cells and islands in 500 of their total is indicated. In every strain an average of 4 tumors.

in the course of many years is common to every strain. Of great interest is a change that occurs suddenly in the picture of a strain.

In the AH-66 strain which was distributed to the Iatrochemical Institute, a striking change occurred in the ascitic picture without any noticeable inducement; the tumor changed in about three serial transplantations from island-type into perfect free-cell type (Plate IIE,F). The strain AH-66F was established with this changed tumor.

A similar change also occurred in AH-62. Strain AH-62F is the free-cell-type substrain of AH-62 which is itself a typical island type (Plate IIC,D). In this case, the tumor bank seemed to have provoked the change. On one occasion, the ascites of AH-62 which had been kept in the tumor bank ($-80\,^{\circ}$C) for 111 days was transplanted. It was successful, but the growth unexpectedly presented a free-cell type which was entirely different from the original one, and the new strain AH-62F was established therefrom. In the original strain which had been kept through animal passages, no such change occurred.

So far the changes are only in the direction of island to free-cell type (changes in the reverse direction will be discussed in Section V).

Both strains AH-66F and AH-62F have been kept as independent strains through more than 770 and 330 transplant generations (at the end of 1969), respectively, without showing any further change in the ascitic picture since their establishment. It was of interest to see what kind of other changes would take place in these substrains accompanying the change in their ascites pictures. The results of related examinations are summarized in Table XII. Most remarkable was the change in their drug resistance. Whereas the original AH-66 is resistant to nitrogen mustard N-oxide (Nitromin) (see Section IV,F), its substrain AH-66F proved quite sensitive to the same substance, but such a difference was not noted between AH-62 and its substrain. As to the survival time, whereas it was rather shortened in AH-66F, it was

TABLE XII

COMPARISON OF STRAINS AH-66, AH-62, AND THEIR
FREE-CELL SUBSTRAINS

Parameters	AH-66	AH-66F	AH-62	AH-62F
Condition at the conversion	—	—	—	Kept 111 days at $-80\,^{\circ}$C
Survival (days)	13	10	13	19
Transplantation rate	90.0	87.7	92.2	90.5
Ascites				
Red blood cells (%)	0–1	0–1	2	3
Free cells (%)	39.8	100.0	22.9	98.6
Sensitivity to nitrogen mustard N-oxide, MED (mg/kg)[a]	50	1	20	20

[a] MED—minimal effective dose.

obviously prolonged in AH-62F. Changes in chromosomes of the substrains will be discussed below (Section IV,E).

The fact that hepatoma cells sometimes show free-cell growth without any cell bonding, and look as if they have lost the epithelial character, is of interest from the point of view of morphology. As stated above, this is observed as a transformation during the continuation of serial transplantation of the tumors, but there are several instances in which this free-cell growth was seen from the beginning of ascitic conversion. As indicated in Table XI, in seven out of twenty-eight strains the percentage of individually isolated (free) cells in the tumor ascites is more than 90%. That the percentage of free cells is not 100%, except for AH-66F, means that by thorough examinations, the formation of small islands is occasionally found in the ascites (seemingly indicating that the loss of epithelial character is not complete).

In ascites hepatomas which have almost 100% free cells, it is not always easy to assume their epithelial origin by looking at the smear preparations. Their appearances are very closely, almost indistinguishably, similar to that of the Yoshida "sarcoma" which is a tumor of 100% free cells. Almost all cytological characteristics attributed to the Yoshida sarcoma cells will be found in free cells of ascites hepatomas (Plate IIIA–F).

This may not be a special problem for ascites tumors, because the epithelial and nonepithelial character is not a matter of distinction on the basis of individually separated cells—tiny spherical bodies—but it should not be disregarded from the point of view of pathological diagnosis of malignant growth. For instance, the ascites tumor S-37 was a mammary carcinoma originally, but it has entirely lost the morphological characteristics of epithelial cells and is designated as "sarcoma," a nonepithelial tumor. With the Ehrlich ascites tumor, this relation is the same. The Yoshida sarcoma will be discussed later in Section V.

There is a series of small experiments relating to individual isolation of tumor cells. Substances such as trypsin and Tween 80 are effective, *in vitro*, in causing hepatoma cells forming islands to become scattered, individually isolated cells (Yoshida *et al.*, 1951; Sato and Aruji, 1952; Essner *et al.*, 1954). Transplantation with material of such released isolated cells was successful just as with untreated original material but did not result in free-cell growth but instead in formation of islands characteristic to the original tumor (Yamada, 1962).

E. CHROMOSOMES

In 1956, only four strains were studied for the number of chromosomes. Although the technique of chromosome studies at that time was

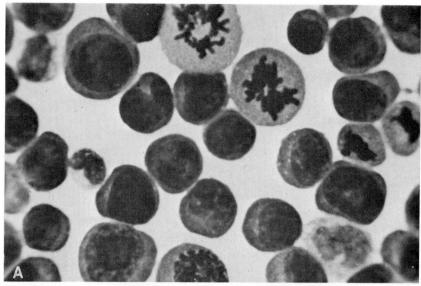

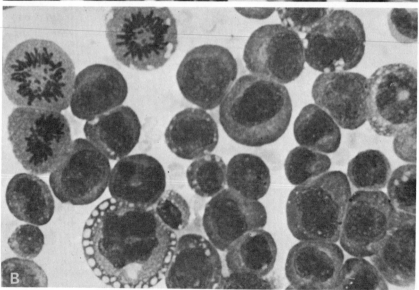

PLATE III. A: Yoshida sarcoma; B: AH-66F.

inadequate, the results obtained were unexpectedly interesting (Fig. 8A).

In each strain, 100 nuclear plates of 4-day-old tumors were examined for their chromosome number, and the results were compared with each other. Most striking was the fact that the modes of distribution of chromosome number differed between AH-130 and AH-601 (AH-602) by about 20. The

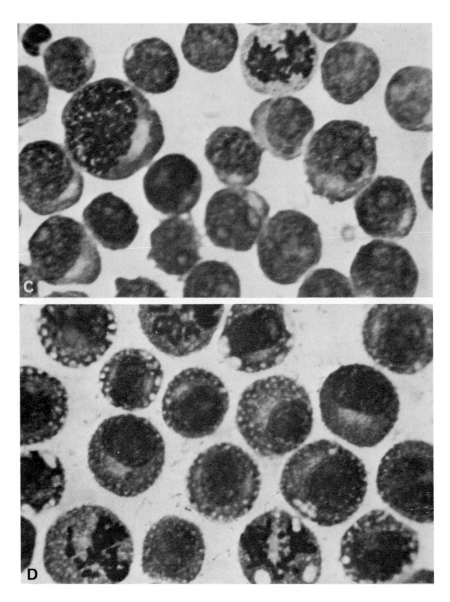

PLATE III. C: AH-414; D: AH-13.

difference between AH-7974 and AH-130 was 3, comparatively slight, but significant. It is probably not surprising that the chromosome number of AH-601 and AH-602, tumors of the same descent, was identical.

As is well known, the regular chromosome number of the rat is 42 and any fluctuation of this chromosome number is not observed as a rule. From this point of view, the most striking fact among the results

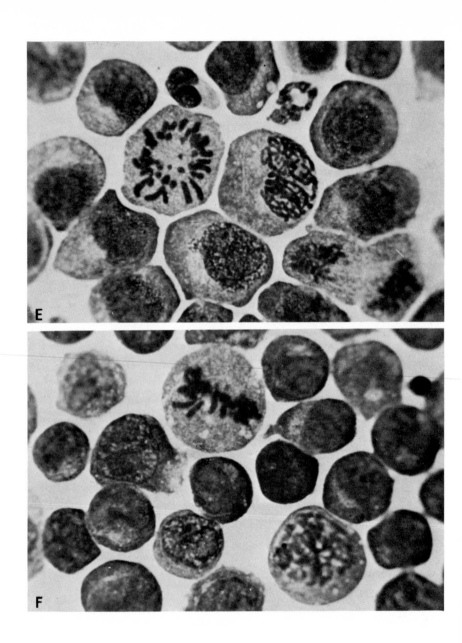

Plate III. E: AH-39; F: AH-62F.

was that in every hepatoma this regular number was lost and the number of chromosomes fluctuated over a wide range. This fluctuation had a mode and the range of fluctuation around the modal number, that is, the pattern of the distribution of chromosome number, seemed to be characteristic to each strain.

This became more evident by the experiment of establishing single cell-derived, clonal sublines of AH-130 (Fig. 8B). Examinations for the chromosome number in each clonal substrain were performed employing 4-day-old tumors after passage through forty-one transplant generations. The modes of chromosome distribution of the three substrains agreed with each other and also with the mode of the mother strain AH-130. This conformity of the three clonal substrains to the mother strain suggested strongly not only the stability of chromosomal pattern of each tumor but that it was imparted to each descendant cell.

These preliminary studies that resulted in the demonstration of individual chromosomal type of hepatomas were carried out by Isaka, Nakamura, and Odashima (1954, 1955). Isaka has pursued further this line of work and has so far carried out the examination of chromosome number along with morphological studies in twenty-four strains.

It has been demonstrated, confirming preliminary studies, that each hepatoma has its own distribution pattern of the chromosome number. Among several tumors, the patterns looked quite similar to one another, but these tumors always showed differences in the idiogram of the chromosomes (see below). These findings showed that no two hepatomas have been observed which agreed entirely with each other in the chromosome pattern.

Only two among twenty-four strains had a mode in the slightly hypodiploid region, and seven strains in the slightly hyperdiploid region. In these strains, the modal number has a very narrow fluctuation range (Fig. 9A). On the contrary, in strains which have the modal number in either hypo- or hypertetraploid regions the fluctuation range is generally very wide, without showing a predominantly high peak of the modal number (Fig. 9B and C). In tumors with the predominant modal number in the diploid region, there is often a small variant mode in the tetraploid region (Fig. 9A).

The chromosome pattern of each strain remains unchanged, as a rule, throughout years of serial transplantations. For example, AH-39 and AH-66F were examined for the chromosome number twice at 2-year intervals. The results are shown in Fig. 10. Both strains showed marked stability in the chromosome pattern. However, it is not rare that a slight shift of the modal number in either the increasing or the decreasing direction is observed during hundreds of transplant generations.

Incidentally, a complete shift of the mode from the hypodiploid region to the hypotetraploid region was observed in strain AH-66F which had exhibited, as stated above, a marked stability of the chromosome pattern for many years. This shift occurred as a gradual process during about 150 transplant generations (about 3 years) and this process was recorded by Isaka as shown in Fig. 11.

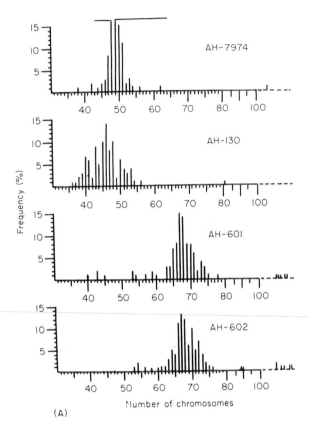

FIG. 8. (A) Different mode of distribution of chromosome number of four ascites hepatoma strains.

The shift of the modal number which is, in principle, the same as that described above, also occurred in the experiment of cloning with the same AH-66F tumor (Fig. 12). Before AH-66F had undergone a shift of the mode, a clonal substrain of the tumor was established (original clone in Fig. 12; the mode at 38). From this clonal strain, six subclones were established and in one of these (subclone-3), the mode was found to have shifted to 76.

These observations offered interesting subjects for further population analysis of the ascites hepatoma; these investigations are being carried on by Isaka.

In almost every idiogram of ascites hepatoma strains, there are striking and peculiar chromosomes which are considered the extreme examples of unevenness or loss of uniformity in the chromosome

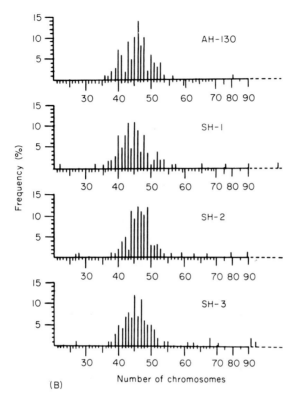

(B)

Number of chromosomes

Fig. 8. (B) Agreement in the mode of chromosome number of clonal three substrains, SH-1-3, and their mother strain, AH-130.

formation in hepatoma cells (Nakamura, 1955). Some outstanding examples taken from idiograms of six strains (Fig. 14) are collected in Fig. 13; they are always alone, missing analogous partners. Besides these extremes there are many chromosomes belonging to this category, which show different grades of irregularity.

Obviously, these chromosomes are abnormal or pathological from the general point of view, but they are "regular" constituent members of the metaphase chromosome plate of the particular hepatoma in which they are found (Fig. 14). In some hepatomas, they are so striking in their shape or size that they are called "marker" chromosomes, distinguishing a strain. A marker chromosome does not appear as such in another strain which has, in turn, its own marker or markers. On the other hand, in some strains there are no chromosomes sufficiently outstanding to be called markers.

Thus, it is obvious (Fig. 14) that the chromosome formation of

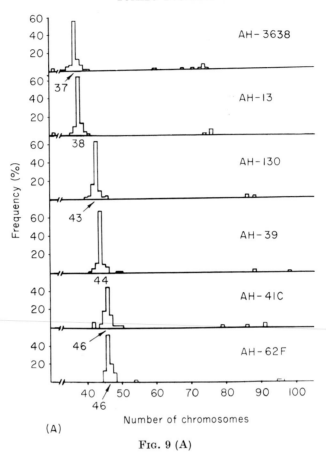

(A)

FIG. 9 (A)

FIG. 9. Histograms of chromosome number of twenty-four ascites hepatoma strains. Ascites hepatomas transformed from Morris hepatomas are included: AH-3638 (in A) and AH-3924A (in C) [S. Odashima and H. P. Morris, *Gann Monograph* **1**, 55 (1966)]; AH-H-35tc2 (in B) [M. D. Reuber, *Gann Monograph* **1**, 43 (1966)]. (Compiled by H. Isaka.)

hepatoma cells is irregular. On the other hand, each strain has its own "principle" which regularly produces its own metaphase plate of chromosomes. As stated earlier, there were several strains in which the modal number of chromosome distribution coincided, but there have been no two strains which showed the same type of the metaphase chromosome formation.

F. DRUG RESISTANCE

In Table XIII, different sensitivities of different ascites hepatoma strains to nitrogen mustard *N*-oxide, an anticancer agent, are summarized.

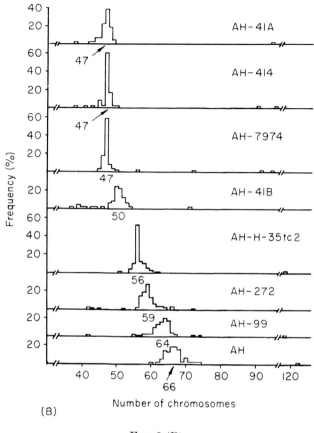

(B)

Fɪɢ. 9 (B)

The cytostatic effect of nitrogen mustard and its derivatives is recognized by cytological examination of their mitotic effects and consequent formation of irregularly polynuclear as well as giant cells, the "NM effect." Such an effect is more or less common to compounds belonging to alkylating agents (Plate IV) and is useful for screening of various derivatives for cancer chemotherapy. (Compounds to be tested are injected into the peritoneal cavity of ascites tumor animals, and every 24 hours after the injection the smears of the ascites are examined for their effect. When typical changes are confirmed in more than 50% of mitotic cells present, positive NM effect is marked for that case.) The nitrogen mustard N-oxide (Nitromin) was a product of studies on cancer chemotherapy, which utilized this screening method with Yoshida sarcoma.

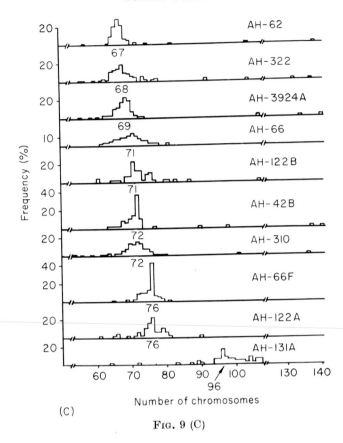

(C)

FIG. 9 (C)

Table XIII is the result of comparative studies on the minimal effective dose (MED) required for inducing the NM effect in different ascites hepatoma strains with Nitromin. In this table, MED is indicated in two ways; *in vivo* MED and *in vitro–in vivo* MED. In the latter procedure, developed by Satoh, the compound to be tested is added to the tumor ascites in the test tube and after 30 minutes at 37°C, the ascites is inoculated in normal rats. The minimal amount of the compound for inducing the NM effect in the inoculated tumor is examined. This technique may be regarded as a test for MED on the cell level, bringing the cells into direct contact, as much as possible, with the compounds.

It is, of course, a problem to determine whether the cytological effect of a compound, such as the NM effect, would parallel the therapeutic effect of that compound; however, this particular NM effect proved to be in quite satisfying agreement with the therapeutic effect (Figs. 15 and 16).

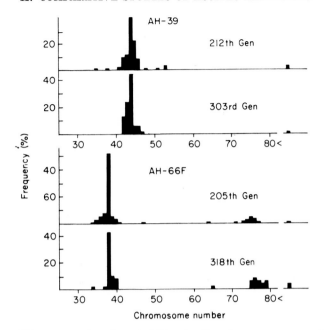

FIG. 10. Histograms showing stability in the chromosome constitution of ascites hepatomas AH-39 and AH-66F, analyzed at 2-year intervals. (Compiled by H. Isaka.)

The first finding of a difference in the drug sensitivity of ascites hepatomas was an entirely unanticipated observation, i.e., the striking difference between AH-130 and AH-7974 in the sensitivity to Nitromin, first observed by Satoh. In strain AH-130, Nitromin showed chemotherapeutic (as well as cytological) effects that surpassed those in Yoshida sarcoma, whereas AH-7974 showed a complete resistance to the same compound (Satoh, 1956) (Fig. 15). Further experiments, repeated more than 10 times, showed the same result. Moreover, experiments carried out with thirteen different derivatives of nitrogen mustard besides Nitromin also gave the same result (Fig. 16).

It is not correct to speak of "complete" resistance of AH-7974. As indicated in Table XIII, *in vivo* MED in this strain corresponds to the maximal tolerated dose (MTD) of the rat to this substance. Examination by the *in vitro–in vivo* technique (on the cell level) demonstrated that tumor cells responded to the compound at 5.0 μg (minimum dose).

There are four strains in Table XIII that proved sensitive to Nitromin in the *in vitro–in vivo* MED, in grades either surpassing (AH-49 and AH-149) or equal (AH-601 and AH-173) to AH-7974. These dose differences are first observed by *in vitro–in vivo* techniques since they are above the dose level that kills the animal.

TABLE XIII

DIFFERENT SENSITIVITIES TO NITROGEN MUSTARD
N-OXIDE (NITROMIN) OF ASCITES HEPATOMA STRAINS[a]

Strain	In vitro– in vivo MED[b,c] (μg/ml)	In vivo MED[b] (mg/kg)	MTD[d] (mg/kg)	Strain	In vitro– in vivo MED[b,c] (μg/ml)	In vivo MED[b] (mg/kg)	MTD[d] (mg/kg)
AH-13	0.1	1	50	AH-7974	5.0	50	50
AH-66F	0.1	1	50	AH-49	10.0	10	50
AH-99	0.1	1	50	AH-318	10.0	10	50
AH-130	0.1	1	50	AH-62	10.0	20	50
AH-272	0.5	1	50	AH-62F	10.0	10	50
AH-602	0.5	10	50	AH-310	10.0	25	50
AH-39	1.0	5	50	AH-66	10.0	50	50
AH-601	5.0	1	50	AH-408	10.0	50	50
AH-21	5.0	10	50	AH-423	10.0	50	50
AH-63	5.0	10	50	AH-149	50.0	50	50
AH-414	5.0	10	50	AH-386	50.0	50	50
AH-127	5.0	25	50	AH-322	50.0	50	50
AH-173	5.0	50					

[a] From H. Satoh, 1956.

[b] In vivo MED—Minimal effective doses for inducing nitrogen mustard (NM) effect in 4-day-old tumors by intraperitoneal injection.

[c] In vitro–in vivo MED—To 1.0 ml tumor ascites is added 1.0 ml solution of the compound. After 30 minutes at 37°C, the ascites is transplanted. The MED for inducing NM effect in the inoculated tumor is determined every 24 hours.

[d] MTD—Maximal tolerated doses.

In Table XIV, the results of sensitivity tests of ascites hepatoma strains to X-ray irradiation are summarized (Irako, 1953). Here again differences among strains are apparent. In this examination, tumor ascites was irradiated in vitro and the dose of X-ray needed to suppress completely the transplantability of each strain of the tumor was measured. A parallelism between sensitivity of the tumor to irradiation and to Nitromin was not demonstrated.

Our program of studies on cancer chemotherapy employed the ascites tumors, beginning with Yoshida sarcoma; as long as only one kind of tumor was used, the work seemed to progress with considerable success. However, the individuality or individual differences inherent in each malignant growth which has been demonstrated in drug sensitivity became an obstacle which must be overcome before proceeding with cancer chemotherapy screening using ascites tumors. Thus, a line is now being pursued by our group, particularly by Satoh, to establish a "hepatoma spectrum" for screening by bringing together and

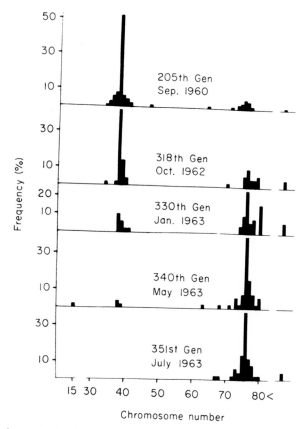

FIG. 11. A complete shift of chromosome number of AH-66F during serial transplantation. During approximately 140 transplant generations (from 205 to 340) the modal number 38 shifted gradually to tetraploid region. In 351st generation the shift was complete. (Compiled by H. Isaka.)

arranging those ascites hepatomas that proved to have several distinctive characteristics in drug sensitivity. On the other hand, a conspicuous cytological effect other than the NM effect, which is rather limited to alkylating agents series, is another object of research. In screening work using ascites tumors, obvious and repeated cytological findings such as NM effect are most helpful as a first guide (Yoshida, 1959).

The drug resistance of ascites hepatomas discussed above may be regarded as "natural" resistance. In the practice of cancer chemotherapy, however, "acquired" resistance is most often the problem. Sakurai and others of our group followed this problem using the

TABLE XIV

In Vitro Lethal Doses of X-Ray Irradiation
to Ascites Hepatoma Cells (10^7)

X-Ray (R)	Strain
2,000	AH-39, 149,[a] 601
3,000	AH-49, 62, 64, 66,[a] 130,[b] 322,[a]
	414, 423,[a] 602
5,000	AH-13,[b] 66F,[b] 99,[b] 7974[a]

[a] Nitrogen mustard *N*-oxide-resistant strains.
[b] Nitrogen mustard *N*-oxide-sensitive strains.

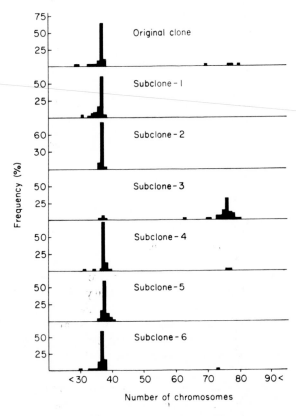

Fig. 12. A complete shift of chromosome number induced by cloning (subclone-3). (Compiled by H. Isaka.)

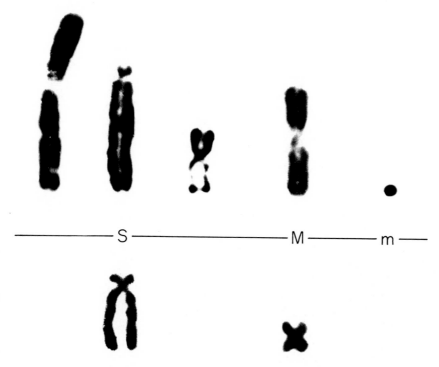

Fig. 13. Examples of "marker" chromosomes in ascites hepatomas. (Above) Markers, from left to right: large submetacentric chromosome with a second constriction (AH-13); large subtelocentric chromosome (AH-13); submetacentric chromosome with thin arm (AH-414); large metacentric chromosome (AH-13), and minute chromosome (AH-39). (Below) For comparison, the largest subtelocentric and metacentric chromosomes of a normal rat (same magnification). (Prepared by H. Isaka.)

Yoshida sarcoma (Sakurai, 1964). They employed the above-mentioned *in vitro–in vivo* technique, that is, the direct contact of the tumor cells with Nitromin *in vitro* and their transplantation repeated with the same tumor line. The dose of the compound for the *in vitro* contact was gradually increased. The resistance has been increased gradually, so that they obtained, at last, a tumor strain as high as 20,000 times more Nitromin-resistant than the original Yoshida sarcoma. They demonstrated, further, by experiments of population analysis performed at different stages of increasing resistance, that, in this increased resistance which showed rather rapid decrease after its acquisition, the possibility of selection of preexisting high resistant cells should be discarded.

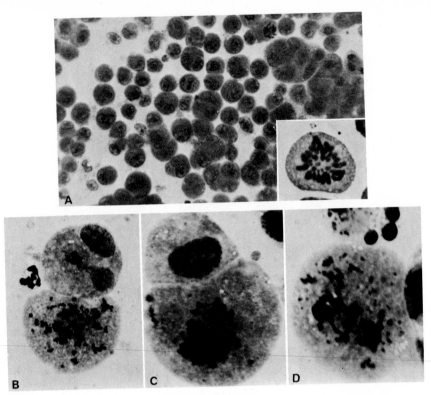

PLATE IV. A: Ascites of 4-day tumor (AH-13 ; control); B–D: Chromosomes 48 hr after administration of nitrogen mustard N-oxide. Breakage and scattering of chromosomes in one cell of a doublet (B); coagulation of chromosomes (C); scattering of chromosome in a free cell (D).

V. Origin of Yoshida Sarcoma

The question of the origin of Yoshida sarcoma has been of interest during the 27 years since this tumor was found. An attempt is made here to summarize the findings and observations which relate to this question.

As stated in Section II, Yoshida sarcoma originated in one of the rats which underwent experiments for hepatoma induction by azo dye feeding; in the liver of that animal hepatoma nodules developed. At the time it was not possible to relate the tumor ascites found in the animal to these hepatomas. The sarcomatous character of the ascites and its infiltrative growths were evident. However, with the progress of studies with the ascites hepatoma the following observations suggested the possibility of the origin of the Yoshida sarcoma in the hepatoma.

First, the ascitic pictures of free-cell-type ascites hepatomas are practically indistinguishable from the picture of Yoshida sarcoma

144

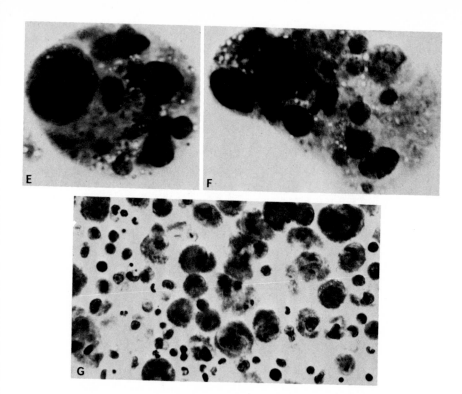

PLATE IV. E–G: Chromosomes 72 hr after administration of nitrogen mustard N-oxide. Formation of polynuclear giant cells in one of a doublet (E) and a triplet (F). Degeneration and necrosis of giant cells with reactive immigration of leukecoytes and mononuclear cells.

(Plate III), and the free-cell-type tumor is not exceptional. Five free-cell-type ascites hepatoma strains are now being kept in this laboratory. One out of these five was a complete free-cell type from the very beginning of ascitic conversion, whereas in two cases the free-cell state was not complete at first. They were almost 95% in the free-cell state, i.e., the ascites contained small island formations in a very small amount, and they had become gradually a 100% free-cell-type tumor. The remaining two cases were at first island-type tumors and after hundreds of transplant generations transformed into 100% free-cell-type tumors (AH-66F and AH-62F; Section IV,D). These transformations from island to free-cell types which were observed in these four strains, although in different ways, may evidently indicate the possibility of transition of tumors from epithelial to sarcomatous (non-epithelial) growth types.

Second, it is a frequent occurrence that primary hepatoma animals are accompanied with production of tumor ascites with which an ascites hepatoma strain is established. There are eighteen strains

TOMIZO YOSHIDA

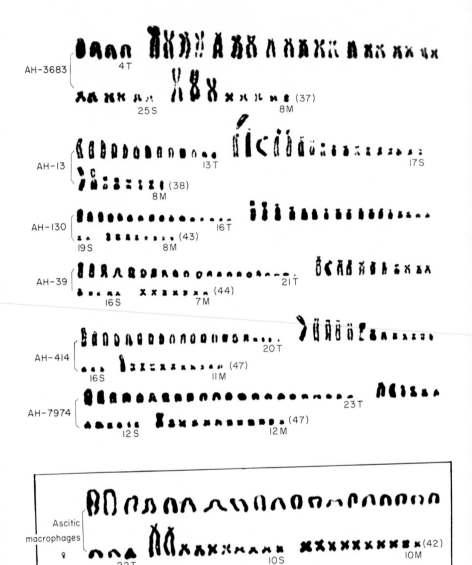

Fig. 14. Metaphase chromosomes of ascites hepatomas (six examples). Arranged from left to right in groups of the same type; telocentric (T), submeta- and subtelocentric (S), and metacentric (M), in the order of decreasing size. (Bottom) Metaphase chromosomes of macrophage of normal rat. Eleven pairs of telocentrics (including X · X), five pairs of submeta- and subtelocentrics, and five pairs of metacentrics. (Prepared by H. Isaka.)

derived from the primary tumor ascites, but all of these primary ascites were island-forming types and none of these was a free-cell type from the beginning like the primary ascites of Yoshida sarcoma. In this particular respect, Yoshida sarcoma does not agree with these cases, but this difference does not seem to be an obstacle to accepting the hepatoma origin of the Yoshida sarcoma.

In addition to these materials collected from observations during the long course of studies with ascites hepatoma, a series of observations of striking changes occurred in the morphology as well as biological behavior of the growth of Yoshida sarcoma, which threw a new light on the problem.

In 1961, Satoh observed that in a rat which underwent an experiment in relation to transplantation resistance, the ascites picture of Yoshida sarcoma suddenly changed into the island-forming type. This was an unexpected finding repeated in experiments in the same line and in other experiments (Yoshida *et al.*, 1964).

Satoh's first series of experiments were designed to learn whether transplantation of a mouse leukemia (SN-36) in rats might cause resistance to transplantation of Yoshida sarcoma, and it was known that a kind of cross-immunity in transplantation would be established between SN-36 and Yoshida sarcoma. Further, to learn the limit of this transplantation resistance, repeated challenges were made with increasing numbers of Yoshida sarcoma cells. The fifth challenge resulted in the growth of a transplanted Yoshida sarcoma, but not

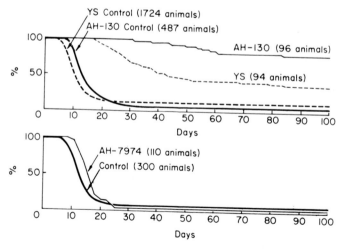

FIG. 15. Difference in therapeutic effect of nitrogen mustard *N*-oxide on Yoshida sarcoma (YS) and two ascites hepatoma strains, AH-130 and AH-7974. (Compiled by H. Satoh.)

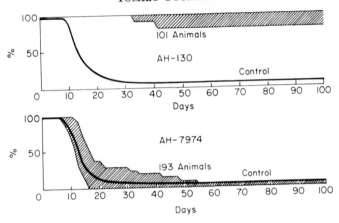

FIG. 16. Completely different therapeutic effect of nitrogen mustard derivatives on AH-130 and AH-7974 strains. Thirteen derivatives were examined. In
AH-130, all compounds were effective and all percentage survival curves (101
animals in total) were in the shaded area, whereas in AH-7974, all compounds
were ineffective and there was no cure among 193 animals in total. (Compiled
by H. Satoh.)

with the original ascites picture of that tumor. The successfully growing
tumors showed island formation just like ascites hepatomas (Figs. 17
to 19). Tables XV and XVI summarize this experimental procedure.
This transformation of ascites picture was observed in 5 of 12 series
of animals. These new types of Yoshida sarcoma have been maintained
by serial transplantation and three transplant strains have been
established from them.

Accompanying this morphological transformation, there was an extra-
ordinarily prolonged survival of animals in which this transformation

TABLE XV

PRETREATMENT (UNSUCCESSFUL TRANSPLANTATION) OF RATS
IN WHICH ISLAND FORMATION OF YOSHIDA SARCOMA
CELLS WAS OBSERVED[a]

| | Challenge | | |
1st	2nd	3rd	4th
SN-36[b]	Y.S.[c]	Y.S.[c]	Y.S.[c]
(0.3 ml)	(10^3)	(10^4)	(5×10^7)

[a] Twelve animals were treated in the same way.
[b] SN-36—Mouse leukemia with ascitic growth (amount of ascites transplanted).
[c] Y.S.—Yoshida sarcoma (number of cells transplanted).

had taken place (Table XVI). Also, in animals transplanted with the three strains, unusually long survival was evident (Table XVII). One of them actually lived more than 300 days. The sublines of these long-living Yoshida sarcoma have been marked with a sign LY and this sign has been used for all sublines of Yoshida sarcoma which

TABLE XVI

FIFTH CHALLENGE OF PRETREATED RATS
WITH YOSHIDA SARCOMA CELLS[a].

Strain	Rats (gm)	Days after pretreatment	No. of cells	Latent days	Survived (days)[b]
LY-306	♀90	21	10^5	12	84
LY-336	♀80	55	10^5	3	145
LY-346	♀80	55	10^6	3	289
LY-320	♀100	21	10^6	2	142
LY-323	♀88	55	10^5	3	245

[a] Successful challenge in five out of twelve pretreated strains of rats; island formation observed in all successfully growing tumors.

[b] These animals survived a remarkably long time compared with the 7–8-day average survival of Yoshida sarcoma animals.

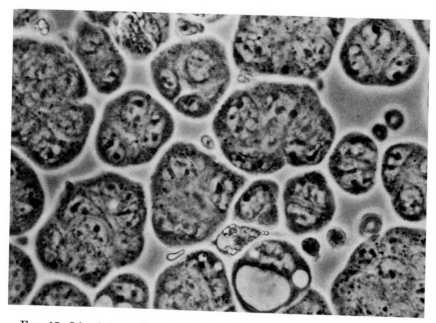

FIG. 17. Island formation in the ascites of LY-336 strain (Table XVI).

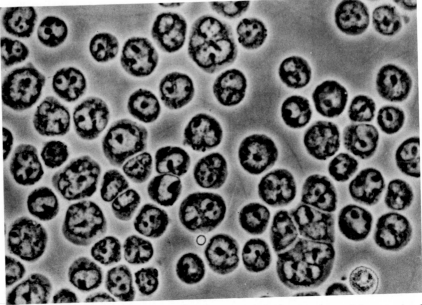

FIG. 18. Island formation in the ascites of LY-54 strain (induced in an animal pretreated with intraperitoneal injection of full blood). Islands are rather small but evident.

underwent transformation to an island-forming type in further experiments, irrespective of the long or short life of their tumor animals. Animals that lived for a long time bearing tumors of these slowly growing LY sublines showed extremely large extension of the abdomen, due to accumulation of an enormous amount of rather "thin" ascites. One such example of a rat is shown in Fig. 19.

In view of the experimental procedure, there is no doubt that the cells transplanted and grown are the Yoshida sarcoma cells, and the animals used in this experiment were normal rats which had not been subjected to any kind of experiments. In addition, the chromosome pattern of the three LY strains differed with each strain, differed from that of the original Yoshida sarcoma, and differed from any of the existing ascites hepatomas kept in our laboratory, excluding the possibility of any of these having been erroneously mixed with the existing ascites hepatomas (Fig. 20).

The histological picture of sections of tumor tissues formed by infiltration of LY strains cells into the omentum and other tissues or by distant metastasis, also presents an adenomatous (epithelial) pattern (Fig. 21).

Bringing all the observations together, one may suggest that the

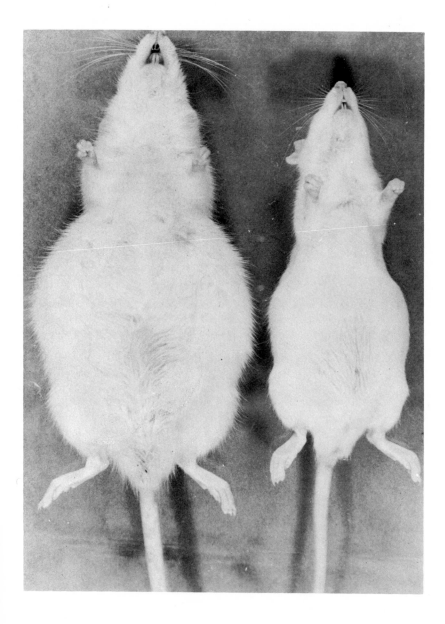

FIG. 19. Distention of the abdomen of an LY tumor-bearing animal (LY-336) on the left and a Yoshida sarcoma animal on the right. The LY animals reach this state generally in about 30 days after transplantation and remain so until they die even after hundreds of days.

epithelial cell nature of Yoshida sarcoma cells that had been "masked" for a long time was "unmasked" by a presently unknown effect and that the original "island" nature became "revealed."

Apart from interpretations as to conditions that caused this kind of phenomenon, the only fact emerging from the experimental procedure was that an immunological conditioning had been presented to the host animals. Simply based on this fact, a further series of experiments were carried out. Satoh carried out two experiments; in one, normal

TABLE XVII

SURVIVAL DAYS OF LY TUMOR-BEARING RATS[a,]

Strain	Generations										
	1	2	3	4	5	6	7	8	9	10	→
LY-306	144	101	148	60	51	41	82	115	126	276	→
LY-336	195	135	113	177	51	186	—[b]	305	168	266	→
LY-346	58	98	226	95	275	88	123	31	58	43	→

[a] For all the strains, the first ten transplant generations are indicated in the table. Transplantation is continued further. In every generation of every strain, the tumor was transplanted only in one animal. When a tumor took in an animal, the tumor was transferred to the next animal and the original host animal lived for a long time, as indicated in the table.

[b] Complete regression of the tumor occurred after transplantation to the next recipient.

rats were pretreated with an intraperitoneal injection of whole blood from a normal rat and, in the other, rats were pretreated with intraperitoneal injection of an emulsion of the liver tissue obtained from a normal rat after removing the blood by perfusion. In both experiments, transplantation of the Yoshida sarcoma resulted in production of LY tumors. New LY strains have been established from positive cases, and it was noted that in these new LY strains, islands formed in the ascites were much smaller in size and less in number than in the first three LY strains. The survival days of animals bearing tumors of new LY strains were certainly longer than those of the original Yoshida sarcoma but not as long as that of the first three LY strains.

Besides these new LY strains, a number of other LY strains have been induced from the Yoshida sarcoma. These facts support Satoh's first observation of the transformation of the Yoshida sarcoma into a tumor of epithelial type and further support the assumption of a hepatoma origin of Yoshida sarcoma.

A question that arose in connection with the LY transformation of Yoshida sarcoma was that if this transformation is induced in Yoshida sarcoma, the same "LY-transformation" must be induced in the free-cell type of ascites hepatomas which are thought to be tumors of the same category as the Yoshida sarcoma. This had been a long-standing question and has been answered positively (Nakamura and collaborators, 1956). A free-cell type of ascites hepatoma, AH-66F, was transplanted into the spleen of a normal rat. The animal died after 39 days. Autopsy revealed the presence of a hemorrhagic ascites, infiltration into the omentum, and tumor nodules in the spleen. Island formation was seen in the ascites. A new LY strain has been established with this ascites. The mean lifespan of tumor animals of this new LY strain remained unchanged, i.e., the same as the original AH-66F.

In this case, the strain **AH-66F** is actually a free-cell-type subline of AH-66 which is an ordinary ascites hepatoma with island formation. However, the ascites picture of the new LY type and that of AH-66, despite the fact that both are island-forming types, differ markedly from each other. In addition, their chromosome types are vastly different, and they both differ from that of AH-66F. The new LY type

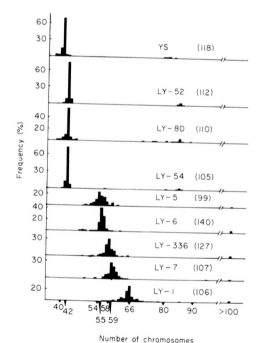

Number of chromosomes

FIG. 20. Examples of the distribution of chromosome number in LY strains. Incidentally, in three strains the modal number is 42, but their idiograms are entirely different from those of the normal rat. (YS) Yoshida sarcoma; number of cells examined is shown in parentheses. (Compiled by H. Isaka.)

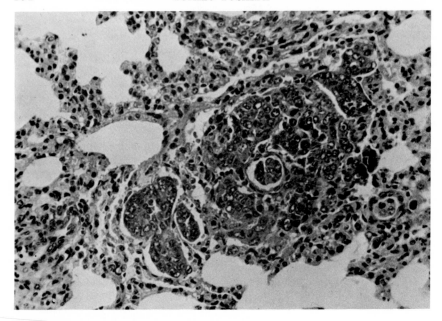

Fig. 21. Histological picture of a metastasis of an LY-336 strain tumor showing epithelial nature.

is, therefore, truly a newly produced type and not a reversion to the original type.

This finding agrees well with the fact that all of the LY strains induced from Yoshida sarcoma to date differ in chromosome type from each other and from that of the original Yoshida sarcoma. Therefore, every LY strain is a new type of tumor.

Transformation of the Yoshida sarcoma and free-cell-type ascites hepatomas into the island-forming or "epithelial" LY types would be attractive to the interpretation of a reversion from a more anaplastic (sarcomatous) type toward a more highly differentiated (epithelial) type, but the facts do not easily permit such an explanation. In other words, the transformation of growth type that took place in these malignant growths was merely a change in direction which does not seem to permit a simple definition such as a vertical movement along the axis of cell differentiation, i.e., differentiation and dedifferentiation, and vice versa.

VI. Concluding Remarks

Ascites hepatomas became a long-term research subject of our group, although this was not originally intended. As it became clear that each ascites hepatoma had its own characteristics, it seemed desirable to establish as many transplant strains of the tumor as possible for their comparative studies. In the 12 years after 1951, almost sixty strains were established, and the work of establishing further strains for comparison has gradually come to a close.

During these long-term studies, the same tumor strains have been kept under observation, i.e., the Yoshida sarcoma for almost 27 years and the oldest strains of ascites hepatoma for almost 18 years.

Studies such as these are different from research projects which follows a definite program designed and calculated to succeed in attaining an objective. In such project research, the guiding principle for research is found inside the program. The present studies were guided from outside. As the studies progressed, many events occurred that suggested directions for investigation. It is obvious that such research programs become long-term ones, and many results obtained do not permit conclusive formulations. There have been, however, many points relevant to the general problem of malignant growth.

First, a given cancer cell population as a whole (a malignant growth) has characteristics of its own, but those of individual constituent cells of the population are not stable, fluctuating over a certain range which is confined by the nature of the population as a whole. They can present, within this limitation, different characteristics after every mitotic multiplication. This relation is demonstrated by the fact that a single cell-derived clonal subpopulation presents, as a rule, the same pattern of characteristics as the mother cell population. A shift of the pattern of a population to a different one can occur. This is not evident in a short period but takes place at intervals of several years or decades. This kind of shift of the pattern can also be induced by cloning, i.e., by single-cell transplantation. Several years may appear long in the laboratory but compared to the passage of time in nature, it is a moment. When the changes observed in cancers are compared, for instance, with the stability of a mutation occurring in nature, cancer would be regarded as a rapidly changing, very unstable, and perhaps fragile creation.

Second, the cellular polymorphism is frequently stated to be a characteristic of the malignant growth. Actually, in ascites tumors, polymorphism is obvious in the terminal stage. However, when one examines the early stages of ascites tumor growth in a new host after transplantation, one may find a beautiful conformity of the cells growing there. As the growth progresses, it moves gradually to the polymorphic state. Polymorphism is, therefore, merely a terminal manifestation of the tumor growth. When a tumor is transplanted to a new host at an early stage when the tumor cells are still in the uniform state, and the same procedures are repeated, the state of uniform cell growth of this tumor is maintained without showing any polymorphy as long as the transplantation is continued. As a result, polymorphism cannot be accepted as a specific characteristic of malignant growth, although the rapidity with which the growth acquires the polymorphic state may be a characteristic of malignancy.

Third, as cancer research is, in the end, an effort to find out what is characteristic, possibly specific, of malignant growth, it seems that laboratory workers are required to be always aware of both conditions; what kind of malignant growth they are working with and how many kinds of tumors are involved in the comparison of results.

REFERENCES

Essner, E., Sato, H., and Belkin, M. (1954). *Exp. Cell Res.* **7**, 430–437.
Goldie, H., and Felix, M. D. (1951). *Cancer Res.* **11**, 73–80.
Goldie, H., Jefferies, B. R., Maxwell, M. D., and Hahn, P. F. (1952). *Cancer Res.*, **12**, 422–425.
Hauschka, T. S. (1953). *J. Natl. Cancer Inst.* **14**, 723–740.
Hauschka (T. S., 1956). *Ann. N. Y. Acad. Sci.* **63**, 637–1036.
Hesse, F. (1927). Centralbl. Bakteriol. I. Abt. **102**, 367–374.
Irako, Y. (1953). *Gann* **49**, Suppl., 319–320.
Isaka, H., Nakamura, K., and Odashima, S. (1954). *Gann* **45**, 434–436.
Isaka, H., Nakamura, K., and Odashima, S. (1955). *Gann* **46**, 194–196.
Ishidate, M. (1968). *Gann* **59**, 341–356.
Klein, G., and Klein, E. (1953). *Nature* **171**, 398–399.
Klein, G., and Klein, E. (1956). *Ann. N. Y. Acad. Sci.* **63**, 640–661.
Kurata, T. (1959). *Trans. Soc. Pathol. Japon.* **48**, 1329–1337 (in Japanese).
Löwenthal, H., and Jahn, G. (1932). *Z. Krebsforsch.* **37**, 439–447.
Muta, Y. (1943). *Gann* **37**, 298–300 (in Japanese).
Nakamura, K. (1955). *Gann* **46**, 196–199.
Nakamura, K., Odashima, S., Isaka, H., and Kurata, T. (1956). *Gann* **47**, 502–504.
Odashima, S. (1964). *Natl. Cancer Inst. Monograph* **16**, 51–87.
Rössle, R. (1936). *Sitzber. Preuss. Akad. Wiss., Physik. Math. Kl.* **III**.
Sakurai, Y. (1964). *Natl. Cancer Inst. Monograph* **16**, 207–239.
Sato, H., and Aruji, T. (1952). *Gann* **43**, 254–257.
Satoh, H. (1952). *Gann*, **43**, 272–274.
Satoj, H. (1954). *Gann*, **45**, 436–438.
Satoh, H. (1955). *Trans. Soc. Pathol. Japon.* **44**, 392–406 (in Japanese).
Satoh, H. (1956). *Gann* **47**, 334–337.
Satomi, M. (1941). *Gann* **35**, 430–448.
Yamada, T. (1962). *Z. Krebsforsch.* **65**, 75–86.
Yoshida, T. (1942). *Gann* **36**, 9–38.
Yoshida, T. (1947). *Trans. Soc. Pathol. Japon.* **36**, 3–4 (in Japanese).
Yoshida, T. (1949a). Yoshida sarcoma (a monograph in Japanese).
Yoshida, T. (1949b). *Gann* **40**, 1–29.
Yoshida, T. (1952). *J. Natl. Cancer Inst.* **12**, 947–969.
Yoshida, T. (1957). *Arch. Pathol. Anat. Physiol.* **330**, 85–105.
Yoshida, T. (1958). *Jikken Dobutsu* **7**, 85–91 (in Japanese).
Yoshida, T. (1959). *Ann. N. Y. Acad. Sci.* **76**, 610–618.
Yoshida, T. (1963). *Deut. Med. Wochschr.* **88**, No. 46, 2229–2238.
Yoshida, T., and Kim, C. (1943). *Gann* **37**, 343–344 (short report in Japanese).

Yoshida, T., and Tsurusaki, H. (1943). *Gann* **37**, 404–424 (in Japanese).
Yoshida, T., Shimauchi, T., Tsurusaki, H., and Sasaki, J. (1943). *Byorigaku Zasshi* **3**, 122–130 (in Japanese); *Gann* **37**, 341–342 (1943).
Yoshida, T., Mura, Y., and Sasaki, Z. (1944). *Proc. Imp. Acad. (Tokyo)* **20**, 611–616.
Yoshida, T., Sato, H., and Aruji, T. (1951). *Proc. Japan. Acad.* **27**, 289–301.
Yoshida, T., Nakamura, K., Odashima, S., and Isaka, H. (1956). *Gann* **47**, 612–615.
Yoshida, T., Odashima, S., Kurata, T., Nakamura, K., Irako, Y., Isaka, H., and Ishizawa, T. (1957). *Gann* **48**, 551–553.
Yoshida, T., Odashima, S., Ishizawa, T., and Irako, Y. (1958). *Gann* **49**, Suppl., 191–192.
Yoshida, T., Isaka, H., and Satoh, H. (1964). *Arzneimittel.-Forsch.* **14**, 735–741.

CHAPTER III

TUMOR MITOCHONDRIA*

LOUIS A. SORDAHL AND ARNOLD SCHWARTZ†

I. Introduction

The wide variety of neoplastic tissues makes any generalization on the isolation and properties of tumor mitochondria very difficult. Since Warburg's (1930) original discovery of high glycolytic activity in tumor tissues, considerable evidence (Warburg, 1956; Aisenberg, 1961; Burk et al., 1967) has accumulated to substantiate the hypothesis that increased glycolysis is a fundamental characteristic of many tumor cells. However, in recent years, studies with a number of hepatomas have questioned the universality of this concept (Morris, 1965; Weinhouse, 1966). Oxidative phosphorylation might be assumed to be depressed or impaired in a tissue with high glycolytic rates such as tumor. In fact, a number of reports (Schneider et al., 1949–1950; Schneider, 1946; Boxer and Devlin, 1961; Allard et al., 1952; Miller and Goldfeder, 1965; Mintz et al., 1967) have shown that tumor mitochondria exhibit reduced activities compared to normal control tissues. Moreover, distinct morphological differences between some tumor and normal tissue

* Original studies reported in this paper were supported by U.S. Public Health Service grants HE-05435, P. 8; HE-07906; NSF GB 6895; and ACS-IN-27J-P-17.

† U.S. Public Health Service Career Research Development Awardee (K$_3$-HE 11, 875).

mitochondria have been found (Allard *et al.*, 1952; Mintz *et al.*, 1967; Sordahl *et al.*, 1969). Recent studies (Arcos *et al.*, 1960, 1969a,b) on chemical carcinogenesis have also suggested an effect on mitochondrial structure and function in the induction of neoplasia. The use of appropriate controls in studying neoplastic mitochondria remains a problem of considerable significance.

In the past decade a number of "energy-linked functions" of mitochondria have been discovered (Lehninger, 1965; Chance, 1963). Among these are ion translocation, "swelling–contraction," transhydrogenation [reduced nicotinamide adenine dinucleotide (NADH)→reduced nicotinamide adenine diphosphonucleotide (NADPH)], and reversed-electron transport producing reduced coenzyme. Recent reports (Hackenbrock, 1966; Penniston *et al.*, 1968) have also suggested that rapid *in vitro* changes in mitochondrial ultrastructure are associated with biochemical function. The discovery of a specific mitochondrial deoxyribonucleic acid (DNA) and several types of ribonucleic acid (RNA), as well as RNA polymerase and polysomes, not only has raised new questions regarding mitochondrial replication, but also the role of mitochondrial nucleic acids in cellular growth and development. It is quite possible that, with alterations in cellular metabolism (e.g., neoplastic tissues), mitochondrial function is also altered from its presumably primary function of adenosine triphosphate (ATP) synthesis (oxidative phosphorylation) to some of the other processes mentioned above. Whether a change in mitochondrial function has any primary significance or is secondary in neoplasia or in the development of the tumor remains to be determined.

This chapter presents selected techniques for the isolation and assay of tumor mitochondria.

II. Preparation

The major objective in preparing tumor mitochondria is to isolate a preparation that exhibits coupled respiratory control, so that other energy-linked functions may be studied on a qualitative and quantitative basis. Many types of isolation media have been employed and various mitochondrial cofactors, such as NAD^+, have been included with the intent of obtaining tumor mitochondria that are functionally intact. In this laboratory it was found that a sucrose medium containing 1% bovine serum albumin yields tumor mitochondria with adequate oxidative phosphorylation (Sordahl *et al.*, 1969).

The following method is a modification of that described by Schneider and Hogeboom (1950). The isolation medium consists of 0.25 M sucrose, 1 mM tris–HCl (never use tris–SO_4), 1 mM ethylenediaminetetraacetate

(EDTA), and 1% bovine serum albumin, pH 7.2–7.4. This medium is designated "STEA."

III. Procedure

1. Mice or rats are killed by cervical dislocation or decapitation. The tumors are excised from the surrounding tissues and placed in a beaker of cold STEA medium.

2. The tumor tissue is blotted on a paper towel, weighed, and placed in a fresh solution of STEA medium.

3. The tissue is minced with a sharp scissors, the STEA solution decanted, and the minced tissue is transferred to a homogenizing vessel (A. H. Thomas, size C).

4. Approximately 10 ml of STEA medium per gram of original tumor tissue are added to the homogenizing vessel (10% homogenate, w/v).

5. Homogenization is accomplished with a motor-driven, tight-fitting Teflon pestle until an even suspension is obtained. The number of strokes necessary for complete homogenization depends on the toughness of the tissue. The homogenizing vessel should be kept cold during the procedure.

6. The homogenate is transferred to chilled centrifuge tubes and centrifuged at 600 g for 10 minutes in a refrigerated centrifuge.

7. The supernatant is poured through cheesecloth into clean centrifuge tubes and the pellet discarded. The suspension is centrifuged at 8500 g for 12 minutes.

8. The supernatant is discarded and the mitochondrial pellet is resuspended in approximately half the volume of STEA medium used for the initial homogenization. This suspension is centrifuged at 8500 g for 10 minutes. The washing procedure is repeated at least twice to remove microsomal and other cellular contamination. The mitochondrial pellet will often appear with a light tan layer surrounding a darker pellet. This loose-packing layer should be removed before washing by gently agitating a small volume of STEA medium over the packed pellet.

9. The washed pellet is finally suspended in STEA medium with approximately 0.5 ml medium per gram of original starting tissue. The mitochondrial suspension should contain 20–30 mg of protein per milliliter. Mitochondrial protein determinations are usually done by a biuret method (Jacobs et al., 1956).

The foregoing procedures are carried out at 0°–4°C. All materials that are used for these procedures should be kept cold. Solutions used for the preparation and assay of mitochondria should be made up in glass distilled water. The bovine serum albumin (BSA) used in these experiments does not have to be fatty acid-free. Crude preparations of BSA (e.g., Sigma, Fraction V) are quite satisfactory for preparing adequate mitochondria. The inclusion of BSA in the isolation medium has been shown to be beneficial in obtaining mitochondrial preparations with respiratory control (Sordahl et al., 1969). This is true for a variety of tumors, although a great deal of variability exists. Quite often, mitochondria isolated from tumors which have become necrotic or are bloody, exhibit very low respiratory control activity compared to mitochondria isolated from less contaminated tumors. In general, yields of tumor mitochondria (on a milligrams of mitochondrial protein to grams of original tissue wet weight basis), are much lower than the yields obtained from normal liver tissue. Devlin (1967) has reported a beneficial effect of BSA when included in the isolation or assay medium. Since the serum albumin may be binding certain endogenous uncoupling factors (fatty acids), its inclusion in the *isolation* medium is recommended. Human serum albumin works as well as BSA, but ovalbumin is detrimental to mitochondria. It is probable, too, that BSA protects or preserves the integrity of mitochondrial structure (during isolation) and, hence, its biochemical function (Weinbach et al., 1967; Sordahl et al., 1969).

IV. Assays

A. OXIDATIVE PHOSPHORYLATION AND RESPIRATORY CONTROL

The following is a description of the polarographic technique for the measurement of mitochondrial respiration. The principle of this method is to use a polarized platinum electrode (cathode) and a nonpolarized, saturated calomel electrode (anode) coupled by means of a KCl salt bridge. At a selected applied voltage (0.6–0.8 V), the change in the current is directly proportional to the change in oxygen tension in the assay solution. At least two types of electrodes are available for polarographic assays:

1. *The vibrating platinum electrode* is a system in which a platinum electrode is placed directly in the assay medium separate from the anode and relies on an applied vibration to create a diffusion potential at the cathode.

2. *The Clark electrode* is a system in which the cathode, anode, and KCl bridge are contained in a single housing and separated from the assay solution by an oxygen-permeable membrane. The diffusion potential is created by a magnetic stirring bar.

Both types of electrodes have been found to give comparable results in this laboratory. The amplifier, recorder, and vibrating platinum electrode assembly are available in a compact unit (Oxygraph, Gilson

Medical Electronics Co., Middleton, Wisconsin). The Clark electrode (Yellow Springs Instrument Co., Yellow Springs, Ohio) can be adapted to the Oxygraph apparatus or may be used with component parts.

The control of mitochondrial respiration depends upon the phosphorylation mechanism (Chance and Williams, 1956). Tightly coupled mitochondria, in the absence of a phosphate acceptor [adenosine diphosphate (ADP)], exhibit low respiratory rates; in the presence of a phosphate acceptor (ADP), the phosphorylation mechanism is activated and, in turn, causes a rapid flow of electrons due to mitochondrial oxidation of added substrate. Adenosine diphosphate is phosphorylated to ATP, and, after all of the ADP is phosphorylated, respiration slows approximately to the original resting level (i.e., prior to the addition of ADP). Mitochondrial respiration depends on several factors: oxygen, oxidizable substrate, inorganic phosphate, and ADP. Originally, five steady states of respiratory activity in mitochondria were described by Chance and Williams (1956). The following is the generally accepted terminology in expressing polarographic measurements of mitochondrial oxidative phosphorylation: *state 1*—respiration in the presence of oxygen, but without substrate or ADP; *state 2*—ADP is present, but no substrate; *state 3* (the active state of respiration)—ADP, inorganic phosphate, substrate, and oxygen are present. When all the ADP is phosphorylated, respiration returns to a slower resting rate, *viz.*, *state 4*. *State 5* is the anaerobic state with all reactants present.

Most polarographic measurements are made with all the mitochondrial assay reactants (including the mitochondria) present, but not ADP. A base line for total oxygen concentration is established on the recorder, and the mitochondrial suspension is added (see Fig. 1). All reactants are now present, except ADP, and the mitochondria are essentially in a state 4 respiratory state. Adenosine diphosphate is then added and the active, state 3, "burst" of respiration occurs. When all the ADP is phosphorylated to ATP, respiration returns to the state 4 rate. The ratio of state 3 to state 4 respiration or the respiratory control index (RCI) is an indication of the "tightness" of respiratory coupling to phosphorylation in mitochondria. High respiratory control ratios are considered to be a measure of adequate mitochondrial respiratory and phosphorylating activity. Adenosine diphosphate is added in precise aliquots (determined spectrophotometrically) and the amount of oxygen consumed (state 3) to phosphorylate ADP to ATP is used to calculate the ADP:O ratio. This ratio is essentially the same as the P:O ratio used in the determination of phosphorylation efficiency by the technique of Warburg manometry (Umbreit et al., 1964). The principle behind the determination of the ADP:O ratio is that for every atom of oxygen consumed by the mitochondria during state 3 respiration,

3 moles of ATP are formed when a NADH-linked substrate is used or 2 moles of ATP are formed for each atom of oxygen consumed when succinate is the substrate (see Fig. 2). These are the generally accepted theoretical ADP:O ratios with the respective substrates. Experimentally, with intact mitochondria, these ratios are usually achieved. Table I gives some representative values of the ADP:O ratios, RCI, and the rates of respiration in state 3 (Q_{O_2}) of normal tissue mitochondria and mitochondria isolated from a selected group of tumors. The Q_{O_2} or rate of respiration in state 3 is a measure of the amount of enzymic protein present in mitochondria and is usually expressed in nanoatoms of oxygen consumed per minute per milligram mitochondrial protein. The enzyme assemblies responsible for electron transport and the transduction of energy to form ATP are probably located in the internal membranes (cristae) of the mitochondria.

Several types of media have been used for the above-described oxygen studies and have been found to be optimal for the particular type of

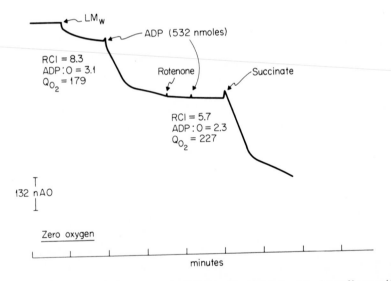

FIG. 1. Oxygen electrode trace showing respiration of normal rat liver mitochondria. The total oxygen base line is indicated by the initial straight line of the trace and the zero oxygen level at the bottom of the figure. Glutamate (5 mM) is the initial substrate. Rotenone (1 μg/mg protein) is added to inhibit glutamate oxidation. Adenosine diphosphate (ADP) produces no stimulation of respiration until succinate (5 mM) is added to bypass the rotenone block. The Q_{O_2} is expressed as nanoatoms oxygen consumed per minute per milligram mitochondrial protein. Temperature, 30°C. Washed liver mitochondria (LM$_W$); respiratory control index (RCI).

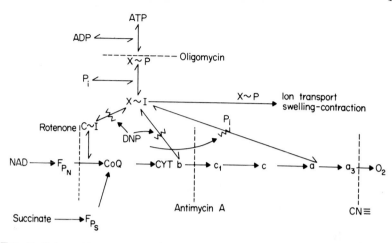

FIG. 2. Schematic representation of the electron transport chain and phosphorylation mechanism. Nicotinamide adenine dinucleotide (NAD) is the acceptor for substrates such as glutamate, pyruvate, β-OH-butyrate, and malate. Electrons are transported through the respective flavoproteins (F_{PN} and F_{PS}), coenzyme Q (CoQ) and the cytochromes (b, c_1, c, a, and a_3) to oxygen. The three energy conservation sites are located between NAD and CoQ (site I), cytochromes b and c (site II), and cytochromes a and a_3 (site III). The phosphorylation mechanism is one of the currently accepted schemes of "chemical coupling" involving initial energized carrier(s) near the chain (C $\sim$ I), the subsequent formation of high-energy intermediate(s) (X $\sim$ I), and finally the energizing of inorganic phosphate (P_i; X $\sim$ P) and phosphorylation of adenosine diphosphate (ADP) to adenosine triphosphate (ATP). The energized carrier (C $\sim$ I) is indicated only at site I for purposes of presentation. Some of the inhibitors (rotenone, antimycin A, and cyanide) of electron transport are indicated by dashed lines. Oligomycin, an inhibitor of terminal phosphate transfer, is also indicated. The approximate locus of action of an uncoupler, 2,4-dinitrophenol (DNP), is indicated by jagged lines. There are other proposed schemes such as the chemiosmotic hypothesis of Mitchell.

mitochondria being assayed (Sordahl *et al.*, 1970). In this laboratory, two types of assay media were found to be best for determining the oxidative phosphorylation characteristics of tumor mitochondria. The sucrose–tris medium described below has been found to be best for assaying mitochondria derived from a large variety of mouse tumors. The KCl–tris medium has been found to be optimal for mitochondria isolated from hepatomas (Sordahl *et al.*, 1969), as well as for normal liver mitochondria.

Sucrose–tris medium: 0.25 M sucrose, 10 mM tris–Cl (pH 7.4); 10 mM K_2HPO_4; and 5 mM substrate (glutamate, β-OH butyrate, α-ketoglutarate, or succinate as sodium or tris salts).

TABLE I

REPRESENTATIVE VALUES FOR MITOCHONDRIAL OXIDATIVE
PHOSPHORYLATION[a]

Tissues	ADP:O	RCI	Q_{O_2}[b]
Normal			
Rat heart	3.2	16	150
Mouse heart	3.1	19	128
Rat liver	2.9	6	110
Mouse liver	2.7	6	91
Tumor			
Mammary adenocarcinoma (mouse)	3.3	10	70
Hepatoma (mouse)	2.3	3	14
Hepatoma (rat)	2.5	6	96
Mammary adenocarcinoma (mouse)	3.2	9	57
Mammary carcinoma (mouse)	2.8	3	50

[a] Glutamate was the substrate and the assay temperature, 30°C. Tumor mitochondria were isolated in the STEA medium described in the text. The liver isolation medium, assay medium, and respiratory control index (RCI) are described in the text.

[b] Q_{O_2} expressed as nanoatoms O_2/minute per milligram mitochondrial protein.

KCl–tris medium: 75 mM KCl; 50 mM tris–HCl; 12.5 mM K_2HPO_4; 1 mM EDTA, 5 mM substrate; and 5 mM $MgCl_2$*; pH 7.4.

One to three milliliters comprises the final volume of the reaction medium in the oxygen electrode chamber. Approximately 1–1.5 mg of mitochondria protein per milliliter of medium are added to the reaction mixture.

1. Assay Procedure

1. Amplifier and recorder are turned on. Voltage (0.6–0.8 V) is applied to the oxygen electrode. The oscillator is activated in the case of the vibrating platinum electrode and the magnetic stirrer when using a Clark electrode. It is important to establish a constant rate of speed for the magnet and not to vary it during the course of the experiment. Most oxygen electrode apparatus have a water-jacketed chamber around the oxygen electrode chamber. The usual temperature for mitochondrial assays is 30°C, although 37°C can also be employed.

2. The complete reaction (assay) mixture, excluding mitochondria, is

---

* $MgCl_2$ is a required cofactor in the assay medium used for normal liver mitochondria but does not seem to be an essential requirement in the assay medium for hepatoma mitochondria (Sordahl *et al.*, 1969).

added to the reaction chamber. The total oxygen base line is established on the recorder (see Fig. 1).

3. Figure 1 is an oxygen electrode tracing of rat liver mitochondria measured by the vibrating platinum electrode. The recorder pen is set at total oxygen base line, which represents 960 nanoatoms of oxygen in the reaction chamber. The volume in the reaction chamber is 2 ml. Assuming 240 nmoles atmospheric oxygen per milliliter in solution at 30°C, the total oxygen present is equal to 480 nanoatoms of oxygen per milliliter or 960 nanoatoms of oxygen in 2 ml. Zero current at the bottom of the trace is equal to zero oxygen concentration.

4. Washed rat liver mitochondria (LM_W; Fig. 1) are now added to the reaction chamber. A downward deflection is usually seen upon addition of the mitochondrial suspension, indicating oxygen uptake and a slight dilution effect. Respiration quickly equilibrates to a steady state. State 4 respiration has been established. This respiratory rate is usually allowed to proceed for approximately 1 minute before the addition of ADP.

5. A 0.1-ml aliquot of ADP (532 nmoles) is added to produce a state 3 burst of respiration. When all the ADP is exhausted, the rapid state 3 respiratory rate ceases and the mitochondria return to state 4 respiration.

6. The ADP:O ratio, the RCI, and the Q_{O_2} in states 3 and 4 can now be calculated.

7. In the case of the mitochondrial preparation in Fig. 1, the amount of ADP added, 532 nmoles, is divided by the amount of oxygen consumed, 174 nanoatoms, and the resulting figure is the ADP:O ratio (3.1; Fig. 1). The exact concentration of the ADP solution is determined by reading the optical density in a spectrophotometer at 259 mμ, and using a millimolar extinction coefficient of 15.1 to 15.9.* An enzymic analysis can also be carried out to determine the concentration of ADP (Kornberg and Pricer, 1951). This is a more sensitive method, and the direct optical density readings and the enzymic determination are in good agreement.

8. The RCI is the ratio of the respiratory rate in state 4 to that in state 3 and is a primary measurement of the tightness of coupling in mitochondria (see above). The RCI as calculated from Fig. 1 is

$$\frac{Q_{O_2} \text{ state 3}}{Q_{O_2} \text{ state 4}} = \frac{179 \text{ nAO/min/mg}}{21.6 \text{ nAO/min/mg}} = 8.3$$

(where nA = nanoatoms.)

Figure 1 is an oxygen electrode tracing of rat liver mitochondria with

---

* Mann Research Laboratories, New York, supply Na–ADP with the millimolar extinction coefficients indicated for each batch shipped.

glutamate and succinate as substrates. After an initial state 3 burst of respiration with glutamate as substrate, a steady-state respiration in state 4 is again achieved. The inhibitor rotenone (1 $\mu g/mg$ protein) is added. Rotenone inhibits electron transport at the region of the flavoprotein associated with NADH-linked respiration (Fig. 2). Adenosine diphosphate is added to test for complete rotenone inhibition; succinate is then added. Electrons from succinate oxidation enter the chain distal to the rotenone block, and, since ADP is already present, the mitochondria are in state 3 respiration. When the added ADP is exhausted, the state 4 rate is again reached. Since one of the phosphorylation sites is not involved with coupled succinate oxidation, the maximum ADP:O ratio attainable is 2. The state 4 rate of respiration with succinate as substrate is always higher than that of NADH-linked respiration due to some endogenous oxidation of the substrate.

A number of chemicals are used as "tools" to inhibit portions of the electron transport chain and phosphorylation mechanism so that certain segments of the chain can be studied. A diagrammatic representation of the electron transport chain indicating the approximate site of action of the more commonly used inhibitors and uncouplers is shown in Fig. 2. Rotenone, antimycin A, and cyanide are selective, specific inhibitors of certain portions of the electron transport chain. Oligomycin is an inhibitor of terminal phosphate transfer but does not prevent the formation of high-energy intermediate(s) which are postulated to provide the energy for ion translocation, swelling-contraction, and other energy-linked functions. Uncouplers, such as 2,4-dinitrophenol (DNP), release respiration from phosphorylation producing rapid, uncontrolled respiration. Inhibitors are generally used at a concentration of 1 to 2 $\mu g/mg$ mitochondrial protein. Uncoupler concentrations vary. Dinitrophenol is usually used at a final concentration of 10^{-5} M. Higher concentrations may actually inhibit rather than stimulate respiration. Since qualitative differences may exist in the utilization of substrates from various types of mitochondria, it is important that both NADH-linked and succinate-linked respiration be studied.

Figure 3 shows oxygen electrode tracings of tumor mitochondria from a mouse mammary adenocarcinoma isolated in a 0.25 M sucrose-10 mM tris-1 mM EDTA medium (STE). Although the ADP:O ratio is not particularly low, the RCI and Q_{O_2} are markedly depressed as compared to the same tumor mitochondria isolated in the STE medium with 1% BSA present (Fig. 3B). It appears that many of the tumor mitochondria have retained the ability to oxidize succinate in a coupled fashion better than that for NADH-linked substrates. The necessity of including BSA in the *isolation* medium is shown in Fig. 4. Figure 4A is an oxygen electrode tracing of mouse mammary adenocarcinoma mitochondria

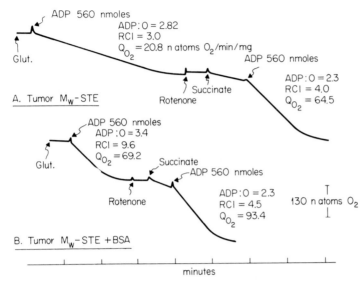

FIG. 3. Oxygen electrode tracings of mitochondria isolated from a mouse mammary adenocarcinoma. Assay conditions are described in the text. Glutamate and succinate are substrates. Tumor mitochondria were added (not shown on traces) to the assay medium with glutamate (Glut.) present. The tracings have been contracted for purposes of presentation and the arrows from glutamate merely indicate this substrate is supporting respiration. (A) Tumor mitochondria isolated in sucrose-tris-EDTA (STE) medium. (B) Tumor mitochondria isolated in STE plus bovine serum albumin (BSA). Washed mitochondria (M_W); adenosine diphosphate (ADP); respiratory control index (RCI).

isolated in the STE medium. Glutamate is the substrate. The ADP:O ratio, RCI, and Q_{O_2} are quite low. Tracing B represents the same mitochondrial preparation, but with BSA (1 mg/ml) added to the *assay medium*. Essentially no improvement is observed. Figure 4C is a tracing of the mitochondria from the same tumor, but isolated in the STE medium containing 1% BSA. There is a marked improvement in the ADP:O ratio, RCI, and Q_{O_2}. Subsequent additions of BSA to the assay medium of the mitochondria (Fig. 4C) *isolated* in BSA produces no further improvement (data not shown).

The respiratory activity during phosphorylation in tumor mitochondria (state 3; Q_{O_2}), even with isolation in albumin, is, for the most part, considerably lower than that seen with normal mouse and rat liver mitochondria. Table I contains some representative ADP:O ratios, RCI's, and Q_{O_2}'s from several types of tumor mitochondria isolated in BSA-containing media. The ADP:O ratios and RCI's of the tumor mitochondria are essentially the same as the controls. However, the Q_{O_2}'s are still generally much lower than those obtained from normal

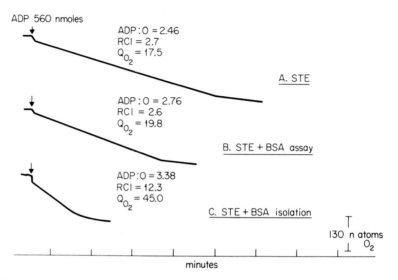

ADP 560 nmoles

ADP:O = 2.46
RCI = 2.7
$Q_{O_2} = 17.5$

A. STE

ADP : O = 2.76
RCI = 2.6
$Q_{O_2} = 19.8$

B. STE + BSA assay

ADP:O = 3.38
RCI = 12.3
$Q_{O_2} = 45.0$

C. STE + BSA isolation

130 n atoms O_2

minutes

Fig. 4. Oxygen electrode tracings of mitochondria isolated from mouse mammary adenocarcinoma. Glutamate is the substrate. Isolation and assay conditions described in text. (A) Tumor mitochondria isolated in sucrose–tris–EDTA (STE). (B) Same tumor mitochondria preparation isolated in STE with 2 mg/ml bovine serum albumin (BSA) added to assay medium. (C) Mitochondria from same tumor isolated in STE plus BSA medium. Adenosine diphosphate (ADP); respiratory control index (RCI).

mitochondria. These depressed Q_{O_2} values would suggest that tumor mitochondria do not have the same number of functional respiratory assemblies as normal mitochondria or that the assemblies are not as active as in normal mitochondria. The possible presence of an endogenous inhibitor should be sought.

B. Electron Microscopy of Isolated Mitochondria

In many instances, electron micrographs of both intact and isolated tumor mitochondria have borne out the biochemical evidence that the function of tumor mitochondria might be impaired (Allard et al., 1952; Mintz et al., 1967; Sordahl et al., 1969). Tumor mitochondria from many tissue sources appear to have less dense matrices, fewer cristae, and are smaller in size than the mitochondria seen in normal liver tissue. It also appears that isolated tumor mitochondria are unable to undergo the rapid transitions in ultrastructural configuration reported for liver (Hackenbrock, 1966; Mintz et al., 1967; Sordahl et al., 1969). The following techniques are an outline of the procedures used for the rapid fixation of isolated mitochondria while undergoing transitions in biochemical state. The reader is referred to other sources for the preparation of intact tissues for electron microscopy (Pease, 1964; Kay, 1967).

Freshly prepared stock suspensions of liver mitochondria are primarily in a condensed morphology as shown in Fig. 5A. This ultrastructural configuration is characterized by an increased intracristal space, increased density in the matrix, and a marked folding of the inner membranes. After 15 minutes incubation of the liver mitochondria in state 4 respiration (monitored in an oxygen electrode chamber) the mitochondria undergo a transition to the "orthodox" configuration which is similar to that seen in mitochondria from intact tissue (Fig. 5B). Upon addition of ADP to a mitochondrial suspension, the organelles undergo a rapid transition back to the condensed morphology originally seen in the stock suspension (Fig. 5C). These rapid transitions in liver mitochondrial morphology were first reported by Hackenbrock (1966) who used the applied terminology. The following fixation method of isolated mitochondrial suspensions is that of Hackenbrock (1966), which is a modification of that of Malamed (1963).

1. Reagents

Millonig's phosphate buffer (100 ml): monobasic sodium phosphate (2.26%; 140 mM), 83.0 ml; and sodium hydroxide (2.52%; 108 mM), 17.0 ml.

Fixative for centrifuged pellets—osmium tetroxide 2% in Millonig's phosphate buffer, pH 7.4 (320 mOsM): 4% osmium tetroxide in water, 2.5 ml (filter before use); phosphate buffer 0.4 ml; 1 M sucrose 1.1 ml; and distilled water 1.0 ml.

2. Centrifuges

Coleman, Model 6-811 (Herbach and Rademan, Inc. Philadelphia, Pennsylvania), or Beckman-Spinco, 152 Microfuge.

3. Rapid Fixation of Isolated Mitochondrial Pellets

1. A 5–20 μl aliquot of the freshly prepared mitochondrial suspension or a 100–200-μl sample from the oxygen electrode chamber is centrifuged for 30 seconds. The concentration of the suspension is adjusted so that the volume of the aliquot allows for a pellet thickness of 0.2 to 0.3 mm.

2. The supernatant is quickly withdrawn and 2% osmium tetroxide in 10 mM phosphate buffer added. Complete fixation occurs in seconds and is noted by a blackening of the pellet. Alternatively, 2% glutaraldehyde in 10 mM phosphate buffer may be used with no postfixation. The

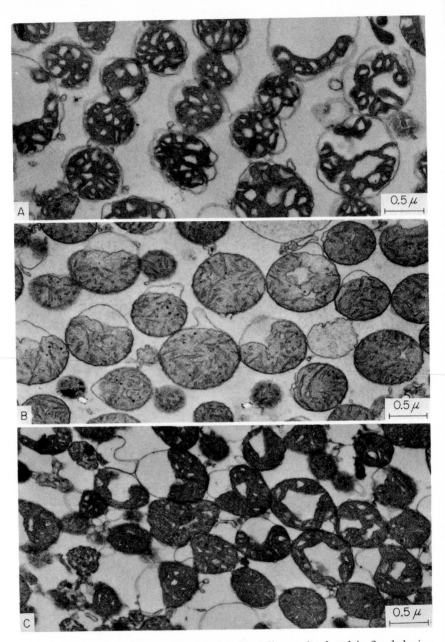

Fig. 5. Electron micrographs of isolated rat liver mitochondria fixed during various respiratory states. (A) Freshly prepared stock suspension. (B) suspension fixed after incubation for 15 minutes in state 4 respiration. (C) Same suspension fixed after 1.5 minutes in state 3 respiration. The cyclic transitions from the condensed configuration in the fresh suspension (A) to orthodox (B) after 15 minutes in state 4 respiration are seen. Addition of adenosine diphosphate to produce state 3 respiration reveals that all the mitochondria have undergone transition to the condensed or intermediate configuration (C). Glutamate is the substrate. Magnification: ×16,280. (Reproduced courtesy of Archives of Biochemistry and Biophysics, Academic Press, New York.)

mitochondrial suspension may be added directly to the cold fixative (Penniston, *et al.*, 1968).

3. Fifteen minutes to 2 hours after addition of the osmium, the fixative is removed and the pellet is dehydrated in graded concentrations of ethanol (30, 50, 70, 90%, absolute; approximately 5 minutes in each).

4. The pellet may be removed from the bottom of the tube by cutting off the tip of the tube just below the pellet and pressing inward on the resulting flat surface with a blunt probe.

C. EMBEDDING OF THE MITOCHONDRIAL PELLET

Fixed mitochondrial pellets may be handled like intact tissue and may be embedded in a variety of materials. Araldite 502 and Epon 812 have been satisfactorily used in the authors' laboratory by the method of Luft (1961), which is summarized as follows:

1. The embedding mixture consists of resin—Araldite 502, 27 ml; hardener—dodecenyl succinic anhydride (DDSA), 23 ml; and accelerator—tridimethylaminomethylphenol (DMP-30), 0.75–1.0 ml. The resin and hardener may be mixed in advance and stored frozen in an airtight container until ready for use. Accelerator is added carefully immediately before use.

2. Transfer the fixed and partially dehydrated pellet to a small vial and complete dehydration with absolute ethanol for 15 minutes.

3. Replace absolute ethanol with propylene oxide (2 changes of 15 minutes each).

4. Replace the propylene oxide with a 50% solution of the embedding mixture containing accelerator. Let stand for 1 hour at room temperature.

5. Add an equal volume of Araldite embedding mixture (containing accelerator) and let stand at room temperature for 3 to 6 hours.

6. Transfer the pellets to undiluted Araldite embedding mixture (with accelerator). This is conveniently done in $\frac{1}{8}$ in. wide strip molds of silastic rubber.

7. Polymerization is carried out in a 60°C oven for 12 to 24 hours.

8. When polymerization is complete the Araldite strips are cut so that the pellets can be mounted on Plexiglas rods with epoxy resin. The pellets are oriented so that they may be sectioned perpendicular to the plane of the pellet.

9. Sections may be cut with glass or diamond knives on any quality ultramicrotome. If staining is desired, Reynold's lead citrate is satisfactory.

10. Sections should be large enough to include both top and bottom surfaces of the pellet. The composition of the mitochondrial population should be closely examined at all levels of the pellet. As many

photographs as practical should be taken and studied from enlarged prints.

The above procedures have been used successfully in the authors' laboratory to prepare isolated mitochondrial pellets fixed during rapid transitions in biochemical state. The electron micrographs in Figs. 5, 6, and 7 were prepared by this method. However, these techniques are still not rapid enough to immediately fix rapidly respiring mitochondria in a particular respiratory steady state. A more rapid fixation technique, and one that allows for a better preparation and visualization of the mitochondrial pellets, is now currently being used in the authors' laboratory. It involves the *rapid* fixation of the mitochondrial suspensions by their direct addition to the buffered fixative and the subsequent distribution of the mitochondrial pellets on a Millipore filter; this method was originally described by Baudhuin et al. (1967). Recently a fluorochrome (8-anilino-1-naphthalenesulfonic acid) has been used to correlate changes in mitochondrial membrane configurations with changes in steady-state kinetics of the electron transport chain (Azzi et al., 1969).

Figure 6 is a set of electron micrographs of isolated mitochondria from the mouse mammary adenocarcinoma. Figures 6A and C are tumor mitochondria isolated in the STE medium and Fig. 6B and D are mitochondria from the same tumor isolated in the STE medium, but with 1% BSA included (STEA). The mitochondria isolated only in the sucrose medium (Fig. 6A and C) exhibited very poor respiratory activity and showed no transitions in morphological ultrastructure. The same is true for the mitochondria isolated in the medium containing BSA. Although these mitochondria exhibited respiratory control, they also showed no rapid transitions in ultrastructural morphology associated with changes in biochemical state (Sordahl et al., 1969). The tumor mitochondria isolated in the BSA have retained a condensed morphology throughout, whereas those isolated without BSA in the medium have exhibited an orthodox morphology throughout (Fig. 6A and C). These preparations of tumor mitochondria also are much smaller in size than those of normal liver, have fewer cristae, and very light matrices. Figure 7A are rat hepatoma mitochondria isolated in an STEA medium. These mitochondria exhibit a condensed morphology in the freshly prepared state. After incubation in state 4 for 15 minutes, the mitochondria underwent a transition in ultrastructural configuration to the orthodox form. However, upon addition of ADP no further changes in ultrastructural configuration were observed, unlike that normally seen with liver mitochondria (Fig. 5). These mitochondria did, however, exhibit changes in their biochemical function. The only apparent differences in the mitochondria of Reuber hepatoma

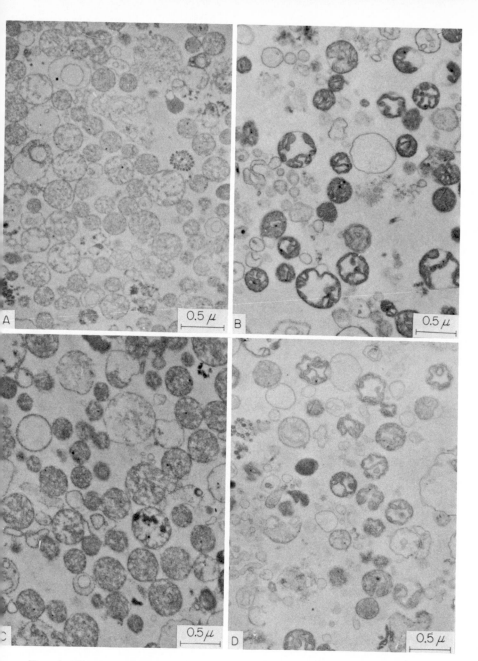

Fig. 6. Electron micrographs of isolated mouse mammary adenocarcinoma mitochondria. (A) Freshly prepared stock suspension of tumor mitochondria isolated in sucrose–tris–EDTA (STE). (B) Freshly prepared stock suspension of mitochondria from the same tumor isolated in STE plus bovine serum albumin (BSA). (C and D) Tumor mitochondria isolated in STE and STE plus BSA, respectively, and fixed after 15 minutes incubation in state 4 respiration. These mitochondria are smaller, have fewer cristae, and less dense matrices compared to those of liver. It is notable that the mitochondria isolated in STE exhibited an orthodox morphology, whereas those isolated in STE plus BSA retain a condensed morphology. No changes in configuration occurred in either preparation upon addition of adenosine diphosphate (state 3). Magnification: ×20,160.

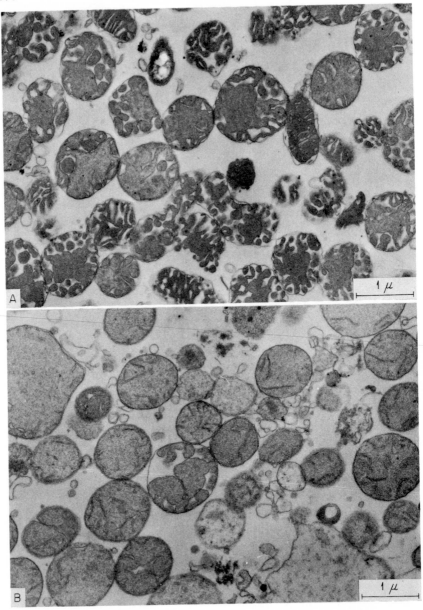

Fig. 7. Electron micrographs of isolated rat hepatoma mitochondria. (A) Freshly prepared stock suspension of mitochondria isolated in sucrose–tris–EDTA plus bovine serum albumin. These mitochondria are in a condensed configuration. (B) Same preparation of mitochondria fixed after incubation for 2 minutes in state 4. All the mitochondria are in an orthodox configuration with some swollen forms evident. Subsequent addition of adenosine diphosphate (state 3) produced no further changes in morphological appearance. Magnification: × 16,280.

and those of normal liver are the lower rates of respiration in state 3 (Q_{O_2}) that are obtained with the hepatoma mitochondria.

In contrast to the various mouse tumors, mitochondria from Reuber hepatomas have higher oxidative phosphorylation values when *assayed* in the KCl–tris medium (optimal assay medium for normal liver mitochondria). The inclusion of BSA in the isolation medium is still necessary in order to obtain optimal values (Fig. 8). The Reuber hepatoma mitochondria are capable of coupled oxidative phosphorylation when isolated in the same medium as liver (STE), but addition of BSA to the isolation medium is necessary to obtain optimal values. The inclusion of $MgCl_2$ in the assay medium generally has little effect on the respiratory rates of hepatoma mitochondria (Sordahl *et al.*, 1969), although added Mg^{++} is required for liver mitochondria (Baltscheffsky, 1957). Other energy-linked functions of tumor mitochondria (ion translocation, swelling–contraction, etc.) are also restored when mitochondria are isolated in BSA-containing media.

D. ENERGY-LINKED POTASSIUM TRANSPORT

Ion transport is one of the energy-linked functions of mitochondria. Theoretically, the high-energy intermediates generated during electron transport are used to facilitate the movement of cations across the

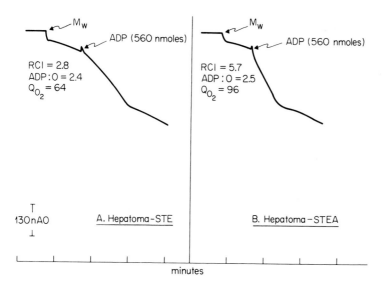

FIG. 8. Oxygen electrode tracings of mitochondria isolated from Reuber rat hepatoma. (A) Hepatoma mitochondria isolated in sucrose-tris-EDTA (STE). (B) Mitochondria from same tumor isolated in STE plus bovine serum albumin (STEA). Glutamate is the substrate. Adenosine diphosphate (ADP); respiratory control index (RCI).

mitochondrial membrane at the expense of the transduction of energy for the production of ATP. Mitochondria transport potassium ions under a variety of conditions. At low salt concentrations in the medium, a combination of the electron transport chain activity and the use of a facilitating agent (valinomycin) are usually required to induce rapid potassium transport (Moore and Pressman, 1964). The antibiotic valinomycin causes the active uptake of potassium. The qualitative and quantitative ability of mitochondria to translocate ions through their membranes is a direct reflection of the intactness of their energy-transducing system. The determination of the actual ion content of isolated mitochondria can also be made and will be discussed later in this chapter. Histones and parathyroid hormone have been shown to cause an energy-linked *efflux* of potassium from mitochondria (Johnson *et al.*, 1967).

1. Procedure

1. Mitochondria are prepared as described earlier in this chapter with the exception that the final suspension of the mitochondria is made at a higher protein concentration. It is desirable to obtain an initial mitochondrial suspension of 40 to 50 mg protein/ml for these experiments. Care should also be taken to reduce the presence of monovalent cations by using tris salts (EDTA) in the isolation medium.

2. Any buffer medium having no monovalent cations may be used. The following media have been employed in this laboratory: (*i*) 0.125 M choline–Cl,20 mM tris, pH 7.4; (*ii*) 0.25 M sucrose–10 mM tris, pH 7.4; (*iii*) 0.225 M mannitol–75 mM sucrose-20 mM tris, pH 7.4. Substrate, 1–10 mM (as tris salt); 5–10 mM tris phosphate.*

3. Changes in the potassium ion concentration of the medium are detected by a cationic sensitive electrode with standard reference electrode connected to a sensitive pH meter and a potentiometric recorder. The cationic electrode is sensitive to all monovalent cations, so it is essential that no monovalent cations, other than potassium, be present in the medium.

4. The electrodes are immersed in the basic assay medium (4–10 ml) which is stirred by a small magnetic flea. The recorder is disconnected from the pH meter, the solution is allowed to stand for several minutes until the millivolt reading stabilizes (usually between $+30$ and $+70$ mV for solutions containing no potassium). The initial millivolt reading is noted; the recorder is connected to the pH meter and turned to "Record." A small volume of the concentrated mitochondrial suspension

---

* Small amounts of potassium (about $500\mu M$) are added when measuring potassium uptake.

is added to yield a final concentration of 1 to 2 mg/ml. An increase in the millivolt reading usually occurs due to the presence of ions in the mitochondrial suspension. Following this increase, the curve should stabilize at a slow, passive potassium efflux, and, after a 1–2 minute equilibration period, agents (valinomycin) that induce potassium-ion movement may be added. At the end of the recording, the recorder is quickly disconnected from the pH meter and the millivolt reading is immediately determined. The initial and final millivolt readings are used to calibrate the recorder chart in terms of millivolt changes.

5. To convert the chart millivolt readings to changes in potassium concentration, the electrode system may be calibrated by repeating the above procedure, but in place of the mitochondria, exact small volumes of standard KCl solution are added sequentially. Eight to ten additions of 10 μl each of a 0.01 M KCl standard are sufficient for an adequate calibration curve. Between additions 0.5 minute should be allowed so that the electrode can stabilize. Since the output of the pH meter is logarithmic, it is necessary to construct a calibration curve by plotting the millivolt readings against the log of the potassium concentration. The millivolt readings, at various intervals along the experimental trace, may be converted to the actual potassium concentration. The use of a computer facilitates this operation.

2. Sample Experiment

The following experiment is included as a demonstration of basic techniques involved in this procedure. Liver mitochondria and tumor mitochondria from a Reuber hepatoma-145 were isolated in STE medium, and half of the mitochondria from the tumor were isolated in the STE medium containing 1% BSA. Since the mitochondria were isolated in a sucrose medium, the sucrose–tris assay medium (see 2, (ii) under *Procedure* above) was used in these assays. The electrode system was first calibrated by the sequential addition of aliquots of a standardized KCl solution (10 mM). Figure 9A presents the calibration curve for this particular experiment. The basic assay medium consisted of 0.25 M sucrose–10 mM tris, pH 7.4; 10 mM tris phosphate; and substrates 10 mM glutamate and 5 mM malate as the tris salts. A 0.1-ml. aliquot of water was also added in place of the mitochondrial suspension. Twenty-microliter aliquots of 10 mM standardized KCl solution were added sequentially until the concentration in the assay medium reached 250 μM. The millivolt readings were noted at each sequential addition (Fig. 9A). After calibrating the electrode system, a fresh beaker of assay medium containing the inorganic phosphate and substrates was allowed to equilibrate with the electrode system (Fig. 9B). This assay medium also contains 500 μM KCl. After allowing approximately 1

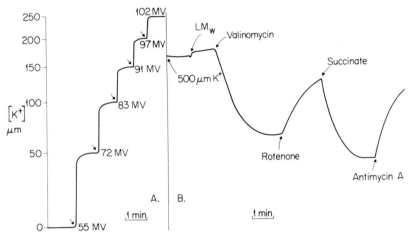

FIG. 9. Measurement of energy-dependent K^+ uptake by rat liver mitochondria with a cationic sensitive electrode. (A) Calibration of a K^+-free assay medium (no mitochondria present) by addition of precise aliquots (50 μM) of K^+ from a standardized KCl solution. A calibration curve of K^+ concentration vs. millivoltage can be plotted on semilog paper. (B) Energy-dependent uptake of K^+ by liver mitochondria in a medium containing 500 μM K^+. Glutamate–malate is the initial substrate. Valinomycin (0.05–0.1 μg/mg mitochondrial protein) is added to induce ion uptake. Addition of rotenone blocks glutamate oxidation, and K^+ efflux is observed. Addition of succinate restores electron transport and K^+ is again taken up until succinate oxidation is blocked by antimycin A (1 μg/mg protein).

minute for equilibration of the electrode system, an aliquot of normal liver mitochondria containing 11.9 mg of mitochondrial protein was added to the assay medium (Fig. 9B). A slight rise in the curve is noted due to the passive efflux of potassium ions (and other monovalent cations) from the mitochondria. After allowing time for equilibration, 1-μg valinomycin is added to induce the energy-linked uptake of potassium from the medium by the mitochondria. After an initial rapid uptake of potassium, the mitochondrial suspension equilibrates and retains the transported K^+. Addition of rotenone to block the NADH-linked respiration (see Fig. 2) now produces a rapid efflux of the potassium from the mitochondria. Subsequent addition of the tris salt of succinate (5 mM) now reestablishes electron flow (and the production of high-energy intermediates) and with this restoration the potassium ion is again taken up by the mitochondrial suspension. After equilibrating at a lower millivolt reading, antimycin-A (which produces a block of electron transport between cytochrome b and c) is added and a rapid efflux of potassium from the mitochondria is again seen. A similar experiment carried out using tumor mitochondria from a Reuber hepatoma isolated only in the STE medium is shown in Fig. 10A. Upon the addition of valinomycin, no potassium uptake occurs. The same tumor mitochondria isolated in the STE medium containing BSA (STEA) show an uptake of potassium by these mitochondria as contrasted to those isolated only in the STE medium (Fig. 10B). However, the rate and total uptake, even by these mitochondria, is not as great as that observed in the normal liver mitochondrial preparation (Fig. 9B). The tumor mitochondrial preparation isolated without BSA exhibited very little respiratory activity and the results of the energy-linked uptake of potassium ion would tend to verify the fact that these mitochondria had a very low ability to transduce energy. In many cases hepatoma mitochondria isolated in the STE medium exhibit fairly good respiratory activity, and in these cases also exhibit an ability to transport potassium ion in an energy-linked fashion. However, when BSA is included in the isolation medium, these particular tumor mitochondria qualitatively and quantitatively transport potassium faster and to a

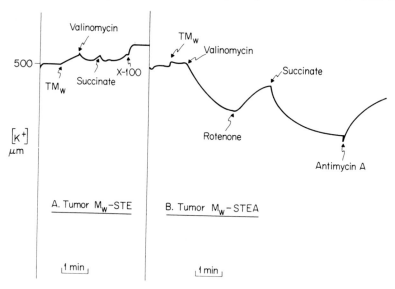

FIG. 10. Measurement of energy-dependent K^+ uptake by mitochondria isolated from Reuber rat hepatoma. Glutamate–malate is the initial substrate. (A) Hepatoma mitochondria isolated in sucrose–tris–EDTA (STE). These mitochondria had no respiratory control (measured polarographically) and exhibit no appreciable uptake of K^+ with either glutamate or succinate as substrates. The nonionic detergent, Triton X–100, was finally added to solubilize the mitochondria and release any endogenous K^+. (B) Mitochondria from the same hepatoma isolated in STE plus bovine serum albumin (STEA). These mitochondria had respiratory control and exhibited the ability to transport K^+ with both glutamate and succinate as substrates. Washed tumor mitochondria (TM_W).

greater extent compared to the same tumor mitochondria isolated without BSA present.

Both the limited and massive uptake of cations, such as potassium and calcium, can also be measured utilizing radioactive isotopes of these ions coupled with scintillation counting techniques. Isotopes ^{42}K and Ca^{45} are available for these types of studies and the reader is referred to various sources for these particular techniques (Bielawski and Lehninger, 1966; Harris et al., 1967). These measurements are also done in a system requiring the expenditure of energy generated within the mitochondrion.

Atomic absorption spectrophotometry* (Cohn et al., 1968) can also be used for the determination of mitochondrial ion content. This particular technique can be used after the uptake of a specific cation has been induced in an assay system. This involves the incubation of mitochondria with a given cation and the subsequent rapid precipitation (usually Millipore filters) and solubilization in appropriate solutions (usually diluted trichloroacetic acid). Total ion content of freshly prepared mitochondria may also be determined utilizing the atomic absorption spectrophotometer techniques. Most ions can be analyzed by solubilization of the mitochondria with trichloroacetic acid and aspiration of the solution through the atomic absorption spectrophotometer. The Ca^{++} presents a problem because of its tendency to combine with phosphate. Modified techniques (Zettner and Seligson, 1964; Rodgerson and Moran, 1968, Malbica and Hall, 1968) for Ca^{++} analysis by atomic absorption spectroscopy are available. Deviations in the ion content of tumor mitochondria, as compared to that of normal tissue mitochondria, may be significant with respect to the role of mitochondria in the overall metabolic economy of the tumor cell. For example, if the tumor mitochondrial ion content was significantly higher than that found in many normal tissue mitochondrial preparations, it may reflect an attempt by these mitochondria to restore or equilibrate the ionic milieu of the tumor cells. In doing so, these mitochondria would have to expend internal energy, and this would greatly reduce their ability to supply ATP to other endergonic processes of the tumor cell. Since Ca^{++} ion is also a known uncoupler and inhibitor of mitochondrial respiration (Carafoli and Lehninger, 1967), it is quite possible that high calcium ion content in tumor mitochondria could produce a complete inhibition of the respiration of these mitochondria in the tumor cell. The massive accumulation of calcium as discrete granules can also be visualized in mitochondria by electron microscopy and appear as dark

---

* Various manufacturers' manuals can be consulted for the operation of these instruments.

electron-opaque bodies within the mitochondrial matrix (Lehninger, 1965, p. 165).

V. Conclusions

It would be impossible within the scope of this chapter to present all the available techniques for the assay of various mitochondrial functions. It is hoped that the reader, if interested, will be able to utilize the basic techniques of isolation presented here and then go to other source material for more specific and appropriate assay techniques. A large number of these techniques involving the assay of the partial reactions of energy coupling and of electron transport, transhydrogenation, "reversed-electron transport," analysis of total pyridine and adenine nucleotide content, and many others are available in a single volume (Estabrook and Pullman, 1967). The techniques of isolation and of assay presented in this chapter have been found to give the optimal results with respect to tumor mitochondrial oxidative phosphorylation and for other energy-linked functions of these mitochondria (Mintz et al., 1967; Sordahl et al., 1969). Preparations of tumor mitochondria vary from tissue to tissue, and subsequent assay of oxidative phosphorylation may require certain minor changes. However, utilizing the basic techniques presented here for the isolation and assay, it should be possible to determine whether a given tumor mitochondrial suspension possesses respiratory activity. If coupled respiration is intact, then subsequent studies may be done to assay for the capability of these mitochondria to carry on other energy-linked functions. If a given mitochondrial preparation does not possess the coupled respiratory activity normally found in mitochondria, additional enzymic assays are available that could be conducted with the isolated membrane fraction to determine what enzymes or properties of these mitochondria from a given tumor have been lost. Electron microscopy of tumor mitochondria, whether or not they exhibit respiratory activity, should also be carried out to determine the intactness of the "double"-membrane system. However, electron micrographs could show relatively intact mitochondrial membranes, yet the preparations themselves may exhibit little or no respiratory activity. A possible loss of some critical cofactor on the mitochondrial enzyme assemblies or the presence of some inhibitory substance in the tumor tissue might then be indicated.

It should be emphasized that mitochondrial preparations from a *single* tumor type can vary greatly in oxidative phosphorylation capacities. Tumor mitochondria appear to possess a greater lability of enzymes or fragility of structure, which is particularly evident during isolation procedures (Kielly, 1952). Possibly albumin protects an already fragile membrane system against the trauma of isolation. Weinbach *et al.*, (1967) have demonstrated a change in the morphology of normal mitochondria in the presence of an uncoupler. The morphology of these mitochondria in the presence of the uncoupler resembles that of many of the tumor preparations in our studies. Oxidative phosphorylation could be restored in these uncoupled mitochondria by the addition of BSA, although there were no changes in the altered morphology of the organelles. Weinbach *et al.* (1967) have suggested that albumin prevents further structural deterioration of mitochondria in the presence of the uncoupler. Feo (1967) has observed a marked insensitivity of tumor mitochondria to digitonin-induced swelling and has suggested a different structural state of tumor mitochondrial membranes. The inability of tumor mitochondria to undergo transitions in ultrastructural morphology during changes in biochemical state is consistent with this view (Sordahl *et al.*, 1969). Even though tumor mitochondria appear more swollen, suggesting greater permeability of the outer membrane, very few preparations of tumor mitochondria oxidized added NADH; the latter cannot penetrate carefully prepared mitochondria. This is considered a criterion for an intact outer membrane in mitochondria (Lehninger, 1951). Borst (1962) has also demonstrated that ascites tumor cells are totally impermeable to NADH. It is apparent that the relationship between ultrastructure and biochemical activity is quite complex, both in normal and in tumor mitochondria. A great many more studies appear to be necessary before the role of mitochondria will be fully understood in the metabolism of the tumor cell.

ACKNOWLEDGMENTS

The Reuber rat hepatomas used in these studies were generously supplied by Dr. Melvin Reuber of the National Cancer Institute. The assistance of Miss Gwendolyn H. Kraft is gratefully appreciated. Our appreciation is also extended to Dr. Z. Blailock for some of the electron micrography.

REFERENCES

Aisenberg, A. C. (1961). "The Glycolysis and Respiration of Tumors." Academic Press, New York.
Allard, C., Mathieu, R., De Lanurande, G., and Cantero, A. (1952). *Cancer Res.* **12**, 407–412.
Arcos, J. C., Griffith, G. W., and Cunningham, R. W. (1960). *J. Biophys. Biochem. Cytol.* **7**, 49–60.

Arcos, J. C., Mathison, J. B., Tison, M. J., and Mouledoux, A. M. (1969a). *Cancer Res.* **29**, 1288–1298.

Arcos, J. C., Tison, M. J., Gosch, H. H., and Fabin, J. A. (1969b). *Cancer Res.* **29**, 1298–1306.

Azzi, A., Chance, B., Radda, G. K., and Lee, C. P. (1969). *Proc. Nat. Acad. Sci. U.S.* **62**, 612–619.

Baltscheffsky, H. (1957). *Biochim. Biophys. Acta* **25**, 382–388.

Baudhuin, P., Evrard, P., and Berthet, J. (1967). *J. Cell Biol.* **32**, 181–191.

Bielawski, J., and Lehninger, A. L. (1966). *J. Biol. Chem.* **241**, 4316–4322.

Borst, P. (1962). *Biochim. Biophys. Acta* **57**, 270–282.

Boxer, G. E., and Devlin, T. M. (1961). *Science* **134**, 1495–1501.

Burk, P., Woods, M., and Hunter, J. (1967). *J. Nat. Cancer Inst.* **38**, 839–863.

Carafoli, E., and Lehninger, A. L. (1967). *Methods Enzymol.* **10**, 745.

Chance, B. (1963). "Energy-Linked Functions of Mitochondria." Academic Press, New York.

Chance, B., and Williams, G. R. (1956). *Advan. Enzymol.* **17**, 65–134.

Cohn, D. V., Bawdon, R., Newman, R. R., and Hamilton, J. W. (1968). *J. Biol. Chem.* **243**, 1089–1095.

Devlin, T. M. (1967). *Methods Enzymol.* **10**, 110.

Estabrook, R. W., and Pullman, M. E., eds. (1967). *Methods Enzymol.* **10**.

Feo, F. (1967). *Life Sci.* **6**, 2417–2425.

Hackenbrock, C. R. (1966). *J. Cell. Biol.* **30**, 269–297.

Harris, E. J., Catlin, G., and Pressman, B. C. (1967). *Biochemistry* **6**, 1360–1370.

Jacobs, E. E., Jacob, M., Sanadi, D. R., and Bradley, L. B. (1956). *J. Biol. Chem.* **223**, 147–156.

Johnson, C. L., Mauritzen, C. M., Starbuck, W. C., and Schwartz, A. (1967). *Biochemistry* **6**, 1121–1127.

Kay, D. (1967). "Techniques for Electron Microscopy." Davis, Philadelphia, Pennsylvania.

Kielly, R. K. (1952). *Cancer Res.* **12**, 124–128.

Kornberg, A., and Pricer, W. E., Jr. (1951). *J. Biol. Chem.* **193**, 481–490.

Lehninger, A. L. (1951). *J. Biol. Chem.* **190**, 345–359.

Lehninger, A. L. (1965). "The Mitochondrion." Benjamin, New York.

Luft, J. H. (1961). *Biophys. Biochem. Cytol.* **9**, 409–417.

Malamed, S. (1963). *J. Cell Biol.* **18**, 696–700.

Malbica, J. O., and Hall, J. C. (1968). *Amer. J. Physiol.* **214**, 1054–1062.

Miller, L. A., and Goldfeder, A. (1965). *Proc. Soc. Exp. Biol. Med.* **119**, 759–763.

Mintz, H. A., Yawn, D. H., Safer, B., Bresnick, E., Liebelt, A. G., Blailock, Z. R., Rabin, E. R., and Schwartz, A. (1967). *J. Cell Biol.* **34**, 513–523.

Moore, C., and Pressman, B. C. (1964). *Biochem. Biophys. Res. Commun.* **15**, 562–567.

Morris, H. P. (1965). *Advan. Cancer Res.* **9**, 227–302.

Pease, D. C. (1964). "Histological Techniques for Electron Microscopy," 2nd Ed. Academic Press, New York.

Penniston, J. T., Harris, R. A., Asai, J., and Green, D. E. (1968). *Proc. Nat. Acad. Sci. U.S.* **59**, 624–631.

Rodgerson, D. O., and Moran, I. K. (1968). *Clin. Chem.* **14**, 1206–1210.

Schneider, W. C. (1946). *Cancer Res.* **6**, 685–690.

Schneider, W. C. and Hogeboom, G. H. (1950). *J. Biol. Chem.* **183**, 123–128.

Schneider, W. C., Hogeboom, G. H., and Ross, H. E. (1949–1950). *J. Nat. Cancer Inst.* **10**, 977–982.

Sordahl, L. A., Blailock, Z. R., Johnson, C., and Schwartz, A. (1970). *In* "Methods in Pharmacology" (A. Schwartz, ed.), Appleton-Century-Crofts, New York, in press.

Sordahl, L. A., Blailock, Z. R., Liebelt, A. G., Kraft, G. H., and Schwartz, A. (1969). *Cancer Res.* **29**, 2002–2009.

Umbreit, W. W., Burris, R. H., and Stauffer, J. F. (1964). "Manometric Techniques," 2nd Ed. Burgess, Minneapolis, Minnesota.

Warburg, O. (1930). "The Metabolism of Tumors." translated by F. Dickens. Constable, London.

Warburg, O. (1956). *Science* **123**, 309–314.

Weinbach, E. C., Garbus, J., and Sheffield, H. G. (1967). *Exp. Cell Res.* **46**, 129–143.

Weinhouse, S. (1966). *Biol. Biochem. Eval. Malignancy Exp. Hepatomas, Proc. U.S.-Jap. Conf., Kyoto, 1965* Gann Monogr. No. 1, pp. 99–115.

Zettner, A., and Seligson, D. (1964). *Clin. Chem.* **10**, 869–890.

MOLECULAR BIOLOGY

CHAPTER IV

PROTEIN BIOSYNTHESIS*

A. CLARK GRIFFIN† AND DIANNE D. BLACK

I. Introduction

One of the initial cell-free amino acid-incorporating systems was isolated from Ehrlich mouse ascites tumor. Littlefield and Keller (1957) obtained ribonucleoprotein particles from the microsomal fraction, and the accessory enzymes were precipitated at pH 5.0 from the soluble portion of the tumor cells. These fractions incubated in the presence of a ^{14}C-amino acid and guanosine triphosphate (GTP) incorporated the radioactivity in a hot perchloric acid-insoluble form. In the relatively short span of just over a decade, many major advances have emerged and the components and mechanism of protein synthesis are now better understood in a wide spectrum of cells and tissues. The preparation and partial characterization of ribosomes, purification and characterization of transfer ribonucleic acid (tRNA), elucidation of the formation

---

* Work supported by grants from the American Cancer Society and The Robert A. Welch Foundation.

† American Cancer Society Professor of Biochemistry.

and function of aminoacyl tRNA's, isolation of the initiation and transfer factors, as well as the contributions resulting from the coding studies have made it possible to construct model systems that accurately describe the events occurring in protein synthesis. There is reason to believe that this model, as illustrated in Fig. 1, is generally universal in nature. Although this ribosomal mechanism probably accounts for a high percentage of all protein synthesis, there are other methods by which proteins or polypeptides may be formed. The synthesis of proteins in nuclei or mitochondria, the synthesis of some peptides by mechanisms not involving nucleic acids (Kleinkauf et al., 1969), end group additions of amino acids to polypeptides certainly occur in many cells. This chapter will be restricted largely to the ribosomal mechanism.

In acknowledging that the general mechanism of protein synthesis

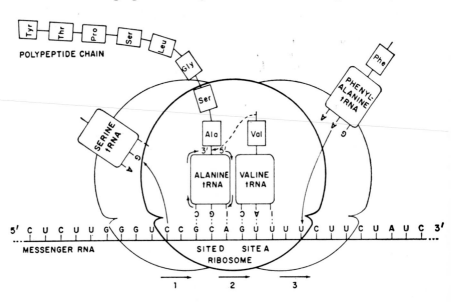

Fig. 1. This survey of sequential addition of amino acids is adapted from Crick (1966). The messenger ribonucleic acid (mRNA) is gliding along the 30 S ribosomal subunit; the peptidyl and aminoacyl terminals of the two interacting transfer ribonucleic acids (tRNA's) are bound to the 50 S unit, and through anti-codon–codon interaction, are hydrogen-bonded to mRNA on the 30 S subunit. On the left, after peptidyl transfer, the tRNA, freed of its charged serine, is leaving the ribosome; in the middle, transpeptidation to the newly adding valyl tRNA is shown taking place; and, on the right, elongation continues with phenylalanyl tRNA approaching its anti-codon with the succeeding codon triplet on mRNA. The 5′ → 3′ arrows around the alanine tRNA emphasize the antiparallel nature of the binding between anticodon on tRNA and codon on mRNA. Site D, donor site; site A, acceptor site. (Reprinted with permission from Lipmann, 1969.)

may be universal, the inclusion of a special section on this subject may not appear warranted in a book devoted to methods in cancer research. However, it will become evident that specialized methods of preparation are required for the isolation of components from different cellular or tissue types. Although the microbial systems are comparable in many respects to mammalian systems, different procedures must be employed for the isolation and study of the two different types. Special refinements must be employed in order to isolate the transfer enzymes from different mammalian cells. The importance of the preparative and the assay procedures employed to study the various stages of protein synthesis must be emphasized.

The objectives of this chapter will be concerned with (a) a consideration of the procedures used for preparing components of protein synthesis in cancer cells and several normal cellular systems, (b) ascertaining if there are differences in components or at any stage of protein synthesis between cancer cells and normal counterparts, (c) ascertaining the extent or degree of specificity that may exist among varying species, and (d) attempting to determine if alterations may occur in the components or the mechanism of protein synthesis that may be involved in either the origin or the behavior of cancer cells.

II. Mammalian Amino Acid-Incorporating Systems

A. TUMOR CELLS

Many *in vitro* amino acid-incorporating systems have been derived from various biological sources. The essential components required for the incorporation of amino acylated tRNA's into polypeptides include: ribosomes, messenger RNA (endogenous or synthetic), transfer enzymes (enzymatic factors), GTP, and monovalent cations. An attempt will be made to present some of the established methods employed in the preparation and isolation of these cell-free components involved in protein synthesis.

1. Novikoff Ascites Tumor Cells

Twenty female, albino rats (125–150 gm)* were each inoculated intraperitoneally (IP) with 1 ml of Novikoff ascites fluid. The inoculum normally contained 40–60 × 10^6 cells per milliliter. This strain of tumor cells, induced by maintaining rats on diets containing an azo carcinogen,

---

* Animals used in this laboratory were obtained from Sprague-Dawley, Inc. Madison, Wisconsin, or Holtzman Laboratory Animals, Madison, Wisconsin.

was obtained from the original Novikoff ascites tumor (Novikoff, 1957). Seven days following the tumor cell transplant, the animals were sacrificed and the cells harvested.

The ascites cells were removed with a 10–20 ml hypodermic syringe and needle (18G, $1\frac{1}{2}$). The fluid was transferred to 250-ml centrifuge bottles containing 30 ml of cell wash buffer. All procedures were conducted at 4°C and processed as outlined in Fig. 2. Eight hundred milliliters of the ascites fluid were centrifuged at 600 rmp for 5 minutes in an International centrifuge, Model PR-2, No. 284 Head. After discarding the supernatant fraction, the packed cells were suspended in 200 ml of cell wash buffer (0.14 M NaCl, 0.02 M dextrose, 0.04 M tris–HCl, pH 8.5) and centrifuged at 800 rpm for 5 minutes. Usually, four washes were sufficient to free the cells of contaminating erythrocytes. The cells were packed on the last washing by centrifugation at 1600 rpm for 5 minutes.

The tumor cells were "plasmolyzed" before homogenization, by adding 5 volumes of cold, deionized water to 50 ml of the packed ascites cells, and were then allowed to stand for 5 minutes. The cells were mechanically broken in an Elvehjem–Potter, Teflon–glass homogenizer. Homogenization was continued until approximately 90% of the cells were broken as judged by observation under the phase microscope. The ionic strength was readjusted by the addition of a 2.5 M sucrose solution containing 0.25 M KCl and 0.05 M MgCl$_2$ (1 ml/9 ml of cell homogenate). This mixture was centrifuged at 45,000 g_{max} (Beckman 42 rotor) for 20 minutes and the cell-free supernatant material recentrifuged at 275,000 g_{max} (Beckman 50.1 rotor) for 60 minutes to sediment the tumor microsomes.

a. *Preparations of Tumor Ribosomes.* (*i*) *Twice deoxycholate (DOC)-washed ribosomes.* It is possible to obtain active incorporating ribosomes exhibiting a requirement for NH$_4^+$, GTP, and transfer enzymes by deoxycholate washings of the microsomal pellets (A. C. Griffin, 1967; A. C. Griffin *et al.*, 1968). The microsomal pellets were suspended in 12 ml of a 2.5% sodium deoxycholate–0.2 M glycylglycine buffer, pH 8.0 (DOC), and gently homogenized. To prepare the DOC buffer, 0.660 gm of glycylglycine was dissolved in 25 ml of deionized water and the pH of this solution adjusted to pH 8.0 with concentrated NaOH. Sodium deoxycholate (0.625 gm) which became readily solubilized at this pH was added. The homogenized pellets were diluted to 240 ml with standard buffer (0.25 M sucrose, 0.025 M KCl, 0.005 M MgCl$_2$, 0.05 M tris–HCl, pH 7.6) and centrifuged at 150,000 g_{max} (Beckman 50 Ti rotor) for 60 minutes. The supernatant material was discarded and the pellets washed an additional time with 6 ml of the DOC buffer and

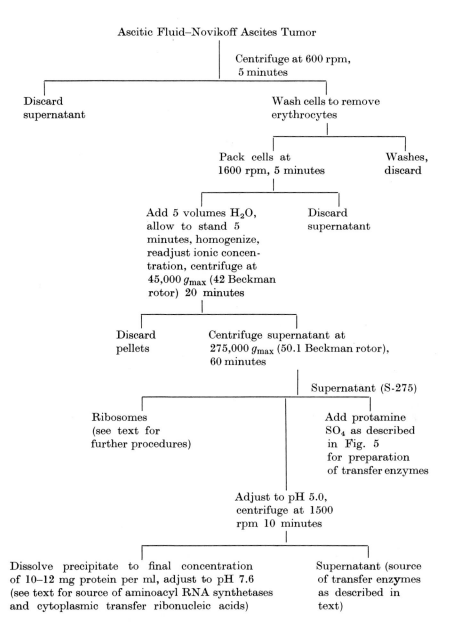

Fig. 2. Fractionation of components of protein synthesis from Novikoff ascites tumor cells.

120 ml of standard buffer. Finally, the pellets were homogenized in 8 ml standard buffer and stored at $-10°C$ to serve as a source of tumor ribosomes. These preparations contained approximately 10 mg ribosomal protein per milliliter (adsorption at 260 mμ assuming 1 mg of ribosomal protein per milliliter is equivalent to 11.2 OD units).

(ii) *Twice DOC–low* Mg^{++}–0.5 *M* NH_4Cl-*washed ribosomes*. Further purification of the 2 × DOC-washed ribosomes was achieved by modification of the procedures of Takanami (1960) and of Gasior and Moldave (1965). Approximately 8 ml of the 2 × DOC tumor ribosomes were solubilized by a tenfold dilution with buffer composed of 0.05 *M* tris–HCl (pH 7.5), 0.001 *M* $MgCl_2$, 0.5 *M* NH_4Cl, 0.01 *M* 2-mercaptoethanol. This suspension was gently homogenized, and centrifuged at 150,000 g_{max} (Beckman 50 Ti rotor) for 40 minutes. The pellets were homogenized in 8 ml standard buffer, sedimented at 40,000 g_{max} for 15 minutes, and resuspended in standard buffer to a final concentration of 1 to 2 mg ribosomal protein per milliliter. The ribosomes purified by this procedure were unstable and were used immediately in the polymerization assays.

(iii) *Deoxycholate–sucrose gradient–0.5 M* NH_4Cl-*washed ribosomes*. Tumor ribosomes were prepared by the method of E. B. Keller and Zamecnik (1956) as modified by Felicetti and Lipmann (1968). Following the original high-speed centrifugation, the microsomes were suspended by mechanical homogenization in 100 ml of buffer composed of the following; 0.35 *M* sucrose, 0.035 *M* $KHCO_3$, 0.004 *M* $MgCl_2$, 0.025 *M* KCl, and DOC added to a final concentration of 0.5%. Five milliliters of the tumor mixture were layered on a discontinuous sucrose gradient of 3 ml 0.5 *M* sucrose over 2 ml of 2 *M* sucrose buffers containing 0.004 *M* $MgCl_2$, 0.05 *M* tris–HCl, pH 7.3. The preparation was centrifuged at 150,000 g_{max} for 3 hours. Maintaining a concentration of 1 mg ribosomal protein per milliliter, the DOC–sucrose ribosomes were diluted in 0.25 *M* sucrose buffer containing 0.05 *M* tris–HCl (pH 7.3), 0.01 *M* $MgCl_2$, 0.5 *M* NH_4Cl, and centrifuged for 90 minutes at 150,000 g_{max}. The washed ribosomes were resuspended in 8 ml of the 0.25 *M* sucrose buffer without 0.5 *M* NH_4Cl and retained full activity for 2 weeks when stored at $-10°C$.

(iv) *Deoxycholate–diethylaminoethyl* (*DEAE*)–*cellulose–0.5 M* NH_4Cl-*washed ribosomes*. The procedure of Kirsch *et al.* (1960) has been adapted for preparation of active, low background, ribosomes. After sedimenting the microsomes in the first 275,000 g_{max} centrifugation, the pellets were homogenized in 32 ml standard buffer and the suspension diluted fivefold to 160 ml with a 0.9 *M* sucrose, 0.004 *M* $MgCl_2$, and 0.025 *M* KCl solution. The suspension was adjusted to 0.009 *M* by the addition of

0.1 M $MgCl_2$ with constant shaking. A 2.5% DOC solution was pipetted dropwise until a 0.25% DOC concentration was obtained. Following centrifugation at 175,000 g_{max} (50.1 rotor) for 20 minutes, the precipitate was discarded and the supernatant fraction recentrifuged at 275,000 g_{max} for 60 minutes. The pellets were rewashed 3 times with standard buffer, resuspended in 2.0 ml of the same, and passed over a DEAE–cellulose column (0.5 × 16 cm) previously equilibrated with 0.05 M tris–HCl (pH 7.3), 0.004 M $MgCl_2$ buffer.

Approximately 70–80 mg of tumor ribosomes (ribosomal protein) were chromatographed on the DEAE–cellulose column. Fractions were eluted with the 0.05 M tris–HCl, (pH 7.3) buffer containing 0.25 M sucrose and collected in 1-ml volumes at 5 minute intervals. Tubes containing the eluted ribosomes appeared turbid. A yield of 28–44 mg of ribosomal protein was obtained from the initial 50 ml of packed ascites cells. These ribosomes were essentially free of one of the transfer enzymes, T_1, but still remained saturated with T_2. Varying designations have been used for the transfer enzymes or factors in different laboratories. A comparative chart has been prepared (see Table III). The designations, T_1 and T_2, will be used to describe the two major transfer enzymes obtained from the tumor cells. Salas et al. (1965) have also described a DEAE–cellulose chromatographic procedure for the removal of nuclease activity from *Escherichia coli* ribosomes.

Prior to use, the DOC–DEAE–cellulose ribosomes were washed further with 0.5 M NH_4Cl to remove T_2. One milliliter of the tumor ribosomes was diluted tenfold with the 0.05 M tris–HCl (pH 7.3) buffer containing 0.25 M sucrose, 0.004 M $MgCl_2$, and 0.5 M NH_4Cl. Following centrifugation at 150,000 g_{max} for 60 minutes, the pellets were resuspended in 1.2 ml of the same buffer without the 0.5 M NH_4Cl. The final ribosomal concentration ranged between 1 and 4 mg of ribosomal protein per milliliter.

b. pH 5 Fractionation. The clear supernatant fraction from the first 275,000 g_{max} centrifugation served as an excellent source of tRNA's, aminoacyl synthetases, and transfer enzymes. The pH of the supernatant material was lowered to pH 5.0 with 1 N acetic acid, and the solution was allowed to stand for 15 minutes. The cloudy suspension was centrifuged at 1500 rpm (International Centrifuge, No. 253 Head) and the resulting precipitate dissolved in 0.02 M tris–HCl, (pH 7.6), 1 × 10⁻³ M ethylenediaminetetraacetate (EDTA), 0.01 M 2-mercaptoethanol buffer to a final concentration of 10 to 12 mg protein per milliliter. Adjustment of this pH 5 fraction to pH 7.6 helped retain full activity of the aminoacyl synthetases and tRNA's during storage at −10°C. The supernatant material contained transfer enzymes.

(i) *Crude transfer enzyme fraction.* The supernatant material from the pH 5.0 soluble fraction was adjusted to pH 7.1 and fractionated with solid ammonium sulfate. The precipitate that formed between 22 and 60% ammonium sulfate saturation was collected by centrifugation at 40,000 g_{max} (Beckman 50 Ti rotor) for 15 minutes, dissolved in 0.01 M tris–HCl (pH 7.5) buffer containing 0.2 M sucrose, and 1×10^{-3} M dithiothreitol (DTT), and dialyzed overnight against the same buffer to remove the excess ammonium sulfate.

(ii) ^{14}C-*Aminoacyl tRNA preparation.* The tumor ^{14}C-aminoacyl tRNA's were prepared by the methods of Canning and Griffin (1965) and Yang and Novelli (1968b). Approximately 100 ml of the tumor S-275 (pH 5) material was incubated at 37°C for 30 minutes in a solution prepared by mixing 20 ml of 0.025 M adenosine triphosphate (ATP) (pH 7.0), 20 ml 0.01 M $MgCl_2$, and 5.0 ml of a ^{14}C-amino acid mixture (pH 7.0). Following incubation, the reaction mixture was chilled and an equal volume of 1 M sodium acetate, adjusted to pH 4.5, was added. The tRNA's were extracted in an equal volume of 80% phenol and the solution centrifuged at 10,000 g (International centrifuge, Model B-20). The aqueous upper layers were collected and 20% potassium acetate added (1 ml/9 ml of solution). Precipitation of the tRNA's was allowed to develop in 2 volumes of cold ethanol for 1 hour in the cold. This ethanol solution was centrifuged at 3000 rpm (International Centrifuge, No. 253 Head), the pellets dissolved in 1×10^{-3} M EDTA, and dialyzed against the same to remove bound GTP and other nucleotide phosphates. Specific activity was approximately 100,000 counts/minute per milligram of RNA.

(iii) *Tumor amino acid-incorporating system.* The ability of the transfer enzymes to catalyze the incorporation and polymerization of amino acids into polypeptides was measured in the following assay system: 0.05 ml ribosomes (9 mg ribosomal protein per milliliter for crude and 3 mg/ml for purified ribosomes), transfer enzymes (as indicated in Tables I and VII), 0.5 μmole phosphoenolpyruvate (PEP), 5–10 μg PEP kinase, 0.04 μmole GTP, 0.6 μmole 2-mercaptoethanol, 10 μmoles $(NH_4)_2SO_4$, 0.01 ml ^{14}C-aminoacyl–tRNA mixture in a total volume of 0.1 ml. The mixture was incubated at 37°C for 25 minutes, and adsorbed on a Whatman No. 3 MM paper disc placed directly into the assay tube. The discs were washed once in cold 5% trichloroacetic acid (TCA), heated in 5% TCA (90°C) for 10 minutes, and washed once in cold TCA and twice in ethanol. After drying, the discs were counted in a Packard scintillation counter with a 60% counting efficiency. Counts per minute were based on the 0.05 ml ribosomes present in the assay mixture.

Incorporation of amino acids by this tumor system was dependent upon transfer enzymes and GTP. The addition of 10 to 15 μmoles ammonium sulfate and 0.6 μmoles 2-mercaptoethanol per assay tube was required for optimal incorporation. Other monovalent cations, such as Na^+ and K^+, were active to a lesser extent (A. C. Griffin et al., 1968).

(iv) Separation of tumor transfer enzymes. In order to compare the tumor with other in vitro incorporating systems, it was necessary to purify and resolve the crude source of transfer factors into two or more enzymes catalyzing the transfer of aminoacyl tRNA to the ribosome–messenger complex with subsequent formation of a peptide linkage. Following pH 5 fractionation, the crude 22–60% $(NH_4)_2SO_4$ material was chromatographed on triethylaminoethyl (TEAE)–cellulose columns as described by Richter and Klink (1967) for yeast transfer factors. The crude $(NH_4)_2SO_4$ material was also treated with alumina Cγ-gel as reported by Nishizuka and Lipmann (1966a) for Escherichia coli. Utilizing another approach, the crude 22–60% $(NH_4)_2SO_4$ material was adsorbed to a 3% calcium phosphate $[Ca_3(PO_4)_2]$ gel suspension. The fraction eluting from the gel with a 0.25 M potassium phosphate buffer (pH 6.8) was subsequently filtered on Sephadex G-200 columns. However, the tumor transfer enzymes did not appear to separate into two complementary factors as did the factors from normal rat liver (Gasior and Moldave, 1965).

The various TEAE–cellulose, alumina Cγ-gel, and Sephadex G-200 fractions were assayed in the amino acid-incorporating system to identify the complementary transfer factors. For these studies the ribosomes were prepared by the techniques employing 2 × DOC, 2 × DOC–low Mg^{++}–0.5 M NH_4Cl, or DOC–sucrose gradient–0.5 M NH_4Cl (see above). Data from these incubations did not show any additive effects with the various transfer enzyme fractions that were obtained nor provide an indication of resolution of the transfer enzyme complex.

Preparative polyacrylamide columns were also used in order to fractionate the transfer enzymes. The 22–60% $(NH_4)_2SO_4$ material (Section II, A, 1, b, i) was concentrated with Acquacide II (Calbiochem, Los Angeles, California) to approximately 60 mg/ml (assuming 0.6 OD unit is equivalent to 1.0 mg protein per milliliter) and dialyzed overnight against the 0.01 M tris (pH 7.6) buffer. One milliliter of the sample containing 0.1 ml 50% sucrose was applied to a 7-cm preparative polyacrylamide gel column that previously had been perfused with the electrolyte buffer for 20 minutes (Shandon Scientific Company, Ltd., London). The gel medium, Cyanogum-41, was polymerized with the chemical catalysts N,N,N',-tetramethylenediamine (TMED) and ammonium persulfate (AP). Separation was achieved in a continuous electrophoresis system using a modified buffer of Davis et al. (1967),

0.035 M asparagine, 5×10^{-4} M DTT, and 1.0 M tris, to bring the pH
to 7.9. Electrophoresis proceeded at 10 mA for 20 minutes, followed by
an increase to 19 mA at constant current until completion of the run
(10–12 hours). The flow rate of the eluting buffer (asparagine, DTT,
tris, pH 7.9) was 2 ml/10 minutes, and all fractions were assayed for
amino acid incorporation. The area of peak activity was pooled, concentrated to 2 to 3 ml with Acquacid II, and dialyzed overnight against
the 0.01 M tris–HCl (pH 7.6) buffer.

Under the same conditions, purity of the preparative gel fractions
was checked with an E-C vertical gel system. A 3%, 3-mm thick, running gel, supported by a 5% gel plug was prepared by the procedure in
the "Vertical Gel Electrophoresis Manual" (E-C Apparatus Corporation,
Philadelphia, Pennsylvania). The protein samples (80–750 μg) containing sucrose and bromphenol blue were applied to slots of 1 cm
widths. Electrophoresis proceeded with 60 mA at a constant voltage of
300 V until the marker dye migrated 11 cm. The separated proteins
were fixed with 10% TCA for 15 minutes, and the gel stained with 0.2%
Amido Black 10 B in 5:5:1 methanol–water–glacial acetic acid solution
for 1 hour. Destaining with the methanol–water–glacial acetic acid
solution was allowed to continue overnight. After destaining, the gel
was cleared with 5% aqueous glycerine.

Fractions eluted from the preparative acrylamide columns were
tested for ^{14}C-amino acid incorporation employing the DOC–DEAE–
cellulose ribosomes. Although the assays showed that a peak emerged
with high transfer enzyme activity when tested in this ribosomal
system, there was no indication of complementation with any other
fraction. Patterns developed from analytical acrylamide electrophoresis
of this active fraction revealed a single band. It was concluded from
these results that the tumor transfer enzymes existed as a homogeneous
complex or that the ribosomes were contaminated with one or more of
the transfer enzymes.

The DOC–DEAE–cellulose ribosomes were purified further by washing with 0.5 M NH$_4$Cl, and the concentrated acrylamide fraction was
reassayed for enzymic activity and complementation. These ribosomes,
in the presence of the crude 22–60% (NH$_4$)$_2$SO$_4$ preparation, were
active as determined by the amount of radioactive amino acid incorporated into hot, TCA, precipitable material. However, no incorporating
activity was obtained with the above acrylamide fraction. It now
appeared certain that only one enzyme was present in the acrylamide
fraction and that the other complementary fraction was attached to the
DOC–DEAE ribosomes. This enzyme was apparently extracted by the
NH$_4$Cl wash.

Identification of the enzyme present in the tumor acrylamide fraction finally was resolved by cross-checking the tumor ribosomes and active transfer enzymes in a known system. Reticulocyte transfer enzymes, TF-1 and TF-2 (Table III), were prepared and purified by the procedure of Arlinghaus et al. (1968a). The results disclosed reticulocyte TF-1 to be extremely active when assayed with the tumor DOC–DEAE–cellulose ribosomes, whereas reticulocyte TF-2 appeared to be inactive. Complementation between the two factors could not be detected, indicating the presence of TF-2 on the ribosomes as noted above. When these same transfer enzymes were tested in the presence of the tumor 0.5 M NH_4Cl-washed ribosomes, neither TF-1 nor TF-2 was active, but when incubated together, the system exhibited the requirement for two enzymes participating in amino acid incorporation.

The concentrated tumor acrylamide fraction was then assayed with the 0.5 M NH_4Cl-washed ribosomes and reticulocyte TF-1 or TF-2. The tumor material appeared to be inactive in the absence or presence of reticulocyte TF-1; however, when the tumor acrylamide fraction and reticulocyte TF-2 were tested, complementation between the two components occurred. It was concluded that the tumor DOC–DEAE–cellulose ribosomes were saturated with T_2, and active, purified tumor T_1 could be obtained by preparative acrylamide electrophoresis. A region corresponding to tumor T_2 from the acrylamide fractions was not located through complementation assays with either tumor T_1 or reticulocyte TF-1.

The resolution and demonstration of two transfer enzymes in a tumor amino acid-incorporating system was accomplished in this laboratory using essentially the procedure developed for rabbit reticulocytes (Arlinghaus et al., 1968a). The initial S-275,000 g supernatant material was precipitated with protamine sulfate, the resulting supernatant fraction made 0.1 M with respect to tris, and the pH adjusted to pH 6.5 with 1 M acetic acid. The precipitate collected between 40 and 70% ammonium sulfate saturation was subjected to $Ca_3(PO_4)_2$ gel fractionation. Tumor T_2 was eluted from the gel at 0.1 M potassium phosphate buffer (pH 7.0), and T_1 at 0.3 M potassium phosphate buffer (pH 7.5). The only modifications for adapting this procedure to the tumor cell-free system was the substitution of 1×10^{-3} M DTT as a constant sulfhydryl source, and storage of the $Ca_3(PO_4)_2$ T_1 in the presence of 1×10^{-3} M DTT. Specific details of this procedure can be found in Section II, C.

In agreement with studies with reticulocyte transfer enzymes, tumor T_1 displayed maximal activity when assayed with the tumor DOC–DEAE–cellulose ribosomes, whereas T_2 possessed slight activity. Complementation between tumor T_1 and T_2 did not occur in these ribosomes, again indicating the association of substantial amounts of T_2 with these ribosomes as noted with reticulocyte TF-1 and TF-2. Neither tumor T_1 nor T_2 showed any individual activities when incubated with the 0.5 M NH_4Cl-washed ribosomes. As observed with the reticulocyte factors, T_2 was evidently extracted from the ribosomes by the NH_4Cl wash. Moreover, when tumor T_1 and T_2 were incubated with the washed ribosomes, complementation between the two enyzmes was evident (Table I). It was concluded, therefore, that two transfer enzymes were involved in the tumor amino acid-incorporating system, but that the demonstration of an absolute requirement for these factors depended upon the purity of the ribosomes. Considerable difficulty was encountered in removal of transfer enzymes from the ribosomes. Usually, the procedures that were employed to remove both T_1 and T_2 reduced the incorporating activity of the ribosomes to a considerable extent.

2. Mouse Ascites Leukemia

Ochoa and Weinstein (1964) isolated a protein-synthesizing system from the L1210 mouse ascites leukemia. This cell-free system depended upon the presence of microsomes or ribosomes and added soluble constituents (pH 5 fractions). Optimal polypeptide synthesis required an energy source, Mg^{++} and spermine. Binding and incorporation of the aminoacyl tRNA's occurred with endogenous and synthetic polyribonucleotide messengers.

Some DBA × Swiss hybrid mice were inoculated IP with approximately 2×10^6 L1210 mouse ascites leukemia cells in 0.15 M NaCl. After 6 days, the cells were collected and washed 3 times with 0.01 M tris–HCl (pH 7.8), 0.15 M NaCl, and 0.02 M dextrose buffer. The cells were homogenized (Potter–Elvehjem-type homogenizer) in 1 volume of standard buffer—0.01 M tris–HCl (pH 7.8), 0.005 M Mg(Ac)$_2$, 0.06 M KCl, 0.006 M 2-mercaptoethanol, and 0.25 M sucrose. Another volume of this buffer was added following homogenization, and the cellular debris removed by centrifugation at 9500 rpm (mean RCF* 10,800 g) for 20 minutes using a SS-34 rotor of a Servall centrifuge. The supernatant material was centrifuged at 45,000 rpm (mean RCF 122,000 g) for 60 minutes in the 50-rotor of the Spinco Model L centrifuge. The sedimented microsomes were suspended by homogenization in 1 to 2 ml of standard buffer and the suspension centrifuged at 755 g for 10 minutes to remove aggregated material. These crude microsomes were used directly for amino acid incorporation studies or washed once with 1% sodium deoxycholate in standard buffer. The pH of the initial microsomal supernatant fraction was adjusted to pH 5.2 with 1 M acetic acid and the suspension centrifuged at 5000 rpm for 10 minutes

---

* RCF, relative centrifugal force.

TABLE I

DEMONSTRATION OF A REQUIREMENT FOR TWO TRANSFER ENZYMES FOR
AMINO ACID INCORPORATION BY PURIFIED TUMOR RIBOSOMES[a, b]

Ribosomes	Transfer enzymes	Counts/min
Deoxycholate–diethylaminoethyl	None	70
	Tumor 40–70% $(NH_4)_2SO_4$	1500
	Tumor acrylamide	1100
	Retic. T_1	650
	Retic. T_2	100
	Retic. $T_1 + T_2$	590
	Tumor T_1 $(Ca_3(PO_4)_2)$	1200
	Tumor T_2 $(Ca_3(PO_4)_2)$	234
	Tumor $T_1 + T_2$	1150
Deoxycholate–diethyl-aminoethyl–0.5 M NH_4Cl	None	50
	Tumor 40–70% $(NH_4)_2SO_4$	525
	Tumor acrylamide (T_1)	100
	Retic. T_1	130
	Retic. T_2	70
	Retic. $T_1 + T_2$	570
	Tumor acrylamide + retic. T_1	100
	Tumor acrylamide + retic. T_2	370
	Tumor T_1 $(Ca_3(PO_4)_2)$	95
	Tumor T_2 $(Ca_3(PO_4)_2)$	100
	Tumor $T_1 + T_2$	360
	Tumor T_1 + retic. T_2	455
	Tumor T_2 + retic. T_1	210

[a] The complete amino acid-incorporating system, in a total volume of 0.1 ml, consisted of 0.05 ml ribosomes (450 μg ribosomal protein for deoxycholate–diethylaminoethyl (DOC–DEAE)-washed and 150 μg ribosomal protein for 0.5 M NH_4Cl-washed ribosomes), 0.5 μmole phosphoenolpyruvate (PEP), 5–10 μg PEP kinase, 0.04 μmole guanosine triphosphate, 0.6 μmole 2-mercaptoethanol, 10 μmole $(NH_4)_2SO_4$, 60 μg ^{14}C-amino acid mixture tRNA, 64 μg tumor $(NH_4)_2$ SO_4 fraction, 8.0 μg tumor acrylamide fraction, and 15 μg tumor T_1, 18.5 μg tumor T_2, 20 μg reticulocyte T_1, and 35 μg reticulocyte T_2 when assayed with the DOC-DEAE ribosomes, or 30 μg tumor T_1, 18.5 μg tumor T_2, 40 μg reticulocyte T_1, and 7.0 μg reticulocyte T_2 in presence of 0.5 M NH_4Cl-washed ribosomes. The tumor 40–70% $(NH_4)_2SO_4$ fraction and T_1 and T_2 factors were prepared according to the procedure of Arlinghaus et al. (1968a). The tumor acrylamide fraction was prepared from the 22–60% $(NH_4)_2SO_4$ material electrophoresed on preparative polyacrylamide columns. Reticulocyte transfer factors T_1 and T_2 were prepared by the procedure of Arlinghaus et al. (1968a). The mixture was incubated at 37°C for 25 minutes, and adsorbed on a Whatman No. 3 MM paper disc placed directly into the assay tube. The disks were prepared for liquid scintillation counting as described in Section II, A1, b. (DOC) Deoxycholate–glycylglycine, pH 8.0; (DEAE) DEAE–cellulose (Carl Schleicher and Schuell Co.); (Retic.) reticulocyte.

[b] Protein concentrations determined from Warburg and Christian nomograph (1941–1942).

in the Servall SS-34 rotor. The precipitate was dissolved in 5 ml of the standard buffer and adjusted to pH 7.8 with 0.1 M KOH.

The *in vitro* ^{14}C-amino acid-incorporating assay consisted of 0.20 mg washed ribosomes; 0.2 mg of pH 5 fraction protein; 0.5–1.2 mμ moles ^{14}C-L-amino acid; 0.0125 μmole each of twenty ^{12}C-L-amino acids, minus the radioactive amino acid; 4 μmoles tris–HCl buffer (pH 7.8); 2 μmoles Mg(Ac)$_2$; 24 μmoles KCl; 2–4 μmoles 2-mercaptoethanol; 0.25 μmole ATP; 0.01 μmole cytidine triphosphate (CTP); 0.01 μmoles GTP; 0.01 μmole uridine triphosphate (UTP); 1.25 μmoles PEP; 12 μg PEP kinase in a total volume of 0.4 ml. Following incubation at 37°C for 30 minutes, the reaction was stopped by the addition of 5% TCA and 2% casamino acids (Difco Laboratories), and heated at 90°C for 30 minutes. The precipitates were placed on membrane filters, washed 3 times with a 1% TCA–casamino acids solution, and twice with 70% ethanol. The membrane filters were dried and prepared for counting.

Results obtained from studies with the L1210 ascites leukemia cells were in general agreement with those established for normal mammalian tissues (von Ehrenstein and Lipmann, 1961; Allen and Schweet, 1962; Arnstein *et al.*, 1962; Maxwell, 1962; Weinstein and Schechter, 1962; Gardner *et al.*, 1962; Fessenden *et al.*, 1963). Efficiency of the *in vitro* incorporating assays was approximately 1–3% that of *Escherichia coli*. The specific activity of deoxycholate-washed ribosomes was 50% that of the crude microsomes. Optimal incorporating concentrations of magnesium ions ranged between 3 and 5 mM; 300–400 μg of poly A and poly U (synthetic polyribonucleotides) were needed for maximum polymerization. Chloramphenicol did not interfere with aminoacyl tRNA-binding or polymerization. A. C. Griffin *et al.* (1968) have reported that the addition of chloramphenicol to an ascites tumor system was not inhibitory for amino acid incorporation.

B. LIVER

E. B. Keller and Zamecnik (1956) reported that liver cell-free systems would incorporate ^{14}C-amino acids into polypeptide structures. They established many of the requirements, such as microsomes, soluble cell fractions, ATP and GTP, for incorporation, and fractionated the soluble cell fraction by adjusting the pH to 5.0. The pH 5 precipitate possessed the tRNA-activating enzymes (aminoacyl synthetases) and the transfer factors essential for amino acid polymerization remained in the soluble phase.

Moldave and co-workers (Moldave, 1960; Fessenden and Moldave, 1963; Gasior and Moldave, 1965; Ibuki *et al.*, 1966; Skogerson and Moldave, 1967; Rao and Moldave, 1967; Ibuki and Moldave, 1968a,b;

Schneir and Moldave, 1968; Skogerson and Moldave, 1968a,b,c) have studied the mechanism of polypeptide synthesis in normal rat liver. Aminoacylated tRNA, in the presence of GTP, monovalent cations, Mg^{++}, a reduced sulfhydryl reagent, and transfer enzymes, is bound to the ribosome with subsequent formation of a peptide bond. In order to study the individual requirements for protein synthesis, it was essential to isolate, purify, and characterize the two enzymes involved in the transfer of the aminoacyl tRNA to the ribosomes with formation of a peptide bond between tRNA peptide already present on the polysome and the newly transferred aminoacyl tRNA. Also, the ribosomes had to be freed of the transfer enzymes.

Normal rat livers were homogenized in a 0.35 M sucrose, 0.035 M $KHCO_3$, 0.025 M KCl, and 0.004 M $MgCl_2$ solution to obtain a 20–33% homogenate. The mitochondrial and nuclear elements were removed by centrifugation at 12,000 g for 15 minutes. The supernatant fraction was centrifuged at 100,000 g for 2 hours to sediment the microsomes. This first high-speed supernatant fraction served as a source of the transfer enzymes. When preparing microsomes, the 12,000 g supernatant fraction was diluted with 7 volumes of buffered salt–sucrose solution and centrifuged at 100,000 g for 2 hours. Resulting microsomes were resuspended in a volume equivalent to one-half of the volume of the original 12,000 g supernatant.

Crude ribosomes were prepared from the sedimented microsomes employing a 3% sodium deoxycholate solution. Earlier purification procedures employed Takanami's method (1960) of dissolving the ribosomes in low Mg^{++} (0.001 M) followed by reprecipitation with an increased Mg^{++} concentration (0.01 M). The deoxycholate concentration was maintained at 0.3% during the low Mg^{++} wash. In order to remove contaminating transfer enzymes, the crude liver ribosomes required centrifugation through a discontinuous sucrose gradient for 24 hours. The bottom layer consisted of 10 ml of 1.0 M sucrose overlaid with 10 ml of 0.5 M sucrose each in 0.5 M NH_4Cl, 0.01 M tris–HCl (pH 7.6), and 0.01 M $MgCl_2$ buffer.

The postmicrosomal supernatant fraction containing the transfer factors, transferase I and transferase II, was adjusted to pH 5.0 and the supernatant fraction was passed through a Sephadex G-25 (coarse) column, previously equilibrated with 0.05 M tris buffer (pH 8.0). The Sephadex G-25 filtrate was mixed with a 3% calcium phosphate gel suspension, stirred for 30 minutes, and centrifuged at a low speed. After washing the gel 3 times with the 0.05 M tris buffer, 0.25 M potassium phosphate buffer (pH 6.8) was added, stirred for 5 minutes, and centrifuged at a low speed. Elution with the 0.25 M potassium phosphate buffer was repeated 3 times and all eluates combined. Solid $(NH_4)_2SO_4$

was added to 25% saturation, while maintaining the pH at 7.0 with $KHCO_3$. The suspension was centrifuged at 12,000 g, and the supernatant was adjusted to 65% saturation with $(NH_4)_2SO_4$. The resulting precipitate was resuspended in 0.05 M tris, 0.15 M KCl, 1 $\times$ 10^{-4} M EDTA, and 1 $\times$ 10^{-3} M glutathione (GSH) buffer (pH 7.2). This partially purified soluble protein fraction was passed through a Sephadex G-200 column, previously equilibrated with the resuspending buffer minus GSH. Elution proceeded with the equilibrating buffer plus GSH at a flow rate of 10 to 15 ml/hour.

By means of the aminoacyl transfer assay, as shown in Figs. 3 and 4, two enzymic activities, transferases I and II, were detected. The original

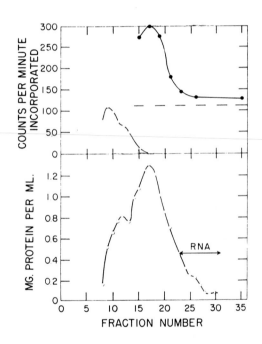

FIG. 3. Gel filtration of partially purified soluble protein fraction on Sephadex G-200. Approximately 80 mg of protein, in 2.7 ml, were applied to a column, 30 $\times$ 2.4 cm, and eluted with tris buffer containing KCl, ethylenediaminetetraacetate, and glutathione as described in the text. After the first 15 ml, 5-ml fractions were collected. Lower half (open circles)—protein distribution in eluate fractions. Upper half—amino acid incorporation from ^{14}C-aminoacyl soluble ribonucleic acid into fresh, crude ribosomes, in the presence of 0.05 ml of column fractions assayed individually (open circles) or in combination with 0.05 ml of Fraction 9 (closed circles). The difference in counts per minute between the dashed horizontal line and the closed circles, in the upper part of the figure, represents the increase in incorporation obtained when Fraction 9 (about 115 counts/minute, individually) is supplemented with Fractions 15 and 25. (Reprinted with permission from Gasior and Moldave, 1965.)

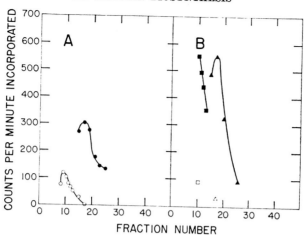

FRACTION NUMBER

FIG. 4. The effect of column fractions on aminoacyl transfer with (A) crude ribosomes and (B) purified ribosomes. (A) Open circles—0.05 ml of column fractions assayed individually. Closed circles—0.05 ml of column fractions assayed in combination with 0.05 ml of Fraction 9. (B) Approximately 40 μg of Fraction 10 protein incubated individually (open square) or in the presence of approximately 100 μg of various column fractions (closed triangles): approximately 100 μg of Fraction 17 protein incubated individually (open triangle) or in the presence of various column fractions (closed squares). (Reprinted with permission from Gasior and Moldave, 1965.)

assay procedure contained 100 μmoles tris–HCl (pH 7.4), 12 μmoles MgCl$_2$, 160 μmoles NH$_4$Cl, 8 μmoles GSH, 0.4 μmole GTP, 0.5–1.0 mg crude or purified ribosomes, 25 μg of ^{14}C-aminoacyl tRNA, and saturating amounts of the complementary factors, transferases I and II (total volume 2.0 ml). Following incubation for 25 minutes at 37°C, perchloric acid was added to a final concentration of 0.4 M. The acid-insoluble protein was extracted with perchloric acid, ethanol–ether at 45°C, and heated in 5% TCA at 90°C for 15 minutes. In the routine assays of the column fractions the reactions were stopped with 5% TCA, heated at 90°C for 15 minutes, and the acid-insoluble protein collected on Millipore filters.

When the individual fractions were incubated in the presence of the crude ribosomes, transferase I activity was enhanced, but added transferase II did not enhance incorporation. However, the addition of both transferases I and II to the same assay tube resulted in a several-fold increase of ^{14}C-aminoacyl tRNA incorporation. With purified ribosomes, neither transferase I nor transferase II activities could be demonstrated. Amino acid transfer occurred only if transferases I and II were added to the assay medium. The active transfer fractions were stable when stored at −80°C.

To achieve better resolution of the two transferases, hydroxylapatite was substituted for the calcium phosphate gel (Table II). Dithiothreitol was added to the Sephadex G-25 filtrate to obtain a final concentration of 1×10^{-3} M. After mixing the suspension for 1 hour at 4°C, the mixture was centrifuged at 10,000 g for 10 minutes, and the hydroxylapatite gel washed once with 0.05 M tris–HCl (pH 8.0), 1×10^{-3} M DTT buffer. Fractions containing the active transferases I and II were eluted from the gel with increasing concentrations of potassium phosphate buffers at pH 6.8 (0.125 M, 0.175 M, 0.25 M, and 0.50 M potassium phosphate). Transferase II was released from the gel at 0.125 M concentration, whereas 0.250 M potassium phosphate was required to remove transferase I. The active fractions were saturated to 70% with $(NH_4)_2SO_4$, maintaining a pH of 7.0 with concentrated NH_4OH. The precipitates were resuspended in the tris–HCl (pH 8.0), 1×10^{-3} M DTT buffer and concentrated by dialysis under vacuum. Preparations were applied separately to Sephadex G-200 columns. The 0.05 M tris–HCl (pH 8.0) buffer was substituted for equilibrating the Sephadex G-200 columns and used as the eluting buffer in the presence of 1×10^{-3} M DTT.

TABLE II

RESOLUTION OF TRANSFERASES I AND II ON HYDROXYLAPATITE[a, b]

Preparation	Total volume (ml)	Protein (gm/total volume)	Transferase I[d]	Transferase II[d]
Sephadex G-25 filtrate	500	9.00	19 870 000	84 620 000
Hydroxylapatite gel supernatant	500	6.24	1 028 000	10 620 000
Hydroxylapatite gel wash	300	0.59	0	69 000
0.125 M Eluate	900	1.09	338 000	8 660 000
0.150 M Eluate	900	0.19	702 000	1 731 000
0.175 M Eluate	900	0.12	1 258 000	1 566 000
0.250 M Eluate	900	0.19	10 554 000	2 148 000
0.500 M Eluate	300	0.11	510 000	511 000

[a] Values presented are the average of two such fractionation procedures.

[b] Reprinted with permission from Schneir and Moldave (1968).

[c] Aliquots of the preparations indicated were assayed for transferase I and II activity, as described in the text, in the presence of saturating amounts of the complementary factor. The eluates were dialyzed against buffer for 3 hours before assay.

[d] Values are expressed as total activity of the particular enzyme in the preparation: counts per minute incorporated with aliquots assayed × total volume per aliquot.

Further modifications of the above methods included adsorption of the Sephadex G-25 filtrate to the calcium phosphate gel and chromatography of the 0.25 M potassium phosphate eluate on hydroxylapatite. The active transferase I was eluted with 0.25 M potassium phosphate (pH 6.8). To resolve transferase II, the calcium phosphate eluate was chromatographed on phosphocellulose and eluted with a 0.01 M potassium phosphate, 0.12 M KCl buffer (pH 6.8). An extension of these and related procedures are described by Moldave (1967, 1968).

Felicetti and Lipmann (1968) have also separated the transferases (T_1 and T_2) from rat liver duplicating essentially the methodology described for rabbit reticulocytes (below). In view of the growing complexity of the literature terminology employed for describing the transfer factors, they proposed a common nomenclature for identification of the transfer enzymes—T_1 to be connected with the GTP-linked binding of aminoacyl tRNA to the ribosomes, and T_2 with the polymerization factor. The various designations are listed in Table III.

C. Reticulocytes

Employing a reticulocyte amino acid-incorporating system, Schweet and associates (Schweet et al., 1958) demonstrated the biosynthesis of hemoglobin. Proof for the synthesis of this soluble protein was based largely on a comparison of ratios of the incorporated amino acids with the ratios of these amino acids in globin. However, with this hemoglobin-synthesizing system, difficulty was encountered in elucidating the functions of the two transfer enzymes associated with aminoacyl tRNA incorporation. Consequently, a reticulocyte polyuridine system was developed which incorporated phenylalanyl tRNA into ribosome-bound polyphenylalanine. With these systems, they demonstrated that the two enzymes needed for incorporation of aminoacyl tRNA into soluble hemoglobin also stimulated the synthesis of polyphenylalanine. Both enzymes were required for the addition of a single amino acid to a growing peptide chain (Arlinghaus et al., 1963, 1964; Hardesty et al., 1963).

The procedure for the isolation of the components of the reticulocyte system developed by Schweet's laboratory is outlined below.

Rabbits weighing 5–6 lb received daily, subcutaneous injections of 1.0 ml of 2.5% phenylhydrazine for 5 days (Allen and Schweet, 1962), and the reticulocytes were obtained by cardiac puncture on the seventh day. The heparinized blood was centrifuged to remove plasma and the cells washed in a 0.13 M NaCl, 0.005 M KCl, and 0.0075 M MgCl$_2$ solution. Following this second centrifugation, the packed cells were lysed in 4 volumes of 0.002 M MgCl$_2$ for 2 minutes, and lysis was stopped by the addition of 1 volume of 1.5 M sucrose, 0.15 M KCl solution. This

A. CLARK GRIFFIN AND DIANNE D. BLACK

TABLE III

LITERATURE DESIGNATION OF TRANSFER ENZYMES OR FACTORS

| System | Terminology | | Ref. |
	Binding enzyme	Polymerizing enzyme	
Rat or calf liver	Transferase I	Transferase II	Gasior and Moldave, 1965
	FII	FI	Klink et al., 1967a
	T_1	T_2	Felicetti and Lipmann, 1968
Rabbit reticulocyte	TF–1	TF–2	Arlinghaus et al., 1968a
	TF–I	TF–II	McKeehan et al., 1969
	T_1	T_2	Felicetti and Lipmann, 1968
Microbial *Escherichia coli*	$T (T_s + T_u)$	G	Lucas-Lenard and Lipmann, 1966
	F–I (F–IB + F–IA)	F–II	Ravel et al., 1968
	T–I, T–II	G–I, G–II	Parmeggiani, 1968
Bacillus stearo-thermophilus	$S (S_3 + S_1)$	S_2	Skoultchi et al., 1968
Yeast	FII	FI	Richter and Klink, 1967
	A^a	B	Ayuso and Heredia, 1967

^{a} The roles of these transfer factors are presently being elucidated; they have been arbitrarily assigned to the functions as shown.

mixture was centrifuged for 10 minutes at 15,000 g and the resulting supernatant recentrifuged at 78,000 g for 90 minutes. The diagram in Fig. 5 outlines the procedures for separation of the transfer enzymes TF-1 and TF-2 and preparation of 0.1 M KCl-treated ribosomes (Arlinghaus et al., 1968a). The degree of purification of the two enzymes at various stages of this procedure is shown in Table IV. The 0.1 M KCl-washed ribosomes essentially were free of contaminating transfer enzymes, especially TF-2, and supported hemoglobin synthesis using the natural or endogenous messenger still present in the ribosomal preparation.

^{14}C-Aminoacyl tRNA's were prepared by the method of Leahy et al. (1960). The pH 5 enzyme fraction from guinea pig liver was incubated with the following components: 12 mμmoles each of twenty amino acids per milliliter, including either DL-leucine-1-^{14}C, DL-lysine-^{14}C, DL-valine-1-^{14}C, or ^{14}C-algal hydrolyzate. The ^{14}C-aminoacyl tRNA's were dialyzed for 6 hours against 0.01 M potassium acetate (pH 5.1), 0.05 M

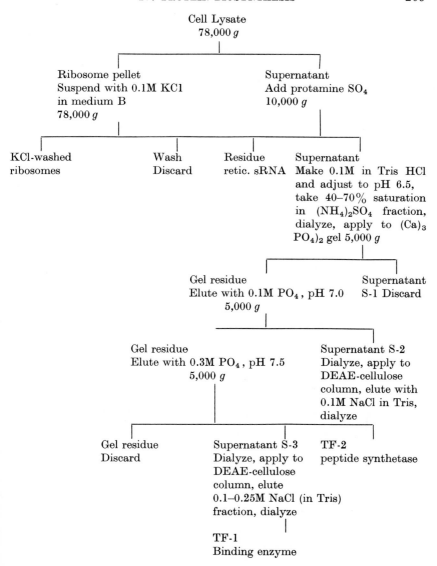

FIG. 5. Preparation of transfer enzymes and KCl-washed ribosomes. sRNA—soluble ribonucleic acid; DEAE—diethylaminoethyl.

KCl buffer in the cold and passed through a 2 × 35-cm column of Sephadex G-25, previously equilibrated with the above buffer. The solution was diluted to 3 mg RNA per milliliter.

The assay procedure employed in this hemoglobin-synthesizing system was as follows: 0.1 μmole GTP, 5 μmoles $MgCl_2$, 100 μmoles KCl, 50 μmoles tris–HCl (pH 7.5), 15 μmoles GSH, 0.1 μmole each of twenty amino acids, 300 μg each TF-1 and TF-2, 3 mg ribosomes, and ^{14}C-aminoacyl tRNA as specified were added to a total volume of 1.5 ml. Following incubation at 37°C for 3 minutes, two general assay procedures were used for determination of the labeled products. The tubes were either chilled, followed by the addition of casein as a carrier and 5% TCA directly to the incubation assay mixture or the labeled ribosomes were isolated by centrifugation followed by precipitation with cold TCA. The precipitated proteins were treated with 1N NaOH to remove all labeled aminoacyl tRNA's that were not incorporated into polypeptides. The solubilized polypeptides were then collected by reacidification with 1 N HCl and acidified acetone and the products analyzed for radioactivity (Arlinghaus et al., 1968a). Both acid-soluble and -insoluble products were determined if the ribosomes were sedimented by centrifugation. However, these investigators emphasized that not only were the free amino acids removed by the above procedures but also some of the short-chain peptides were too small to be precipitated by the acid treatment and, therefore, would render deceptive results. The presence of reduced glutathione in the assays maintained TF-2 in a stable and active form. If the crude enzyme preparation contained ample amounts of hemoglobin, the protein was precipitated with acidified acetone to remove the heme groups, which would quench the radioactive samples.

TABLE IV

PURIFICATION OF TWO ENZYME FRACTIONS REQUIRED FOR TRANSFER OF AMINO ACIDS FROM AMINOACYL RNA TO POLYPEPTIDES[a]

Enzyme fractions[b]	Volume (ml)	Protein (mg)	Total activity (%)	Specific activity[c]
78,000 g supernatant	1700	94,000	100	10.4
40–70% $(NH_4)_2SO_4$	188	3752	51	130.0
$(Ca)_3(PO_4)_2$ gel S-1	236	2030	6	26.0
$(Ca)_3(PO_4)_2$ gel S-2[d]	71	405	—	—
$(Ca)_3(PO_4)_2$ gel S-3	77	330	12	340.0
DEAE–cellulose TF-1[d]	25	100	—	—
DEAE–cellulose TF-2[d]	23	60	—	—

[a] Reprinted with permission from Arlinghaus et al. (1968a).

[b] Enzyme fractions were isolated as described. The transfer assay contained 3 mg of KCl-washed ribosomes, 300 μg of leucyl-^{14}C RNA, and limiting amounts of the enzyme fractions.

[c] Specific activity is expressed as pmoles leucine-^{14}C transferred per milligram of enzyme protein.

[d] These fractions were inactive for transfer of leucine-^{14}C by themselves. DEAE, diethylaminoethyl.

A further purification of the reticulocyte ribosomes was achieved by treatment with 5% sodium deoxycholate. Exposure to a KCl solution (Mg^{++}-free), preincubation, and DOC treatments of the ribosomes were required to reduce endogenous hemoglobin synthesis in the poly U phenylalanyl tRNA system (Arlinghaus and Schweet, 1962; Arlinghaus et al., 1964). The microsomes were adjusted to a concentration of approximately 8.7 mg/ml (assuming 1 mg ribosomes per milliliter had an absorbance of 11.2) with 0.25 M sucrose. This suspension was incubated with a mixture containing 46 mM tris–HCl, (pH 7.5) 92 mM KCl, and 18 mM GSH at 37°C for 25 minutes. The mixture was chilled and preincubated for an additional 40 minutes at 37°C with the other components required for complete ^{12}C-amino acid incorporation. Following this incubation, the mixture was diluted 8 times with the 0.1 M KCl buffer and centrifuged at 78,000 g for 90 minutes. The pellets were homogenized in 0.25 M sucrose and recentrifuged at 10,000 g for 10 minutes. A 5% sodium deoxycholate solution (0.25 volume of supernatant) was added to the ribosomal supernatant fraction and the mixture incubated at 37°C for 3 minutes. The ribosomes were further diluted tenfold with 0.25 M sucrose, 70 mM KHCO$_3$, and 8 mM MgCl$_2$ solution and centrifuged at 78,000 g for 90 minutes. Finally, the pellets were homogenized in 0.25 M sucrose and the homogenates centrifuged at 10,000 g for 10 minutes to remove any aggregated material from the suspended ribosomes.

The complete reticulocyte–poly U reaction mixture (1.5 ml) employed for the synthesis of polyphenylalanine contained 6.7 mM MgCl$_2$, 67 mM KCl, 33 mM tris–HCl (pH 7.5), 67 μM GTP, 10 mM GSH, 67 μM L-phenylalanine, 70 mμM ^{3}H-phenylalanyl tRNA, 100 μg poly U, 300 μg each of TF-1 and TF-2, and 1.5 mg deoxycholate-washed ribosomes. Following incubation at 37°C for 10 minutes, the tubes were chilled, casein was added as a carrier, and the phenylalanine peptides were precipitated and treated as described for the hemoglobin-synthesizing system. A more detailed description of the other procedures employed by Schweet's group have been presented elsewhere by Arlinghaus et al. (1968b).

In recent studies, both TF-I and TF-II have been purified to homogeneity. The TF-I was assigned a molecular weight of 186,000 ± 5000, and TF-II a molecular weight of 70,000 (McKeehan et al., 1969).

D. Human Tissues

Matthaei and colleagues have investigated the efficiency of various human tissues to direct in vitro protein synthesis. Some of the tissues used in their studies included tonsils, placenta, adrenals, spleen, and tumor (Neth *et al.*, 1968; Bermek, 1969; Schöch and Matthaei, 1970; Gros and Matthaei, 1968).

Generally, the minced tissues were homogenized in a buffer [50 mM tris–HCl (pH 7.4), 25 mM KCl, 5 mM MgCl$_2$, 250 mM sucrose, and 2 mM 2-mercaptoethanol] by an Ultra Tunax for 4 to 5 minutes. The homogenates were centrifuged for 20 minutes at 30,000 g and the resulting supernatant recentrifuged at 130,000 g for 2 hours. For preparation of ribosomes, the microsomal pellets were either resuspended in buffer containing 0.6% sodium deoxycholate, 250 mM sucrose, 10 mM tris–HCl (pH 7.6), 100 mM KCl, and 10 mM MgCl$_2$ or 500 mM NH$_4$Cl, 250 mM sucrose, 50 mM tris–HCl (pH 7.4), 10 mM MgCl$_2$, and 2 mM 2-mercaptoethanol.

The suspensions were layered over a discontinuous sucrose gradient of 1 M and 2 M sucrose in the respective ribosome buffers, and the ribosomes were sedimented by centrifugation between 105,000 and 130,000 g for 5 hours. If the 0.6% DOC buffer was used, the sedimented ribosomes were resuspended in a buffer [10 mM tris–HCl (pH 7.6), 100 mM KCl, and 10 mM MgCl$_2$] and centrifuged at 10,000 g for 10 minutes. The supernatant fraction contained the suspended ribosomes. For the 0.5 M NH$_4$Cl-treated ribosomes, the pellets were resuspended in the initial homogenizing buffer minus sucrose.

Separation of the incorporating factors from tRNA and amino acid synthetases was achieved through pH 5 fractionation. Both synthetases and tRNA were separately eluted from DEAE–cellulose columns, and the ^{14}C- or ^{3}H-aminoacyl tRNA prepared by the usual phenol procedure. The fraction containing the transfer enzymes was precipitated between 25 and 65% (NH$_4$)$_2$SO$_4$ saturation. This precipitate was dissolved in 50 mM tris–HCl (pH 7.4), 0.1 mM K–EDTA, 250 mM sucrose, and 2 mM DTT, dialyzed against the same buffer, and passed over a Sephadex G-25 column. Activity of these components was measured in a ribosomal binding system.

E. OTHER SYSTEMS

A list of references for procedures pertinent to the isolation of protein-synthesizing components from other systems are given below.

Liver systems: Hoagland *et al.* (1964); Wettstein *et al.* (1964); Sutter and Moldave (1966); Klink *et al.* (1967a,b,); Rosen *et al.* (1967).

Nuclear systems: McLean *et al.* (1958); Campbell and Greengard (1959); Rendi and Warner (1960); Wang (1963); Maggio (1966); Sekeris *et al.* (1966); Tsuzuki and Naora (1968).

Other mammalian systems: Zamecnik *et al.* (1958); Penman *et al.* (1963); Zimmerman (1963); P. J. Keller *et al.* (1963); Madison and

Dickman (1963a,b); Brewer *et al.* (1964); Stenzel *et al.* (1966); Rich (1967); Mahler and Brown (1968); Grau and Favelukes (1968); Goodwin *et al.* (1969); Means *et al.* (1969).

Microbial systems: Nathans and Lipmann (1961); J. E. Allende *et al.* (1964); Spyrides (1964); E. B. Keller and Ferger (1965); Nishizuka and Lipmann (1966a,b); Lucas-Lenard and Lipmann (1966); Seeds and Conway (1967); Parmeggiani (1968); Gordon (1968); Johnson *et al.* (1968); Skoultchi *et al.* (1968); Hollis and Furano (1968); Ertel *et al.* (1968a,b); Ravel *et al.* (1968).

Yeast systems: Wettstein *et al.* (1964); Heredia and Halvorson (1966); Ayuso and Heredia (1967); Richter and Klink (1967).

III. Preparation and Study of Properties of Components of Protein Synthesis

A. TRANSFER RIBONUCLEIC ACIDS

1. Isolation

The procedure of Brunngraber (1962) was employed in this laboratory for the preparation of crude tRNA fractions (Goldman *et al.*, 1969). One hundred grams of rat liver was extracted with 150 ml of a buffer (1.0 M NaCl, 0.1 M tris–HCl, 0.005 M EDTA, pH 7.5) and 150 ml 80% redistilled phenol (in H_2O) by mixing for 5 to 10 minutes in a Waring blender. The homogenate was centrifuged at 8000 g for 10 minutes and the resulting aqueous phase was re-extracted with an equal volume of 80% phenol and centrifuged as above. The aqueous phase was precipitated by the addition of 2 volumes of cold ethanol. The mixture was allowed to stand in the cold for at least 1 hour and was centrifuged at 8000 g for 10 minutes. Precipitates were dissolved in 150 ml of 0.1 M tris–HCl (pH 7.5). This mixture was stirred for 30 minutes in the cold with 2 to 3 gm DEAE–cellulose (previously washed with several volumes of 0.1 M tris–HCl, pH 7.5). The DEAE–cellulose mixture was centrifuged at 2000 rpm (International centrifuge) for 10 minutes. The DEAE pellets were washed batchwise in the centrifuge tubes with 100 ml 0.1 M tris–HCl (pH 7.5) and centrifuged as above. Elution of the pellets was achieved by the addition of 40 ml of the initial buffer (1.0 M NaCl, 0.1 M tris–HCl, 0.005 M EDTA, pH 7.5), by allowing to stand for 10 minutes, and by centrifuging as described above. The resulting supernatant containing the tRNA fraction was precipitated with 2 volumes of cold ethanol and allowed to stand overnight at 0°C. The tRNA was centrifuged at 8000 g for 10 minutes, washed once with cold ether, and finally dissolved in H_2O and stored at 0°C for later use. Activity was retained for several months. From 50 to 60 mg tRNA were obtained per 100 gm rat liver.

Novikoff ascites tumor cells were collected and washed 3 times with several volumes of a buffer (0.14 M NaCl, 0.02 M glucose, 0.04 M tris–HCl, pH 8.5) and centrifuged at 700 rpm for 3 minutes (A. C. Griffin *et al.*, 1965). Then 50 ml of packed tumor cells was extracted with 150 ml of a buffer (1.0 M NaCl, 0.1 M tris–HCl, 0.005 M EDTA, pH 7.5) and 150 ml 80% phenol as described above for rat liver. All subsequent steps were carried out as indicated for the liver tRNA preparation. However, 0.1 gm DEAE–cellulose per milliliter of the suspended precipitate was used in the tumor preparation. By a second DEAE-cellulose treatment of the nonadsorbed solution, yields as high as 50 mg of crude tRNA were obtained from the 50-ml packed tumor cells.

2. Resolution of tRNA'S

a. Countercurrent Distribution. An excellent procedure for the purification of several amino acid acceptor tRNA's has been established by Apgar *et al.* (1962). The solvent system includes: phosphate buffer 1.25 M pH 6.0 (600 gm dipotassium hydrogen phosphate, 938 gm sodium dihydrogen phosphate monohydrate in glass-distilled water to a total volume of 8190 ml.) To 8 liters of this buffer, 800 ml of formamide and 4160 ml of isopropyl alcohol, reagent grade, were added and the mixture was shaken. This solvent system was kept overnight in a constant temperature room at 23°C. The countercurrent apparatus (E-C Apparatus Co., 200 tubes) was filled with the lower phase of the solvent system (10 ml per tube), and 10 ml of upper phase were added to each of the first 20 tubes of the apparatus. A solution of 600 mg of yeast tRNA in 50 ml each of upper and lower phase was prepared by dissolving the RNA in 38 ml of the phosphate buffer plus 38 ml of formamide, 38 ml of the lower phase of the solvent system, and 20 ml of isopropyl alcohol. The RNA solution was introduced in place of the solvents in tubes 1–5 of the apparatus. Insoluble material (approx. 100 mg) separated at the interface and was not introduced into the countercurrent distribution apparatus. A 200-transfer distribution was carried out during approximately 20 hours at 23°C.

The contents of the tubes of the apparatus were combined in groups of five to give forty fractions. Each fraction was mixed with 100 ml of ether in a 500-ml separatory funnel, and the aqueous layer was separated. To the aqueous phase was added 35 ml of 2-methoxyethanol, and the RNA was extracted into the organic layer. The 2-methoxyethanol solution was mixed with 150 ml of ether and 100 ml of *n*-butanol, and the aqueous layer was drained into a Visking, size 20, dialysis casing, and dialyzed solutions were assayed for amino acid acceptor activity and for RNA content by absorbancy at 260 mμ. Ribonucleic acid was obtained from the dialyzed fractions by the addition of sodium chloride and 3 volumes of 95% ethanol. The distribution of alanine, valine, histidine, and tyrosine acceptor activity from the 500 mg of yeast soluble RNA is shown in Fig. 6. The recovery of UV-absorbing material and the recoveries of the alanine-, valine-, histidine-, and tyrosine-acceptor RNA activities were all approximately 80%.

The major fractions were redistributed in the countercurrent apparatus. Phosphate buffer, 1.9 M (pH 6.0) was prepared by dissolving 666 gm of dipotassium hydrogen phosphate and 1044 gm of sodium dihydrogen phosphate monohydrate in 6000 ml water. To 5900 ml of this solution was added 590 ml of formamide and 2596 ml of isopropyl alcohol and the mixture shaken. The apparatus was filled with lower phase and partially with upper phase as described for the initial distribution. The RNA fractions indicated in Fig. 6 were combined and dissolved in 20 ml of the above buffer. To this solution were added 20 ml of formamide, 10 ml of the lower phase of the solvent system, and 8.8 ml of isopropyl alcohol. Twenty milliliters each of upper and lower phases were added to the RNA solution, and the mixture was placed in the first two tubes of the apparatus. After the completion of 200 transfers,

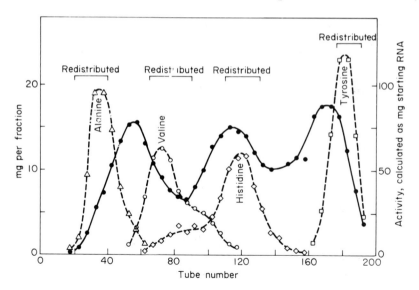

FIG. 6. 200-Transfer countercurrent distribution of 500 mg of yeast "soluble" RNA. Filled circles—mg of RNA; triangles—alanine–acceptor activity; open circles—valine-acceptor activity; "diamonds"—histidine–acceptor activity; squares—tyrosine–acceptor activity. (Reprinted with permission from Apgar et al., 1962.)

the countercurrent apparatus was set to recycle and the distributions were continued until a high degree of resolution of acceptor activity for each tRNA was achieved. With a 875-transfer countercurrent distribution of alanine-acceptor RNA, a high recovery (60–80% of the fractions from Fig. 6) of activity and UV-absorbing material were obtained. There was little indication of inactivation of the tRNA. This procedure has been used for the preparation of tRNA's for structural studies.

b. *Methylated Albumin Kieselguhr (MAK)*. Columns composed of diatomaceous earth and serum albumin have proved useful for the separation of nucleic acids. Mandell and Hershey (1960) have described an efficient chromatography system that contains kieselguhr (Hyflo Supercel, Johns-Manville Products Corporation, New York) and Fraction V bovine serum albumin powder (Armour Laboratories, Chicago, Illinois). The albumin was esterified by treatment with methyl alcohol. Sueoka and Yamane (1962) prepared a soluble RNA fraction from *Escherichia coli*. ^{14}C-Aminoacyl-tRNA's were prepared and applied to MAK columns (1.8 × 8 cm). A NaCl gradient (0.3 - 1.0 M) was used for elution of the columns. Characteristic profiles were obtained for each of sixteen aminoacyl tRNA's. More than one acceptor tRNA was evident for certain of the amino acids, i.e. leucine, isoleucine, tryptophan, and serine.

Many investigators have employed MAK chromatography for the resolution of tRNA's or for determining the possible role played by tRNA's in cellular regulatory processes (Wettstein, 1966; Doi and Kaneko, 1966). These procedures have been used to determine changes induced in tRNA's by infection with phage or virus (Sueoka et al., 1966; Subak-Sharpe et al., 1966). Baliga et al. (1968, 1969), employing MAK columns, observed that the histidyl and tyrosyl tRNA's from Novikoff hepatoma showed major alterations from the normal liver patterns.

c. *Reversed-Phase Chromatography*. The reversed-phase column chromatography system developed by Weiss and Kelmers (1967) may be employed for the resolution of tRNA's. Mixtures of aminoacylated tRNA's or uncharged tRNA's may be applied to the reversed-phase columns. With the former, it is possible to make direct comparisons of the aminoacyl tRNA patterns of two tissues or cell types by pre-charging the tRNA from one tissue with ^{14}C-labeled lysine, for example, and the other tRNA with ^{3}H-lysine. The charged mixtures are chromatographed on the same column and the radioactivity profiles are plotted.

In this procedure, 336 ml of a washed solution containing 5% tricaprylmethylammonium chloride (General Mills, Kankakee, Illinois) in Freon 214 (tetrachlorotetrafluoropropane, E. I. du Pont de Nemours and Co.) was mixed with 600 gm Chromosorb W (Applied Sciences Laboratories, Inc., State College, Pennsylvania) and stored in buffer A containing 0.25 M NaCl, 0.01 M MgCl$_2$, 0.01 M sodium acetate (pH 4.5). A column (250 × 0.9 cm) was filled with this buffer, and the chromosorborganic phase was packed by gravity.

Combinations of tritium and ^{14}C-labeled aminoacyl tRNA's were applied to the above column. Charging of the tRNA's was accomplished by employing combinations of the synthetases and tRNA fractions of the liver and tumor, i.e., liver synthetases, liver tRNA, and amino acid-^{14}C; liver synthetases, tumor tRNA, and amino acid-^{3}H; tumor synthetases, tumor tRNA, and amino acid-^{14}C, tumor synthetases, liver tRNA, and amino acid-^{3}H. It, therefore, was possible to make direct comparisons of the enzyme and the tRNA activity of the liver and tumor cells on the same column.

A linear gradient was employed to develop the column [1 liter each of buffer A and buffer B (0.5 M NaCl, 0.01 M MgCl$_2$, 0.01 M sodium acetate, pH 4.5)]. The column flow rate was 1 ml/minute. Initial runs were carried out in jacketed columns maintained at 27°C. However, it was observed subsequently that identical chromatograms were obtained if the columns were insulated and developed at room temperatures. Fifteen-milliliter fractions were collected, and the absorption at 260 mμ was ascertained. One-milliliter aliquots of each sample were precipitated by the addition of 10 ml of cold 5% TCA (allowed to stand for 15 minutes). The precipitates were collected by filtration on Millipore filters (type H. A., pore size 0.45 μ) and washed with an additional 10 ml of 5% TCA. Each filter was washed with 5 ml of ethanol and dried at 80°C for 10 minutes. The filters were counted in vials containing 10 ml of scintillation fluid (4 gm of poly(propylene oxide), 0.2 gm of 1,4-bis-2-(5-phenyloxazolyl)-benzene, 1 liter of sulfur-free toluene) in a Packard Tri-Carb liquid scintillation spectrometer with maximal setting for simultaneous tritium and ^{14}C counting.

Recently, Weiss et al. (1968) described two new reversed-phase chromatographic systems for the separation of tRNA's. These systems employ the water-insoluble quarternary ammonium salts, trioctyl-propyl ammonium bromide or dimethyldilauryl ammonium chloride, immobilized on a hydrophobic diatomaceous earth support. Sodium chloride gradients were employed to develop the columns and proved useful for resolution of tRNA's near the front of the chromatogram. Two formylmethionine tRNA's were resolved by this method.

(i) Precharging of tRNA's. Aminoacyl synthetase preparations for precharging tRNA were obtained as follows: The initial high-speed supernatant fraction of rat liver or tumor cells (S 275; see Section II, A, 1) was adjusted to pH 5.0 with 1 N acetic acid and centrifuged for

7 minutes at 1500 rpm (Internation centrifuge, Model PR-2). Resulting precipitates were dissolved in buffer (0.25 M sucrose, 0.005 M $MgCl_2$, 0.025 M KCl, 0.05 M tris–HCl, pH 7.6).* The pH was adjusted to 7.0 with 1 N KOH and the precipitate carefully stirred until solution was essentially complete. Diethylaminoethyl–cellulose, previously equilibrated with the buffer, was added (0.8 gm/2 ml synthetase solution) and the mixture stirred for 10 minutes in the cold. Centrifugation at 1500 rpm for 10 minutes then was carried out and the supernatant fraction adjusted to 0.01 M with 2-mercaptoethanol and 20% (by volume) with glycerol. This synthetase preparation, stored at 0°C, will retain activity for several weeks. From 5 to 7 mg tRNA were incubated for 30 minutes at 37°C in a reaction mixture containing 50 mg of the aminoacyl synthetase preparation, 12.5 μmoles ATP, 12.5 μcuries of ^{14}C-amino acid or 16 μcuries of ^{3}H-amino acid, and 0.25 volume of a buffer (0.2 M tris–HCl, 0.02 M $MgCl_2$, 0.02 M KCl, pH 7.5). Following incubation the mixture was extracted once with an equal volume of 80% phenol at 0°C and centrifuged at 8000 g for 10 minutes. The aqueous layer was precipitated with 2 volumes of cold ethanol for 30 minutes and centrifuged at 10,000 g. The resulting labeled aminoacyl tRNA was dissolved in 1.0 ml H_2O (pH 4.5) for application to the reversed-phase columns.

(ii) *Postcharging.* The reversed-phase column chromatography procedure of Weiss and Kelmers (1967) may also be used for separation of the different isoaccepting tRNA's from a large batch of previously uncharged tRNA. A sample of 25 mg of rat liver or tumor tRNA in 5.0 ml H_2O was applied to the column. The column was operated under the same conditions as described above. Fifteen-milliliter fractions were collected at a rate of 1.0 ml/minute. Upon completion of the column, each fraction from Nos. 31 to 130 was concentrated as follows. Each fraction was precipitated by the addition of 2 volumes of cold ethanol and allowed to stand overnight at 0°C. The tRNA precipitates were collected over Millipore filters (type H.A., pore size 0.45 μ, diameter 47 mm), and the tRNA from each fraction was eluted from the filter with 2.0 ml of a buffer (0.05 M NaCl, 0.01 $MgAc_2$, 0.001 M EDTA, pH 7.0). These were allowed to stand for 30 minutes at room temperature with occasional shaking. The filters were removed, and the resulting concentrated fractions were frozen and stored.

In order to determine the elution profile of the uncharged tRNA's from the above columns 50 μl of each concentrated fraction, 50 μl of a mixture of synthetase protein, ATP, buffer, and a [14]C- or ^{3}H-amino acid were incubated for 20 minutes at 37°C. Ten milliliters of cold 5% TCA were added to each tube and allowed to stand for 10 minutes. The

---

* Note: use 35 ml buffer per 40 gm rat liver.

aminoacyl tRNA of each fraction was collected over Millipore filter, washed with 10 ml cold 5% TCA, followed by 5.0 ml 95% ethanol. The filters were dried for 10 minutes at 80°C and counted for activity. Although elution patterns of the free tRNA's followed in general those obtained for the aminoacyl tRNA's, there were some interesting differences in the two patterns for certain tRNA's.

d. *Other Procedures. Hydroxylapatite columns*: Pearson and Kelmers (1966); Muench and Berg (1966b).

Sephadex columns (G-25): Muench and Berg (1966a).

Diethylaminoethyl–cellulose: Bergquist et al. (1965).

Benzoylated DEAE–cellulose: Wimmer et al. (1968); Gillam et al. (1967).

Methylated albumin–silicic acid. This material appears to have a much greater adsorption than MAK. N-Carbobenzyloxyphenylalanyl tRNA elutes from this column at a considerably higher salt concentration than phenylalanyl tRNA or any of the other tRNA's (Stern and Littauer, 1968).

3. Structural Studies on tRNA

Transfer RNA's are the smallest of the biologically active nucleic acids, and it has been possible to characterize these macromolecules in terms of nucleotide sequence as well as other properties. Recently, Kim and Rich (1968), Hampel et al. (1968), and Fresco et al. (1968) have reported the crystallization of tRNA which enables one to obtain meaningful diffraction data for ascertaining three-dimensional structures.

The general procedures for the characterization of tRNA's were developed by Holley and associates (Penswick and Holley, 1965). The complete structure of alanine tRNA was elucidated by this group in 1965 (Holley et al., 1965). Structural determinations involved the identification of small fragments formed by the complete digestion of the RNA with pancreatic ribonuclease and takadiastase ribonuclease T_1. Pancreatic ribonuclease cleaves the RNA chain to the right of nucleotides containing bases with pyrimidine structures (C, U, Ψ and T). Digestion with ribonuclease TI produces fragments terminating in nucleotides whose bases contain purine structures, G, MG and I. The small fragments are then separated on DEAE cellulose or DEAE-Sephadex columns.

Since the elaborate studies of Holley and associates reporting the complete structure of yeast alanyl tRNA, structures for at least twelve additional tRNA's have been reported. The nucleotide sequence of these tRNA's are shown in Table V. The number of tRNA's for which the complete nucleotide sequence has been established is increasing rapidly. Although most of the structural studies have been made on microbial

TABLE V

Ribonucleic acid	5'-Terminal	D and MG Region	Anticodon region
Yeast Ala	GGGCGUGU	(¹M · · · ᴰM) GGCGCGUAGDCGGDAGCGCG	(¹M) CUCCCUUIGCIΨGGGAG
E. coli Ala			
Yeast SerI	GGCAACUU	(ᴬᶜ ᴼM · · · ᴰM) GGCCGAGDGGDDAAGGCGAA	(ᴵP · · · ᴼM) AGAΨUIGAAAΨCUUUUG
Yeast SerII	GGCAACUU	(ᴬᶜ ᴼM · · · ᴰP) GGCCGAGDGGDDAAGGCGAA	(ᴵP · · · ᴼM) AGAΨUIGAAAΨCUUUUG
Rat liver Ser	GUAGUCGU	(ᴬᶜ ᴼM · · · ᴰM) GGCCGAGDGGDDAAGGCGAΨ	(³M ᴵP ᴼM · · · ᴼM) GGACUIGAAAΨCCAUUG
Yeast Tyr	CUCUCGGU	(²M ᴼM · · · ᴰM) AGCCAAGDDGGDDDAAGGCG	(ᴵP) CAAGACUGΨAAAΨCUUG
E. coli Tyr	GGGUGGGP	(ᴼM) UCCCCGAGCGGQCAAAGGGA	GCAGACURUASAΨCUGC
E. coli Tyr StI Su	(⁺ˢᵘ) GGUGGGGU	(ᴼM) UCCCGAGCGGCCAAAGGGAG	CAGACUCUAAAΨCUGCC (G)
Yeast Phe	GCGGAUUU	(²M · · · ᴰM) AGCUCAGDDGGGAGAGCGCC	(ᴼ ᴼ M M · · · ⁵M) AGACUGAAYAΨCUGGAG
E. coli B Phe	GCCCGCUC	AGCGGDCGASCCAGDAGGUA	GAGCAGGGGGAΨUGGAA
Wheat germ Phe	GCGGGGAU	(²M · · · ᴰM) AGCUCAGDDGGGAGAGCGΨC	(ᴼ ᴼ M M) AGACUGAAYAΨCUGAAG
E. coli F Met	CGCGGGGU	GGAGCAGCCUGGDAGCUCGU	(²M) CGGGCUCAUAACCCGAA
Yeast ValI (Torula)	GGUUUCGU	(¹M) GGUCΨAGDDGGDCAUGGCAΨ	CUGCΨUIACACGCAGAA
Yeast Val (Baker's)	GGUUUCGU	(¹M) GUGGUΨCAGDCGGDAUGGGG	CAΨUCGCΨUIACACGCA

ᵃKey to abbreviations:

A—adenylic acid	P, Q, R, S, Y—Unidentified nucleotides
C—cytidylic acid	AcC—N^4-acetylcytidylic acid
G—guanylic acid	1MA—1-methyladenylic acid
U—uridylic acid	1MG—1-methylguanylic acid
I—inosinic acid	5MC—5-methylcytidylic acid
T—ribothymidylic acid	3MC—3-methylcytidylic acid
D—dihydrouridylic acid	OMU—2'-O-methyluridylic acid
Ψ—pseudouridylic acid	OM Ψ—2'-O-methylpseudouridylic acid

STRUCTURES OF TRANSFER RIBONUCLEIC ACIDS[a]

	T Ψ C region	3'-Terminal	Ref.
AGUC	UCCGGTΨCGAUUCCGGA	CUCG UCC ACCA C UCC ACCA	Holley et al., 1965 Alvino and Clarke, 1968
$\overset{5}{\overset{M}{}}$GGCUCUGCCCGC	GCAGGTΨCAAAUCCUGC	AGUU GUC GCCA	Zachau et al., 1966
$\overset{5}{\overset{M}{}}$GGCUUUGCCCGC	GCAGGTΨCGAGUCCUGC	AGUU GUC GCCA	
$\overset{3}{\overset{M}{}}\overset{5}{\overset{M}{}}$GGGUCUCCCCGC	$\overset{1}{\overset{M}{}}$GCAGGTΨCGAAUCCUGC	CGAC UAC GCCA	Staehelin et al., 1968
$\overset{5}{\overset{M}{}}$AGADC	$\overset{1}{\overset{M}{}}$GGGCGTΨCGACUCGCCC	CCGG GAG ACCA	Madison et al., 1966
CGGUCACAGACUUC	GAAGGTΨCGAAUCCUUC	CCCA CCC ACCA	Doctor et al., 1969
GUCAUCGACUUC	GAAGGTΨCGAAUCCUUC	CCCC ACC ACCA	Goodman et al., 1968
$\overset{7}{\overset{M}{}}$GUC	$\overset{5}{\overset{M}{}}$CUGUGTΨ$\overset{1}{\overset{M}{}}$CGAUCCACAG	AAUU CGC ACCA	RajBhandary et al., 1967
$\overset{7}{\overset{M}{}}$AΨCCCCGUGC	CUUGGTΨCGAUUCCGAG	UCCG GGC ACCA	Gassen and Uziel, 1969
$\overset{7}{\overset{M}{}}$GDC	GCGUGTΨ$\overset{1}{\overset{M}{}}$CGAUCCACGC	UCAC CGC ACCA	Dudock et al., 1969
$\overset{7}{\overset{M}{}}$GGUC	GUCGGTΨCAAAUCCGGC	CCCC GCA ACCA	Dube et al., 1968
$\overset{5}{\overset{M}{}}$CC	CCCAGTΨ$\overset{1}{\overset{M}{}}$CGAUCCUGGG	CGAA AUC ACCA	Takemura et al., 1968
GAACCCCD	$\overset{5}{\overset{M}{}}$CAGTΨ$\overset{1}{\overset{M}{}}$CGCGAUCCUDGG	CGAA AUA CCCA	Bayev et al., 1967

[a]Key to abbreviations (cont.)

IPA—isopentenyladenylic acid	Ala—alanine
DMG—N^2-dimethylguanylic acid	Ser—serine
OMG—2'-O-methylguanylic acid	Tyr—tyrosine
7MG—7-methylguanylic acid	Phe—phenylalanine
2MC—2'-O-methylcytidylic acid	Met—methionine
1MI—1-methylinosinic acid	Val—valine
2MG—N^2-methylguanylic acid	St—strain

E. coli—Escherichia coli

tRNA's, Staehelin et al. (1968) reported the nucleotide sequence for rat liver serine tRNA. With the increasing refinement of these procedures, it is possible to determine the effect of such factors as phage, virus, carcinogens, and radiation upon the primary nucleotide sequence and to ascertain if the tRNA's are involved in vital cellular processes such as differentiation, regulation, and carcinogenesis (Goodman et al., 1968).

From Table V some interesting observations may be made: (a) the amino acceptor region (3'-terminal nucleotides) is identical for all of the tRNA's studied thus far; (b) the total number of nucleotides of the tRNA's characterized thus far range from 75 to 87; (c) nucleotides Nos. 20–24 (from 3'-terminal end) GTψCG have been the same in almost all of the tRNA's studied, with the exception of yeast serine I and *Escherichia coli* F methionine which have GTψCA; (d) methylated C and G appear most frequently in the dihydrouridylic and anticodon regions; (e) a region between the anticodon and TψC regions varies considerably in chain length from 2 nucleotides in yeast valine to 12–14 nucleotides in some of the serine and tyrosine tRNA's; (f) a comparison of the nucleotide sequence of yeast and rat liver seryl tRNA's reveals a difference in 21 of the 85 nucleotides and mostly in the base-paired regions adjacent to the CCA terminal and the anticodon loop.

4. Influence of Carcinogens, Including Ultraviolet Light, on tRNA's

Several investigators (Farber et al., 1967) have demonstrated that ethionine interacts with liver RNA and more specifically with the tRNA's. This interaction is mostly through ethylation of one or more of the bases and ribose. Many of the methyl groups of the methylated compounds present in liver tRNA's are derived from methionine via S-adenosylmethionine. In addition, the methylation probably occurs after RNA's are formed. Since ethionine is converted to S-adenosylethionine, it is possible that the ethionine ethyl group participates in alkylation of the RNA's. Hancock (1968) has reported that embryonic and neoplastic liver are more active in ethylating tRNA *in vitro* than is normal liver. The most extensively ethylated nucleotide in tRNA was guanylic acid. Axel et al. (1967) also reported that ethionine-fed rats have a loss of tRNA[leu] which codes for UUG. There is increasing indication that ethylation of tRNA may be of major importance in ethionine carcinogenesis. Magee et al. (1967) reviewed the role of alkylation of nucleic acids in the origin of tumors of the liver and other organs.

It has been shown (J. A. Miller and Miller, 1967; Poirier et al., 1967) that N-hydroxylation is apparently an essential step in the metabolic activation of several of the important carcinogens: 2-acetylaminofluorene, 4-acetylaminobiphenyl, 4-acetylaminostilbene, 2-acetylaminophenanthrene, N-methyl-4-aminoazobenzene, and other aminoazo carcinogens. The N-hydroxy metabolites are more carcinogenic than the parent compounds and have been shown to react *in vitro* with protein, RNA, and DNA. Five nucleophilic components of these macromolecules—methionine, cysteine, tryptophan, tyrosine, and guanine—will react with the N-hydroxy compounds.

Several investigators (see Weinstein, 1970) have shown that acetylaminofluorene (AAF) will react, *in vivo* and *in vitro*, with nucleic acids. The high affinity of AAF–tRNA complexes on BD*–cellulose makes it possible to isolate this fraction from other tRNA's. The amino acid-accepting capacity of *Escherichia coli* tRNA, after treatment with N-acetoxy AAF, has been studied by Weinstein (1970). Most of the tRNA's examined had reduced activities, i.e., arginine to 35% of the control. However, the valine and alanine acceptance was enhanced considerably. These findings point out the importance of alteration of tRNA through interaction with carcinogens in terms of biological activity. Altered tRNA may influence the codon response by the interaction with the aminoacyl synthetase, ribosome, or the transfer enzymes.

Studies have been initiated in this laboratory to ascertain if the liver tRNA patterns are altered by the feeding of diets containing the highly active aminoazo carcinogen, 3'-methyl-4-dimethylaminoazobenzene. Male albino rats were fed *ad libitum* for 7 to 8 weeks a diet containing the carcinogen at a level of 0.06%. The livers at this time were grossly enlarged, cirrhotic and fibrotic, but without evidence of visual tumors. Transfer RNA was prepared from these livers as described in Section III, A, *1*. Aliquots of the tRNA (approximately 5 mg) were charged with specific labeled amino acids and co-chromatographed with an aminoacyl tRNA (same amino acid carrying a different label) from normal liver. The patterns of the precancerous livers exhibiting the greatest deviation from normal liver are shown in Fig. 7. Early peaks emerged when the lysyl, leucyl, phenylalanyl, and tyrosyl tRNA's of the precancerous liver tissues were chromatographed on the reversed-phase columns. Slight distortions were observed between the normal rat liver and precancerous liver patterns for arginyl, glutamyl, seryl, and isoleucyl tRNA's, but the patterns for valyl, histidyl, threonyl, and methionyl tRNA's of the two tissues were identical according to this investigative approach. There is no immediate explanation to account for the altered patterns seen in several of the aminoacyl tRNA's following the administration of the carcinogenic aminoazo compounds. However, it is possible that these tRNA's have undergone methylation or have reacted with

---

* BD, benzoylated diethylaminoethyl.

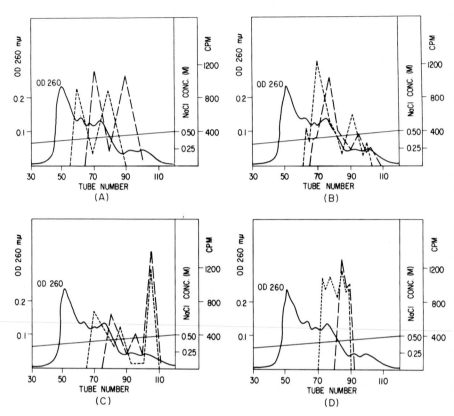

FIG. 7. Comparison of aminoacyl transfer ribonucleic acid (tRNA) patterns from normal rat liver and from livers of rats fed diets containing 3'-methyl-4 dimethylaminoazobenzene (3' Me DAB). —— Liver tRNA; —————— 3' MeDAB Liver tRNA. (A) Lysyl tRNA; (B) leucyl tRNA; (C) phenylalanyl tRNA; (D) tyrosyl tRNA.

N-hydroxylated or other metabolites of the 3'-methyl-4-dimethylamino-azobenzene. Direct methylation of liver tRNA with diazomethane (B. E. Griffin et al., 1967) or with dimethyl sulfoxide prior to charging with either phenylalanine or tyrosine resulted in profiles similar to those obtained from the precancerous liver in that some of the aminoacyl tRNA's emerged early from the reversed-phase columns. Capra and Peterkofsky (1968) obtained a new species of leucine tRNA from $E.\ coli$ grown on a methionine-deficient medium. These studies also utilized reversed-phase column chromatography. When the "methyl-deficient" leucyl tRNA was methylated and rechromatographed on these columns the methylated species emerged earlier from the column. What role the alteration of tRNA's by cancer-inducing chemicals may play in the process of malignant tumor cell transformation is still unknown. Since it is possible to resolve and characterize the tRNA's, this approach affords an unusual opportunity to study the effects of carcinogens upon nucleic acids.

Chambers and co-workers have conducted an interesting study relative to specific lesions produced by direct exposure of highly purified yeast alanyl tRNA to ultraviolet light. Some of the photoreactions that cause inactivation of tRNA include: (a) photohydration of C and U residues; (b) dimerization of adjacent C and U residues; (c) chain cleavage at ψ residues; and (d) modification of ψ residues without chain cleavage (Schulman and Chambers, 1968). During the course of this investigation, these workers (Reeves et al., 1968) isolated a new species of yeast alanyl tRNA (tRNA[ala lab]). Full amino acid acceptor activity was obtained by chromatography of phenyoxyacetylaminoacyl tRNA on BD–cellulose. They reached the conclusion that tRNA[ala lab] undergoes extensive photochemical modification without loss of amino acid acceptor activity and that inactivation may occur by the formation of a single photoproduct in the nucleotide region (5, 6, 7) from the acceptor end of the molecule. Based on these UV inactivation studies and the structural data in the literature for tRNA's of which the nucleotide sequence has been established, these workers proposed that the specific recognition site for the aminoacyl tRNA synthetases may involve the first hydrogen-bonded nucleotide pairs of the tRNA but that the entire stem region has a role in maintaining the stereochemical integrity of this recognition site. This approach of pinpointing the lesions produced in biologically active macromolecules by carcinogenic agents such as ultraviolet light would appear to be of great value in studying the mechanism of cancer induction.

5. Transfer RNA Patterns of Tumor Cells

Yang and Novelli (1968a), working with mouse plasma cell tumors, demonstrated the presence of multiple isoaccepting tRNA's for twenty amino acids. However, no attempt was made to compare the tRNA profiles with those of normal mouse tissues. Baliga and associates 1968 and Weinstein, 1970 studied the aminoacyl tRNA patterns (MAK chromatography) of Novikoff hepatoma and normal rat liver. Differences between the tumor and liver cells were observed for histidine, tyrosine, and asparagine. Taylor et al. (1967, 1968) observed differences in specific tRNA's in mouse tumor when comparisons were made with normal organs. A new species of tyrosyl tRNA in tumors produced by SV 40 virus has been reported by Holland et al. (1967). The studies of Mach et al. (1968) and Yang and Novelli (1968a) indicate that some tRNA's specific for amino acids may differ from one plasma cell tumor to another.

The reversed-phase chromatography developed by Weiss and Kelmers (1967) has been employed in this laboratory to study the aminoacyl tRNA synthetase and tRNA patterns of normal rat liver and of Novikoff ascites tumor cells (tumors of hepatic origin; Novikoff, 1957). The tRNA and aminoacyl synthetases of tumor and liver were prepared and charged as described in the preceding section. Direct comparisons of aminoacylated tRNA's of the tumor and liver were made on the same columns. The initial amino acid studied was arginine, and the patterns that were obtained by using various combinations of aminoacyl synthetases and tRNA's from the two cell types are shown in Figs. 8 and 9 (Goldman *et al.*, 1969). The 260-mμ adsorbing material emerged from the columns at Fraction No. 55 and the initial arginyl tRNA peak appeared at Fraction No. 70. Four subsequent peaks emerged. The profiles for the liver and tumor were almost identical (Figs. 8 and 9). If differences exist at either the synthetase or tRNA levels, these would be reflected in the aminoacyl tRNA patterns by the absence of peaks, shifting of peak areas, or the appearance of new peaks. From these findings it must be concluded that the arginyl synthetase and tRNA's for liver and tumor are similar.

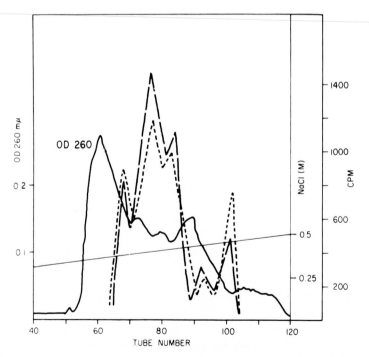

FIG. 8. Comparison of arginyl transfer ribonucleic acid (tRNA) patterns from liver and ascites tumor cells. ------ Liver tRNA and liver synthetase; — — tumor tRNA and tumor synthetase.

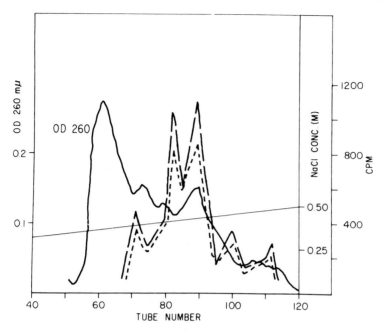

FIG. 9. Comparison of arginyl transfer ribonucleic acid (tRNA) patterns from liver and ascites tumor cells. ------ Liver tRNA and tumor synthetase; — — tumor tRNA and tumor synthetase.

Tumor and liver tRNA's were charged with ^{3}H- or ^{14}C-labeled phenylalanine and co-chromatographed on the reversed-phase columns. The liver phenylalanine tRNA profile differed from tumor as shown in Fig. 10. Three distinct peaks were observed for the liver, whereas the tumor exhibited an absence of the first peak and a displacement of the second phenylalanine peak. A normal pattern was obtained from the combination of tumor synthetase and liver tRNA suggesting that a difference does exist between tumor and liver with respect to the tRNA's that will accept or react with phenylalanine.

Several additional studies of the aminoacyl tRNA's of liver and tumor were carried out (A. C. Griffin, 1970). Comparisons of the elution profiles revealed that the tumor and liver were almost identical with respect to the RNA's of each of the following amino acids: threonine, histidine, methionine, glutamic acid, and tyrosine. Some deviations in the aminoacyl tRNA patterns were observed in the asparagine, valine, and serine studies. These findings are not in agreement with those reported by Weinstein (1970) for the histidyl and tyrosyl tRNA patterns of the liver and tumor tissues. Weinstein employed MAK chromatography, and it is also possible that a variation exists in the Novikoff hepatoma employed in the two laboratories. Further studies will have

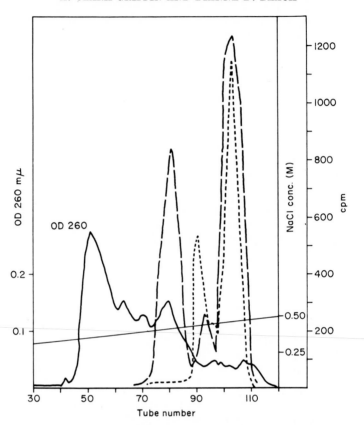

Fɪɢ. 10. Comparison of phenylalanyl transfer ribonucleic acid (tRNA) patterns from liver and ascites tumor cells. ----- Liver tRNA and liver synthetase; — — tumor tRNA and tumor synthetase.

to be carried out in order to explain this difference in findings. When definite alterations have been established in the chromatographic profile for tRNA's in the tumor tissues, an attempt will be made to establish the chemical alteration (i.e., methylation and base substitution) responsible for the change. An extension of this approach may make it possible to ascertain the role of the aminoacyl synthetases and tRNA's in cancer induction and in the function and behavior of malignant tumor cells.

B. Aɴᴏᴀᴄʏʟ Sʏɴᴛʜᴇᴛᴀꜱᴇꜱ

Several of the aminoacyl–RNA synthetases have been obtained in highly purified states. These include the synthetases for arginine (C. C. Allende and Allende, 1964; Mitra and Mehler, 1967); phenylalanine

(Conway *et al.*, 1962; Stulberg, 1967); isoleucine (Baldwin and Berg, 1966); glutamic acid (Deutcher, 1967); tyrosine (Calendar and Berg, 1966); valine (Lagerkvist and Waldenström, 1967); methionine (Lemine *et al.*, 1968); and threonine (C. C. Allende *et al.*, 1966). In many tissues two or more synthetases for specific amino acids may be present.

A procedure for the preparation of a highly purified and stable arginyl–RNA synthetase from rat liver has been developed (Ikegami and Griffin, 1969).

Rat liver (100–150 gm fresh weight) was homogenized in a Teflon–glass homogenizer with 3 volumes of buffer (0.25 M sucrose, 5 mM $MgCl_2$, 25 mM KCl, and 50 mM tris–HCl, pH 7.6). The homogenate was centrifuged at 15,000 g for 30 minutes in the Spinco preparative centrifuge, Model L-2 rotor No 19. The resulting supernatant solution then was centrifuged at 105,000 g for 60 minutes. A 0.5 volume of calcium phosphate gel suspension (Bio-Rad Laboratories) was added to the above supernatant fraction and stirred for 30 minutes. The suspension was centrifuged at 5000 g for 15 minutes and the supernatant layer discarded.

The gel was stirred for 20 minutes with one-half the original volume of 0.02 M potassium phosphate buffer (pH 6.8), containing 10% glycerol and 6 mM 2-mercaptoethanol, and centrifuged; the supernatant layer was discarded. The gel was mixed with one-third the original volume of 0.1 M potassium phosphate buffer (pH 7.5), containing 10% glycerol and 6 mM 2-mercaptoethanol, stirred for 30 minutes, and centrifuged. The resulting supernatant solution contained most of the enzyme. Glycerol was added to a final concentration of 20%. The 0.1 M phosphate buffer-extracted fraction could be stored for 2 months at $-20°C$ without appreciable loss of activity. The gel, which still retained some enzyme activity was discarded.

a. Diethylaminoethyl Cellulose–Column Chromatography. Diethylamino-ethyl–cellulose (Whatman DE-52, 1.0 meq/gm) was washed with 0.1 M potassium phosphate buffer (pH 6.5) until the pH of the supernatant solution was 6.5 and then stored in the same buffer. A column (2 × 20 cm) was packed with this material and equilibrated with buffer A(0.005 M potassium phosphate, 6 mM 2-mercaptoethanol, 10% glycerol, pH 7.5). After the enzyme solution was applied, the column was washed with 300 ml of buffer A at a rate of 60 ml/hour and eluted under pressure with a linear gradient of phosphate ion concentration and of decreasing pH. The mixing chamber contained 300 ml of starting buffer, and the reservoir contained 300 ml of 0.25 M potassium phosphate (pH 6.5), containing 10% glycerol and 6 mM 2-mercaptoethanol. Ten-milliliter fractions were collected and the absorbance at 280 mμ was followed.

Fractions that had highest activities were pooled and concentrated by dialysis against buffer A containing 20% polyethylene glycol.

An approximate 100-fold purification of the enzyme was achieved (Table VI). The purified arginyl RNA synthetase (4B) contained low activities of the synthetases for lysine, glutamic acid, aspartic acid, and proline. No activity was detected by the assay procedures employed for other aminoacyl synthetases. The purified enzyme migrated as a single major band on acrylamide-gel electrophoresis with two additional, faster moving components in trace quantities. The kinetic properties of

TABLE VI

SUMMARY OF PURIFICATION OF ARGINYL TRANSFER RIBONUCLEIC ACID SYNTHETASE

Fraction	Total protein (mg)	Specific activity[a]	Total activity ($\times 10^3$)	Yield (%)	Relative purification
1. 105,000 g Supernatant fraction	6600	2796	18480	100	1
2. Calcium phosphate gel eluate	647	9800	6341	34.3	3.5
3. DEAE-cellulose eluate[b]	38	44426	1688	9.0	16
4A. Hydroxylapatite, eluate I	2.9	200425	581	3.2	72
4B. Hydroxylapatite, eluate II[c]	1.6	273350	431	2.3	98

[a] Specific activity is expressed by picamoles of arginyl tRNA formed per milligram of protein.

[b] DEAE, diethylaminoethyl.

[c] Three preparations were combined for the hydroxylapatite rechromatography and the yield of enzyme was calculated as one preparation (Ikegami and Griffin, 1969).

the enzyme were similar to those of other aminoacyl RNA synthetases. The K_m values for arginine, ATP, and rat liver tRNA were 1.25, 1.9, and 0.37 μM, respectively. The purified enzyme was used to charge tRNA's of normal liver and Novikoff ascites tumor cells. The arginyl tRNA's were chromatographed on reversed-phase columns as described in Section III, A, 2, c. The profiles obtained were almost identical to those shown in Figs. 8 and 9 indicating that (1) this highly purified liver arginyl tRNA synthetase was capable of charging five tRNA's (this was also observed when a crude liver synthetase preparation was employed); (2) the purified liver arginyl synthetase also charged five tRNA's of tumor origin; (3) the tumor and liver arginyl tRNA's must be similar; (4) the liver arginyl synthetase has a low degree of specificity in that it is active for the several isoaccepting arginyl tRNA's of liver and tumor.

C. Enzymes and Related Factors

1. Transfer Factor Complex

Incorporation of aminoacyl tRNA by rat liver ribosomes requires transferase I and transferase II, GTP, NH_4^+, Mg^{++}, and a sulfhydryl compound. Initial studies demonstrated that transferase I catalyzed the transfer of aminoacyl tRNA to ribosomes only in the presence of GTP or the GTP analog, 5'-guanylyl methylenediphosphonate (GMP= PCP). Transferase I was inactivated by prior exposure to GTP, the GTP analog, and guanosine diphosphate (GDP). Aminoacyl tRNA protected the enzyme against this GTP inhibition, whereas deacylated tRNA was less than 25% as efficient as the aminoacyl tRNA (Ibuki et al., 1966; Ibuki and Moldave, 1968a). Similar findings have been reported for TF-I isolated from rabbit reticulocytes (McKeehan et al., 1969).

Preincubation of transferase I in a buffer salts medium at 37°C for 5 minutes, followed by the addition of other components in the amino acid-incorporating system, resulted in a 70% decrease in overall incorporation. Guanosine diphosphate, other nucleotide diphosphates, GTP, and GMP=PCP resulted in an even greater loss in activity during preincubation with transferase I. The addition of aminoacyl tRNA to the mixture protected transferase I against GTP and the GTP analog, but was ineffective against the temperature or GDP initiated loss of activity.

By means of Sephadex G-200 chromatography, the complex formed between transferase I and ^{14}C-aminoacyl tRNA was isolated from the unbound aminoacyl tRNA's (Rao and Moldave, 1967). When inactivated by GTP, transferase I lost this ability to complex with aminoacyl tRNA's. Guanosine triphosphate, however, was required for the binding of the stable transferase I–aminoacyl tRNA complex to the ribosomes (Ibuki et al., 1966; Ibuki and Moldave, 1968b).

Two transfer enzymes, TF-1 and TF-2, are required for the synthesis of hemoglobin on reticulocyte ribosomes with endogenous mRNA, or for the synthesis of polyphenylalanine on poly U templated ribosomes (Bishop and Schweet, 1961; Arlinghaus et al., 1963; Hardesty et al., 1963). It was observed that phenylalanyl tRNA was bound to the poly U-charged ribosomes at high Mg^{++} concentrations (10 mM) in the absence of TF-1 or GTP (Shaeffer et al., 1968a). Additional studies employing low Mg^{++} concentrations revealed that TF-1 catalyzed binding of the initial phenylalanyl tRNA to the poly U-charged ribosomes and that GTP was required for this reaction. Enzymic binding occurred at 6.7 mM MgCl$_2$ and 67 mM KCl. This enzyme was not activated by a sulfhydryl compound nor did deacylated tRNA interfere with enzymic binding. Similarly, the T$_1$ factor isolated from normal rat liver and rabbit reticulocytes by Felicetti and Lipmann (1968) catalyzed binding of phenylalanyl tRNA in the presence of GTP to the poly-uridine–ribosomal complex. However, when incorporated into the hemoglobin transfer system, TF-1 did not demonstrate the same potential for binding aminoacyl tRNA's to the 0.1 M KCl-treated ribosomes (Arlinghaus et al., 1968a). Klink et al. (1967b) separated two amino acid transfer enzymes, FI and FII, from rat and calf livers, but did not identify the binding enzyme using a calf liver system. Both enzymes were required for binding of aminoacyl tRNA to the ribosomes (endogenous mRNA) with simultaneous formation of a peptide bond.

Two systems were developed by Ibuki and Moldave (1968b) to study aminoacyl tRNA binding to liver ribosomes without peptide bond formation. The ribosomal–aminoacyl tRNA complex was isolated from the incubation mixture containing puromycin or puromycin-treated ribosomes by adsorption onto Millipore filters or by discontinuous sucrose density gradient centrifugations. The binding of aminoacyl tRNA to ribosomes was examined by incubating approximately 0.5 mg of ribosomes, 20 μg of ^{14}C-aminoacyl tRNA (10,000 counts/minute), and 0.2 mM GTP, in the presence or absence of 5 to 15 μg of transferase I. Incubations in a total volume of 0.5 ml were carried out at 37°C in buffered salts solution containing 60 mM tris–HCl buffer (pH 8 at 0°C), 6 mM MgCl$_2$, 80 mM NH$_4$Cl, 2 mM DTT, and 0.5 mM puromycin in most cases. Ribosomal-bound radioactivity was expressed as counts per minute per 0.5 mg of ribosomes.

For the isolation of ribosomes by the centrifugation procedure, the incubation mixture was layered directly onto a discontinuous sucrose gradient. The top layer was 4 ml of 10% sucrose in 0.05 M tris buffer and 0.004 M MgCl$_2$; the bottom layer was 25% sucrose in the same tris–MgCl$_2$ solution. After 4 hours of centrifugation at 100,000 g, the sedimented pellets were resuspended in 1 ml of the buffered salts solution. The total TCA-insoluble and the hot (90°C) TCA-insoluble (protein) fractions were prepared and assayed for radioactivity. The total acid-insoluble fraction contained aminoacyl tRNA and polypeptidyl tRNA bound to ribosomes, whereas the hot acid-insoluble fraction measured radioactivity associated with polypeptides.

In order to facilitate the isolation of ribosomes by the Millipore filtration procedure, the incubation mixtures were diluted with 3 ml of cold (4°C) buffered salts solution, filtered through 25-mm membrane discs (mean pore size, 0.45 μ), and washed with three portions (3 ml each) of buffered salts solution. Gentle suction was used to insure a slow flow rate of approximately 8 ml/minute. Under these conditions and with the concentrations of ribosomes and aminoacyl tRNA used, 90–98% of the former and none of the latter was retained by the filter. The filters were then glued to planchets and dried, and radioactivity was determined. This procedure measured the total amount of ^{14}C-aminoacyl tRNA-bound to ribosomes.

Puromycin-treated ribosomes were also used to study aminoacyl tRNA binding. These particles were prepared by incubating approximately 10 mg of ribosomes in 1 ml of buffered salts solution containing 0.5 mM puromycin. After 10 minutes at 37°C, the incubation mixture was layered on and centrifuged through a discontinuous sucrose gradient for 4 hours at 100,000 g. The top layer of the gradient was 4 ml of 10% sucrose in buffered salts solution, and the bottom layer was 4 ml of 25% sucrose in the same solution. The ribosomes were resuspended in buffered salts solution and aliquots, containing approximately 500 μg of ribosomes, were used in the incubations as described above. When assayed for aminoacyl transfer from aminoacyl tRNA to peptidyl tRNA, in the presence of transferases I and II and GTP, puromycin-treated ribosomes were 25% as active as ribosomes treated similarly but without puromycin.

Addition of puromycin to the ribosomal transferase I mixture increased the amount of charged tRNA bound to the ribosomes by at least 50%, whereas peptide synthesis was minimal. This enhanced effect was temperature-dependent, binding did not occur at 0°C, and was not influenced by transferase II. The enzymic binding of aminoacyl tRNA to the endogenous messenger–ribosomal complex occurred at concentrations of 6 mM Mg^{++}, 80 mM NH$_4^+$, and 1×10^{-4} M GTP. The GTP analog, GMP=PCP, likewise, initiated enzymic binding of aminoacyl tRNA to the ribosomes and was not inhibited by the presence of deacylated tRNA. A nonenzymic binding of aminoacyl tRNA to rat liver ribosomes occurred at 20 mM MgCl$_2$. This binding was inhibited by deacylated tRNA. Several possibilities were proposed to explain the puromycin stimulatory effect upon binding of aminoacyl tRNA to the ribosomes: (a) the artifactual removal of some of the peptidyl tRNA present at the aminoacyl tRNA site; (b) the binding of aminoacyl tRNA to sites normally occupied by peptidyl tRNA removed by puromycin; and (c) the translocation of some peptidyl tRNA from the aminoacyl tRNA site to the peptidyl tRNA position, making additional aminoacyl tRNA acceptor sites available.

Studies with this liver peptide chain-elongating system indicated that transferase I, GTP, Mg^{++}, and NH$_4^+$ were essential for the binding of aminoacyl tRNA to ribosomes. The GTP analog, GMP=PCP could be substituted for GTP at this stage of protein synthesis indicating that hydrolysis of the terminal phosphate was not necessary for enzymic binding of aminoacyl tRNA. Ertel *et al.* (1968a,b) also replaced GTP with the analog for enzymic binding of phenylalanyl tRNA in a microbial system and suggested the absence of GTP hydrolysis.

Klink *et al.* (1967b) reported the separation of calf liver FI into three peaks of activity with Sephadex G-200 chromatography. Following elution from hydroxylapatite, transferase I derived from rat liver, resolved into three components by Sephadex G-200 filtration (Schneir and Moldave, 1968). Molecular weights of these three forms of transferase I were estimated to be greater than 300,000 for A, 300,000 for B, and 100,000 for C. The molecular weight of rabbit reticulocyte TF-I has been calculated to be 186,000 $\pm$ 5000 (McKeehan *et al.*, 1969).

Preincubation of rat liver transferase II, ribosomes, and GTP with subsequent addition of aminoacyl tRNA, GTP, Mg^{++}, NH_4^+, a sulfhydryl compound, and transferase I resulted in a marked stimulation and increase in the incorporation of aminoacyl tRNA into peptides (Skogerson and Moldave, 1967, 1968a,b,c). They proposed the following sequence of events. A complex is formed between transferase II and the ribosomes in the presence of GTP. This is followed by a "priming of the ribosomes," i.e., translocation of endogenous peptidyl tRNA from aminoacyl to the peptidyl site, thereby making additional sites available for the binding and incorporation of the next aminoacyl tRNA. Thus it would appear that transferase II effects translocation and that peptide bond formation is an inherent property of the ribosomes. Monro *et al.* (1968), working with *Escherichia coli*, reported that the peptidyl transferase is a constituent of the 50 S ribosome. Lipmann (1969) proposed this enzyme must be centered between the donor and acceptor sites in order to catalyze or initiate transfer of the peptidyl moiety from the donor to the amino acceptor on the aminoacyl or acceptor site and that peptide bond formation is dependent upon the proximity of the two tRNA's.

The liver ribosomal–transferase II complex was isolated by a discontinuous sucrose density gradient method (Skogerson and Moldave, 1967, 1968a,b,c). This complex supported amino acid incorporation with transferase I, aminoacyl tRNA, and other components of the transfer reaction without additional transferase II. Generally, binding of transferase II to the ribosomes occurred with GTP or GMP=PCP and a sulfhydryl compound, but required 37°C specifically for translocation. Once transferase II catalyzed translocation, the bound enzyme was removed by sedimenting the ribosomes through a sucrose gradient containing 0.5 M NH_4Cl. Aminoacyl tRNA was then enzymically bound (transferase I) to these "primed" ribosomes with concurrent peptide bond formation in the absence of bound transferase II. Likewise, a peptide bond formed when aminoacyl tRNA was nonenzymically bound to the ribosomes. Peptide bond synthesis also occurred between puromycin and endogenous peptidyl tRNA since the ester carboxy group of the peptidyl tRNA attached to the amino group of puromycin through a peptide linkage (Monro, 1967). Concomitantly, the peptidyl moiety was shifted to the acceptor or aminoacyl site. The addition of ^{3}H-puromycin or aminoacyl tRNA to the system resulted in a decrease in the amount of puromycin-reacting material and a reduction in the number of free binding sites. Clearance of the aminoacyl site, holding the peptidyl moiety, and the peptidyl site with the deacylated tRNA required transferase II to translocate the peptidyl tRNA to the peptidyl site. The mechanism for removal of this deacylated tRNA from the peptidyl site for translocation to be completed is still largely unknown.

Recently, Schneider et al. (1968) presented data confirming the association of rat liver transferase II with translocase activity. Transfer factor T_2, isolated from normal rat liver, and rabbit reticulocytes required a sulfhydryl compound to catalyze polymerization of the phenylalanyl tRNA's bound to the polyuridine-charged ribosomes (Felicetti and Lipmann, 1968) and demonstrated ribosomal linked GTPase activity not influenced by the addition of aminoacyl tRNA. Three transfer factors from rabbit reticulocytes displayed GTPase activity (Hardesty et al., 1967). Further purification of these three proteins revealed TF-I, TF-II, and a nonspecific nucleoside, triphosphate phosphohydrolase, to be linked with a ribosome-dependent GTP hydrolysis (McKeehan et al., 1969). In addition, the GTPase activity of the binding enzyme was dependent upon phenylalanyl tRNA. The FI obtained from calf liver possessed a ribosomal and sulfhydryl-dependent GTPase which was not influenced by added aminoacyl tRNA (Klink et al., 1967b). The reticulocyte system, in contrast to the liver, required TF-2 for peptide bond formation. A dipeptide was established as the first product of the TF-2 giving support to the two-site-binding theory (Arlinghaus et al., 1964). It was speculated from data obtained with the reticulocyte poly U–phenylalanyl tRNA system, that TF-1, in the presence of GTP, bound the phenylalanyl tRNA to the poly U–ribosomal complex. The TF-2 then catalyzed peptide bond synthesis, and TF-1, plus GTP, initiated translocation of the peptidyl tRNA. Shifting of the peptidyl tRNA, now one amino acid longer, provided a free site for the next aminoacyl tRNA. Regardless of how the phenylalanyl tRNA was bound, enzymically or nonenzymically, TF-2 was still needed to catalyze the synthesis of a peptide linkage between the two phenylalanines. During the process of polyphenylalanine elongation, the growing peptide chain always remained attached to a tRNA bound from the incubation mixture (Shaeffer et al., 1968b).

2. Initiation and Release

Components stimulating in vitro initiation of protein synthesis by mammalian systems have not been clearly identified. Thus far, evidence is lacking for the involvement of N-acetyl or N-formyl derivatives of aminoacyl tRNA's in stimulating peptide chain initiation (Marcker and Sanger, 1964; Mosteller et al., 1968b). Valine has been detected as the NH_2-terminal amino acid with a free amino group for most nascent globin peptides (Rahamimoff and Arnstein, 1967), whereas, N-acetyl-serine appeared as the first amino acid in hypophyseal hormones (Harris, 1959; Li, 1959). Several investigators were successful in achieving incorporation of deaminated valine into the NH_2-terminal position of nascent globin chains (Rich et al., 1966; Arnstein and Rahamimoff, 1968). Moreover, initiation of globin synthesis may involve deacylated tRNA (Culp et al., 1968; Mosteller et al., 1968a,b). Such initiation studies with a poly U–phenylalanyl tRNA system showed tRNA^{Phe} to be functional in the initial reaction of polyphenylalanine synthesis. A protein fraction (Fraction I) extracted from reticulocyte ribosomes was required for the de novo synthesis of hemoglobin and was associated with initiation of peptide chains, rather than completion of nascent ones (R. L. Miller and Schweet, 1968). Comparable to the Escherichia coli initiating factors, the poly U-dependent phenylalanine reticulocyte system utilized Fraction I at low Mg^{++} concentrations. Recently, Galper and Darnell (1969) discovered N-formylmethionyl tRNA in HeLa cell cytoplasmic and mitochondria fractions but have not demonstrated a relationship between this species of tRNA and initiation.

Another stage of protein synthesis is concerned with the mechanism by which a completed peptide can be released from the ribosome. Preliminary studies with several mammalian systems have made it evident that the release of a completed protein was an enzymic function requiring GTP, perhaps cyclic adenosine monophosphate (AMP), and a monovalent cation (Hultin, 1962, 1966; Morris, 1963, 1966, 1968; Khairallah and Pitot, 1967). Khairallah and Pitot (1967) presented methods for determining the in vitro release of the nascent proteins from polysomes prepared from rat liver.

In a recent review of protein biosynthesis, Lipmann (1969) has covered several aspects of release including the studies of Scolnick et al. (1968). Their experiments with an E. coli B system linked the release of free f-methionine from the ribosomes with messenger termination triplets, UAA, UAG, or UGA, and a supernatant factor R. The R factor was shown to separate into two components, R_1, specific for codons UAA and UAG, and R_2, specific for codons UAA and UGA.

3. Function of GTP, SH, etc.

a. *Guanosine Triphosphate.* A unique characteristic of protein synthesis has been the specific requirement for GTP. This nucleoside triphosphate participates in the following intermediates of mammalian *in vitro* protein synthesis:

1. Although an initiation mechanism has not been established for mammalian systems, GTP was required in the initiation sequence of poly U-directed phenylalanine synthesis for microbial systems (Lucas-Lenard and Lipmann, 1967).

2. It enhanced inactivation of the binding enzyme in the absence of aminoacyl tRNA (Ibuki *et al.*, 1966; Ibuki and Moldave, 1968a; McKeehan *et al.*, 1969).

3. It stimulated enzymic binding of the protein–aminoacyl tRNA complex to the ribosomes (Hardesty *et al.*, 1963; Arlinghaus *et al.*, 1964; Ibuki and Moldave, 1968a,b; Shaeffer *et al.*, 1968a).

4. It was required after the initial binding of aminoacyl tRNA to the ribosomes but prior to peptide bond synthesis (Skogerson and Moldave, 1968a,b,c).

5. It stimulated binding of liver transferase II, in the presence of a sulfhydryl compound, to the ribosomes (Skogerson and Moldave, 1967, 1968b,c).

6. It was found in translocation (Skogerson and Moldave, 1968a,b,c).

7. It was necessary for release mechanism (Hultin, 1962, 1966; Khairallah and Pitot, 1967; Morris, 1963, 1966, 1968).

Skogerson and Moldave have noted that hydrolysis of GTP to guanosine diphosphate (GDP) and inorganic phosphate did not take place during binding since the GTP analog was able to displace the GTP requirement. The analog, however, could not be substituted for GTP prior to peptide bond formation or translocation and was suggestive of GTP hydrolysis. Both transfer enzymes presently have been associated with a ribosomal-dependent GTPase activity, specific for GTP (Hardesty *et al.*, 1963; 1967; Arlinghaus *et al.*, 1964; Klink *et al.*, 1967a,b; Felicetti and Lipmann, 1968; McKeehan *et al.*, 1969).

b. *Sulfhydryl Compounds.* These are involved in protein synthesis. Studies conducted with mammalian reticulocyte and liver systems showed the sulfhydryl compounds to aid in activation and protection of the TF-2 or transferase II enzyme (Sutter and Moldave, 1966; Arlinghaus *et al.*, 1968a; Felicetti and Lipmann, 1968) rather than having a more direct function in the synthesizing mechanism.

c. *Cations.* Incorporation of amino acids into hemoglobin or phenylalanyl tRNA into polyphenylalanine by a rabbit reticulocyte system required Mg^{++} (1.5–6.7 mM) and K^+ (67–100 mM) as the monovalent ion (Allen and Schweet, 1962; Arlinghaus et al., 1968a; Shaeffer et al., 1968a). The NH_4^+ optimum for overall amino acid incorporation by a rat liver system was approximately 80 mM. Enzymic binding of aminoacyl tRNA to the ribosomes did not occur at NH_4^+ concentrations above 60 mM, but a greater need for NH_4^+ appeared during peptide bond synthesis between peptidyl tRNA and the newly bound aminoacyl tRNA. Skogerson and Moldave (1968a) have correlated this NH_4^+ requirement with activation of the ribosomal peptidyl synthetase. Both Mg^{++} and NH_4^+ also were involved in the incorporation of puromycin into peptide linkage with endogenous tRNA. In the tumor-incorporating system, NH_4^+ (100–150 mM) seemed to be more effective than K^+, or Na^+ cations (A. C. Griffin et al., 1968).

Binding of aminoacyl tRNA to ribosomes containing either endogenous mRNA or synthetic polyribonucleotides has been described as being enzymic or nonenzymic, depending upon the Mg^{++} concentration (Arlinghaus et al., 1964; Shaeffer et al., 1968a; Ibuki and Moldave, 1968b). At low levels of Mg^{++}, 6.7 mM for reticulocytes, and 6.0 mM for liver, the protein-aminoacyl tRNA complex, along with NH_4^+ or K^+, and GTP was bound to the ribosomes. In the presence of increased Mg^{++} (10–20 mM) aminoacyl tRNA binding to the ribosomes proceeded without enzyme or GTP. The high Mg^{++} concentrations may induce conformational changes of the ribosomes, thereby exposing the proper sites essential for binding (Skogerson and Moldave, 1968c; Shaeffer et al., 1968a).

4. Specificity

As reported by several laboratories, aminoacyl tRNA's from various microbial, yeast, and mammalian sources are interchangeable in the transfer of amino acids to the ribosomes (Nathans and Lipmann, 1960, 1961; Rendi and Ochoa, 1962; Bloemendal et al., 1964; Canning and Griffin, 1965). It was proposed that a limited degree of species specificity existed between the transfer enzymes that catalyzed the transfer of aminoacyl tRNA to the ribosomes with subsequent peptide bond formation. Meanwhile, the methods for isolation and purification of these transfer enzymes and ribosomes were refined so that it became possible to cross-react these factors from various mammalian sources. Felicetti and Lipmann (1968), employing the method of Arlinghaus et al. (1968a,b), prepared the protein-synthesizing components from rat liver and rabbit reticulocytes. In contrast to the reticulocyte system, it was more difficult to obtain liver ribosomes with low inherent GTPase activity. The liver and reticulocyte transfer factors, T_1 and T_2, were completely interchangeable in a polyuridine–phenylalanine polymerizing system. The reticulocyte ribosomes also interacted with the liver transfer enzymes in executing peptide chain elongation.

Complementary transfer enzymes and purified ribosomes were isolated in this laboratory from Novikoff ascites tumor cells and rabbit reticulocytes according to the method of Arlinghaus et al. (1968a,b). The reticulocyte ribosomes (DOC–DEAE ribosomes), prepared as described in Section II,A,*1,a*, were active for amino acid incorporation, but did not maintain full activity following the 0.5 M NH_4Cl washing (Section II,*A,1,a*). However, the reticulocyte ribosomes (DOC–DEAE) incorporated ^{14}C-aminoacyl tRNA's into hot TCA-insoluble material with either the reticulocyte or tumor transfer enzymes as noted in Table VII. The two factors from each source were complementary and completely interchangeable.

Similarly, as illustrated by Table I, cross-complementation also occurred between these same factors and tumor ribosomes. In order to achieve this complementary effect, it became necessary to wash the

TABLE VII

INTERCHANGEABILITY BETWEEN TUMOR AND RETICULOCYTE TRANSFER ENZYMES[a, b]

Reticulocyte ribosomes	Transfer enzymes	counts/min
Deoxycholate–diethylaminoethyl	None	70
	Retic. T_1	130
	Retic. T_2	109
	Retic. $T_1 + T_2$	915
	Tumor $(NH_4)_2SO_4$	1020
	Tumor T_1 $(Ca_3(PO_4)_2)$	542
	Tumor T_2 $(Ca_3(PO_4)_2)$	148
	Tumor $T_1 + T_2$	1020
	Retic. $T_1 +$ Tumor T_2	737
	Retic. $T_2 +$ Tumor T_1	1844

[a] Basic system: 0.05 ml ribosomes (220 μg ribosomal protein), tumor $(NH_4)_2SO_4$ (64 μg), retic. T_1 (38 μg), retic. T_2 (33 μg), tumor T_1 (15 μg), tumor T_2 (7.4 μg), 0.01 ml amino acid mixture ^{14}C-transfer ribonucleic acid (approximately 7000 counts). The amounts of other components in the total assay system of 0.1 ml and incubating procedure are described in the legend of Table I. (DOC) Deoxycholate–glycylglycine, pH 8.0; (DEAE) DEAE–cellulose; (Retic.) reticulocyte.

[b] Protein concentrations were determined from the Warburg and Christian nomograph (1941–1942).

tumor DOC–DEAE ribosomes with 0.5 M NH_4Cl. Otherwise, the transfer enzymes remained tightly bound to the tumor ribosomes, making it impossible to show any complementation between the transfer factors. As indicated for rat liver, it was very difficult to remove these proteins from the tumor ribosomes without destroying incorporating activity.

Krisko *et al.* (1969) compared the interchangeability of the transfer factors and ribosomes, derived from liver, tumor, and microbial sources (Table VIII). Generally, they observed that microbial T

TABLE VIII

INTERCHANGEABILITY OF TRANSFER ENZYMES AND RIBOSOMES FROM TUMOR CELLS, RETICULOCYTES, AND *Escherichia coli*[a]

Ribosomes	Transfer factors			Phenylalanine polymerized (pmoles)
	Tumor	Reticulocyte	E. coli	
Tumor				0.7
	T_2			0.6
	T_1			5.0
	$T_1 + T_2$			4.9
	$(NH_4)_2SO_4Fr$			5.1
		T		4.7
Reticulocyte		T_1		0.2
		T_2		0.1
		$T_1 + T_2$		2.5
		T_2	T	2.4
		T_1	G	0.2
			T + G	0.1
E. coli			T	<0.1
			G	<0.1
			T + G	6.4
		T_2	T	0.2
		T_1	G	0.3
		$T_1 + T_2$		0.3

[a] Condensed and reprinted with permission of Krisko *et al.* (1969).

($T_u + T_s$) could be substituted for mammalian T_1 when assayed with mammalian ribosomes, but microbial G did not replace mammalian T_2. In the same manner, mammalian T_1 and T_2 were tested for binding and complementation with microbial ribosomes. However, mammalian T_1 would not bind aminoacyl tRNA to these ribosomes.

IV. Mechanism of Protein Synthesis

The ribosomal–polysomal mechanism of protein synthesis appears to be a generally universal one. As indicated, there are species differences in terms of ribosomal structure, aminoacyl synthetases, transfer RNA's and in transfer enzymes. However, the general sequence of events, involvement of aminoacyl tRNA's, two or more specific transfer enzymes, GTP, etc., appear to be quite similar for all of the microbial and mammalian cells that have been studied thus far. The complete cycle of events in protein synthesis, as illustrated by Watson (1965), Crick (1966), Lipmann (1969), and many other investigators, includes the following events (see also Fig. 1):

1. *Chain initiation* begins with the binding of mRNA to ribosomes (30 S) and attachment of a specific aminoacyl tRNA to the ribosome and with the first mRNA codon. N-Formyl methionyl tRNA has been shown by Marcker and Sanger (1964) to be the initiator with AUG as the first codon (5'-terminal of the mRNA). Although f-methionine appears to be the initiator amino acid for proteins of *Escherichia coli* and other microbial cells, the initiator tRNA for mammalian cells has not been established. Three factors, F_1, F_2, F_3, and GTP are required for the initiation steps (Rudland *et al.*, 1969).

2. *Elongation*—the peptidyl chain grows by the stepwise addition of amino acids through a four-stage cycle (Lipmann, 1969). In the starting phase the donor site (peptidyl- or protein-binding site) is occupied by a peptidyl or aminoacyl tRNA. The acceptor site becomes occupied by an oncoming aminoacyl tRNA the anticodon of which matches the next codon's triplet on the mRNA. This binding is facilitated by factor T and GTP. Peptidyl transfer occurs, the free tRNA remains on the donor site on the ribosome, and the newly formed peptidyl tRNA on the acceptor site. Peptidyl transfer activity appears to be an inherent function of the 50 S ribosome subunit. Factor G and GTP promotes the displacement of the free tRNA from the donor site and the transfer of the extended peptidyl tRNA to this site. There is a simultaneous movement of the mRNA in order that the next codon will be at the now vacant acceptor site for the oncoming aminoacyl tRNA.

3. *Termination*—the growing peptide chain remains on the same ribosome until the termination codon on the mRNA is reached (3' terminal of the mRNA). Codons UAA, UAG, and UGA are concerned with termination and release. The completed protein is released from the tRNA by a mechanism that is not completely understood. Supernatant factors apparently are involved in the termination events.

Protein Synthesis in Cancer Cells

There are no conclusive findings that would indicate that the mechanism of protein synthesis in cancer cells differs in any fundamental aspect from that presented above. The possibility does exist that specific components within cancer cells may be altered. At this time, the tRNA's would appear to be the most likely components altered. It has been demonstrated that there is interchangeability of ribosome T_1 and T_2, from Novikoff ascites tumor cells, normal liver, and reticulocytes, in the incorporation of aminoacyl tRNA's into acid-insoluble forms. Krisko et al. (1969) recently reported that the binding of phenylalanyl tRNA to poly U-charged Novikoff tumor and rabbit reticulocyte ribosomes was stimulated similarly by Escherichia coli transfer factor T and by a tumor supernatant fraction. In addition, the bacterial T catalyzed amino acid polymerization in both mammalian systems in the presence of mammalian T_2. However, bacterial G would not replace mammalian T_2. With E. coli ribosomes, it was found that reticulocyte T_1 could not be substituted for bacterial T. These findings do indicate the possibility of species differences in certain of the major components of protein synthesis. However, the tumor cell system, in this case at least, behaved similarly to other mammalian systems. Webb et al. (1964) in studying the polysomal patterns of several liver tumors concluded that the small abberations that were observed were not related to changes essential to the neoplastic process.

The above findings only indicate that the same general mechanisms are operative in the biosynthesis of proteins by the polysomal systems of all cellular types. Most of these studies were conducted with the highly artifactual in vitro systems outside of the control mechanisms inherent in the cell and the body. Subtle structural alterations reflecting changes associated with malignant tumor cell transformation or behavior may not be apparent in the in vitro systems employed for the study of protein synthesis. Further refined methodology will be required to ascertain if the ribosomes, tRNA's or accessory enzymes involved in protein synthesis do differ in cancer cells.

Many specific areas of protein synthesis in normal mammalian cells and in cancer cells will require further extensive study. Some of these areas include:

a. Mechanisms of chain initiation and release. From studies carried out in this laboratory, there is little indication of release of completed polypeptide chains employing liver or tumor in vitro amino acid-incorporating systems; approximately 80% of the incorporated radioactivity, determined by hot TCA insolubility, remained on the polysomes.

b. Removal of inherent mRNA and acceptance of new mRNAs. It is possible to remove, or at least to decrease, the inherent mRNA's from mammalian ribosomes by preparative and preincubation techniques. However, these ribosomes have a limited capacity to accept new mRNA. Addition of poly U to these ribosomes will stimulate the incorporation of phenylalanyl tRNA but only to a limited extent. The development of new methods for the removal of inherent or bound mRNA from ribosomes as well as techniques for the acceptance of new mRNA's from viral and other sources will be of immeasurable help in these studies.

c. Chain elongation. Employing the ascites tumor cell-incorporating system, it was shown that chain elongation during the *in vitro* incubation period is limited. Analysis of the labeled polypeptides obtained from these studies indicated that the C-terminal amino acid corresponding to the last incorporated aminoacyl tRNA accounted for approximately 80% of the total incorporated radioactivity. These findings suggest that the preexisting polypeptide chains added a single amino acid. Further studies are required to determine the reasons for the limited chain elongation in this polysomal system.

d. Amino acid incorporation assay procedures. In most of the *in vitro* studies reported in the literature, "incorporation" is based upon radioactivity present in hot TCA-insoluble fractions. However, certain investigators have based their incorporation data upon procedures that used TCA to stop the reaction, addition of 1 N NaOH to hydrolyze aminoacyl tRNA and dissolve the precipitate, followed by acidification to reprecipitate the polypeptides and proteins prior to counting. Some studies are also based on ribosomal-bound radioactivity. Accordingly, there may be some doubt as to what actually is being measured in the *in vitro* incorporating systems. The procedures of Lucas-Lenard and Haenni (1968) may be used to characterize the products formed by the binding, peptidization, or chain elongation reactions employing ^{14}C-phenylalanine tRNA and polyuridine in *in vitro* systems. Following the incubation period the mixture was chilled, the ribosomes pelleted, hydrolyzed, and subjected to descending chromatography in butanol–ammonium hydroxide. The radioactivity of the strips was analyzed in a radiochromatogram scanner and the counts correlated with spots on the paper corresponding to phenylalanine, diphenylalanine, or triphenylalanine. As indicated above, it is quite possible that in many of the mammalian *in vitro* systems "protein synthesis" or "incorporation" may be restricted to the elongation of existing polypeptide chains by a single amino acid. Some further consideration of the methods and terminology employed in the study of protein biosynthesis, especially in the mammalian systems would be desirable.

e. Compositional and functional aspects of ribosomes isolated from normal mammalian cells and from cancer cells.

f. Finally, the artifactual nature of the mammalian amino acid-incorporating systems should be fully realized. These systems polymerize less than 1% of the potential amino acids that are incorporated into proteins by comparable intact cellular systems. The *in vitro* systems are not subjected to the organizational and regulatory elements present in the living system. A better understanding of these complex mechanisms that exist in the intact cells or groups of cells may provide new insight into the many problems related to cancer. Hoagland's analysis of some of the complexities of protein synthesis is worthy of the most serious consideration: "Indeed, we are now becoming aware that the simplified systems we study in the test tube are but sad reflections of intracellular capabilities. The triumph of mechanistic universality may in fact result from too assiduous efforts to discard those elements of the machinery which contribute to diversity" (Hoagland, 1969).

V. Conclusions

Methods have been presented for the preparation of the components involved in the biosynthesis of polypeptides. The *in vitro* systems described include: reticulocyte, rat liver, certain human tissues, and mouse ascites leukemia and Novikoff ascites tumor cells. Reconstitution of these components under suitable *in vitro* conditions results in the incorporation of labeled amino acids, usually determined by the radioactivity present in the insoluble fraction following treatment with hot TCA. Although this incorporation represents an extremely small percentage of the intracellular capacity, it has been possible to utilize these systems to obtain some understanding of the components and of the events involved in protein biosynthesis. From these studies, an overall mechanism has evolved for nucleic acid-directed protein synthesis. This polysomal system appears to be generally universal, and cancer cells, as indicated by studies with the above tumor cell systems, do not differ from other cellular systems in this respect.

There are many subtleties in the methodology required to isolate and purify the components of the *in vitro* incorporating systems from different mammalian tissues or cells. Most of the components (ribosomes, transfer enzymes, tRNA's, aminoacyl synthetases) required for protein synthesis are interchangeable indicating that there is a low degree of specificity at this level. It is also of interest that several of the components of microbial systems also may be utilized in mammalian systems. It would appear at this time that the most likely components to undergo alteration or change during malignant tumor cell transformation are the tRNA's or possibly the aminoacyl synthetases. With new and improved methodology, it is now possible to characterize the tRNA's and ascertain changes that may be related to the origin of or subsequent behavior of the cancer cell.

Although the findings to date would suggest that cancer cells are not unique in terms of the generalized mechanism of protein biosynthesis, further detailed studies may change this picture. Polypeptide chain initiation and release, chain elongation, removal of inherent mRNA, and acceptance of new messenger are poorly understood in mammalian incorporating systems. In addition, it is quite possible that subtle changes in structures of the ribosomes or accessory components have occurred so that they do not respond to the usual cellular control mechanisms. Such changes would not be apparent in the above *in vitro* studies.

The highly artifactual nature of the *in vitro* systems also must be considered. Emphasis should be given to the low degree of incorporation observed in these systems and to the fact that the essential elements of organization and control present in intact cells have been completely disrupted or eliminated. Refinements in methods of preparation and study of the *in vitro* components may reveal structural or other differences in components obtained from normal and cancer cells. Perhaps of greater importance will be the development of methods and procedures to obtain a greater insight into protein synthesis within the intact cell.

REFERENCES*

Allen, E. H., and Schweet, R. S. (1962). *J. Biol. Chem.* **237**, 760.

Allende, C. C., and Allende, J. E. (1964). *J. Biol. Chem.* **239**, 1102.

Allende, C. C., Allende, J. E., Gatica, M., Celis, J., Mora, G., and Matamala, M. (1966). *J. Biol. Chem.* **241**, 2245.

Allende, J. E., Monro, R., and Lipmann, F. (1964). *Proc. Natl. Acad. Sci. U.S.* **51**, 1211.

Alvino, C. G., and Clarke, H. T. (1968). *Federation Proc.* **27**, 342.

Apgar, J., Holley, R. W., and Merrill, S. H. (1962). *J. Biol. Chem.* **237**, 796.

Arlinghaus, R., and Schweet, R. (1962). *Biochem. Biophys. Res. Commun.* **9**, 482

Arlinghaus, R., Favelukes, G., and Schweet, R. (1963). *Biochem. Biophys. Res. Commun.* **11**, 92.

Arlinghaus, R., Shaeffer, J., and Schweet, R. (1964). *Proc. Natl. Acad. Sci. U.S.* **51**, 1291.

---

* The reader's attention is called to "The Mechanism of *Protein* Synthesis." *Cold Spring Harbor Symp. Quant. Biol.* **34** (1969). This volume covers many of the most recent findings related to the components and mechanisms reported in this chapter.

Arlinghaus, R., Shaeffer, J., Bishop, J., and Schweet, R. (1968a). *Arch. Biochem. Biophys.* **125**, 604.

Arlinghaus, R., Heintz, R., and Schweet, R. (1968b). *Methods Enzymol.* **12**, 700–708.

Arnstein, H. R. V., Cox, R. A., and Hunt, J. A. (1962). *Nature* **194**, 1042.

Arnstein, H. R. V., and Rahamimoff, H. (1968). *Nature* **219**, 942.

Axel, R., Weinstein, I. B., and Farber, E. (1967). *Proc. Natl. Acad. Sci. U.S.* **58**, 1255.

Ayuso, M., and Heredia, C. F. (1967). *Biochim. Biophys. Acta* **145**, 199.

Baldwin, A. N., and Berg, P. (1966). *J. Biol. Chem.* **241**, 831.

Baliga, B. S., Srinivasan, P. R., and Borek, E. (1968). *Federation Proc.* **27**, 794.

Baliga, B., Borek, E., Weinstein, I. B., and Srinivasan, P. R. (1969). *Proc. Natl. Acad. Sci U.S.* **62**, 899.

Bayev, A. A., Venkstern, T. V., Mirzabekov, A. D., Krutilina, A. I., Axelrod, V. A., Li, L., and Engelhardt, V. A. (1967). *In* "Genetic Elements: Properties and Function" (D. Shugar, ed.), pp. 287–301. Academic Press, New York.

Bergquist, P. L., Baguley, B. C., Robertson, J. M., and Ralph, R. K. (1965). *Biochim. Biophys. Acta* **108**, 531.

Bermek, E. (1969). *Proc. F. E. B. S., Madrid, Spain.*

Bishop, J., and Schweet, R. (1961). *Biochim. Biophys. Acta* **54**, 617.

Bloemendal, H., Bont, W. S., and Bosch, L. (1964). *Cancer Res.* **24**, 994.

Brewer, C. B., Davies, M. C., and Florini, J. R. (1964). *Biochemistry* **3**, 1713.

Brunngraber, E. F. (1962). *Biochem. Biophys. Res. Commun.* **8**, 1.

Calendar, R., and Berg, P. (1966). *Biochemistry* **5**, 1681.

Campbell, P. N., and Greengard, O. (1959). *J. Biol. Chem.* **71**, 148.

Canning, L., and Griffin, A. C. (1965). *Biochim. Biophys. Acta* **103**, 522.

Capra, J. D., and Peterkofsky, A. (1968). *J. Mol. Biol.* **33**, 591.

Conway, T. W., Lansford, E. M., Jr., and Shive, W. (1962). *J. Biol. Chem.* **237**, 2850.

Crick, F. H. C. (1966). *Sci. Am.* **215**, 55.

Culp, W. J., Mosteller, R. D., and Hardesty, B. (1968). *Arch. Biochem. Biophys.* **125**, 658.

Davis, C. H., Schliselfeld, L. H., Wolf, D. P., Leavitt, C. A., and Krebs, E. G. (1967). *J. Biol. Chem.* **242**, 4824.

Deutcher, M. P. (1967). *J. Biol. Chem.* **242**, 1123.

Doctor, B. P., Loebel, J. E., Sodd, M. A., and Winter, D. B. (1969). *Science* **163**, 693.

Doi, R. H., and Kaneko, I. (1966). *Cold Spring Harbor Symp. Quant. Biol.* **31**, 581.

Dube, S. K., Marcker, K. A., Clark, B. F. C., and Cory, S. (1968). *Nature* **218**, 232.

Dudock, B. S., Katz, G., Taylor, E. K., and Holley, R. W. (1969). *Biochemistry* **62**, 941.

Ertel, R., Brot, N., Redfield, B., Allende, J. E., and Weissbach, H. (1968a). *Proc. Natl. Acad. Sci. U.S.* **59**, 861.

Ertel, R., Redfield, B., Brot, N., and Weissbach, H. (1968b). *Arch. Biochem. Biophys.* **128**, 331.

Farber, E., McConomy, J., Franzen, B., Marroquin, F., Stewart, G. A., and Magee, P. N. (1967). *Cancer Res.* **27**, 1761.

Felicetti, L., and Lipmann, F. (1968). *Arch. Biochem. Biophys.* **125**, 548.

Fessenden, J. M., and Moldave, K. (1963). *J. Biol. Chem.* **238**, 1479.

Fessenden, J. M., Cairneros, J., and Moldave, K. (1963). *Proc. Natl. Acad. Sci. U.S.* **49**, 82.

Fresco, J. R., Blake, R. D., and Langridge, R. (1968). *Nature* **220**, 1285.

Galper, J. B., and Darnell, S. F. (1969). *Biochem. Biophys. Res. Commun.* **34**, 205.

Gardner, R. S., Wahba, A. J., Basilio, C., Miller, R. S., Lengyel, P., and Speyer, J. F. (1962). *Proc. Natl. Acad. Sci. U.S.* **48**, 2087.

Gasior, E., and Moldave, K. (1965). *J. Biol. Chem.* **240**, 3346.

Gassen, H. G., and Uziel, M. (1969). *Proc. F. E. B. S.*, Madrid, Spain.

Gillam, I., Millward, S., Blew, D. von Tigerstrom, M., Wimmer, E., and Tener, G. M. (1967). *Biochemistry* **6**, 3043.

Goldman, M., Johnston, W. M., and Griffin, A. C. (1969). *Cancer Res.* **29**, 1051.

Goodman, H. M., Abelson, J. N., Landy, A., Brenner, S., and Smith, J. D. (1968). *Nature* **217**, 1019.

Goodwin, F., Shafritz, D., and Weissbach, H. (1969). *Arch. Biochem. Biophys.* **130**, 183.

Gordon, J. (1968). *Proc. Natl. Acad. Sci. U.S.* **59**, 179.

Grau, O., and Favelukes, G. (1968). *Arch. Biochem. Biophys.* **125**, 647.

Griffin, A. C. (1967). *Advan. Cancer Res.* **10**, 83–116.

Griffin, A. C., Canning, L., Holland, B., and Malick, B. (1965). *Cancer Res.* **25**, 318.

Griffin, A. C. (1970). *Advan. Enzyme Regulation* **7**, pp. 361-374 (in press).

Griffin, A. C., Holland, B. H., and Darré, D. L. (1968). *Cancer Res.* **28**, 636.

Griffin, B. E., Haines, J. A., and Reese, C. B. (1967). *Biochim. Biophys. Acta* **142**, 536.

Gros, F., and Matthaei, H. (1968). *In* "Cell Free Protein Synthesis." Max-Planck Inst. Exptl. Medi., Göttingen, Germany.

Hampel, A., Labanauskas, M., Connors, P. G., Kirkegaard, L., RajBhaandary, U. L., Sigler, P. B., and Bock, R. M. (1968). *Science* **162**, 1384.

Hancock, R. L. (1968). *Cancer Res.* **28**, 1223.

Hardesty, B., Arlinghaus, R., Shaeffer, J., and Schweet, R. (1963). *Cold Spring Harbor Symp. Quant. Biol.* **28**, 215.

Hardesty, B., Lin, S., and Culp, W. (1967). *Federation Proc.* **26**, 611.

Harris, J. I. (1959). *Biochem. J.* **71**, 451.

Heredia, C. F., and Halvorson, H. O. (1966). *Biochemistry* **5**, 946.

Hoagland, M. B. (1969). "Symposium, Polypeptides." Sponsored by Miles Laboratories, Inc., New York.

Hoagland, M. B., Scornik, O. A., and Pfefferkorn, L. C. (1964). *Proc. Natl. Acad. Sci. U.S.* **51**, 1184.

Holland, J. J., Taylor, M. W., and Buck, C. A. (1967). *Proc. Natl. Acad. Sci. U.S.* **58**, 2437.

Holley, R. W., Apgar, J., Everett, G. A., Madison, J. T., Marquisee, M., Merrill, S. H., Penswick, J. R., and Zamir, A. (1965). *Science* **147**, 1462.

Hollis, V. W., and Furano, A. V. (1968). *J. Biol. Chem.* **243**, 4926.

Hultin, T. (1962). *Biochim. Biophys. Acta* **61**, 916.

Hultin, T. (1966). *Biochim. Biophys. Acta* **123**, 561.

Ibuki, F., and Moldave, K. (1968a). *J. Biol. Chem.* **243**, 44.

Ibuki, F., and Moldave, K. (1968b). *J. Biol. Chem.* **243**, 794.

Ibuki, F., Gasior, E., and Moldave, K. (1966). *J. Biol. Chem.* **241**, 2188.

Ikegami, H., and Griffin, A. C. (1969). *Biochim. Biophys. Acta* **178**, 166.

Johnson, W., Kuchler, R., and Solotorousky, M. (1968). *J. Bacteriol.* **96**, 1089.

248   A. CLARK GRIFFIN AND DIANNE D. BLACK

Keller, E. B., and Ferger, M. F. (1965). *Federation Proc.* **24**, 283.

Keller, E. B., and Zamecnik, P. C. (1956). *J. Biol. Chem.* **221**, 45.

Keller, P. J., Cohen, E., and Wade, R. (1963). *Biochemistry* **2**, 315.

Khairallah, E. A., and Pitot, H. C. (1967). *Biochem. Biophys. Res. Commun.* **29**, 269.

Kim, S. H., and Rich, A. (1968). *Science* **162**, 1381.

Kirsch, J. F., Siekevitz, P., and Palade, G. E. (1960). *J. Biol. Chem.* **235**, 1419.

Kleinkauf, H., Gevers, W., and Lipmann, F. (1969). *Proc. Natl. Acad. Sci. U.S.* **62**, 226.

Klink, F., Kramer, G., Nour, A. M., and Petersen, K. C. (1967a). *Biochim. Biophys. Acta* **134**, 360.

Klink, F., Kloppstech, K., Kramer, G., and Dimigen, J. (1967b). *Biochim. Biophys. Acta* **134**, 373.

Krisko, I., Gordon, J., and Lipmann, F. (1969). *J. Biol. Chem.* **244**, 6117.

Lagerkvist, U., and Waldenström, J. (1967). *J. Biol. Chem.* **242**, 3021.

Leahy, J., Glassman, E., and Schweet, R. (1960). *J. Biol. Chem.* **235**, 3209.

Lemine, F., Waller, J. P., and Van Rapenbusch, R. (1968). *European J. Biochem.* **4**, 213.

Li, C. H. (1959). *Lab. Invest.* **8**, 574.

Lipmann, F. (1969). *Science* **164**, 1024.

Littlefield, J. W., and Keller, E. B. (1957). *J. Biol. Chem.* **224**, 13.

Lucas-Lenard, J., and Lipman, F. (1966). *Proc. Natl. Acad. Sci. U.S.* **55**, 1562.

Lucas-Lenard, J., and Lipmann, F. (1967). *Proc. Natl. Acad. Sci. U.S.* **57**, 1050.

Lucas-Lenard, J., and Haenni, A. L. (1968). *Proc. Natl. Acad. Sci. U.S.* **59**, 554.

Mach, B., Koblet, H., and Gross, D. (1968). *Proc. Natl. Acad. Sci. U.S.* **59**, 445.

McKeehan, W., Sepulveda, P., Lin, S-Y., and Hardesty, B. (1969). *Biochem. Biophys. Res. Commun.* **34**, 668.

McLean, J. R., Cohn, G. L., Brandt, I. K., and Simpson, M. V. (1958). *J. Biol. Chem.* **233**, 657.

Madison, J. T., and Dickman, S. R. (1963a). *Biochemistry* **2**, 321.

Madison, J. T., and Dickman, S. R. (1963b). *Biochemistry* **2**, 326.

Madison, J. T., Everett, G. A., and Kung, H. (1966). *Science* **153**, 531.

Magee, P. N., Craddock, V. M., and Swvann, P. F. (1967). *In* "Carcinogenesis: A Broad Critique," pp. 421–439. Williams & Wilkins, Baltimore, Maryland.

Maggio, R. (1966). *Biochim. Biophys. Acta* **119**, 641.

Mahler, H. R., and Brown. B. J. (1968). *Arch. Biochem. Biophys.* **125**, 387.

Mandell, J. D., and Hershey, A. D. (1960). *Anal. Biochem.* **1**, 66.

Marcker, K., and Sanger, S. (1964). *J. Mol. Biol.* **8**, 835.

Maxwell, E. S. (1962). *Proc. Natl. Acad. Sci. U.S.* **48**, 1639.

Means, A. R., Hall, P. F., Nicol, L. W., Sawyer, W. H., and Baker, C. A. (1969). *Biochemistry* **8**, 1488.

Miller, J. A., and Miller, E. C. (1967). *In* "Carcinogenesis: A Broad Critique," pp. 387–420. Williams & Wilkins, Baltimore, Maryland.

Miller, R. L., and Schweet, R. (1968). *Arch. Biochem. Biophys.* **125**, 632.

Mitra, S. K., and Mehler, A. H. (1967). *J. Biol. Chem.* **242**, 5490.

Moldave, K. (1960). *J. Biol. Chem.* **235**, 2365.

Moldave, K. (1967). *Methods Enzymol.* **12**, 478–481 and 598–601.

Moldave, K. (1968). *Methods Enzymol.* **12**, 721–725.

Monro, R. E. (1967). *J. Mol. Biol.* **26**, 147.

Monro, R. E., Cerna, J., and Marcker, K. A. (1968). *Proc. Natl. Acad. Sci. U.S.* **61**, 1042.

Morris, A. J. (1963). *Biochim. Biophys. Acta* **11**, 201.
Morris, A. J. (1966). *Biochim. Biophys. Acta* **22**, 498.
Morris, A. J. (1968). *Methods Enzymol.* **12**, 831–837.
Mosteller, R. D., Culp, W. J., and Hardesty, B. (1968a). *Biochem. Biophys. Res. Commun.* **30**, 631.
Mosteller, R. D., Culp, W. J., and Hardesty, B. (1968b). *J. Biol. Chem.* **243**, 6343.
Muench, K. H., and Berg, P. (1966a). *Biochemistry* **5**, 970.
Muench, K. H., and Berg, P. (1966b). *Biochemistry* **5**, 982.
Nathans, D., and Lipmann, F. (1960). *Biochim. Biophys. Acta* **43**, 126.
Nathans, D., and Lipmann, F. (1961). *Proc. Natl. Acad. Sci. U.S.* **47**, 497.
Neth, V. R., Heller, G., and Matthaei, H. (1968). *Z. Physiol. Chem.* **349**, 1514.
Nishizuka, Y., and Lipmann, F. (1966a). *Proc. Natl. Acad. Sci. U.S.* **55**, 212.
Nishizuka, Y., and Lipmann, F. (1966b). *Arch. Biochem. Biophys.* **116**, 344.
Novikoff, A. B. (1957). *Cancer Res.* **17**, 1010.
Ochoa, M., and Weinstein, I. B. (1964). *J. Biol. Chem.* **239**, 3834.
Parmeggiani, A. (1968). *Biochem. Biophys. Res. Commun.* **30**, 613.
Pearson, R. L., and Kelmers, A. D. (1966). *J. Biol. Chem.* **241**, 767.
Penman, S., Scherrer, K., Becker, Y., and Darnell, J. E. (1963). *Proc. Natl. Acad. Sci. U.S.* **49**, 647.
Penswick, J. R., and Holley, R. (1965). *Proc. Natl. Acad. Sci. U.S.* **53**, 543.
Poirier, L. A., Miller, J. A., Miller, E. C., and Sato, K. (1967). *Cancer Res.* **27**, 1600.
Rahamimoff, H., and Arnstein, H. R. V. (1967). *Proc. 7th Intern. Congr. Biochem. IUB, Tokyo,* **4**, p. 698.
RajBhandary, U. L., Chang, S. H., Stuart, A., Faulkner, R. D., Hoskinson, R. M., and Khorana, H. G. (1967). *Proc. Natl. Acad. Sci. U.S.* **57**, 751.
Rao, P., and Moldave, K. (1967). *Biochem. Biophys. Res. Commun.* **28**, 909.
Ravel, J., Shorey, R. L., Froenher, S., and Shive, W. (1968). *Arch. Biochem. Biophys.* **125**, 514.
Reeves, R. H., Imara, N., Schwam, H., Weiss, G. B., Schulman, L. H., and Chambers, R. W. (1968). *Proc. Natl. Acad. Sci. U.S.* **60**, 1450.
Rendi, R., and Ochoa, S. (1962). *J. Biol. Chem.* **237**, 3707.
Rendi, R., and Warner, R. C. (1960). *Ann. N. Y. Acad. Sci.* **88**, 741.
Rich, A. (1967). *Methods Enzymol.* **12**, 481–491.
Rich, A., Eikenberry, E., and Malkin, L. (1966). *Cold Spring Harbor Symp. Quant. Biol.* **31**, 303.
Richter, D., and Klink, F. (1967). *Biochemistry* **6**, 3569.
Rosen, L., Murray, E. L., and Novelli, G. D. (1967). *Can. J. Biochem.* **45**, 2005.
Rudland, P. S., Whybrow, W. A., Marcker, K. A., and Clark, B. F. C. (1969). *Nature* **222**, 750.
Salas, M., Smith, M. A., Windell, S. M., Wahba, A. J., and Ochoa, S. (1965). *J. Biol. Chem.* **240**, 3988.
Schneider, J. A., Raeburn, S., and Maxwell, E. S. (1968). *Biochem. Biophys. Res. Commun.* **33**, 177.
Schneir, M., and Moldave, K. (1968). *Biochim. Biophys. Acta* **166**, 58.
Schöch, G., and Matthaei, H. (1970). *Z. Physiol. Chem.* (in press).
Schulman, L. H., and Chambers, R. W. (1968). *Proc. Natl. Acad. Sci. U.S.* **61**, 308.
Schweet, R. S., Lamfrom, H., and Allen, E. H. (1958). *Proc. Natl. Acad. Sci. U.S.* **44**, 1029.
Scolnick, R., Tompkins, R., Caskey, T., and Nirenberg, M. (1968). *Proc. Natl. Acad. Sci. U.S.* **61**, 768.

Seeds, N. W., and Conway, T. W. (1967). *Biochem. Biophys. Res. Commun.* **28**, 1047.

Sekeris, C. E., Schmid, W., Gallwitz, D., and Lukas, I. (1966). *Life Sci.* **5**, 969.

Shaeffer, J., Arlinghaus, R., and Schweet, R. (1968a). *Arch. Biochem. Biophys.* **125**, 614.

Shaeffer, J., Arlinghaus, R., and Schweet, R. (1968b). *Arch. Biochem. Biophys.* **125**, 623.

Skogerson, L., and Moldave, K. (1967). *Biochem. Biophys. Res. Commun.* **27**, 568.

Skogerson, L., and Moldave, K. (1968a). *Arch. Biochem. Biophys.* **125**, 497.

Skogerson, L., and Moldave, K. (1968b). *J. Biol. Chem.* **243**, 5354.

Skogerson, L., and Moldave, K. (1968c). *J. Biol. Chem.* **243**, 5361.

Skoultchi, A., Ono, Y., Moon, H. M., and Lengyel, P. (1968). *Proc. Natl. Acad. Sci. U.S.* **60**, 675.

Spyrides, A. J. (1964). *Proc. Natl. Acad. Sci. U.S.* **51**, 1220.

Staehelin, M., Rogg, H., Baguley, B. C., Ginsberg, T., and Wehrli, W. (1968). *Nature* **219**, 1363.

Stenzel, K. H., Aronson, R. F., and Rubin, A. L. (1966). *Biochemistry* **5**, 930.

Stern, R., and Littauer, U. Z. (1968). *Biochemistry* **7**, 3469.

Stulberg, M. P. (1967). *J. Biol. Chem.* **242**, 1060.

Subak-Sharpe, H., Shepherd, W. M., and Hay, J. (1966). *Cold Spring Harbor Symp. Quant. Biol.* **31**, 583.

Sueoka, N., and Yamane, T. (1962). *Proc. Natl. Acad. Sci. U.S.* **48**, 1454.

Sueoka, N., Kano-Sueoka, T., and Gartland, W. J. (1966). *Cold Spring Harbor Symp. Quant. Biol.* **31**, 571.

Sutter, R. P., and Moldave, K. (1966). *J. Biol. Chem.* **241**, 1698.

Takanami, M. (1960). *Biochim. Biophys. Acta* **39**, 318.

Takemura, S., Mizutani, T., and Miyazaki, M. (1968). *J. Biochem. (Tokyo)* **63**, 277.

Taylor, M. W., Granger, G. A., Buck, C. A., and Holland, J. J. (1967). *Proc. Natl. Acad. Sci. U.S.* **57**, 1712.

Taylor, M. W., Buck, C. A., Granger, G. A., and Holland, J. J. (1968). *J. Mol. Biol.* **33**, 809.

Tsuzuki, J., and Naora, H. (1968). *Biochim. Biophys. Acta* **169**, 550.

von Ehrenstein, G., and Lipmann, F. (1961). *Proc. Natl. Acad. Sci. U.S.* **47**, 941.

Wang, T. Y. (1963). *Biochim. Biophys. Acta* **68**, 633.

Warburg, O., and Christian, W. (1941–1942). *Biochem. Z.* **310**, 384.

Watson, J. D. (1965). *In* "Molecular Biology of the Gene," p. 336. Benjamin, New York.

Webb, T. E., Blobel, G., and Potter, V. R. (1964). *Cancer Res.* **24**, 1229.

Weinstein, I. B. (1970). *In* "Genetic Concepts and Neoplasia." Williams & Wilkins, Baltimore, Maryland (in press).

Weinstein, I. B., and Schechter, A. N. (1962). *Proc. Natl. Acad. Sci. U.S.* **48**, 1686.

Weiss, J. F., and Kelmers, A. D. (1967). *Biochemistry* **6**, 2507.

Weiss, J. F., Pearson, R. L., and Kelmers, A. D. (1968). *Biochemistry* **7**, 3479.

Wettstein, F. O. (1966). *Cold Spring Harbor Symp. Quant. Biol.* **31**, 595.

Wettstein, F. O., Noll, H., and Penman, S. (1964). *Biochim. Biophys. Acta* **87**, 525.

Wimmer, E., Maxwell, I. H., and Tener, G. M. (1968). *Biochemistry* **7**, 2623.

Yang, W. K., and Novelli, G. D. (1968a). *Biochem. Biophys. Res. Commun.* **31**, 534.

Yang, W. K., and Novelli, G. D. (1968b). *Proc. Natl. Acad. Sci. U.S.* **59**, 208.
Zachau, H. G., Dütting, D., and Feldman, H. (1966). *Angew. Chem.* **78**, 392.
Zamecnik, P. C., Stephenson, M. L., and Hecht, L. I. (1958). *Proc. Natl. Acad. Sci. U.S.* **44**, 73.
Zimmerman, E. F. (1963). *Biochem. Biophys. Res. Commun.* **11**, 301.

CHAPTER V

PREPARATION OF MACROMOLECULES OF VERY HIGH SPECIFIC ACTIVITY IN TUMOR CELLS *in Vitro**

CHARLES M. MAURITZEN†, YONG C. CHOI,
AND HARRIS BUSCH

I. Introduction

The tremendous progress made in the last decade in our understanding of nucleic acid and protein biosynthesis and in the control of these processes has been achieved largely with microbial or viral systems. Similar progress has not been made with the more complex nucleated mammalian cells because of the limitations of available methods. Many modern analytical techniques employed in studies on ribonucleic acid (RNA), including structural (Sanger *et al.*, 1965; Brownlee and Sanger, 1967; Forget and Weissman, 1967a,b) and hybridization studies (Gillespie and Spiegelman, 1956), require highly purified RNA of very

* These studies were supported in part by U.S. Public Health Service Cancer Research Center Grant (CA-10893) and the American Cancer Society Grant P-339.

† Present address: Department of Biochemistry, University of Melbourne, Parkville, N.2, Victoria, Australia.

high specific activity. Analyses of the rates of biosynthesis, turnover, or maturation of RNA species require adequate labeling of these macro-molecules in short (pulse) times (Muramatsu *et al.*, 1966, Gillespie, 1968).

For analytical studies on mammalian cells, systems are required that will yield rapid and extensive labeling of the macromolecules in sufficient quantities to permit their isolation in high activity from nuclei, nucleoli, and other structures; moreover, subfractionation of the components of these organelles is generally necessary because of their complexity.

In vivo experiments have not successfully met these requirements; the labeled precursors are so diluted in the various extracellular and intracellular pools of the animal body that prohibitively high input levels of isotopic precursors are required. Such levels are impractical because of the high costs of isotope, the possibilities of serious radiation damage to the animal and to laboratory personnel, and disturbances of the endogenous levels of precursor in the animal. Although the commonly used *in vitro* tissue culture systems are satisfactory for some purposes, they have drawbacks in that the amounts of cells are gener-ally limiting because cells are conventionally grown in very dilute suspensions (1:5000–1:10,000). For example, the minimum quantity of cells from which nucleoli can satisfactorily be isolated is 4 gm and this would require 20–40 liters of medium.

This chapter describes an *in vitro* system in which Novikoff hepatoma ascites cells have been maintained in relatively concentrated suspen-sions (1:10–1:100) for periods up to 24 hours. Using a phosphate-free medium, ^{32}P-orthophosphate, and a cell concentration of 1:100, 97% of the added isotope was taken up by the cells within 6 hours. More-over, in this time, there was a total conversion of 2% of the added ^{32}P into RNA. The uptake of ^{32}P into nuclear RNA is linear up to 24 hours. The highest specific activity obtained for RNA was 4×10^9 counts/minute per mg for 45 S nuclear RNA or approximately 2 mcuries/mg 45 S RNA.

The system also incorporates ^{3}H-uridine, ^{3}H-adenosine into RNA and ^{3}H-lysine and ^{3}H-tryptophan into the histones and other nuclear proteins with a very high efficiency compared to *in vivo* systems.

II. Procedure

A. Novikoff Hepatoma Ascites Cells

The tumor cells were maintained in male Holtzman rats. Six or seven days after intraperitoneal transplantation, the rats bearing the ascites tumors were sacrificed by decapitation. After the abdominal skin was washed with 70% ethanol, an incision was made in the abdominal wall and the ascites fluid was collected. The ascites fluid from 10 to 20 rats was combined and centrifuged at 12,000 rpm for 10 minutes at 0°C in a Sorvall RC-2B centrifuge. This high-speed centrifugation was found to aid in the packing and separation of contaminating red cells. After centrifugation, the buffy coat of leukocytes and macrophages was manually removed with a spatula from the surface of the tumor cells and discarded. The tumor cells were then separated with a spatula from the underlying layer of red cells. The remainder of the procedure described is that used for ^{32}P-orthophosphate uptake except where specified.

The tumor cells were redispersed by gentle hand homogenization using a very loose-fitting Teflon pestle with 6 to 8 volumes of ice-cold NKM solution (0.13 M sodium chloride, 0.005 M potassium chloride, and 0.008 M magnesium chloride). The cells were again pelleted by centrifugation at 12,000 rpm for 10 minutes and separated from contaminating red cells. Usually, three washes with NKM were sufficient to remove red cells and to deplete the cells of endogenous inorganic orthophosphate and other soluble components. The cells were finally resuspended in 5 to 6 volumes of ice-cold, modified, Eagle's basal medium using gentle hand homogenization with a loose-fitting Teflon pestle. A small aliquot was used to determine the packed cell volume in a hematocrit tube, and the suspension was then diluted to exactly 10% cells (v/v) with medium.

1. Incubation Medium

The medium used is a modified form of Eagle's basal medium (1955a,b). The exact composition of the medium varied with the type of labeling desired (Table I). When very high specific activities were sought, the particular precursor which was to be added in isotopic form was omitted from the medium. If a linear uptake of isotope was desired for a longer period of time, the isotopic precursor was diluted with a known amount of unlabeled carrier prior to addition to the medium.

The principal modification in the medium from the formula of Eagle's basal medium was that all twenty amino acids required for protein synthesis were present in a final concentration of 0.2 mM. In addition, L-glutamine was present at a final concentration of 2.0 mM and the compounds L-ornithine, L-cystine, L-hydroxyproline, and reduced glutathione were also present in a concentration of 0.2 mM. The components of the medium were dissolved as a series of solutions, sterilized, and stored frozen at -20°C until needed (Table II).

TABLE I

COMPLETE COMPOSITION OF MODIFIED EAGLE'S BASAL MEDIUM
USED FOR INCUBATIONS

Compound	Final concentration (mg/liter)	Compound	Final concentration (mg/liter)
L-Alanine	17.8	Biotin	1.0
L-Arginine HCl	42.0	Calcium pantothenate	1.0
L-Asparagine	26.4	Choline chloride	1.0
L-Aspartic acid	26.6	Folic acid	1.0
L-Cysteine HCl	31.2	Inositol	2.0
L-Cystine	48.0	Nicotinamide	1.0
L-Glutamine	292.0	Pyridoxal HCl	1.0
L-Glutamic acid	29.6	Riboflavin	0.1
Glutathione (reduced)	62.0	Thiamine HCl	1.0
Glycine	15.0	Penicillin G	50.0
L-Histidine HCl	41.8	Streptomycin sulfate	50.0
L-Hydroxyproline	26.4	Potassium chloride	400.0
L-Leucine	26.2	Sodium chloride	6800.0
L-Isoleucine	26.2	Magnesium sulfate · $7H_2O$	200.0
L-Lysine HCl	36.6	Calcium chloride	200.0
L-Methionine	29.8	Sodium bicarbonate	2200.0
L-Ornithine HCl	33.5	D-Glucose	1000.0
L-Phenylalanine	33.0		
L-Proline	23.0	Fetal calf serum	10%(v/v)
L-Serine	21.0		
L-Threonine	23.8		
L-Tryptophan	40.8		
L-Tyrosine	36.2		
L-Valine	23.4		

2. Amino Acids and Vitamins

Several amino acid solutions (Table II) were used. A general amino acid solution containing most of the L-amino acids (Mann Research Laboratories, MA quality) was dissolved at a concentration of 10 mM in 0.3 N HCl. Separate solutions of L-arginine, L-cysteine, L-leucine, L-lysine, and L-tryptophan were each prepared in a concentration of 50 mM in 0.3 N HCl. A solution of L-glutamine was prepared in water in concentrations of 100 mM. The vitamin supplement (Table II) contained (in 100× final concentration) biotin, folic acid, choline chloride, calcium pantothenate, inositol, nicotinamide, pyridoxal hydrochloride, riboflavin, and thiamine hydrochloride. The salt solution used (Table II) was that of Earle (1963) in 10× final concentration except that

TABLE II

Additive solution	Components of solution	Concentration of components	Volume required per liter final solution	Order of addition
Amino acid A	L-Alanine, L-asparagine, L-aspartic, L-glutamic, glycine, L-histidine, L-cystine, L-hydroxyproline, L-isoleucine, L-methionine, L-ornithine, L-phenylalanine, L-serine, L-threonine, L-tyrosine, L-valine, reduced glutathione	10 mM in 0.3 N HCl (= 50 × concentrate)	20	1
Amino Acid B	L-Arginine	50 mM in 0.3 N HCl	4	—
Amino acid C	L-Cysteine	= 250 × concentrate	4	—
Amino acid D	L-Leucine	= 250 × concentrate	4	2
Amino acid E	L-Lysine	—	4	—
Amino acid F	L-Proline	—	4	—
Amino acid G	L-Tryptophan	—	4	—
NaOH	0.3 N NaOH	0.3 N	44	3
Amino acid H	L-Glutamine in water	100 mM in water (= 50 × concentrate)	20	4
Vitamin mixture	Calcium pantothenate, folic acid, inositol, riboflavin, choline chloride, nicotinamide, pyridoxal HCl, thiamine HCl	100 × concentrate	10	5
Earle's salts (no phosphate)	Sodium chloride, potassium chloride, magnesium sulfate, calcium chloride, D-glucose	10 × concentrate	80.4	6
Fetal calf serum	—	1 × concentrate	100	7
Water	—	—	500	8
Sodium bicarbonate	—	7% (w/v)	to pH 7.4 (≅30 ml)	9
Water	—	—	to 1 liter	10

orthophosphate was omitted. In experiments not involving ^{32}P-ortho-phosphate uptake, unlabeled phosphate was included in the salt solution at a concentration of 20 mM (2 mM final concentration).

3. Fetal Calf Serum

Fetal calf serum, immunodiffusion-selected (Hyland Division, Travenol Laboratories) was dialyzed at 2°C for 4 days against four (20 volume) changes of NKM to remove inorganic orthophosphate and amino acids. The dialyzed serum was then sterilized by passage through a 0.45-μ Millipore filter and stored frozen until required. In preparing the medium, allowance was made for the salt content of the neutralized amino acid solution and the serum. The solutions were added (see Table I) in the sequence: amino acids, 0.3 N NaOH, vitamins, glutamine, Earle's salts, antibiotics, dialyzed serum, and water to 10% of final volume. Sodium bicarbonate (7% w/v) gassed with CO_2 was used to adjust the pH to 7.4 at 37°C. Water was then added to the final desired volume.

B. RADIOACTIVE SAFETY PROCEDURES

The procedures described involve the use of large quantities of isotope (from 50 to 700 mcuries ^{32}P in a single experiment). Because of the potential radiation hazard, rigorous precautions must be taken concerning the safety of personnel, the possible contamination of equipment, and the disposal of radioactive wastes.

1. Protection of Personnel

The principal radiation hazard to workers is from ^{32}P-orthophosphate. The isotope, obtained in carrier-free form (1 curie/ml 0.1 N HCl; International Chemical and Nuclear Corporation, California) was stored behind a lead shield in a locked fume cupboard until use.

In addition to radiation badges, all workers wore disposable laboratory coats, lead-lined aprons, face masks, shoes (for hot-lab use only), and two pairs of disposable gloves. The outer pair of gloves was discarded and replaced after each manipulation involving high activities of isotope. All operations involving high source activity, e.g., removal and addition of isotope and homogenization of cells, were conducted behind lead glass shields. All incubations were performed in heavy walled, glass Erlenmeyer flasks to reduce radiation and to minimize the risk of breakage.

2. Working Precautions

Benches and floors of work areas in laboratories and cold rooms were covered with sheets of polythene under sheets of heavy brown paper or Benchkote. Glass and plastic ware used in procedures involving high activities (>50 mcuries) were either discarded after use or were carefully rinsed with detergent and cold phosphate solution before normal washing; the rinsings were disposed of as described below. The inside of some glassware, e.g., homogenizers and plastic centrifuge bottles, retained high activity (>5000 counts/minute) even after vigorous washing. This equipment was stored in special cupboards away from other apparatus and could be reused safely. All concentrated radioactive solutions were measured with disposable plastic syringes or with Eppendorf–Marburg pipettes with disposable plastic tips.

All waste solutions obtained during the procedures, e.g., cell supernatants and supernatants from the isolation of nuclei, nucleoli, or ribosomes were carefully transferred to glass bottles for subsequent disposal. During manipulations involving removal of supernatants which were carefully poured off into storage containers, the lip of the tube or bottle was wiped with Kleenex or the supernatants were aspirated using a suction pump. All work areas and equipment were carefully monitored for radioactivity *before and after* use.

3. Disposal of Waste

Solid radioactive wastes, e.g., contaminated glassware, syringes, or absorbent tissues were collected in double-thickness polythene bags and set aside for disposal. All radioactive waste solutions were stored in bottles. Wastes containing ^{32}P were stored in drums in a sealed room for ten half-lives; the radioactivity was then determined and the appropriate dilution was made according to U.S. Atomic Energy Commission regulations before disposal in the sewage system.

Experiments involving large amounts of ^{32}P (50–700 mcuries) have been performed in this laboratory for a considerable time. During these experiments, no workers have been exposed to undue radiation as measured by badge dosimeters and no serious contamination of equipment or laboratory areas has occurred.

C. RADIOACTIVE ISOTOPES

Carrier-free ^{32}P-orthophosphate (1 curie/ml) was diluted to 1 to 10 mcuries/ml with Eagle's medium. This diluted stock solution was then added to the cell suspension in the medium at the level of from 0.5 to 60 mcuries/gm cells. The exact amount of radioactivity used in each experiment was determined by diluting a 50-μl sample of the diluted stock isotope solution to 100 ml with 0.1 M phosphate and measuring the radioactivity in 50-μl portions (in quadruplicate) of this solution with 10 ml of Bray's scintillation fluid (1960).

Other isotopically labeled compounds used, ^{3}H-5-uridine, ^{3}H-L-tryptophan, ^{3}H-8-adenosine, ^{3}H-8-guanosine, or ^{3}H(4,5)L-lysine, were supplied in concentrations of 0.5 to 1.0 mcuries/ml and were added directly to the cell suspension. Samples were diluted with cold carrier as described above for the determination of input radioactivity.

1. Incubation Conditions

Suspensions of washed Novikoff cells (1:9) described above were diluted with Eagle's medium to a final concentration of 1:49 or 1:249 cells in the medium in heavy walled Erlenmeyer flasks. The flasks were previously coated with silicon (Siliclad, Beckman) and were sterilized at 160°C. An air-to-liquid ratio of 4:1 was used. The flasks were then incubated at 37°C under an atmosphere of 95% O_2, 5% CO_2 in gyrorotary shaker baths. Small samples, in 50 to 500-ml flasks were incubated in a Model G-76, New Brunswick shaker and the larger flasks (1–2 liters) were incubated in a Model G-25 controlled-environment incubator shaker (New Brunswick). After 5 to 10 minutes to permit temperature equilibration, the reaction was started by addition of radioisotope.

2. Isotope Uptake into Trichloroacetic Acid-Insoluble Material

The uptake of isotope into total trichloroacetic acid (TCA)-insoluble material of Novikoff cells was determined at various times throughout the incubation by taking 50- or 100-μl samples in triplicate with an Eppendorf pipette and transferring these to tubes containing 1 ml of 0.1 M phosphate (or other carrier) in ice. One milligram of carrier serum protein was also added to each tube followed by 15 ml of ice-cold 10% TCA. After 1 hour, the precipitated material was filtered on Millipore glass fiber filters (♯AP 200) and washed with five portions of 40 ml of cold 10% TCA followed by 10 ml of ethanol. The filters were dried under an infrared lamp and placed in vials along with 10 ml of Bray's scintillation solution (1960).

D. Isolation of Nuclei

In order to obtain "clean" nuclei free from cytoplasmic tags and to minimize degradation of RNA, nuclei were isolated by the citric acid procedure (Higashi et al., 1966; Busch, 1967a). A typical preparation is described. At the end of the incubation period, the cells (2 ml packed volume) were pelleted from the suspension by centrifugation at 2000 g and 0°C for 10 minutes. The supernatant portion was discarded (see Section II, B, 2). All subsequent operations were performed at 2 to 4°C in the cold room. The cells were lysed by homogenization with 20 ml of ice-cold 5% citric acid using twenty to thirty strokes in a tight-fitting 0.005-in. clearance (Teflon pestle) at 2200 rpm. The suspension was diluted to 40 ml with 5% citric acid and centrifuged at 2000 rpm for 10 minutes. The supernatant was discarded.

The crude nuclear pellet was resuspended in 40 ml of 5% citric acid and washed by centrifugation twice more using a total of sixty to eighty strokes with the homogenizer. The nuclear pellet was then resuspended (two to three strokes) in 2 to 3 ml of 0.25 M sucrose containing 1.5% citric acid, and the suspension was layered over 38 ml of 0.88 M sucrose containing 1.5% citric acid. The nuclei were pelleted at 2000 g for 10 minutes. The RNA was extracted immediately (see below); if the preparation was to be used for histone extraction, the nuclei were first washed with 12 to 15 ml of ethanol.

E. ISOLATION OF NUCLEOLI

Nucleoli were obtained from Novikoff cells using the sonication procedure of Muramatsu and Busch (1967). Novikoff hepatoma ascites cells (20 gm) were homogenized with 10 volumes of ice-cold 2.0 M sucrose containing 3.3 mM $CaCl_2$. The nuclei were pelleted by centrifugation at 40,000 g and 2°C for 1 hour and then resuspended in 40 ml of 0.34 M sucrose (without $CaCl_2$). The nuclei were then disrupted by sonication at 10 to 11 amp for 60 to 70 seconds at 2°C using a Branson sonic amplifier. The suspension was then layered over 120 ml of 0.88 M sucrose (without $CaCl_2$), and the nucleoli were pelleted by centrifugation at 2000 g for 10 minutes. The purity of the preparation was checked microscopically after staining with azure C. Satisfactory nucleolar preparations were obtained from Novikoff hepatoma ascites cells which had been incubated for up to 6 hours (Busch, 1967b).

F. EXTRACTION OF RIBONUCLEIC ACID

The RNA was extracted from nuclei, nucleoli, and ribosomal preparations by hot extraction (65°C) with 0.3% sodium dodecyl sulfate–phenol as described previously (Steele and Busch, 1967; Muramatsu and Busch, 1967). The deproteinized RNA was precipitated with 2 volumes of ethanol containing 2% potassium acetate. With nuclear preparations made by the citric acid procedure, no further purification was necessary, but nucleolar preparations were still contaminated with inorganic phosphate and mononucleotides. These were removed by dissolving the RNA sample in 0.5 ml of water and chromatographing it on Sephadex G-25 (0.5 × 20-cm column). The RNA was recovered from the breakthrough peak of the effluent by precipitation with ethanol (Muramatsu and Busch, 1967; Steele et al., 1965).

1. Sucrose Density Gradient Centrifugation

Aliquots of RNA (0.2 mg) were layered on 33-ml linear sucrose gradients (5–40%) containing 0.1 M NaCl, 0.01 M sodium acetate (pH 5.1), and 0.001 M ethylenediaminetetraacetate (EDTA). Centrifugation was carried out in an SW 27 rotor at 26,000 rpm for 16 hours at 4°C in a Spinco L2-50 ultracentrifuge.

The gradients were fractionated and the ultraviolet profile was determined with the aid of an ISCO Model D density gradient fractionator. For isolation of individual sedimentation classes of RNA, 2.5 mg of RNA were fractionated on these gradients. Fractions corresponding to the rapidly sedimenting classes of RNA with approximate sedimentation coefficients of 28, 35, and 45 S were pooled. Each sedimentation class of RNA was purified by two to three density gradient separations until a single symmetrical sedimentation peak was obtained (Steele and Busch, 1967; Quagliarotti et al., 1970).

2. Oligonucleotide Mapping Procedure

For mapping the enzymatic digestion products of RNA, the procedure of Rushizky and Knight (1960) was used, i.e., paper electrophoresis at pH 2.7 (ammonium formate) in the first dimension followed by paper chromatography in a 55:45 t-butanol–ammonium formate (pH 3.8) buffer, pH 4.7–4.8, in the second. Electrophoresis was carried out at pH 2.7 on Whatman No. 3 MM paper (68 × 46 cm) for 17 to 20 hours with a potential of 6 volts/cm and a current of 10 to 20 mA. Electrophoresis was terminated when a picric acid marker reached the buffer level in the anode chamber. For paper chromatography, the tank was completely saturated with the solvent and the chromatogram was developed for 36 to 38 hours at room temperature. The papers were then dried and the spots were located under ultraviolet light.

The spots were then cut out and eluted with 2 to 3 ml 0.01 N HCl. To each sample, 10–20 ml of scintillation solution (Bray, 1960) was added. After thorough mixing, the radioactivity was determined in a Packard Model 3375 liquid scintillation counter.

3. Determination of Nucleotide Composition by ^{32}P-Analysis

Ribonucleic acid was hydrolyzed with 0.3 N KOH for 16 hours at 37°C; the hydrolyzate was neutralized with 5 N perchloric acid at 0 to 2°C. After centrifugation to remove potassium perchlorate, the supernatant fraction was chromatographed on Dowex-1 formate (Hurlbert *et al.*, 1954) to separate the nucleotides.

4. Sanger Procedure for Oligonucleotide Mapping

The methods developed by Sanger, Brownlee, and Barrell (1965) require high specific activity RNA for rapid radioautography and further structural studies. Partial hydrolysis of the RNA was carried out either with pancreatic RNase A or with T_1 RNase, and subsequent hydrolysis of the fragments was carried out by snake venom phosphodiesterase, spleen phosphodiesterase, U2 RNase, or RNase (partial digestion or after CMCT* treatment). Electrophoresis in the first dimension was on cellulose acetate and in the second dimension on DE 81 paper (Reeve Angel). The optimal DE 81 paper is purchased in rolls (150 meters long). In this laboratory, electrophoretic runs were made in a Savant apparatus.

G. Utilization of ³²P-Orthophosphate by Novikoff Cells

The kinetics of uptake of ³²P-orthophosphate into the TCA-insoluble fraction of Novikoff cells are shown in Fig. 1 for 1:50 cell suspension

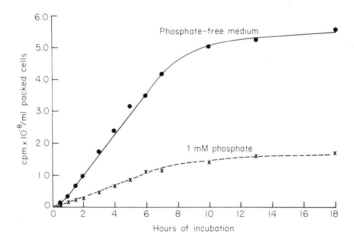

FIG. 1. The kinetics of uptake of ³²P-orthophosphate into trichloroacetic acid-insoluble fractions for Novikoff hepatoma ascites cells incubated *in vitro* in the presence and absence of carrier phosphate. Conditions: 25 ml of cell suspension (1:50) contained 0.44 mcurie ³²P-orthophosphate at zero time. Results are plotted as counts per minute per milliliter packed cells.

---

* CMCT, *N*-cyclohexyl-*N'*-(β-morpholinyl-(4)-ethyl) carbodimide-methyl-*p*-toluene sulfonate.

in phosphate-free medium. After an initial lag period of approximately 30 minutes, the uptake of ^{32}P was linear for 7 hours, after which the rate decreased. The same period of linear uptake occurred in the presence of 1 mM phosphate so that in these cells, which are not phosphate-deficient, the rate of formation of TCA-insoluble substances decreases, probably because some component in the medium is limiting.

That this explanation is probably correct is demonstrated by the results in Fig. 2 which shows the uptake of ^{32}P-orthophosphate into

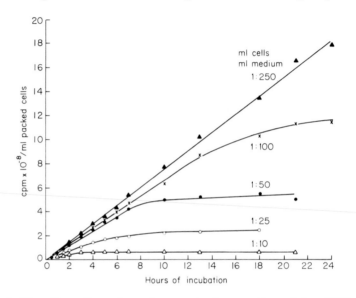

Fig. 2. The effect of varying cell concentrations on the uptake of ^{32}P-orthophosphate into trichloroacetic acid-insoluble material by Novikoff cell, incubated *in vitro* in phosphate-free medium. Conditions: in all experiments, 25 ml of cell suspension contained 0.44 mcurie ^{32}P-orthophosphate at zero time.

TCA-precipitable materials for cell concentrations of 1:10 to 1:250. At the cell concentration of 1:10, which is similar to that found in peritoneal ascites fluid, linear uptake of ^{32}P ceased after 3 hours. However, at cell concentrations of 1:250, linear uptake was observed for as long as 24 hours. The results are plotted as ^{32}P uptake as counts/minute per milliliter packed cells. The most efficient system for the conversion of ^{32}P into TCA-insoluble components was that in which the cells were incubated at a concentration of 1:250. At short times of incubation, there was little difference between cell concentrations of 1:50 to 1:250, i.e., the rate of uptake was very similar.

Analysis of the supernatant fluid for ^{32}P after sedimentation of the cells shows that at all cell concentrations studied, the ability of Novikoff ascites cells to take up ^{32}P-orthophosphate from a phosphate-free medium was very high. Table III compares the input ^{32}P-orthophosphate with the amount remaining in the supernatant medium after incubation.

TABLE III

COMPARISON OF THE TOTAL UPTAKE OF ^{32}P-ORTHOPHOSPHATE
BY NOVIKOFF HEPATOMA ASCITES CELLS *in Vitro* UNDER
VARIOUS CONDITIONS

Cell concentration	Isotope concentration (mcuries ^{32}P/ml cells)	Incubation time (hours)	Input in mixture (mcuries total ^{32}P)	Cell super- natant (mcuries total ^{32}P)	^{32}P Uptake by cells (%)
1:10	0.2	3	0.5	0.015	97.1
1:25	0.5	10	0.5	0.012	97.5
1:50	1.0	6	0.5	0.010	98.0
1:50	24.0	9	480.0	12.5	97.4
1:100	2.0	10	0.5	0.020	96.0
1:100	17.87	15	536.0	17.2	96.8
1:250	4.9	10	0.5	0.026	94.8

The uptake of ^{32}P-orthophosphate into TCA-precipitable material in a 1:10 cell suspension was normally terminated at 3 hours, but if the cell suspension was diluted with additional medium at 1 hour to a final cell concentration of 1:250, the uptake of ^{32}P continued linearly for at least 11 hours (Fig. 3). The pH of the 1:10 cell suspension after 3 hours was 7.35 and, therefore, the failure of continued ^{32}P uptake into TCA-insoluble material was probably due to exhaustion of some essential precursor in the medium or an endogenous factor in the cells.

Exhaustion of some factor in the medium was also shown by another experiment (Fig. 4). Two flasks, A and B, each containing 25 ml of 1:50 cell suspension of Novikoff cells in a phosphate-free medium and 0.5 mcurie of ^{32}P-orthophosphate, were incubated for 5 hours. At this time, the mixture was chilled and the cells were separated from the medium by centrifugation. The supernatant from each flask was set aside. The cells were resuspended (flask A in 24.5 ml of fresh medium and flask B in 24.5 ml of fresh medium containing 0.5 mcurie ^{32}P-orthophosphate).

On reincubation, there was a lag period of 30 minutes during which time no further uptake of ^{32}P was observed; then, there was a linear

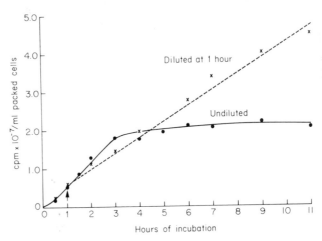

FIG. 3. The effect of dilution of a concentrated cell suspension on the uptake of ^{32}P-orthophosphate in trichloroacetic acid-insoluble material. Conditions: 25 ml of cell suspension (1:10) contained 0.5 mcurie ^{32}P at zero time. At 1 hour, 2 ml of suspension removed and diluted with 48 ml of medium; incubation continued. (●—●) A 1:10 cell suspension; (×---×) a 1:10 cell suspension diluted to 1:250 at 1 hour.

uptake of ^{32}P in both experiments. As the cells had taken most of the ^{32}P-orthophosphate (Table III), the slope of A after fresh medium was added was very close to the initial slope. In experiment B, in which both fresh medium and additional ^{32}P-orthophosphate were added; there was an almost twofold increase in rate of labeling of TCA-insoluble substances by the cells (Fig. 4).

The supernatants from experiments A and B at 5 hours were used to resuspend 0.5 ml (packed volume) of freshly prepared Novikoff cells (experiments C and D, respectively). No further additions were made to experiment C. Figure 4 shows that uptake of ^{32}P was very limited and terminated after 1 to 2 hours. In experiment D, the medium from B at 5 hours was mixed with fresh cells (0.5 ml) and supplemented with 0.5 mcurie of ^{32}P-phosphate, and there was a somewhat greater uptake of isotope which terminated after 4 hours.

Figure 5 shows that the above results were not caused by treatment of the cells. In this experiment, the incubation of cell suspensions with ^{32}P-phosphate was interrupted either by chilling or by chilling and pelleting the cells by centrifugation before resuming the incubation. Chilling alone (Fig. 5) produced no effect on the uptake of ^{32}P into TCA-insoluble material, and chilling and centrifuging produced only a lag period of 30 minutes before normal uptake was resumed.

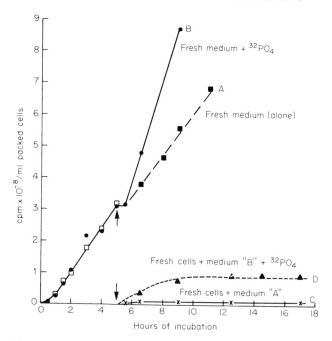

Fig. 4. The effects of replacement of medium, cells and ^{32}P-orthophosphate on the kinetics of uptake of ^{32}P-orthophosphate into trichloroacetic acid-insoluble material by Novikoff cells *in vitro*. Conditions: 25 ml of cell suspension in phosphate-free medium contained 0.5 mcurie ^{32}P-orthophosphate at zero time (experiments A and B). After 5 hours incubation, supernatant medium removed from bath and replaced with fresh medium and incubation resumed. Curve A—fresh medium at 5 hours; curve B—fresh medium containing 0.5 mcurie ^{32}P at 5 hours. The original supernatant medium used in experiments A and B was used to resuspend 0.5 ml (packed volume) fresh cells and incubation resumed. Curve C—fresh cells in original medium from A; curve D—fresh cell in original medium from B plus 0.5 mcurie ^{32}P-orthophosphate.

1. Cold Chase Experiments

The effect of a cold phosphate chase was studied by incubating a cell suspension (1:50) of Novikoff cells with ^{32}P-orthophosphate for 10 hours. At 1 and 2 hours, equal portions of the suspension were removed, chilled in ice, and the cells separated from the medium by centrifugation (3000 rpm for 10 minutes). The supernatants were discarded and the cells were washed twice by resuspension in Eagle's medium containing 5 mM phosphate. The cells were finally resuspended in a volume of medium containing 5 mM phosphate equal to the original supernatant and incubation was resumed. It can be seen from

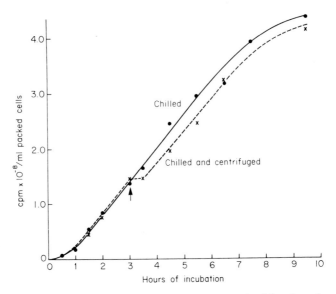

FIG. 5. The effect of chilling and centrifuging on the kinetics of uptake of ³²P-orthophosphate by Novikoff cells *in vitro*. Conditions: 25 ml of cell suspension (1:50) contained 0.5 mcurie ³²P-orthophosphate at zero time. (●—●)— suspension chilled in ice for 30 minutes at 3 hours and incubation resumed; (×---×)—suspension chilled at 3 hours, cells pelleted by centrifugation and resuspended in original medium before resuming incubation. Note: the time delay in chilling or centrifuging has been omitted from the abscissa.

Fig. 6 that a cold phosphate chase at 1 or 2 hours effectively stops the uptake of ³²P into TCA-insoluble material.

2. Biosynthesis of RNA

The above experiments evaluated the uptake of ³²P-orthophosphate into TCA-insoluble material. Although 95–98% of the added isotope was taken up by the cells in a phosphate-free medium (Table III), only 4–15% of the added isotope was converted into TCA-precipitable substances. These include phosphoproteins, phospholipoproteins, and nucleic acids.

The uptake of ³²P-phosphate into RNA was investigated in a series of experiments in which from 2 to 30 gm of Novikoff cells were incubated with varying amounts of ³²P-orthophosphate in phosphate-free medium. After incubation, nuclei, nucleoli, or ribosomes were isolated and these organelles were then used for the extraction of RNA. Tables IV, VA and VB show that nuclear and nucleolar RNA with very high specific activities can be recovered routinely.

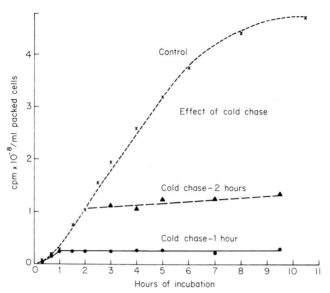

FIG. 6. The effect of cold phosphate "chase" on the uptake of ^{32}P-ortho-phosphate into trichloroacetic acid-insoluble material by Novikoff cells *in vitro*. Conditions: 75 ml of cell suspension (1:50) contained 1.5 mcurie ^{32}P-phosphate at zero time. Curves: ($\times$ --- $\times$) control—cells washed with medium containing unlabeled 5 mM phosphate and reincubated with medium containing 5 mM phosphate B; ($\bullet$—$\bullet$) cold chase at 1 hour; ($\blacktriangle$——$\blacktriangle$) cold chase at 2 hours.

TABLE IV

RECOVERY AND RADIOACTIVITY OF RIBONUCLEIC ACID FROM
NUCLEI AND NUCLEOLI OF NOVIKOFF CELLS INCUBATED
in Vitro WITH ^{32}P-ORTHOPHOSPHATE IN CARRIER-FREE MEDIUM

Type of RNA	Packed volume of cells (ml)	Incubation conditions			RNA recovery	
		Input of ^{32}P-ortho-phosphate (mcurie)	Ratio of cells to medium	Time (hours)	Total (mg)	Total (counts/minute)
Nuclear	2	123	1:50	6	1	5.6×10^9
Nuclear	2	12	1:50	6	2	4.4×10^8
Nuclear	30	500	1:100	15	10	2.1×10^{10}
Nuclear	30	600	1:100	15	10	1.8×10^{10}
Nucleolar	34	170	1:50	6	4.5	9.5×10^8
Nucleolar	20	50	1:100	6	4	3.1×10^9
Nucleolar	20	50	1:100	6	4.5	2.9×10^9
Nucleolar	20	80	1:100	6	5	6.2×10^9

TABLE VA

Specific Activities of Various Ribonucleic Acid Components
Obtained from Isolated Cell Nuclei after Incubation of
Novikoff Hepatoma Ascites Cells *in Vitro* with $^{32}PO_4$
in Phosphate-Free Medium[a]

RNA Component	Specific activity (counts/minute per mg)
4.0 S	3.0×10^8
4.5 S	4.4×10^8
5.0 S	4.8×10^8
U1	1.6×10^8
U2	1.8×10^8
U3	0.8×10^8
18 S	1.3×10^9
28 S	2.0×10^9
45 S	4.0×10^9

[a] Twenty milliliters (packed volume) of cells was incubated with 500 mcuries of $^{32}PO_4$ in 1 liter of medium for 9 hours.

TABLE VB

Specific Activities of Nucleolar Ribonucleic Acid
Components Obtained from Isolated Nucleoli after
in Vitro Incubation of Novikoff Hepatoma Ascites
Cells with $^{32}PO_4$ in Phosphate-Free Medium[a]

RNA Component	Specific activity (counts/minute per mg)
28 S	2.3×10^8
35 S	2.6×10^8
45 S	2.6×10^8
55 S	2.6×10^8

[a] Twenty milliliters (packed volume) cells was incubated with 1 liter of medium containing 150 mcuries $^{32}PO_4$ for 6 hours.

The integrity of the nuclear and nucleolar RNA was shown by sucrose density gradient patterns (Figs. 7 and 8). These patterns demonstrate that no significant degradation of nuclear or nucleolar RNA occurred.

To show that, when 45 S nucleolar RNA was subjected to limited hydrolysis, highly labeled RNA products could be recovered for further degradation procedures, short-term T_1 RNase digests (Wikman *et al.*, 1969) were carried out. The digests then were subjected to

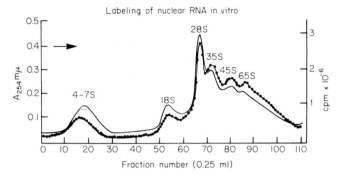

FIG. 7. Sedimentation profile and distribution of radioactivity of nuclear ribonucleic acid (RNA) from Novikoff hepatoma ascites cells labeled *in vitro* with ^{32}P-orthophosphate, 20 mcuries/ml packed cells for 15 hours. The RNA, 250 μg in 100 μl of buffer (0.1 M NaCl, 0.001 M ethylenediaminetetraacetate, 0.01 M acetic acid/sodium acetate, pH 5.1), was layered on a 5–45% (w/w) linear sucrose gradient of the same ionic composition as the sample buffer. Centrifugation was performed in SW-27 rotor in a Spinco Model L2-50 ultracentrifuge at 3°C for 16 hours. The solid line represents the absorbancy at 254 mμ recorded with an ISCO Model UA-20 ultraviolet analyzer, and the dotted line the distribution of radioactivity in 0.25-ml fractions obtained using an ISCO density gradient fractionator Model D. The arrow indicates the direction of sedimentation. The numbers above the peaks indicate the approximate sedimentation coefficients of the RNA components.

electrophoresis on slab gels (20 × 40 cm) and a resultant radioautograph is shown in Fig. 9. These results indicate that it will be possible to use the new procedures developed by Sanger's group (Adams *et al.*, 1969; Nichols, 1970) and by Fellner's group (1970).

Inasmuch as 4.5 S RNA$_\text{I}$ has been isolated in high purity in this laboratory (Ro-Choi *et al.*, 1970), it seemed that this RNA when isolated from the very radioactive nuclear RNA obtained by the present procedure would be a useful test material for such structural analyses. When finally purified, 8 × 10^6 counts/minute was recovered in the 4.5 S RNA$_\text{I}$. The results obtained by the mapping procedures for an RNase digest are shown in Fig. 10. This result demonstrates the feasibility of further structural studies with the present system.

3. Ribosomal RNA

The uptake of ^{32}P-orthophosphate into ribosomal (r)RNA is much slower than into nuclear or nucleolar RNA but proceeds linearly for approximately 24 hours. Novikoff hepatoma ascites cells (20 ml, packed volume) were incubated with 980 ml of phosphate-free medium containing 260 mcuries of ^{32}P-orthophosphate; the suspension being equally divided between four 1-liter flasks. The flasks were incubated

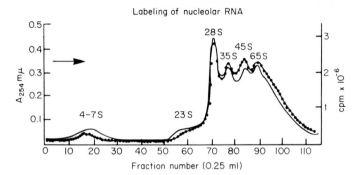

Labeling of nucleolar RNA

Fig. 8. Sedimentation profile and distribution of radioactivity of nucleolar ribonucleic acid (RNA) from Novikoff hepatoma ascites cells labeled *in vitro* with ^{32}P-orthophosphate, 20 mcuries/ml packed cells for 15 hours. The RNA 250 μg in 100 μl of buffer (0.1 M NaCl, 0.001 M ethylenediaminetetraacetate, 0.01 M acetic acid/sodium acetate, pH 5.1), was layered on a 5–45% (w/w) linear sucrose gradient of the same ionic composition as the sample buffer. Centrifugation was performed in an SW-27 rotor in a Spinco Model L2-50 ultracentrifuge at 3°C for 16 hours. The solid line represents the absorbancy at 254 mμ recorded with an ISCO Model UA-20 ultraviolet analyzer, and the dotted line the distribution of radioactivity in 0.25-ml fractions obtained using an ISCO density gradient fractionator Model D. The arrow indicates the direction of sedimentation. The numbers above the peaks indicate the approximate sedimentation coefficients of the RNA components.

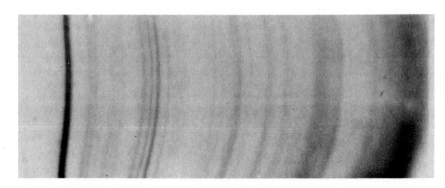

Fig. 9. Radioautographic electrophoregram of ^{32}P-labeled nucleolar 28 S ribonucleic acid (RNA) digested partially with T1 RNase. The ^{32}P-labeled nucleolar RNA (100 μcuries/mg) was treated with T1 RNase (substrate/enzyme = 1 mg RNA/20 units, 300,000 units = 1 mg enzyme) in a buffer containing 0.02 M Na acetate, 0.002 M ethylenediaminetetraacetate, and 0.04 M tris acetate (pH 7.2) at 37°C for 30 minutes. A 8% acrylamide gel (Loening, 1967) was prepared in slab form (17 × 37 × 0.4 cm) and electrophoresis was performed vertically with above buffer at 300 volts (35 mA) for 30 hours at 4°C. The gel was removed and enclosed with a cellophane sheet (Saran wrap). An X-ray film (Cronex-4, 14 × 17 in., Dupont) was exposed to the enclosed gel in close contact for 30 minutes and developed in a Profexray (Profex). Approximately 30 bands were observed, among which the top-most dense band is referred as B3 band (Wikman *et al.*, 1969) and the lowest broad band is a mixture of small oligonucleotides.

272

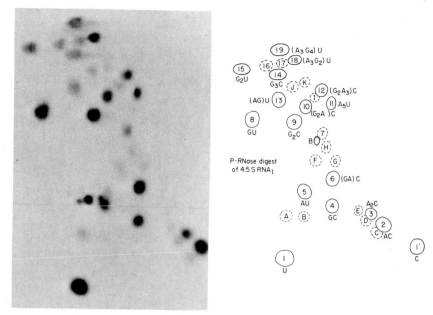

Fig. 10. Radioautograph of electrophoretic separation of pancreatic digest of ³²P-labeled 4.5 S ribonucleic acid (RNA_I). The ³²P-labeled 4.5 S RNA_I (100 µg/20; µcuries per milligram) was digested completely with pancreatic RNase (16 µg; 3000 units/mg) in a volume of 8 µl containing 2 mM ethylenediaminetetraacetate and 0.02 M tris–HCl (pH 7.4) for 3 hours at 37°C. Ionophoresis on cellulose acetate at pH 3.5 and on diethylaminoethyl (DEAE) paper in 7% formic acid was performed according to Brownlee and Sanger (1967). An X-ray film (Cronex-4, 14 × 17 in., Dupont) was exposed to DEAE paper for 10 hours and developed in a Profexray (Profex). These data were obtained by Drs. T. S. Ro-Choi and Y. Moriyama (see Peacock and Dingman, 1968; Wienberg *et al.*, 1967).

at 37°C and the contents were used for the isolation of ribosomes at 10, 18, and 24 hours. Figure 11 shows the specific activities of the 28 S rRNA at these times; linear synthesis continues for at least 24 hours despite the fact that the total uptake of ³²P into TCA-insoluble materials was linear for only 12 to 13 hours under similar conditions.

4. Uptake of Nucleosides and Amino Acid

The same system used to study the uptake of ³²P-orthophosphate into RNA was used to study the uptake of various labeled nucleosides and amino acids into Novikoff cells, except that 2 mM phosphate was present in the medium.

The uptake of ³H-uridine, ³H-adenosine, and ³H-guanosine into the TCA-insoluble fraction is shown in Figs. 12 and 13. The uptake was linear for 2 hours in each case. The total utilization of the isotope is

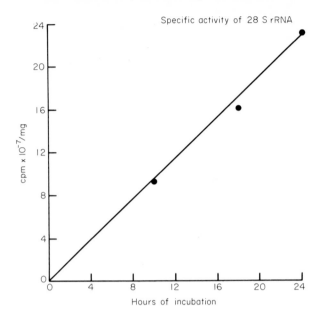

FIG. 11. The kinetics of ^{32}P-orthophosphate labeling of ribosomal 28 S RNA from Novikoff cells incubated *in vitro* in phosphate-free medium. The samples were 5-gm cells, 1:100 suspension, containing 52 mcuries ^{32}P at each time interval. These data were obtained by Dr. Joan Wikman.

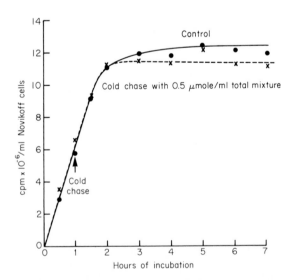

FIG. 12. The kinetics of uptake of ^{3}H-uridine into trichloroacetic acid-insoluble material by Novikoff ascites cells *in vitro*. Conditions: ratio of cells to medium, 1:100; [3]H-[5]-uridine, 23.3 curies/mmole at 1 mcurie/ml packed cells; control and cold chase, 0.5 mM uridine at 1 hour.

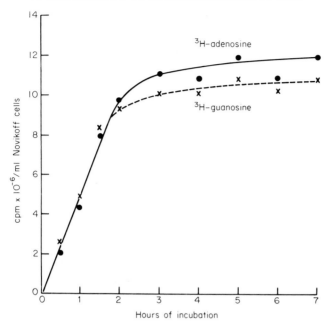

Hours of incubation

Fig. 13. The uptake of ^{3}H-adenosine and ^{3}H-guanosine into trichloroacetic acid-insoluble fraction by Novikoff cells *in vitro*. Conditions: ratio of cells to medium, 1:100; isotope 1 mcurie/ml packed cells; ^{3}H-[8]-adenosine, 26 curies/mmole; ^{3}H-[8]-guanosine, 2.6 curies/mmole.

TABLE VI

ACTIVITIES RECOVERED FROM VARIOUS NUCLEAR AND NUCLEOLAR
FRACTIONS AFTER *in Vitro* INCUBATION OF NOVIKOFF HEPATOMA
ASCITES CELLS WITH ^{3}H-L-LYSINE OR ^{3}H-L-TRYPTOPHAN[a]

Isotope[b]	Nuclei (total counts/minute)		Nucleoli (total counts/minute)[c]	
	Acid soluble	Acid insoluble	Tris 8 M urea-soluble	Tris 8 M urea-insoluble
^{3}H-L-Lysine	6.2×10^6	5.7×10^6	3.4×10^6	4.1×10^6
^{3}H-L-Tryptophan	0.9×10^6	5.7×10^6	1.3×10^6	2.1×10^6

[a] Nuclei and nucleoli were isolated as described in the text. Nuclei from 2 ml packed cells were extracted 3 times with ice-cold 0.25 N HCl. The extracts were concentrated and washed on an Amicon filter. Nucleoli from 4 ml of cells were extracted with Tris buffer in 8 M urea containing β-mercaptoethanol. Radioactivity of each fraction is expressed as counts per minute per milliliter packed cell nuclei or nucleoli.

[b] One millicurie of isotope per milliliter packed cell was incubated for 90 minutes.

[c] Data supplied by Dr. J. Dworak.

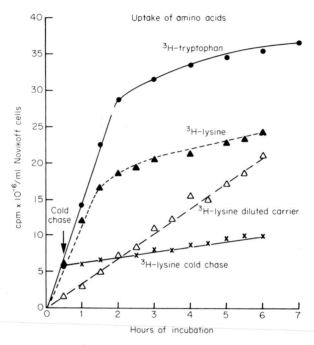

FIG. 14. The kinetics of uptake of ³H-L-tryptophan and ³H-L-lysine into trichloroacetic acid-insoluble fraction by Novikoff ascites cells *in vitro* showing the effects of cold chase with lysine (0.4 mM) at 30 minutes and of cold carrier lysine (0.1 mM). Conditions: ratio of cells to medium, 1:100; isotope input—³H-[4,5]-L-lysine (28 curies/mmole) at 1 mcurie/ml packed cells, ³H-L-tryptophan (6.5 curies/mmole) at 0.5 mcurie/ml packed cells; cold chase, unlabeled L-lysine added to final concentration of 0.4 mM at 30 minutes. In the dilution experiment, ³H-lysine was diluted with unlabeled lysine to a final concentration 0.1 mM.

very efficient, indicating that the "scavenger" pathways for the direct phosphorylation of the three nucleosides were very active in these cells. The addition of unlabeled uridine (0.5 mM) at 1 hour (Fig. 12) did not result in termination of ³H-uridine uptake. However, in this case, the cells were not washed prior to addition of unlabeled uridine, so the experiment was not comparable to the cold phosphate chase (Fig. 6). The specific activities of 45 and 35 S RNA isolated from nuclei after the incubation of Novikoff cells for 2 hours with 1 mcurie ³H-uridine per milliliter cells were 7.2 × 10⁶ and 2.4 × 10⁶ cpm/mg RNA, respectively.

The uptake of ³H-lysine and ³H-tryptophan into the TCA-insoluble fraction of Novikoff cells is shown in Fig. 14. The uptake of both amino acids was linear for 1½ to 2 hours after which the uptake was much slower. Dilution of the ³H-lysine with unlabeled lysine (0.1 mM)

resulted in a linear uptake for at least 7 hours, indicating that lysine starvation was the cause of the loss of linearity in the control. Addition of unlabeled lysine (0.4 mM) to the system at 30 minutes effectively terminated the uptake of ^{3}H-lysine into the Novikoff hepatoma ascites cells.

With 1 mcurie/ml packed cells, high specific activities were found in the nuclear and nucleolar protein fractions with both ^{3}H-lysine and ^{3}H-tryptophan in the medium (Table VI).

III. Discussion

In view of the findings of significant differences in the nucleolar compositions and oligonucleotide frequencies of nucleolar RNA of cancer cells and other cells (Busch and Smetana, .1970), it seems essential to cancer research to determine whether these differences are chemotherapeutically exploitable. None of the sequences of RNA's of tumor cells are known, with the exception of 5 S ribosomal RNA (Forget and Weissman, 1969). Accordingly, it seemed essential to the progress of molecular biology of cancer that improved methods become available at the earliest possible time for studies on individual nuclear and nucleolar RNA's. Although methods have been developed in this laboratory for isolation and purification of nucleolar components from kilogram quantities of tumors, the amounts of the high purity resulting products are insufficient to use the procedures worked out for yeast RNA by Holley *et al.* (Madison, 1970). The objective of the present technique was to obtain nuclear and nucleolar products with very high specific activity and thereby to take advantage of techniques developed (Sanger and Brownlee, 1967).

The technique described above for the *in vitro* incubation of Novikoff hepatoma ascites cells with various isotopic precursors yields very high specific activities of the complex macromolecules of the mammalian cell nucleus. The properties of the system are summarized below.

A. Specific Activities

By using Novikoff cells washed in a medium devoid of precursor, the uptake of the labeled precursor is extremely efficient. With ^{32}PO$_4$, specific activities as high as 9 × 10^9 counts/minute per milligram have been obtained for nucleolar 45 S RNA. With ^{3}H-uridine, specific activities of 7.2 × 10^6 counts/minute per milligram have been obtained for 45 S RNA, and with ^{3}H-lysine, 2.1 × 10^6 counts/minute per milligram for histones.

1. Uniformity of Labeling

Under the conditions described, the endogenous pool of precursors is quickly equilibrated with the isotopic compound. Thus, the UV and ^{32}P-nucleotide compositions and oligonucleotide frequencies are identical after a 2 hour labeling period (Tables VII and VIII). Structural studies on 4.5 S RNA (Ro-Choi et al., 1970) have shown that the labeling of each nucleotide unit in the molecule is equal and uniform.

2. Degradation

The very high specific activities achieved in the macromolecules of the nucleus (5 curies/mmole for 4.5 S RNA) might cause some concern as to the stability of these molecules to radiation-induced degradation. Such degradation has not been found even in a molecule as large as 45 S RNA (mol. wt. 3.5×10^6) in periods up to 1 month.

In any event, radiolytic degradation is unlikely to prove a serious drawback to the system for in nearly all cases the labeled macromolecules are used within a few days after they are isolated and have not been kept for periods of more than 2 months.

3. Kinetics of Labeling

In the case of ^{32}PO$_4$, linear uptake into the cells in a phosphate-free medium continues for up to 24 hours. The endogenous pool of phosphate is thus adequate. In the case of labeled amino acids or nucleosides in a precursor-free medium, linear uptake ceases after $1\frac{1}{2}$ to 2 hours. When the labeled amino acid is diluted with unlabeled carrier, linear uptake persists for at least 7 hours. With ^{32}PO$_4$ there is a lag period of 30 minutes before linear uptake into RNA begins. This effect appears to persist despite preincubation of the cells for up to 1 hour before isotope addition. Presumably this lag period is required for ^{32}PO$_4$ to equilibrate with the organically bound phosphate pools in the cell; the same lag period, however, was not observed with in vivo labeling (Quagliarotti et al., 1970); the reasons for this are not clear.

4. Stability of Cells

The cells remain viable throughout incubation as evidenced by the fact that uptake of isotopes into macromolecules is linear for 24 hours and by the fact that the RNA derived from nuclei and from ribosomes after 24 hours incubation showed no sign of degradation. Moreover, the cells retain their biosynthetic ability, since cells that had been stored at 2°C in medium for 30 hours gave essentially the same uptake of isotope and the same sedimentation profile of ^{32}P in nuclear RNA as cells that had been freshly prepared.

TABLE VII

THE ^{32}P AND ULTRAVIOLET NUCLEOTIDE COMPOSITION OF RAPIDLY SEDIMENTING NUCLEOLAR RIBONUCLEIC ACID FROM NOVIKOFF HEPATOMA ASCITES CELLS[a]

RNA Component	Adenosine (A)		Uridine (U)		Guanosine (G)		Cytidine (C)		Alkaline-resistant residue ^{32}P	A + U / G + C	
	monophosphate ^{32}P	UV[b]	monophosphate ^{32}P	UV[b]	monophosphate ^{32}P	UV[b]	monophosphate ^{32}P	UV[b]		^{32}P	UV[b]
Nucleolar 28 S	16.6±0.3	15.9±0.2	20.1±0.3	20.4±0.3	32.1±0.6	33.9±0.6	31.4±0.4	29.8±0.9	1.4	0.58	0.56
Nucleolar 35 S	16.5±0.3	16.3±0.5	19.6±0.3	20.8±0.8	32.0±0.3	33.3±1.0	31.9±0.4	29.6±1.0	1.0	0.56	0.58
Nucleolar 45 S	15.7±0.3	16.6±0.5	19.4±0.3	19.9±0.2	33.3±0.3	33.0±0.6	31.5±0.4	30.5±0.9	0.6	0.54	0.57
Ribosomal 28 S	16.8		18.0		35.1		30.1			0.53	—

[a] Results obtained following *in vitro* labeling of 20 gm cells with 50 mcuries ^{32}P in 1 liter of medium for 6 hours. The RNA, extracted from nucleoli and purified by density gradient separation, was hydrolyzed with 0.3 N KOH and the mononucleotides separated by Dowex 1 column chromatography. Standard errors were calculated by the following equation:

$$SE = \sqrt{\Sigma(x - \overline{x})^2/n(n - 1)}.$$

[b] Data from Choi *et al.*, 1968.

TABLE VIII

DISTRIBUTION OF RADIOACTIVITY IN MONO- AND OLIGONUCLEOTIDES
OF NUCLEOLAR RIBONUCLEIC ACIDS[a]

Nucleotides[b]	Percentage of total ^{32}P		
	28 S	35 S	45 S
C	28.5	27.8	27.4
U	12.6	12.8	12.7
pseudo U	0.6	0.7	0.7
AC	3.9	3.9	3.7
AU	2.9	2.9	2.9
GC	13.5	13.2	12.0
GU	8.9	9.2	8.8
AAC	1.5	1.6	1.4
AAU	1.9	1.1	1.7
AGC	6.6	7.0	6.7
AGU	3.9	4.1	3.9
GGC	3.8	4.1	3.5
GGU	1.7	1.4	1.3
AAAC	1.5	1.5	1.5
AAGC	3.0	3.6	3.2
AAGU	1.5	1.6	1.4
AAGC	2.7	2.4	2.2
AGGU	0.9	0.9	0.8
Residue	23.3	23.1	22.9

[a] Results obtained after 6 hours *in vitro* labeling of 20 gm Novikoff hepatoma cells (1:100) with 50 mcuries ^{32}P-orthophosphate. The values for each sequence are the percentages of total radioactivity from each RNA found in the nineteen eluted spots.
[b] C—cytidine; U—uridine; A—adenosine; G—guanosine.

B. USEFULNESS OF THE PROCEDURE

The procedures described above can be utilized for a variety of purposes. It is possible to separate nearly all the RNA components by electrophoresis on 2.8% acrylamide slab gels (Loening, 1967). The high specific activity of RNA permits short-exposure radioautographs to detect the position of the bands in the slab gel.

1. Structural Studies

The sequence of RNA molecules can be elucidated on a microscale (Brownlee and Sanger, 1967; Fellner *et al.*, 1970) by radioautographic mapping of the oligonucleotides released by pancreatic and T_1 RNase digestion. Studies in this laboratory (Ro-Choi *et al.*, 1970) on 4.5 S RNA from Novikoff nuclei have shown the feasibility of the present method for structural analysis on mammalian RNA.

2. Hybridization Experiments

The technique of hybridization is a powerful analytical tool which requires activities of the order of 1×10^6 to 1×10^7 counts/minute per milligram RNA if meaningful results are to be obtained.

3. Kinetic Studies on the Biosynthesis and Turnover of RNA and Nuclear Proteins

Using modern techniques, it is possible to isolate nuclei from as little as 2 gm of cells, and nucleoli from 4 gm of cells. The histone and nonhistone protein can be extracted from these organelles and separated by disc gel electrophoresis. Rapid labeling of these proteins, with high specific activities, will permit kinetic studies to be made on their rates of biosynthesis and turnover.

ACKNOWLEDGMENTS

The authors are indebted to Dr. Tae-Suk Ro-Choi and to Dr. Joan Wikman who supplied the data on the 4–7 S RNA and 28 S rRNA, respectively. We also wish to thank Charles Taylor for skilled technical assistance.

REFERENCES

Adams, J. M., Jeppesen, P. G. N., Sanger, F., and Barrell, B. G. (1969). *Nature* **223**, 1009–1014.

Bray, G. A. (1960). *Anal. Biochem.* **1**, 279–285.

Brownlee, G. G., and Sanger, F. (1967). *J. Mol. Biol.* **23**, 337–353.

Busch, H. (1967a). *Methods Enzymol.* **12**, Part A, 421–448.

Busch, H. (1967b). *Methods Enzymol.* **12**, Part A, 448–464.

Busch, H., and Smetana, K. (1970). *In* "The Nucleolus." Academic Press, New York.

Choi, Y. C., Smetana, K., and Busch, H. (1968). *Exptl. Cell Res.* **53**, 582–602.

Eagle, H. (1955a). *Science* **122**, 501.

Eagle, H. (1955b). *J. Biol. Chem.* **214**, 839–852.

Earle, W. R. (1963). *J. Natl. Cancer Inst.* **4**, 165–212.

Fellner, P., Ehresmann, C., and Ebel, J. P. (1970). *Nature* **225**, 26–31.

Forget, B. G., and Weissman, S. M. (1967a). *Nature* **213**, 878.

Forget, B. G., and Weissman, S. M. (1967b). *Science* **158**, 1695.

Forget, B. G., and Weissman, S. M. (1969). *J. Biol. Chem.* **244**, 3148–3165.

Gillespie, D. (1968). *Methods Enzymol.* **12**, Part B, 641–668

Gillespie, D., and Spiegelman, S. (1956). *J. Mol. Biol.* **12**, 829–842.

Higashi, K., Shankar Narayanan, K., Adams, H. R., and Busch, H. (1966). *Cancer Res.* **26**, 1582–1590.

Hurlbert, R. B., Schmitz, H., Bruman, A. F., and Potter, V. R. (1954). *J. Biol. Chem.* **209**, 23–39.

Loening, V. E. (1967). *Biochem. J.* **102**, 251–257.

Madison, J. T. (1970). *Methods Cancer Res.* **5**, 229–250.

Muramatsu, M., and Busch, H. (1967). *Methods Cancer Res.* **2**, 303–359.

Muramatsu, M., Hodnett, J. L., Steele, W. J., and Busch, H. (1966). *Biochim. Biophys. Acta* **123**, 116–125.

Nichols, J. L. (1970). *Nature* **225**, 147–151.

Peacock, A. C., and Dingman, C. W. (1968). *Biochemistry* **7**, 668–674.

Quagliarotti, G. C., Hidvegi, E., Wikman, J., and Busch, H. (1970). *J. Biol. Chem.* **245**, 1962–1969.

Ro-Choi, T. S., Moriyama, Y., Choi, Y. C., and Busch, H. (1970). *J. Biol. Chem.* **245**, 1970–1977.

Rushizky, G. W., and Knight, C. A. (1960). *Proc. Natl. Acad. Sci. U.S.* **46**, 947–952.

Sanger, F., and Brownlee, G. G. (1967). *Methods Enzymol.* **12**, Part A, 361–381.

Sanger, F., Brownlee, G. G., and Barrell, B. G. (1965). *J. Mol. Biol.* **13**, 373–398.

Steele, W. J., and Busch, H. (1967). *Methods Cancer Res.* **3**, 62–152.

Steele, W. J., Okamura, N., and Busch, H. (1965). *J. Biol. Chem.* **240**, 1742–1749.

Weinberg, R. A., Loening, V. E., Willems, M., and Penman, S. (1967). *Proc. Natl. Acad. Sci. U.S.* **58**, 1088–1095.

Wikman, J., Howard, E., and Busch, H. (1969). *J. Biol. Chem.* **244**, 5471–5480.

CHAPTER VI

ELECTRON MICROSCOPY OF NUCLEIC ACIDS

MICHAEL BEER, PAUL BARTL, THEODOR KOLLER, AND HAROLD P. ERICKSON

I. Introduction

Many of the central problems of molecular biology require for their solution extensive understanding of the structure and interactions of nucleic acid molecules. These are often most directly illuminated by examination of nucleic acids or the nucleic acid-containing systems in the electron microscope. Methods have been developed to determine the length and configuration of double- or single-stranded nucleic acids, to find in double-stranded nucleic acids those regions that are rich in AT* base pairs, and to determine the positions of those regions for which deletion mutants are available. Often the diameter of nucleic acid-containing structures and the number of molecules within a complex must be known. The sites of interaction of nucleic acid strands with particular protein molecules is an area demanding increased attention. Finally considerable progress has been made toward an electron-microscopic determination of the sequence of bases in nucleic acids. In this review techniques are presented which have been developed in connection with such problems.

All of the techniques have a number of steps in common. First the nucleic acid must be prepared, and the worker must be assured that it is available in the state optimal for study. Next the material must be transferred to the specimen-supporting films which are suspended over the grids generally used to carry them. Then, to make the nucleic acid molecules on the film more detectable, the preparation can be "stained" appropriately or "shadowed." The first procedure is based on the attachment of electron-scattering heavy ions to nucleic acid molecules. The latter procedure involves evaporating electron-scattering material onto the specimen and highlighting its morphological features. Finally the specimen is ready for examination in the electron microscope where its images can be recorded on photographic emulsions. The plates and films obtained are converted to prints on which the analysis can be conveniently carried out. In the following each of these steps will be reviewed in considerable detail.

II. Preparation of Nucleic Acids

A. EXTRACTION

The extraction of nucleic acids from various biological tissues has been extensively covered in "Methods of Enzymology" (Grossman and Moldave, 1967) or in "Procedures in Nucleic Acid Research" (Cantoni and Davies, 1966). The subject will not be discussed here. However, a few relevant precautions seem in order. When phenol extraction is used it is advisable to use freshly redistilled phenol (from commercially available crystalline or preservative-free liquefied phenol). Oxidation products are formed in phenol by simultaneous action of light and air. Their presence in older preparations of phenol may produce breaks in

---

* AT, adenine-thymine.

polynucleotide chains due to oxidation. To avoid this, phenol should be redistilled in the presence of zinc powder (according to some authors) in nitrogen atmosphere and the product collected under tris or phosphate buffer, pH 7–8, to neutralize the slight acidity of phenol.

Phenol extraction itself does not inactivate nucleases—another source of breaks in polynucleotide chains. The isolation of nucleic acids from bacteriophages by concentrated solutions of sodium perchlorate (Freifelder, 1966) seems to be more effective from this point of view. The cells or particles from which nucleic acids are isolated (Kislina et al., 1968) may not be the only source of nucleases. Ribonucleases are practically ubiquitous, i.e., fingertips, dialysis tubing, some chemicals, and glassware may carry traces of nucleases and activating divalent cations. Therefore, surgical gloves, boiling of dialysis tubing in several changes of sodium bicarbonate solution followed by several exchanges of distilled water and soaking in ethylenediaminetetraacetate (EDTA) solution (Scheffler et al., 1968), fresh buffer solutions, and glassware cleaned with chromic acid are used to reduce the danger of the action of nucleases.

Another precaution to avoid breakage of nucleic acid molecules is to expose them to a minimum of shear forces (Hershey and Burgi, 1960; Josse and Eigner, 1966; Davidson and Freifelder, 1966) during pipetting, stirring, etc. This is of particular importance for preparations of nucleic acid molecules of molecular weights of several tens of millions of daltons. Wide-bore pipettes, very slow flow rates, and slow stirring or rocking during phenol extraction reduce the degradation of long nucleic acid molecules, particularly single-stranded ones.

B. REACTION WITH BASE-SELECTIVE REAGENTS

Some time ago a suggestion was made for an electron-microscopic determination of the sequence of bases in the nucleic acids (Beer and Moudrianakis, 1962). The procedure outlined requires that nucleic acid macromolecules be prepared, in which one of the bases is marked through the selective attachment of an electron-scattering group which might identify the position of the base when the nucleic acid is viewed in the electron microscope. Thus far, no new nucleotide sequence has been determined through electron microscopy. Nevertheless, procedures have been worked out for selective binding of potential markers. The two best understood reagents are (a) the guanine-specific attachment of 2-diazo-p-benzenedisulfonic acid and (b) the thymine-specific reaction of osmium tetroxide in the presence of cyanide ion.

1. Preparation of Nucleic Acids in Which the Guanine Bases are Selectively Marked with Benzenedisulfonic Acid Groups (Moudrianakis and Beer, 1965a,b; Erickson and Beer, 1967)

2-Amino-p-benzenedisulfonic acid is purified by repeated precipitation with concentrated HCl from an alkaline solution. The diazonium salt is made by dissolving 126 gm of the purified amine in 400 ml of water and 22 ml of 50% sodium hydroxide. Forty grams of $NaNO_2$ is added in the cold, the solution is filtered, and 100 ml of 12 N HCl is added. The diazonium salt precipitates as a white slurry. It is filtered in the cold and stored at a concentration of 0.8 M in 0.05 N HCl at $-70°C$. Under these conditions, the diazonium activity decreases by less than 50% during 1 year.

The nucleic acid to be marked is dissolved in 1 ml of water or 0.1 M $NaHCO_3$ buffer at pH 9. One milliliter of diazonium slurry at $0°C$ is brought to pH 8 to 9 by the addition of about 0.03 ml of 50% NaOH. This is added to the nucleic acid solution; thereafter the pH is maintained at 9.0 with a saturated solution of K_2CO_3 adjusted to pH 11.5 with HCl. The reaction is rapid at first, but slows down as the diazonium decays. After 10 or 15 minutes, more diazonium is added and the procedure repeated until necessary. Finally the reacted nucleic acid is purified on Sephadex G-75.

The macromolecular component obtained has benzenedisulfonic groups on both the guanine residues and the others. To convert the product into one where primarily guanines are labeled, the nucleic acid must be incubated at pH 4. To do this the nucleic acid is precipitated by ethanol and redissolved in 0.1 M sodium acetate at pH 4 and incubated for 1 hour at $37°C$. The product obtained is a nucleic acid in which primarily the guanine residues carry the benzenedisulfonic groups.

Often the interaction with the diazonium salt leads to some fragmentation of the nucleic acid molecules, but the unbroken components can be recovered by sucrose gradient centrifugation or appropriate Sephadex chromatography.

2. Preparation of Deoxyribonucleic Acid in Which the Thymine Bases are Selectively Marked (Beer et al., 1966; Highton et al., 1968; Di Giamberardino et al., 1969)

It is possible to produce deoxyribonucleic acid (DNA) in which approximately 90% of the thymines are converted to an addition product of the thymine base with 1 mole of osmium tetroxide and 2 moles of cyanide ion. The reaction which requires single strands is gentle and leaves molecules as long as ϕX-174 DNA essentially unbroken. As the reaction proceeds the buoyant density of the macromolecule increases. This can be shown by cesium chloride, equilibrium, density gradient centrifugation. A convenient method of preparation is the following.

A reagent solution is made using OsO_4 and KCN neutralized with HCl and dissolved in water from a quartz still to give a solution 0.2 M OsO_4 and 0.2 M KCN at pH 7.0. To the solution an equal volume of denatured DNA is added in concentration up to 100 $\mu g/ml$ in 0.01 M NaCl. The resulting solution is sealed in a glass tube and incubated in a water bath at 55°C for 4 hours. After the reaction the solution is passed through a column containing Sephadex G-75 (particle size, 40–120 μ), and eluted with 0.01 M NaCl. The fractions are pooled. It appears that the reaction product is not completely stable and should be used for electron microscopy as soon as possible after preparation. The decay appears to have a half-life of perhaps 100 hours at 25°C.

III. Preparation of Substrate Films

A. CARBON

At present, the usual method used for the preparation of carbon films is that developed by Bradley (1954). Carbon is evaporated in vacuum by passing high electric current through the tips of two pointed carbon electrodes in contact (Spencer, 1959; Cotte, 1960). The heat-evaporated carbon forms a uniform coherent layer by condensation on smooth surface. In this way, thin carbon films can be obtained (several tens of angströms thick); they are transparent to electrons and stable in the beam of the electron microscope.

Freshly cleaved mica is a suitable smooth surface for the condensation of thin carbon layers. Pieces of freshly cleaved mica are placed in high vacuum ($\sim 10^{-4}$ torr) at a distance of perhaps 15 cm from the electrodes. Carbon is evaporated by short bursts of electric current of 50 to 100 amp. The amount of evaporated carbon can be easily determined visually by placing a piece of white filter paper near the mica and folding it so that carbon deposits only on a part of it. The amount of carbon on mica should not exceed an almost undetectable grayish-brown layer on a white paper placed beside the mica.

After removing the mica from the vacuum, the carbon film can easily be floated off by submerging the mica into hot distilled water at a shallow angle with the carbon layer up.

On the bottom of the trough, grids are placed on a piece of filter paper. By slowly draining off the water the carbon film settles on the grids and after drying they are ready for use. As mentioned previously, a thin carbon film should have almost no color and should be visible on the water surface in reflected light only. It can be pushed gently across the water surface by needles to adjust it over the grids before it settles on them. At present, thin carbon films thus obtained are the most easily prepared substrate for high-resolution work.

B. FORMVAR

The Formvar films (Schaefer and Harber, 1942) are prepared by evaporation of 0.5 to 1.0% w/v solution of Formvar (polyvinyl formal) in chloroform from the surface of a clean microscope slide. The microscope slide is held in a vertical position during drying. Thus, at the upper edge, a thinner film is formed than at the lower edge of the slide. The dry film is cut off at the edges with a razor blade and floated off on a water surface in the same way as described previously for carbon films.

A Formvar film of proper thickness ($\sim$100 Å) should not show any interference color on water. Only those areas of the film that appear silver-gray in reflected light should be used for the grids.

C. COLLODION

The collodion films are the most easily prepared substrate for routine low-resolution work (Ruska, 1939). One or several drops of 1.0% w/v solution of collodion (nitrocellulose) in amyl acetate are placed on the water surface in a petri dish, 9–10 inches in diameter. The collodion solution spreads readily over the surface in a very thin layer. By evaporation of the solvent, a collodion film forms, some 200 Å thick with no interference colors. The 200-mesh supporting grids can be carefully placed on the film while it is still floating on water. Then a filter paper is laid from the top onto the film with the grids. The film attaches itself to it and can be lifted from the water; the grids are between the film and the filter paper. After the film is dried, the coated grids are ready for use. The Formvar films can be picked up from water in the same way.

The Formvar films are more resistant to electron bombardment than collodion. The resistance of both types is greatly improved by evaporating a thin layer of carbon onto them.

Both Formvar and collodion films show considerable structure due to semicrystalline micelles. They are suitable for routine work only at lower magnifications and lesser demands on resolution. They are semipermeable, and thus the salts in preparation can be dialyzed out by leaving the film with a drop on it simply floating on water or buffer surfaces. These films are much less stable in the beam than carbon films.

D. COLLODION FILMS WITH HOLES

These films (Drahos and Delong, 1960) are a suitable test object for astigmatism corrections. They can be used, as well, to support ultrathin carbon films which are mechanically not strong enough to stretch over the openings of 400-mesh grids.

The preparation of films with holes has many common features with the preparation of Formvar films. A microscope glass slide is dipped into a 0.25% w/v solution of collodion in isoamyl acetate about 2 cm high in a calibrated cylinder or staining dish. The glass slide is held by forceps for about 0.5 minute in a vertical position just above the solution level where the space is saturated with acetate vapors. Most of the collodion solution drains off and only a very thin layer remains. The slide is taken out vertically and the solution begins to dry from the top. At this moment, one breathes [a short breath (only a fraction of a second)] at the glass from a distance of 2 to 5 inches. Water vapor condenses, and microdroplets on the glass leave holes in the collodion film formed by the drying solution. The short breathing can be repeated several times before the solution from the whole area on the glass slide dries. The cluster of small holes is seen as an opaque strip, about 1 mm wide, at the edge of the drying solution. The wider the strip, the larger the droplets and, consequently, the larger the diameter of the holes. With some practice, holes with average diameters down to tenths of a micron can be produced. After coating with carbon, they are useful in astigmatism correction or as a support for very thin carbon films.

E. THIN CARBON FILMS ON HOLEY FILM SUPPORTS

The use of extremely thin carbon support films is of interest in high-resolution work, since it minimizes the extent of inelastic scattering of the electrons. These films break easily during the specimen preparation and also in the electron beam. Therefore a support by holey film is often required.

A grid already carrying a holey carbon film is covered with a standard collodion membrane as described above. Then a very thin carbon layer is evaporated onto this collodion film. The very small amount evaporated is best controlled by the indirect evaporation method: about 1 inch below the carbon rods a glass plate is mounted horizontally, to prevent the carbon from reaching the grids directly. The amount evaporated should be less than what is visible on a filter paper, which is partially covered with a mask. It is best checked in the electron microscope after dissolving the collodion or Formvar membrane as described below. Breakage of the carbon films over the largest holes but not over the smaller ones indicates that the films are as thin as possible.

The dissolving of the collodion film is delicate and requires some experience. It is best done in a small dish separated into two compartments by a porous plastic wall. The dish is filled with a solvent (ethanol–ether or acetone). At an angle of 45° to the liquid surface, the grids (not more than 2 or 3) are submerged in one of the compartments. After about 5 minutes, the solvent is slowly removed from the other compartment by suction. The remaining solvent is evaporated under a light bulb until the grids are completely dry.

F. Supporting Films of Single Crystals of Graphite

The supporting films mentioned until now have been traditionally used for the last 20 years. At high magnification, under conditions designed to detect small differences in mass in the specimen, the operator becomes aware of a limitation which is inherent in these supporting films. Electron micrographs of the films show a granularity the magnitude of which is a function of the amount of defocus, being a minimum at exact focus and increasing on either side. This granularity is what sets the limit on the smallest mass which is detectable in the electron microscope today. It is not surprising that considerable effort has gone into attempts to produce supporting films which are free of it. One of the most attractive suggestions for avoiding random granularity was to use single crystal supports (Fernández-Morán, 1960) and of these mica and graphite seem particularly attractive. For both, many claims have been made for successful cleavage by pulling the layers apart using Scotch tape and repeating this process until the thickness is decreased to a usable level. In the final step the Scotch tape is removed from the graphite or mica flake by appropriate solvents. These procedures however, are exceedingly slow. More recently three more convenient methods have been developed for the production of graphite supporting films.

Method 1: Pyrolytic growth of graphite on single crystals of nickel (Karu and Beer, 1966). Strips of high-purity nickel (A. D. Mackay and Co., New York) 0.0025 inch thick are heated in a very clean vacuum chamber at 10^{-7} torr by passing current to a temperature of 900°C for a period of 8 to 10 hours. Such strips when cooled and examined under a metallurgical microscope give clear evidence of single crystals in the size range of a few microns. When these nickel films are returned to the vacuum system, heated again to a temperature of 1100°C, and methane gas is passed into the chamber to a pressure of 5×10^{-3} torr, a dark surface will begin to cover the hot nickel. The pyrolitic reaction is allowed to continue for a period of 1 to 5 minutes, after which time the heating current is switched off, the nickel strip is allowed to cool, and the graphite is floated off the nickel on the surface of HCl. The graphite is transferred to water and washed by changing it several times with fresh water. Finally it is picked up on standard grids in a manner typical for evaporated carbon films. Such grids are then ready for use. This method is simple but does not yield very thin graphite films.

Method 2: Chemically cleaved graphite support films (Dobelle and Beer, 1968). Graphite crystals can be cleaved into extremely thin layers by chemical treatment. A procedure based on drastic oxidation to graphite oxide has been successful and is described here.

The following chemicals are thoroughly mixed with a magnetic stirrer in a 150-ml beaker: (*a*) 1 gm of 325-mesh powdered graphite flake (obtainable from Asbury Graphite Mills, Inc., Asbury, New Jersey); (*b*) 0.5 gm sodium nitrate; and (*c*) 23 ml of concentrated sulfuric acid. The flask is immersed in an ice bath and the contents allowed to cool; 3 gm of potassium permanganate are added slowly while stirring and the temperature is maintained below 20°C. After complete solution, stirring is continued for 5 minutes. The reaction mixture is removed from the ice bath, warmed to 35°C, and stirred on a magnetic stirrer. As the temperature rises, the beaker is returned to the ice bath to maintain the temperature between 32° and 40°C. Stirring is continued for 30 minutes.

An equal volume of distilled water is slowly added and the temperature is maintained for 10 to 15 minutes at $98° \pm 5°$C. This is very conveniently done by occasionally warming the mixture on a hot plate. Subsequently the beaker is removed from the hot plate and allowed to cool, and 10 ml of 3% hydrogen peroxide is added. The contents of the beaker are centrifuged at 500 rpm in a desk top Sorvall centrifuge for 1 minute. The precipitate is discarded; the supernatant is centrifuged and the new precipitate is washed by several resuspensions and sedimentations. The last suspension is diluted in 10 volumes of ethanol and allowed to settle 48 hours in the refrigerator. The yellow supernatant suspension is suitable for spraying on a holey carbon film. The ethanol wets the carbon film and the suspended thin graphite flakes are stretched across the holes. The films so produced are exceedingly thin and appear to be less granular than evaporated carbon films.

Method 3: Pyrolitic conversion of evaporated carbon films into graphite films (White *et al.*, 1969). At high temperature in an inert atmosphere it is known that amorphous carbon can be converted to graphite. This fact has recently been used to produce highly crystalline graphite films in a form convenient for support of specimens for electron microscopy.

To withstand the high temperatures necessary, the standard grids must be replaced by ones made of graphite. These can be produced by cleaving thin slices from a graphitized carbon rod with the crystal C axis running along the cylinder axis, and drilling holes into this graphite disc by blasting with an abrasive drill through a mask of stainless steel mesh. This procedure has been described by Turnbull and Williamson (1963). Subsequently the carbon grid is covered with a holey carbon film produced as mentioned previously. The grid covered with holey film is finally covered with a thin film of evaporated carbon produced as previously described (Section III, E). This grid is dried and is ready for the heat treatment.

This heat treatment is carried out in a furnace (e.g., Astro Model 2570 C) at a temperature of 2500° to 2600°C for a time of 1 to 5 minutes in an inert atmosphere of argon or nitrogen. The absence of oxygen in the atmosphere surrounding the grids is important since small traces are enough to lead to the loss of the thin films used.

The graphite films here described appear less grainy than similar films of evaporated carbon. However a reliable quantitative comparison is not yet available.

IV. Deposition of Nucleic Acids

A. SPRAYING OF NUCLEIC ACIDS ONTO MICA

Hall (1956) introduced a technique for spraying nucleic acids onto mica. This procedure is convenient for short macromolecules or in cases where fragmentation due to shear is unimportant. High quality mica in rectangles 1×2 inches can be commercially obtained (Essex Wire Corporation, Peabody, Massachusetts). The mica is cleaved by inserting a razor blade at the edge and separating the layers. Nucleic acid solution is sprayed onto the freshly cleaved surfaces. This solution must contain only volatile salts, such as acetic acid, ammonium acetate, or ammonium carbonate to avoid residual salt on the specimen. The concentration of the nucleic acid is conveniently approximately 10 μg/ml. The spraying is readily accomplished through a Vaponephrin nebulizer using perhaps ten puffs at a distance of 5 cm. The puffs should not be given in too rapid succession so that there is time for drying between them. In this way, puddles on the mica are avoided. After the nucleic acid has been sprayed, the mica is transferred to a vacuum system where the specimen is shadowed in a conventional way. In this technique, as originally described by Hall, platinum shadowing was used, but since then finer grain materials have also been employed successfully. Shadowing angles

θ, with tan $\theta = 1/7$ to $1/10$ are usual. After shadowing, carbon is deposited from a direction perpendicular to the plane of the mica in a manner which is usual for carbon film production, and to a thickness which is again comparable to the film thicknesses used for specimen supports. The use of carbon at this stage is again a deviation from Hall's original use of silicon monoxide, possibly followed by collodion, but appears satisfactory and simpler. The mica is then removed from the vacuum chamber and the carbon and platinum are floated off with water in the usual way, and the films are picked up on grids. These are now ready for examination in the electron microscope.

B. PREPARATIONS INVOLVING PROTEIN MONOLAYERS

The original method of adsorbing DNA or ribonucleic acid (RNA) molecules from a bulk solution to a monomolecular protein film (Kleinschmidt and Zahn, 1959) has been perfected and good reproducibility can be obtained. Through the use of this and related methods, much information has been collected on the structure of a wide variety of single- and double-stranded nucleic acid molecules.

Many globular proteins (e.g., cytochrome c, chymotrypsin, trypsin, albumin, lysozyme, and ribonuclease) can be spread in the form of a monomolecular film on the surface of water or aqueous solutions. By denaturation on the surface, the polypeptide chain unfolds. Thus, a predominantly two-dimensional molecular network is formed. The side chains of the polypeptide network carry positive charges on their basic groups. The DNA or RNA molecules, with negative charges on the phosphate groups, are adsorbed to the polypeptide film. By touching it, the surface film can be transferred to a grid, covered by a supporting membrane. Specimens thus obtained can subsequently be contrasted and observed in the electron microscope.

Several modifications of this method exist (Kleinschmidt, 1968):

1. The Spreading Procedure (Kleinschmidt and Zahn, 1959)

A shallow trough with hydrophobic surface (paraffin-coated glass, Teflon, or Teflon-coated metal) is filled with an aqueous solution or water, the so-called subphase, which may contain a variety of reagents to suit the designed experiment. Surface-active compounds should be avoided since they interfere with the formation of a uniform and coherent protein film. For the same reason, the surface of the subphase should be perfectly clean. The cleaning of the surface can be achieved by streaking a glass rod or a Teflon bar several times over the meniscus of the subphase (e.g., 0.25 M ammonium acetate in H_2O, pH 7) in the trough.

A small volume of a solution containing both the protein and the nucleic acid studied (e.g., 1 M ammonium acetate, 2 mg/ml double-stranded DNA, and 100 mg/ml cytochrome c) is spread on the surface of the subphase via a ramp (a clean glass slide) submerged at a shallow angle into the subphase. Dusting the surface onto which the film is going to be spread, with a little talcum powder, makes it simple to locate the film and to observe the spreading. The adsorption of nucleic acid molecules occurs simultaneously during the spreading of the surface film. During the spreading, salt concentration gradients occur between the spread solution and the subphase. Also, the protein molecules undergo reorientation in the surface by movements in two directions. Thus the nucleic acid molecules are exposed to some un-defined shearing forces and their two-dimensional arrangement may be affected. One has to bear this in mind when interpreting the electron micrographs.

A number of studies have already been carried out where single-stranded nucleic acid molecules were readily observed (Freifelder et al., 1964; Inman, 1967; Westmoreland et al., 1969). In the former two cases, precautions had to be taken to insure that, after the hydrogen bonds are broken to produce the single strands, these bonds are not re-formed. This is readily done by adding formaldehyde to the system to a concen-tration of 1 to 4%. The spreading procedure can be carried out equally well with this material in solution.

2. The Diffusion Procedure (Lang et al., 1964, 1967)

In this procedure, the spreading of the protein film and the adsorption of nucleic acid molecules to it occur independently. The trough is filled with a solution of nucleic acid 20–100× more dilute (0.01–0.05 μg/ml) than that used for spreading. A protein film, as in the procedure de-scribed previously, is then spread over the nucleic acid solution. The nucleic acid molecules in the surface of the solution become adsorbed irreversibly to the protein film. If one leaves the protein film over the nucleic acid solution for a longer time, more molecules diffuse to it and get attached. Thus the amount of nucleic acid molecules adsorbed to the film increases with time.

In this procedure, the nucleic acid molecules are not exposed to any shearing forces. Yet, in the interpretation of electron micrographs of heterogeneous nucleic acids, one must not forget that shorter mole-cules have a higher diffusion coefficient; therefore relatively more of them will be adsorbed to the film and the distribution of the lengths of molecules on the film will not represent the situation in the bulk solution.

3. The One-Step Release Procedure (Kleinschmidt et al., 1962; Dunne-backe and Kleinschmidt, 1967)

This technique is suitable in those cases where the release process of the nucleic acid (e.g., from a bacteriophage) is to be demonstrated or if only a very small amount of the source of nucleic acid is available. The spreading of the protein film and the extraction of the nucleic acid occur at the same time. The release of the nucleic acid may be induced by an osmotic shock (high salt concentration in the spread solution and low salt in the subphase) or by protein denaturing compounds (sodium perchlorate or urea) in the subphase. The expelled nucleic acid is immediately adsorbed to the protein film and thus can often be found near, or still attached, to the virus or cell from which it originates.

The methods described have found great use in length measurements of nucleic acid molecules, usually plotted in the form of histograms showing the length distribution. The factors affecting the observed length of nucleic acid molecules have been reviewed by Inman (1967). Information may also be obtained on the tertiary and quaternary structure of nucleic acid molecules (coils, branched molecules, circles, supercoiled or intercalated circles, etc.) as well as on molecular products of denaturation and annealing. The interpretation of width measurements of filamentous molecules is less reliable since insufficient information is available on the state of nucleic acid molecules in the protein film from this point of view, i.e., whether they are enveloped in or nakedly adsorbed by the protein film.

C. DIRECT ADSORPTION OF NUCLEIC ACIDS TO SUPPORTING FILMS

In this section a group of techniques is discussed which allows the preparation of specimens of unbroken nucleic acid strands without the use of a protein film. The molecules are directly adsorbed onto the supporting film, which in most of the cases is already mounted on a grid.

This method was first described by Beer (1961). The films can be a copolymer of styrene and vinylpyridine, which has weakly basic ion exchange properties, or standard evaporated carbon. The DNA is adsorbed as parallel, straight molecules on the film as the grid is streaked along the surface of a nucleic acid solution for a distance of about 2 cm and at a speed of 2 cm/sec. The direction of streaking is noted on the grids. The excess liquid is immediately drawn off by touching the edge of the grid to absorbent filter paper so that the flow direction of the receding excess liquid is the same as the direction of streaking. The abundance of the strands transferred depends on the pH, the ionic strength, and the concentration of the DNA solution. Satisfactory conditions are DNA concentration, 1–3 μg/ml, and buffer, 0.1 M ammonium acetate, pH 6.1.

Highton and Beer (1963) demonstrated unbroken, single-stranded, tobacco mosaic virus (TMV) RNA molecules. The RNA was heated to 45°C in the presence of 4% formaldehyde to obtain a configuration without hydrogen bonding at room temperature. Grids covered with carbon films were streaked as described by Beer (1961) across the surface of 1 ml of RNA solution. This had a concentration of 25 μg/ml of RNA in 0.01 M sodium phosphate buffer at pH 6.8 with 4% formaldehyde, 10^{-4} M EDTA. The RNA solution was heated for 15 minutes at 45°C and then cooled rapidly to about 10°C. On the grids, strands were observable as a uniform distribution of well-separated straight strands, oriented parallel to one another and to the direction of streaking.

The number of molecules deposited on the carbon films increased with increasing ionic strength and RNA concentration. Below 0.01 M ionic strength, almost no strands were observed.

Length measurements indicated that most of the molecules were either unbroken or suffered only one break. From the known molecular weight of TMV RNA the base spacing was calculated to be between 5 and 6 Å, indicating a certain amount of stretching of the strands during the deposition on the grid.

Similar results can be obtained by putting a drop of double- or single-stranded nucleic acid (2–5 μg DNA/ml in 0.02 M salt) on a grid carrying a carbon film. The liquid is then removed by touching the edge of the grid to a piece of filter paper.

A similar technique was described by Bendet et al. (1962). The DNA strands were obtained by mild alkali treatment of the virus. One or two milliliters of a solution containing 0.5–1 μg/ml T3 in 0.1 M ammonium acetate and 10^{-4} M EDTA is placed on a collodion-covered microscope slide. The slide is then tilted to an angle of 45° and the excess liquid allowed to flow off onto bibulous paper. After shadowing the films are floated on water and picked up on grids. With this procedure Bendet et al. (1962) were able to measure the length of T3 DNA molecules with a remarkably narrow length distribution.

The techniques described suffer from three major drawbacks:

1. Since the strands are oriented in one direction, the study of the contour of the molecules is difficult, e.g., circular nucleic acid molecules, such as ϕX-174 DNA, are seldom recognizable as ring-shaped. Mostly they appear as two intertwisted, parallel strands or as a "double" strand.

2. Depending upon the nucleic acid concentration the molecules tend to form multistranded, longitudinal aggregates, which are an artifact of the preparation procedure. This fact makes difficult the identification

of a particular strand as a single molecule (Erickson and Beer, 1968).

3. In order to reduce the frequency of aggregated molecules, it is advisable to work at the lowest possible nucleic acid concentration (0.5–2 μg/ml in 0.01 M salt). Under these conditions, however, the distribution of molecules over the grid is irregular and inconvenient for finding the individual strands.

It has been possible to overcome these problems. A standard carbon film is treated with a surface-active quaternary ammonium salt, which apparently adsorbs to it. In a recent paper, Koller et al. (1970) describe the use of a very dilute solution (10^{-5} %) of alkyl dimethylbenzyl-ammonium chloride (BAC), which is commercially available as a disinfectant (Zephiran, Winthrop). The grids with carbon, collodion, or Formvar films are floated on BAC overnight, blotted dry on a filter paper, and then touched to the surface of a solution containing 0.1–1.0 μg DNA/ml and 0.001–0.1 M salt (ammonium acetate or potassium chloride) at pH 5 to 7. The excess liquid is left on the grid for about 15 seconds and then removed with absorbent filter paper. The grid is finally washed on distilled water. Under these conditions, the distribution of small DNA molecules, such as ϕX-174, is regular over the whole grid.

The adsorption can be carried out with the nucleic acid solution at elevated temperature, and so one can gain some insight into the configurational changes accompanying warming. For example, ϕX-174 DNA at 20°C appears as a compact structure whereas at 55°C it occurs as a larger and thinner ring. Similarly, the gradual melting of double-stranded DNA can be readily followed if samples are taken at different temperatures during warming.

V. Shadowing

Most biological objects including DNA give rise to low inherent contrast in conventional electron microscopes. Consequently it is necessary to emphasize their structural features by either staining or shadowing. This latter procedure involves depositing strong electron-scattering metal by evaporation in vacuum onto the specimen in a direction which is far from parallel to the ultimate electron beam direction. Shadowing is either done from a fixed point relative to the fixed specimen or it is done while the specimen is rotated in its own plane so that, in effect, shadowing metal is deposited onto the specimen from all directions under a certain angle. The former procedure is more suitable in studies where the dimensions of the structure perpendicular to the plane of the film are of importance; the latter in cases where the length of a strand with variable direction has to be followed.

The operation is carried out in a vacuum system at pressures below

5×10^{-5} torr. The shadowing is generally deposited by evaporation from either a tungsten wire bent into a hairpin or from a tungsten wire basket for lumps of metal. The tungsten wire is heated with a heavy current to bring about the evaporation.

The choice of material to be evaporated determines the granularity of the deposited layer. For moderate resolution, platinum or gold, palladium, or uranium are being used and appear satisfactory. For finest detail, tungsten or osmium dioxide are used (Hart, 1963; Murphy and Goodman, 1960). When such detail is needed it is important to keep the thickness of the evaporated layer to a minimum—preferably less than the smallest dimensions to be identified.

A piece of paper can be placed beside the grids with a corner folded up to give a boundary between a region with, and another without metal deposition. Here the extent of deposition is readily judged: a barely visible film which may have a thickness of perhaps 5 to 10 Å leads to a level of contrast that allows easy visualization on the fluorescent screen of the electron microscope.

The clarity of the shadows can generally be improved by an aperture placed in front of the source of evaporating metal. This leads to a small and fixed effective source and so gives sharper shadows.

Before evaporation, when adequate vacuum is obtained, the tungsten wire is degassed by heating to a temperature that leads to near melting of the platinum metal. This preheating will invariably lead to a rise in the pressure within the vacuum system as gases trapped in the wire and adsorbed to it are released. It is desirable to maintain this heating for 5 minutes by which time again high vacuum should be obtained. In some evaporating systems it is possible to cover the grids during degassing and so prevent the deposition of the desorbed material. Subsequently the current can be raised gradually but never so high that the pressure exceeds 10^{-4} torr. The current is turned off when shadowing is judged adequate by the darkness of the filter paper.

When circular shadowing is desired the procedure is essentially the same as in linear shadowing with the exception that the grids are placed on a horizontal platform which can rotate in its own plane via a low-speed electric motor—generally a speed of 0.5 to 1 rps is satisfactory. This way several revolutions will occur during the process of evaporation of the metal.

VI. Staining

The contrast of nucleic acid molecules can be enhanced also by staining, that is, the chemical attachment of electron-scattering groups to the nucleic acid. The visibility by these procedures is generally less than that obtained by shadowing, but the structural information is generally more faithfully preserved.

In high-resolution studies, particularly on single-stranded nucleic acids, there is a clear need for a stain in which each cation has sufficient density to be individually detectable. Such a cation could indicate the position of each cation-binding group. With this possibility in view, tests have begun on the massive cation $(Ta_6Br_{12})^{2+}$ as a stain for DNA. The results so far indicate that this stain may, indeed, be superior to other stains in that the molecules are uniform in density and show high contrast.

A. URANYL ACETATE

One of the most popular stains is uranyl acetate which is generally used either in aqueous solution at a concentration of about 0.1 M (2%) with an unadjusted pH of 4.6 (Beer and Zobel, 1961) or in a solution of an organic solvent such as acetone (Gordon and Kleinschmidt, 1968) at a concentration of 10^{-5} M. In both cases, it is desirable that the preparation be stained immediately after it is made. Staining is usually carried out by floating the grid on the stain solution for a minute and then removing the excess stain by dabbing off with a filter paper or washing for a few seconds in ethanol.

B. DODECA-μ-BROMOHEXATANTALUM ACETATE

The anhydrous halide $(Ta_6Br_{12})Br_2$ can be produced according to Kuhn and McCarley (1965) by reduction of tantalum(V) halides with aluminum foil in a temperature gradient. Aqueous and alcoholic solutions of $(Ta_6Br_{12})^{2+}$ show distinct infrared absorption spectra (Kuhn and McCarley, 1965; Robin and Kuebler, 1965), the maxima at 15650 and 13300 cm^{-1} being characteristic for the complex with a 2+ charge. The $(Ta_6Br_{12})Br_2$ can be converted to the acetate or sulfate by ion-exchange on Dowex AG-1X-8(O'Hara 1968). Concentration of the stain is best done by rapid boiling of small volumes. At OD_{640} of about 15 to 20, the concentration of the solution seems to be suitable for staining nucleic acid molecules.

The authors generally use the acetate salt of the complex cation. In aqueous solution a good contrast of double-stranded DNA and nucleohistones can be obtained. The contrast of single strands, however, is at the limit of the visibility. For higher contrast, a fresh aqueous solution can be dried and the salt redissolved in 95% ethanol. The use of the ethanolic solution leads to overstaining with generally good visibility of single-stranded DNA (Koller et al., 1970).

Recently it has been found that single-stranded nucleic acid stains far better when deposited on the nonconducting substrate collodion than it does on carbon. Under these conditions a brief washing of the grids in water is necessary (Y. K. Lee, unpublished).

The grids are washed for 15 to 30 minutes on water from a quartz still immediately after the adsorption of the nucleic acid molecules and without drying in between. Immediately before use the staining solution is filtered through a Millipore filter (10 mμ). The grid is transferred to a first drop of staining solution on a Teflon surface to remove the adhering water droplet and then floated on a second one for 30 seconds to 2 minutes. Excess stain is removed from the specimens by washing in a mixture of 30% ethanol and 70% cyclohexane for 10 seconds.

C. Use of Polystyrene Sphere Shadow to Find Low-Density Nucleic Acid

Stained nucleic acid molecules may have a density that is too low for easy identification of the molecules on the fluorescent screen of the electron microscope. Yet these molecules are readily identified in shadowed preparation. A convenient procedure is to scatter polystyrene spheres on the preparation, shadow the grid, and concentrate on those nucleic acid molecules that traverse the shadow created by the polystyrene sphere. These molecules are easily found by virtue of the shadow contrast outside the sphere shadow. Within the sphere shadow, however, visibility is due to the staining (Beer and Zobel, 1961).

VII. Measurement of Strands

The magnification at which the images are recorded in the electron microscope depends first of all on the information sought. Clearly the magnification must be high enough so that the finest detail required is not lost in the grain of the plates used. For high-resolution work this question is discussed in detail in Section VIII. When contour lengths of linear molecules are required, often the detail needed is not less than 100 Å and instrumental magnifications of × 5000–10,000 are satisfactory provided the visibility is adequate for good focusing.

For quantitative work, an accurate calibration of the magnification of the electron microscope is essential. This is best done by obtaining micrographs of commercially available replica gratings with known spacing of lines. The micrographs of the grating naturally must be obtained under the same operating conditions as used on the sample. If, however, either of the grids is buckled the microscope will require refocusing when the grids are exchanged and, therefore, will be operating at a different magnification. A correction for this can be made if the amount of adjustment in focus is noted. Indeed, if after the first micrograph the objective lens requires overfocusing by Δf to give a correctly focused image of the second specimen, then the second magnification will be greater than the first by a factor of $[1 + \Delta f/f]$, where f is the focal length of the objective lens.

The calibration of magnification at high magnifications poses a problem since large numbers of grating lines cannot be included within one high-magnification micrograph. The grating rulings are sufficiently irregular so that only if several are included within one micrograph can one obtain an accurate calibration of the magnification. A good calibration at high magnification can, however, be based on a good calibration at low magnification and a ratio of the high magnification to the low magnification. This is readily obtained if the portion of the grating recorded at high magnification is included in the portion recorded at low magnification.

Alternatively, calibration at high magnification can be based on the observed separation of planes in crystals known through studies with X-ray diffraction. Many materials are suitable and calibration grids are readily prepared or are even available commercially.

When low magnification is used, micrographs must be checked for any variation in magnification over the area covered. This is easily recognized through the curvature of the grating lines. It is, of course, possible still to obtain precise dimensions of macromolecules, as was elegantly done by Lang et al. (1967).

Length measurements on nucleic acid molecules are most conveniently carried out with a map measurer. These devices give results which are generally reproducible to within 1% provided the lengths to be traced are at least tens of centimeters. To realize this the electron micrographs must either be enlarged or a tracing made of the projected enlarged image. In either case, it is important again to determine the magnification and to test its constancy over the field.

The length of double-stranded nucleic acid molecules is a measure of the molecular weight with the most thoroughly examined cases indicating a linear density of 192 daltons/Å, when the molecules are deposited either by the protein monolayer technique (Lang et al., 1967; Thomas and MacHattie, 1967) or on carbon films (MacHattie and Thomas, 1964). At ionic strengths below about 0.14 M, however, increased but variable lengths were observed, and it seems preferable to work above this level (Lang et al., 1967).

The linear density of single-stranded nucleic acid molecules appears more sensitive to the details of the preparation technique. Freifelder, Kleinschmidt, and Sinsheimer (1964) using the protein monolayer technique observed with formaldehyde-treated circular denatured ϕX-174 DNA a length of $1.77 \pm 0.13\,\mu$. This value is virtually the same as found for the double-stranded circle in which the same ϕX-174 DNA molecule forms a duplex with its own complement, suggesting that the internucleotide separation is the same, namely, 3.4 Å. On the other hand, Highton and Beer (1963) observed that for TMV RNA, under conditions which lead to strong orientation of the molecules, the average internucleotide distance was increased to about 5 to 6 Å.

Estimates of the strand diameter can be made on either stained or shadowed preparations. Naturally the former give information mainly about the diameter parallel to the supporting film. Staining also raises the question of whether the dimensions of the stained region are equal to the dimensions of the total structure of interest. Discrepancies in this regard might be illuminated by comparing data from negative staining with positive staining.

When small dimensions are to be measured in the electron microscope the accuracy of focus becomes important. Since most electron microscopes operate with a numerical aperture of about 10^{-2}, the tolerance in focus suggested by simple geometrical considerations is about $100\times$ the tolerance in the quantity to be measured. Thus for accuracies within 10 Å the focus must be correct to within 1000 Å.

When shadowed preparations are used, information is obtained generally about diameters perpendicular to the plane of the supporting film. The magnitude of the observed shadow, the angle of the shadowing, and the diameter are easily related through simple geometrical considerations. These lead to the relation

$$D = L \tan \theta$$

where D is the diameter of the strand, L is the length of shadow obtained when the shadowing occurs at right angles to the strand, and θ is the angle between the path of evaporating shadow materials and the surface of the specimen. The angle θ is best inferred from the ratio of the length of shadow and diameter of polystyrene spheres scattered on the specimen prior to shadowing.

When accurate diameters are required on structures not wider than a few angströms, it is important that the amount of metal deposited during shadowing not be too extensive. This is best assured by using varying amounts of shadowing metal and checking that this variable has no influence on the inferred diameter.

VIII. High-Resolution Microscopy and the Study of Nucleotide Sequences

In this section a brief discussion will be given of considerations relevant in high-resolution microscopy and particularly as it applies to the problem of the electron-microscopic determination of nucleotide sequences.

Modern commercial electron microscopes are capable of routinely achieving a resolution of 5 to 8 Å, and in favorable circumstances even 3 Å. It should be possible, then, to distinguish details in the object separated by this distance and, more important, to locate small details in the image with a comparable precision. Measurements on molecular models have shown that adjacent nucleotides will be about 8 Å apart in a completely extended polynucleotide chain. Length measurements on micrographs of specimens of RNA indicate that the average separation of nucleotides is actually only about 5.5 Å (Highton and Beer, 1963). In any case it is within the resolving power of the microscope to locate image details to within the precision of one nucleotide position. This is not to say that the individual nucleotides can be resolved. Each nucleotide will be several angströms in size, so that their images will normally overlap even at 5 Å resolution. The nucleic acid should, therefore, appear as a more or less continuous strand. To see and resolve specific nucleotides, stain groups are needed that are dense enough to be visible or detectable along the image of this strand and small enough to be located precisely.

The visibility of small stain groups can be considered in terms of the contrast produced by single atoms, in that the contrast of a group of atoms closer together than the resolution of the instrument should be additive. The amplitude contrast, due to the loss of electrons scattered outside the objective aperture, is variously calculated to be on the order of 0.1 to 1% (Haine, 1961; Scherzer, 1949) for a single heavy atom. Contrast can be enhanced significantly by underfocusing the objective lens to introduce phase-contrast effects. With optimum focus setting this phase contrast can be several times greater than the amplitude contrast (Scherzer, 1949; Eisenhandler and Siegel, 1966). In either case the contrast should be sufficient to allow one to detect an "isolated" atom by proper photographic recording techniques. The problem is that the atoms and molecular structures of interest are not "isolated" but are on the surface of a thin carbon film, which is itself many atomic layers thick. Random fluctuations in the number of carbon atoms and differences in the three-dimensional ordering over different small areas of the film produce a varying contrast or granularity in the image of carbon film. The granularity has an average size close to the resolution of the microscope, and the contrast of different 6-Å spots varies in magnitude by ± 3 to 10% for in-focus and moderately underfocused micrographs. This substrate noise is thus comparable in magnitude and generally greater than the contrast expected for the image of a single atom or small molecule. The problem of visualizing molecular details is one of distinguishing them from this noise. This problem was examined experimentally by Highton and Beer (1968).

Over structures much larger in size than the substrate granularity (or resolution) the noise will tend to be averaged out, as background spots with both positive and negative contrast will be included in the area. Inasmuch as this noise can be considered random over the area, so that the summation of contrast follows Poisson statistics, the expected random contrast of the whole area will be proportional to $1/(\text{area})^{1/2}$. Thus, if the average random contrast is $\pm 5\%$ for small 10-Å squares, it will be only $\pm 0.5\%$ for 100-Å square areas. Or if one is interested in visualizing areas 20 Å wide and 200 Å long, which might contain a section of a DNA molecule, the contrast of different areas of this size would be expected to vary randomly by $\pm 5/(40)^{1/2}$ or $\pm 0.8\%$. A section of DNA of this size and shape might be reliably detected if its contrast were $3 \times$ as large as this random noise. Any given small section of the molecule, however, could not be distinguished from the substrate noise. It clearly follows that the lower the contrast of a linear molecule, the greater the length that must be considered to give a signal significantly higher than the noise.

An illustration of these considerations can be found in the detectability of stained and unstained double-stranded DNA. For this purpose, micrographs have been taken at a magnification of $\times 30,000$ using plates developed for fine grain (Valentine, 1965; *Kodak Tech. Bits*, 1966). An accelerating voltage of 60 kV and a 50-μ objective aperture are generally used. Several micrographs are generally taken at focal increments of 1000 Å to obtain one in the desired range of underfocus. For this low-resolution imaging of the strands, it is convenient to take advantage of phase contrast by using underfocused micrographs. Underfocusing of 1000 to 3000 Å should give maximum contrast enhancement for a 10–20-Å wide strand and has, in fact, been found to give the most visible and clear images. Astigmatism is not disturbing if it is less than one-third of the amount of underfocus and is routinely corrected quickly before each micrograph.

Micrographs were obtained of native double-helical DNA and denatured, single-stranded RNA, both unstained and stained with 1% aqueous uranyl acetate (Erickson and Beer, 1968). The stained double-helical DNA is easily visible over most of its length (Fig. 1A–C), although some variation in contrast can be noted. Many sections are straight and visible for several hundred angströms and can be reliably traced and located within a 20-Å wide strip. Other sections are less visible or are more crooked, and the exact course of the strand is more ambiguous. Figure 1D and E shows micrographs of unstained DNA. These strands are only marginally visible and the course of the strand, which should have about the same crookedness and bends as can be seen in the stained DNA, can only occasionally and with ambiguity be traced to within 20 Å. Micrographs of denatured single-stranded RNA, stained with uranyl acetate, have a range of visibility and contrast comparable to the unstained DNA. The variation in contrast from one strand to another and along different sections of the same strand seemed to be greater with the RNA, possibly reflecting nonuniformity in the staining or stretching of these strands.

The stained molecule which has greater contrast can be discerned over the background even when examination is restricted to a short segment of the strand. The lower-contrast unstained molecule can be detected only if much larger segments are examined.

It is clear from the above that there is a compelling need to increase the signal-to-noise ratio in electron micrographs. Two attractive methods for doing this have already been indicated. The first involves the use of graphite substrates to diminish the major source of noise discussed in Section III,F. The second is the use of the massive cationic stain, $Ta_6Br_{12}^{2+}$ discussed in Section IV,B.

To look for specific marked nucleotides one must examine the nucleic acid at high resolution and look for spots or small regions of high contrast along the strands. This involves taking micrographs at $\times 100,000$ or higher magnification, and operating the microscope to obtain the highest possible resolution. With modern microscopes it is possible to correct astigmatism to less than 500 Å, and in many cases to less than 250 Å, and to take a through focal series with focal increments of, say, 125 Å. Micrographs near focus will then demonstrate point-to-point resolution of 5 or even 3 Å.

Other than focus, astigmatism, and instrumental instabilities all of which can significantly reduce resolution, the most important factors that were found to affect the contrast and visibility of the nucleic acid strands were specimen contamination and damage in the electron beam. Contamination was generally seen and measured on the edges of a dense object on the specimen, such as the shadowed side of a polystyrene sphere. As little as 30 Å of contamination reduced the contrast markedly, making unstained DNA completely invisible. The use of an efficient cooling anticontamination device, which will reduce the contamination to less than 15 Å a minute, is thus essential. However, even in the absence of measurable contamination, prolonged exposure in the electron beam reduced the visibility; thus, exposure of any area is kept to less than a minute.

One approach to high-resolution microscopy is directed toward obtaining a "parafocal image" (Van Dorsten and Premsela, 1966), where phase contrast effects are reduced to a minimum by taking a micrograph very close to focus and using a small objective aperture. Although the contrast is very low, this gives a picture which is easy to interpret since the contrast is due almost entirely to scattering of

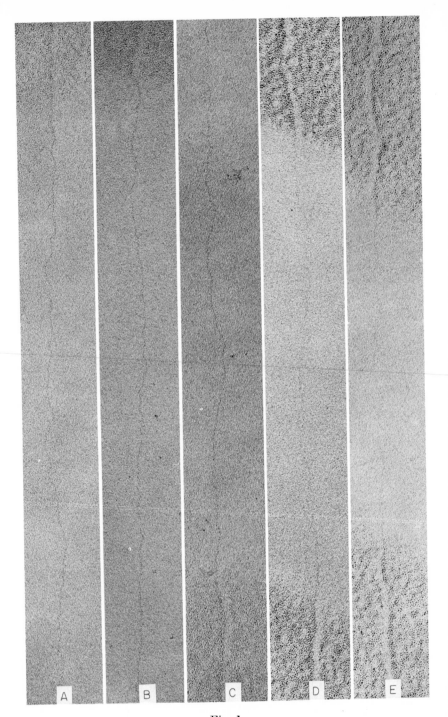

Fig. 1

electrons outside the objective aperture and is, thus, simply related to the mass density in the object. The use of the small aperture, however, makes this method difficult in practice, as the astigmatism changes frequently and usually needs correction before each micrograph or focal series. This quick and precise correction of astigmatism can be achieved routinely by using an image intensifier, television display system. Otherwise one must make the best correction possible by observing the image on the fluorescent screen, and afterward reject those micrographs for which the correction is inadequate, i.e., in which phase-contrast granularity or streaking due to the astigmatism are evident.

An alternative procedure for high-resolution microscopy is to make use of the phase-contrast effects by taking micrographs underfocused. An amount of underfocusing to give maximum contrast consistent with high-resolution can be calculated from the diffraction theory of image formation (Hanszen and Morgenstern, 1965; Heidenreich, 1967). This depends on the spherical aberration and focal length of the objective lens, but is generally in the range of 600 to 1200 Å underfocus. Unfortunately, the contrast enhancement is not a simple and uniform effect, but varies depending on the spatial frequency of Fourier coefficients of the image. Thus the contrast of different details in the image is not simply related to the mass density in the object, but also depends on their size, shape, and surroundings. The interpretation of these micrographs requires a consideration of the details of the imaging process and of possible artifacts. On the other hand, this system gives the advantage of a several fold increase in contrast over the "parafocal" image; since the amplitude contrast is only a small fraction of the total it is possible to forgo the use of an objective aperture. With no objective aperture the astigmatism of the microscope is usually found to be stable for hours or days, thereby eliminating the problems of correcting astigmatism before each micrograph is made. Instead, one can spend an hour or two at the beginning of the day correcting astigmatism with a holey carbon film test specimen, taking micrographs and making adjustments until a satisfactory correction is achieved. Analytical procedures for determining these adjustments are quite useful (O'Hara and Beer, 1962). Then a number of micrographs can be taken before the astigmatism is seen to change and needs another correction.

FIG. 1. Electron micrograph of double-stranded DNA. These micrographs were obtained from shadowed preparations carrying polystyrene spheres. Any DNA molecule crossing the shadow of a polystyrene sphere can be seen there by virtue of its density. At the edge of the shadow region the molecule appears shadowed. (A–C) Deoxyribonucleic acid stained with 1% aqueous uranyl acetate; (D, E) DNA unstained. × 400,000.

The foregoing discusses the instrumental factors relevant to high-resolution electron microscopy. The preparation of the specimens suitable for the study of nucleotide sequence is now reiterated.

In Section II,B the procedures for producing nucleic acid molecules with selectively marked bases have been indicated. In Section III,E the preparation of thin carbon films is described. These are suitable for the detection of masses that give a density greater than the film granularity. The theoretically attractive graphite films have not been sufficiently tested to assure a reliable improvement. The labeled nucleic acid molecule is best deposited on the supporting film by direct adsorption without protein monolayer. The quaternary ammonium salts mentioned in Section IV,C are clearly helpful and can apparently be removed by the washing procedures described. To indicate the positions of the selectively coupled anionic marking groups the grid carrying the nucleic acid must be stained. The best procedure so far found for accomplishing this is the aqueous uranyl acetate staining mentioned in Section VI,A. The results unfortunately are not completely reproducible but in the most favorable cases—apparently on slightly hydrophilic grids—dense clusters are found along the nucleic acid molecules and these are attributable to the markers which have bound dense cations (Beer and Moudrianakis, 1962; Bartl et al., 1970). Although some satisfactory results have been obtained by the aqueous staining procedure, it must at present be considered incompletely worked out, and reliable sequence data require improvements in at least some of the procedures of cationic counterstaining or smooth substrate preparation.

REFERENCES

Bartl, P., Erickson, H. P., and Beer, M. (1970). *Micron* **1**, 374.

Beer, M., (1961). *J. Mol. Biol.* **3**, 263.

Beer, M., and Moudrianakis, E. N. (1962). *Proc. Nat. Acad. Sci. U.S.* **48**, 409.

Beer, M., and Zobel, C. R. (1961). *J. Mol. Biol.* **3**, 717.

Beer, M., Stern, S., Carmalt, D., and Mohlhenrich, K. H. (1966). *Biochemistry* **5**, 2283.

Bendet, I., Schachter, E., and Lauffer, M. A. (1962). *J. Mol. Biol.* **5**, 76.

Bradley, D. E. (1954). *Brit. J. Appl. Phys.* **5**, 65.

Cantoni, G. L., and Davies, D. R., eds. (1966). *Procedures Nucleic Acid Res.* Pt. II.

Cotte, G. (1960). *C. R. Acad. Sci.* **250**, 621.

Davidson, P. F., and Freifelder, D. (1966). *J. Mol. Biol.* **16**, 490.

Di Giamberardino, L., Koller, T., and Beer, M. (1969). *Biochim. Biophys. Acta* **182**, 523.

Dobelle, W. H., and Beer, M. (1968). *J. Cell Biol.* **39**, 733.

Drahos, V., and Delong, A. (1960). *Nature (London)* **186**, 104.

Dunnebacke, T. H., and Kleinschmidt, A. K. (1967). *Z. Naturforch. B* **22**, 159.

Eisenhandler, C., and Siegel, B. (1966). *J. Appl. Phys.* **37**, 1613.

Erickson, H. P., and Beer, M. (1967). *Biochemistry* **6**, 2694.

Erickson, H. P. and Beer, M. (1968). *Electron Microsc. 1968, Proc. Eur. Reg. Conf.,* 4th, Rome, p. 87.

Fernández-Morán, H. (1960). *J. Appl. Phys.* **31**, 1840.

Freifelder, D. (1966). *Virology* **28**, 742.

Freifelder, D., Kleinschmidt, A. K., and Sinsheimer, R. L. (1964). *Science* **146**, 254.

Gordon, C., and Kleinschmidt, A. K. (1968). *Biochim. Biophys. Acta* **155**, 305.

Grossman, L., and Moldave, K., eds. (1967). *Methods Enzymol.* **12**, Pt. A, Sect. IV.

Haine, M. E. (1961). "The Electron Microscope," p. 79. Wiley (Interscience), New York.

Hall, C. E. (1956). *J. Biophys. Biochem. Cytol.* **2**, 625.

Hanszen, K. J., and Morgenstern, B. (1965). *Z. Angew. Phys.* **19**, 215.

Hart, R. G. (1963). *J. Appl. Phys.* **34**, 434.

Heidenreich, R. D. (1967). "Fundamentals of Transmission Electron Microscopy." Wiley (Interscience), New York.

Hershey, A. D., and Burgi, E. (1960). *J. Mol. Biol.* **2**, 143.

Highton, P. J., and Beer, M. (1963). *J. Mol. Biol.* **7**, 70.

Highton, P. J., and Beer, M. (1968). *J. Roy. Microscop. Soc.* **88**, 23.

Highton, P. J., Murr, B. L., Shafa, F., and Beer, M. (1968). *Biochemistry* **7**, 825.

Inman, R. B. (1967). *J. Mol. Biol.* **18**, 464.

Josse, J., and Eigner, J. (1966). *Annu. Rev. Biochem.* **35**, 789.

Karu, A. E., and Beer, M. (1966). *J. Appl. Phys.* **37**, 2179.

Kislina, O. S., Naroditsky, V. S., Mazzarelli, M., and Tikhonenko, T. I. (1968). *Acta Virol. (Prague)* **12**, 435.

Kleinschmidt, A. K. (1968). *Methods Enzymol.* **12**, Pt. B, 361.

Kleinschmidt, A. K., and Zahn, R. K. (1959). *Z. Naturforsch. B* **14**, 730.

Kleinschmidt, A. K., Lang, D., and Zahn, R. K. (1962). *Biochim. Biophys. Acta* **61**, 857.

Kodak Tech. Bits (1966). No. 2. Eastman Kodak Co., Rochester, New York.

Koller, T., Harford, G. H., Lee, Y. K., and Beer, M. (1970). *Micron* **1**, 110.

Kuhn, P. J., and McCarley, R. E. (1965). *Inorg. Chem.* **4**, 1482.

Lang, D., Kleinschmidt, A. K., and Zahn, R. K. (1964). *Biochim. Biophys. Acta* **88**, 142.

Lang, D., Bujard, H., Wolff, B., and Russell, D. (1967). *J. Mol. Biol.* **23**, 163.

MacHattie, L. A., and Thomas, C. A. (1964). *Science* **144**, 1142.

Moudrianakis, E. N., and Beer, M. (1965a). *Biochim. Biophys. Acta* **95**, 23.

Moudrianakis, E. N., and Beer, M. (1965b). *Proc. Nat. Acad. Sci. U.S.* **53**, 564.

Murphy, A. P., and Goodman, J. F. (1960). *Nature* **188**, 689.

O'Hara, D. S. (1968). Ph.D. Thesis, Johns Hopkins Univ., Baltimore, Maryland.

O'Hara, D. S., and Beer, M. (1962). *Sci. Instrum. News, RCA* **7**, 16.

Robin, M. B., and Kuebler, N. A. (1965). *Inorg. Chem.* **4**, 978.

Ruska, H. (1939). *Naturwissenschaften* **27**, 287.

Schaefer, V. J., and Harber, D. (1942). *J. Appl. Phys.* **13**, 427.

Scheffler, I. E., Elson, E. L., and Baldwin, R. L. (1968). *J. Mol. Biol.* **36**, 291.

Scherzer, O. (1949). *J. Appl. Phys.* **20**, 30.

Spencer, M. (1959). *J. Biophys. Biochem. Cytol.* **6**, 125.

Thomas, C. A., and MacHattie, L. A. (1967). *Annu. Rev. Biochem.* **36**, 485.

Turnbull, J. A., and Williamson, G. K. (1963). *Trans. Brit. Ceram. Soc.* **62**, 807.

Valentine, R. C. (1965). *In* "Quantitative Electron Microscopy" (G. F. Bahr and E. H. Zeitler, eds.), p. 596. Williams & Wilkins, Baltimore, Maryland.

Van Dorsten, A. C., and Premsela, H. F. (1966). "Electron Microscopy," p. 21. Maruzen Co., Tokyo.

Westmoreland, B. C., Szybalski, W., and Ris, H. (1969). *Science* **163**, 1343.

White, J. R., Koller, T., Beer, M., and Bartl, P. (1969). *Proc. 27th Annu. Meet. Electron Microsc. Soc. Amer., St. Paul, Minnesota.*

CHAPTER VII

METHODS FOR STUDYING MAMMALIAN TRANSFER RIBONUCLEIC ACID*

I. BERNARD WEINSTEIN† AND LOUIS M. FINK‡

* This research was supported by U. S. Public Health Service Research Grant No. CA-02332 from the National Cancer Institute.

† Career Scientist of the Health Research Council of the City of New York (I-190).

‡ Trainee, supported by U. S. Public Health Service Training Grant No. CA-05001 from the National Cancer Institute.

I. Introduction

A. ROLE OF TRANSFER RIBONUCLEIC ACID IN TRANSLATION OF THE GENETIC MESSAGE

Translation of the genetic message during protein synthesis is mediated by a specific set of ribonucleic acid (RNA) molecules, the tRNA's* (Crick, 1958, 1966a). These molecules serve as "adaptors" in the translation mechanism, since they serve to deliver amino acids to their corresponding positions on mRNA. Each amino acid is first attached to a specific tRNA by an aminoacyl–tRNA synthetase. The aminoacyl–tRNA's are then aligned on corresponding triplets of nucleotides (codons) in the mRNA. Specificity of the translation mechanism depends on base pairing between a specific nucleotide region in tRNA, the anticodon, and nucleotides in the codon. The amino acid plays only a passive role in this recognition process (Chapeville et al., 1962; Grunberger et al., 1969). The fidelity of translation, therefore, is highly dependent on the structure of tRNA's and their precise function.

The above mechanism predicts that all cells must contain at least one type of tRNA for each amino acid. Degeneracy, i.e., the existence of multiple code words for the same amino acid, is a prominent feature of the genetic code of bacteria (Nirenberg et al., 1966; Khorana et al., 1966) and also of higher organisms (Weinstein, 1963; Marshall et al., 1967; Nishimura and Weinstein, 1969). Indeed, 61 out of a possible 64 triplets have been assigned to the twenty amino acids incorporated into protein. Weisblum et al. (1962, 1965) were the first to establish

---

* Abbreviations and terms used, in addition to those specified by the IUPAC-IUB Commission on Biochemical Nomenclature and the *Journal of Biological Chemistry*, include: transfer RNA (tRNA); messenger RNA (mRNA); multiple tRNA's accepting the same amino acid (isoaccepting tRNA's). Aminoacylated tRNA's are designated phenylalanyl–tRNA, seryl–tRNA, etc.; amino acid-specific tRNA's that are not acylated are designated tRNA^{Phe}, tRNA^{Ser}, etc.; where isoaccepting tRNA's exist these are designated tRNA^{Phe}I, tRNA^{Phe}II, etc. One A$_{260}$ unit is defined as the amount of material per milliliter of solution that produces an absorbance of 1 in a 1-cm light path cell at 260 mμ.

that in certain cases the physical basis for degeneracy is the existence of multiple types of tRNA for the same amino acid, each type recognizing a different codon.

Subsequent data on patterns of codon recognition of purified species of tRNA led Crick (1966b) to formulate the "wobble hypothesis." This hypothesis states that wherever a given amino acid has more than one codon, and when these codons differ in the first position (5' end) of the codon, there is a unique set of tRNA's to read each type of codon. An individual tRNA, however, can recognize multiple codons for the same amino acid, if these codons differ from each other only in the third position (3' end) of the codon. Crick has postulated that the first and second positions of the codon pair with bases in the anticodon of tRNA by the usual Watson–Crick base-pairing rules (A to U or G to C). The pairing of the third base in the codon with its corresponding base in the anticodon follows these rules: U in the anticodon will pair with either A or G in the codon; C in the anticodon with G in the codon; A in the anticodon with U in the codon; G in the anticodon with U or C in the codon; and I in the anticodon with either U, C, or A in the codon (Crick, 1966a,b). Studies on codon recognition by isolated *Escherichia coli* and yeast tRNA's have yielded results which are generally in agreement with this hypothesis (Kellogg *et al.*, 1966; Söll *et al.*, 1967; Söll and RajBhandary, 1967). Recent studies suggest an additional wobble mechanism in which it appears that a derivative of uridine present in the 5' end of the anticodon of a valine tRNA (Yaniv and Barrell, 1969; Harada *et al.*, 1969) can base pair with both A and G, and to a lesser extent U, in the 3' end of the codon (Kellogg *et al.*, 1966; Mirzabekov *et al.*, 1968; Nishimura and Weinstein, 1969). Although the wobble mechanism was formulated on the basis of data obtained from microorganisms, recent studies with purified tRNA's from guinea pig liver (Caskey *et al.*, 1968) and rat liver (Nishimura and Weinstein, 1969) indicate that this mechanism extends to mammalian cells.

B. Changes in Transfer Ribonucleic Acid Population during Development, Viral Infection, and Neoplasia

The central role of tRNA in translation of the genetic code makes it likely that changes in the abundance and specificity of individual tRNA's play an important role in metabolic regulation, cellular differentiation, and neoplastic transformation (Ames and Hartman, 1963; Stent, 1964; Sueoka *et al.*, 1966; Weinstein, 1968a). Changes in the tRNA population have been demonstrated in bacteria after T2 phage infection (Kano-Sueoka and Sueoka, 1968), after infection with an RNA phage (Hung and Overby, 1968), during sporulation (Kaneko and Doi, 1966; Lazzarini, 1966), and as a consequence of changes in the growth media (Doi *et al.*, 1966; Yegian and Stent, 1969a,b). Changes in tRNA's have been described in higher plants (Vold and Sypherd, 1968; Anderson and Cherry, 1969), during early development and differentiation of sea urchins (Yang and Comb, 1968; Zeikus *et al.*, 1969), during metamorphosis of bullfrog tadpoles (Tonoue *et al*, 1969), and in erythrocytes of developing chicks (Lee and Ingram, 1967).

Evidence is accumulating that marked alterations in the tRNA population of mammalian cells may accompany viral infection and neoplasia. Changes in tRNA profiles have been described after herpes virus infection (Subak-Sharpe *et al.*, 1966), and in hamster cells transformed with adenovirus 7 or SV40 virus (Taylor *et al.*, 1968). In an extensive study of mammalian tissues (Taylor *et al.*, 1967; Holland *et al.*, 1967; Taylor *et al.*, 1968), it was found that methylated albumin kieselguhr (MAK) column profiles of tRNA's from different normal organs were usually similar. The elution profiles of phenylalanyl–, seryl–, glycyl–, and tyrosyl–tRNA's from the Ehrlich ascites tumor, however, differed appreciably from those of the corresponding normal organ tRNA's. Yang and Novelli (1968) have described differences in the seryl–tRNA A elution profiles of two mouse plasma cell tumors; and Mushinski and Potter (1969) found variations in the abundance of different leucyl–tRNA's in a series of mouse plasma cell tumors. Baliga *et al.* (1969) have found that the elution profiles on MAK columns of aminoacyl–tRNA's for histidine, tyrosine, and asparagine differed markedly from the corresponding tRNA's of normal rat liver. Additional but less striking differences between the Novikoff hepatoma and normal liver were observed in isoleucyl–, lysyl–, methionyl–, and tryptophanyl–tRNA's. The total tRNA of certain tumors appears to have a higher content of methylated bases than the tRNA of the corresponding normal tissue (Bergquist and Matthews, 1962; Viale *et al.*, 1968), and Borek and his colleagues have amassed evidence for an increase in the tRNA methylases of several tumors—a finding confirmed by others. (See Borek and Srinivasan, 1966, and Baliga *et al.*, 1969, for a review of this subject.) Recent studies suggest that at least two hepatic carcinogens, ethionine and N-2-acetylaminofluorene, produce chemical modifications of tRNA (Axel *et al.*, 1967; Fink *et al.*, 1970; Agarwal and Weinstein, 1970).

It is apparent, therefore, that in both lower and higher organisms extensive qualitative changes in the tRNA population accompany physiological or developmental changes, viral infection, and tumor formation, though at the present time it is difficult to separate cause from effect. Further studies are required, to determine the physiological significance of these changes. Although there have been rapid advances in the purification and sequence analysis of bacterial and yeast tRNA's, there are relatively few studies on the characterization of individual mammalian tRNA's. The purpose of the present article is to summarize basic methods employed in the isolation, fractionation, and assay of mammalian tRNA's. Many of the methods are derived from those originally developed for bacterial and yeast tRNA's. In general, these methods have been scaled down to utilize the relatively small amounts of tRNA which are obtained from mammalian tissues. Techniques employing column chromatography rather than counter-current fractionation will be emphasized since these are simpler, capable of a high degree of resolution, and require smaller amounts of material.

II. Isolation of Transfer Ribonucleic Acid from Tissues and Cells

A. BULK PREPARATION

Transfer RNA can be extracted directly with phenol from various mammalian tissues (Brunngraber, 1962; Delihas and Staehelin, 1966). The following procedure has been employed in our laboratory for the isolation of rat liver tRNA (Fink *et al.*, 1968). With minor modifications it has also been employed for the extraction of tRNA from other normal tissues and tumors. Rats are decapitated and their livers removed and quickly frozen in liquid nitrogen. Batches of 100 gm of liver are homogenized with 200 ml of 0.01 M tris HCl (pH 7.0), 0.2% bentonite (prepared as described by Fraenkel-Conrat *et al.*, 1961), 0.3 M sucrose, and 200 ml of water-saturated phenol containing 0.1% 8-hydroxy-quinoline, in a Waring blender at high speed for 2 minutes. The homogenate is stirred vigorously at 20°C for 1 hour and then centrifuged at 13,000 g for 25 minutes at 4°C. The aqueous layer is re-extracted 3 times with water-saturated phenol containing 0.1% sodium dodecyl sulfate (SDS) and 0.1% 8-hydroxyquinoline. Two volumes of 95% ethanol and 0.1 volume of 2 M sodium acetate (pH 5.0) are added to the aqueous layer and the mixture placed at −20°C for 4 hours or longer. The precipitate is collected by centrifugation at 13,000 g for 30 minutes at 4°C, suspended in 40 ml of 1 M NaCl, stirred gently at 4°C for 8 hours, and the insoluble RNA (largely ribosomal RNA) removed by centrifugation at 13,000 g at 4°C for 30 minutes. The 1 M NaCl soluble RNA is precipitated with two volumes of 95% ethanol at −20°C, the precipitate is collected at 13,000 g for 30 minutes, and resuspended in distilled water containing 0.01 M MgCl$_2$. Analysis of this material by sucrose gradient centrifugation and polyacrylamide gel electrophoresis reveals predominantly 4 S RNA (tRNA), a small amount of 5 S RNA, and less than 5% contamination with ribosomal RNA. The yield for rat liver is between 0.5 and 0.8 mg tRNA per gram wet weight of liver.

The above preparation of tRNA contains variable amounts of polysaccharides, which can be reduced but not completely eliminated if the animals are fasted prior to sacrifice. Polysaccharides and other low-molecular-weight contaminants can be removed by chromatography on diethylaminoethyl (DEAE)–cellulose. A DEAE–cellulose column (2.5 × 20 cm) is equilibrated with 0.1 M tris–HCl (pH 7.2) buffer containing 0.01 M MgCl$_2$ and 0.2 M NaCl, and the tRNA (approximately 200 mg) is applied. The column is washed with three to four column volumes of the same buffer, which removes the low-molecular-weight contaminants, then the tRNA is eluted with 0.8 M NaCl in 0.1 M tris–HCl (pH 7.2) and 0.01 M MgCl$_2$, and recovered by ethanol precipitation.

An alternative to the DEAE step is isopropanol fractionation of RNA, as described by Zubay (1962), which can also be used to separate tRNA from higher-molecular-weight RNA's and DNA. Further separation of tRNA from other RNA's and DNA may be accomplished by gel filtration chromatography using Sephadex G-100 (Watson and Ralph, 1967; Kirtikar and Kaji, 1968). If the crude tRNA is to be used for the isolation of specific amino acid tRNA's, it can be applied directly to the appropriate columns (see Section IV) after the 1 M NaCl procedure, since other nucleic acids, polysaccharides, and low-molecular-weight contaminants will usually be removed during purification of the individual tRNA.

The above procedure yields mainly cytoplasmic tRNA. If one wants to exclude completely mitochondrial and nuclear tRNA, as well as 5 S ribosomal RNA, unfrozen livers are first homogenized in 0.25 M sucrose in a Potter–Elvehjm homogenizer and a microsomal supernatant fraction isolated by ultracentrifugation (Weinstein, 1968b; also see Section III, A). The latter is then extracted with phenol, as described above, and the 1 M NaCl step can be omitted.

B. PROCEDURE FOR STRIPPING

Most of the tRNA isolated as described above appears to be "uncharged" and can be aminoacylated *in vitro*. To be certain that the tRNA is completely uncharged, a stripping procedure can be included. This may be important in experiments where one wants to quantitate accurately the total *in vitro* amino acid acceptance capacity of the tRNA. Several procedures for stripping tRNA's have been described (von Ehrenstein and Lipmann, 1961; Sarin and Zamecnik, 1964; Yang and Novelli, 1968). Incubation of the tRNA in 0.3 M tris–HCl (pH

7.5), 0.01 M magnesium acetate, 0.001 M ethylenediaminetetraacetate (EDTA)–disodium at 35°C for 30 minutes, and reprecipitation with two volumes of ethanol are adequate for stripping most tRNA's; this is a relatively mild procedure (Yang and Novelli, 1968). It must be mentioned however, that even mild alkaline treatment can produce chemical modifications in certain tRNA's (Yoshikami and Keller, 1969).

C. PREPARATION OF TRANSFER RIBONUCLEIC ACID FROM NONCYTOPLASMIC SOURCES

Small amounts of tRNA are present in the nucleus (Hodnett and Busch, 1968) and mitochondria (Buck and Nass, 1968) of mammalian cells. The tRNA's present in mitochondria differ appreciably from cytoplasmic tRNA's (Buck and Nass, 1968; Smith and Marcker, 1968; Galper and Darnell, 1969). A method for the isolation of mitochondrial tRNA is described by Buck and Nass (1968). The avian myeloblastosis virus contains tRNA and this can be extracted with phenol from purified viral preparations and separated from viral RNA on density gradients (Trávniček, 1968; Erikson and Erikson, 1969).

D. *In Vivo* CHARGING OF TRANSFER RIBONUCLEIC ACID

Frequently only very small amounts of starting material are available for analysis. This is particularly true when tissue culture cells, nuclei, or mitochondria are the source of the tRNA. For these reasons, it may be convenient to add a radioactive amino acid to the tissue culture media or inject it into the intact animal. After a suitable period of *in vivo* charging, the tRNA is extracted from the cells with phenol and the radioactive aminoacyl–tRNA can be analyzed directly by column chromatography. It is important that during extraction and column chromatography the pH be kept mildly acid because of the lability of the aminoacyl–tRNA bond in mild alkali. For further details on the application of this method to tissue culture cells, the reader is referred to Taylor *et al.* (1968).

III. Assays of Biological Properties of Transfer Ribonucleic Acid

The first major function of tRNA's is to react with "synthetases" to yield aminoacyl tRNA's. This reaction is termed aminoacylation or "charging." The first step in this reaction is activation of the amino acid, by reaction with adenosine triphosphate (ATP), to produce an enzyme-bound aminoacyladenylate. The second step, performed by the same enzyme, is esterification of the amino acid to the 3' OH of the terminal adenosine of the corresponding tRNA. The overall reaction can be described as follows (for an extensive treatment of this subject, see Novelli, 1967):

1. Amino acid + ATP + enzyme → amino acid–adenosine monophosphate (AMP)–enzyme + inorganic pyrophosphate;

2. amino acid–AMP–enzyme + tRNA → aminoacyl–tRNA + AMP + enzyme.

The first step can be assayed by the hydroxamate reaction or by the liberation of inorganic pyrophosphate (Novelli, 1967). The second step can be assayed by measuring the conversion of radioactive amino acid into a cold trichloroacetic acid-insoluble form, and it is convenient to assay the overall two-step reaction in the same way (see below). Assays for measuring the binding of free amino acid or tRNA to their corresponding enzyme, which employ membrane binding (Yarus and Berg, 1967), gel filtration (Lagerqvist et al., 1966), or electrophoresis (Okamoto and Kawade, 1967; Seifert et al., 1968), have also been developed.

The other major function of tRNA is codon recognition. This involves interaction between the anticodon region of tRNA and a specific triplet of nucleotides (or "codon") in mRNA, as well as a less specific binding of tRNA's to the ribosome. This aspect of tRNA function can be measured in the triplet-directed ribosomal binding assay of Nirenberg and Leder (1964). Codon recognition of a purified tRNA can also be assayed in a subcellular protein-synthesizing system in which one measures the transfer of labeled amino acid, previously bound to a given tRNA, into protein, under the direction of a defined mRNA. This is called the "transfer reaction" and will also be described in detail.

A. Preparation and Properties of Aminoacyl–Transfer Ribonucleic Acid Synthetases

The activity and amino acid specificity of a given tRNA is most conveniently measured by determining its acceptance activity for a labeled amino acid in an aminoacylation reaction containing a crude mixture of aminoacyl–tRNA synthetases, the appropriate radioactive amino acid, ATP, the necessary salts, and buffer.

For the above assay one needs a crude mixture of synthetases which is free of endogenous tRNA. This can be prepared from rat liver as follows. Six rats (150–250 gm) are decapitated and the livers are excised and rinsed in a small amount of cold homogenizing buffer (0.01 M tris–HCl, pH 7.8; 0.06 M KCl; 0.005 M magnesium acetate; 0.006 M mercaptoethanol; 0.25 M sucrose). All subsequent procedures are performed at 0° to 4°C. The tissue is minced and homogenized in an equal volume of homogenizing buffer, employing a Potter-Elvehjm homogenizer with a loosely fitting Teflon pestle. The homogenate is centrifuged twice at 15,000 g for 30 minutes, and the pellets discarded. The supernatant fraction is then centrifuged at 122,000 g for 1 hour to obtain a microsomal supernatant fraction. To remove endogenous tRNA, 1% protamine sulfate is slowly added (0.05–0.1 ml per milliliter extract) to the microsomal supernatant fractions until no further precipitate is formed and the mixture stirred for 30 minutes. The precipitate is removed by centrifugation at 16,000 g for 10 minutes. Synthetases are precipitated from the supernatant fraction by the addition of saturated ammonium sulfate (pH 7.5) to 70% concentration (2.3 ml saturated ammonium sulfate per milliliter extract) and collected by centrifugation at 16,000 g for 10 minutes. A concentrated suspension of the pellets is dialyzed against 4 liters of 0.1 M tris–HCl (pH 7.2) and 0.005 M MgCl$_2$ for 3 hours, which solubilizes most of the protein. A small amount of insoluble residue is removed by centrifugation at 10,000 g for 10 minutes and aliquots of the soluble material frozen rapidly in Dry Ice and acetone. The preparation is stable for several weeks when stored at $-20°C$.

Other methods for the preparation of crude aminoacyl–tRNA synthetases have been described. A microsomal supernatant fraction can be placed on a DEAE–cellulose column and the column washed with 0.1 M tris–HCl (pH 7.2) buffer containing 0.01 M MgCl$_2$, 0.2 M NaCl, 0.005 M mercaptoethanol. The synthetases will be eluted but the endogenous tRNA, and other nucleic acids will remain on the column. The protein fraction can be used as such or concentrated by ammonium sulfate precipitation (Mushinski and Potter, 1969). Gel filtration on Sephadex G-100 can also be used to obtain an enzyme fraction which is free of endogenous tRNA (Taylor et al., 1968).

Aminoacyl–tRNA synthetases specific for a given amino acid have been purified from a number of species, including *Escherichia coli*, yeast, and mammalian tissues. Enzymes purified from mammalian tissues include: arginyl–tRNA synthetase, 100-to 280-fold (Ikegami and Griffin, 1969; Allende and Allende, 1964); seryl–tRNA synthetase, 600-fold (Rouge, 1969); glutamyl–tRNA synthetase, 150-fold (Deutscher 1967); threonyl–tRNA synthetase, 400-fold (Allende et al., 1966), and phenylalanyl–tRNA synthetase, 260-fold (Fink et al., 1969). An apparently homogeneous preparation of tryptophanyl–tRNA synthetase has been purified from bovine pancreas (Preddie, 1969). Their molecular weights range from 59,000 to 180,000, and the presence of subunits has been described in some cases (Bruton and Hartley, 1968; Preddie, 1969).

Most of the evidence obtained with bacterial extracts indicates that a single synthetase can recognize isoaccepting tRNA's even if the tRNA's differ in their codon recognition (Bruton and Hartley, 1968; Cassio and Waller, 1968; Goodman et al., 1968; Sundharadas et al.,

1968). At the same time, there are studies suggesting the presence of multiple aminoacyl–tRNA synthetases for the same amino acid in the cytoplasm of neurospora (Kull and Jacobson, 1969) and mammalian cells (Strehler *et al.*, 1967). The significance of this heterogeneity is not apparent at present. There is considerable species specificity in recognition between tRNA's and synthetases, but there are also many cases of *in vitro* recognition with heterologous mixtures (Doctor *et al.*, 1966; Anderson, 1969). The fact that rat liver cytoplasmic synthetase preparations cannot acylate certain liver mitochondrial tRNA's suggests that there exist synthetases which are unique to mitochondria (Buck and Nass, 1968). The actual mechanism of recognition between a tRNA and its corresponding synthetase is not known with certainty (see Section V).

Studies by Williams and Neidhardt (1969) indicate that the synthesis of certain aminoacyl–tRNA synthetases is subject to repression or depression in response to the amino acid supply in *E. coli*. In collaborative studies (Agarwal *et al.*, 1969), the authors did not detect a significant change in the activity of aminoacyl–tRNA synthetases in rat liver after cortisone administration. Further studies are required, however, to determine whether or not this is an important regulatory mechanism in higher organisms.

B. Assay of Amino Acid Acceptance

The system for assaying the amino acid acceptance of liver tRNA, or column fractions containing tRNA, employed in the authors' laboratory is a modification of that previously described for *Escherichia coli* tRNA's (Nishimura *et al.*, 1967). The reaction mixture contains in a total volume of 0.1 ml approximately 50 to 200 μg of unfractionated tRNA, or 0.01–0.03 ml of column fractions; 10 μmoles of tris–HCl, pH 7.5; 1 μmole of magnesium acetate; 1 μmole of KCl; 0.2 μmole of ATP; 0.01–0.02 μcurie of ^{14}C-labeled amino acid (100–500 μcuries/μmole); and 0.04 ml (approximately 1.4 mg of protein) of crude aminoacyl–tRNA synthetase, prepared as described in Section III, A. It is convenient to employ the following stock solutions: tris–HCl (0.1 M, pH 7.0)–MgCl$_2$ (0.1 M); ATP (0.02 M), neutralized KCl (0.1 M); and ^{14}C-amino acid (10–50 μcuries/ml). A typical 0.1 ml assay then contains: tris–MgCl$_2$, 0.01 ml; ATP–KCl, 0.01 ml; ^{14}C-amino acid, 0.01 ml; crude enzyme, 0.03 ml; tRNA, 0.01–0.03 ml; and water to give a total volume of 0.1 ml. The reaction mixture is incubated at 37°C for 10 minutes by which time the reaction has in most cases reached a plateau. Aliquots (0.08 ml) are pipetted onto Whatman No. 3 MM filter paper discs (24 mm in diameter). The discs are prelabeled with pencil and pierced with pins which support them on a Styrofoam block. After applying the samples, the discs, with their pins still attached to prevent them from sticking to each other, are immersed in 5% trichloroacetic acid containing 1% casamino acids (DIFCO), and kept on ice for 15 minutes with occasional mixing. The solution is changed 3 times at 15-minute intervals. The discs are then immersed in ethanol-ether (1:1) for 15 minutes and ether for 15 minutes. Finally, they are dried, placed in counting vials containing toluene and phosphor, and counted in a liquid scintillation counter.

The above assay conditions may not be optimal for all extracts and amino acids. High concentrations of salt may impair aminoacylation of specific tRNA's and this must be borne in mind when assaying column fractions directly. In certain cases, the above concentration of amino acid may be limiting. Yang and Novelli (1968) have described variations in the optimal ATP to Mg ratio for different tRNA's. In general, the authors have not found a requirement for sulfhydryl reagents in the charging reaction but this may exist in other systems.

The above reaction mixture can be used to synthesize radioactive aminoacylated tRNA for preparative purposes. The reaction is scaled up to a total volume of 1 ml. After charging with a ^{14}C-amino acid at 37°C for 10 minutes, an equal volume of water-saturated phenol is added, the mixture is shaken at room temperature for 3 minutes, and then centrifuged for 5 minutes at 1500 rpm. The supernatant fluid is removed, made 0.01 M with sodium acetate (pH 4.3), dialyzed at 4°C for 16 hours against at least 300 volumes of 0.05 M sodium acetate buffer (pH 5.0)–0.002 M MgCl$_2$, then dialyzed for 5 hours against 300 volumes of 0.002 M MgCl$_2$, and stored at −20°C. Alternatively, the radioactive aminoacyl–tRNA can be recovered after phenol extraction, by ethanol precipitation and suspended in the appropriate buffer.

A simple method for isolating radioactive aminoacyl–tRNA which avoids phenol extraction is as follows. At the end of the charging reaction, 1 ml of reaction mixture is brought to 0°C, 0.02 ml of 1 M sodium acetate (pH 5.0) is added, and the material is applied on a 1 × 5-cm DEAE–cellulose column which has been preequilibrated with 0.2 M NaCl in 0.1 M sodium acetate buffer, pH 5.0. The column is washed with 20 ml of the latter buffer to elute unbound free amino acid, ATP, and protein. The aminoacyl–tRNA can then be eluted with 0.8 M NaCl in the same buffer and concentrated by ethanol precipitation or dialyzed to remove the NaCl (Reeves et al., 1968).

C. Ribosomal Binding and Codon Recognition

The codon recognition of a specific tRNA can be assayed by aminoacylation with the appropriate radioactive amino acid (see above) and then determining which polynucleotide triplets (synthetic codons) or polymers stimulate the binding of that aminoacyl–tRNA to ribosomes. The aminoacyl–tRNA–triplet–ribosome complex can be trapped on a nitrocellulose filter and assayed for radioactivity (Nirenberg and Leder, 1964). A typical reaction mixture (0.05 ml) contains 0.1 M tris–HCl (pH 7.5), 0.05 M KCl, 1–2 A_{260} units of $E. coli$ ribosomes and 0.02 M magnesium acetate. Approximately 1000 to 10,000 cpm of the appropriate ^{14}C-aminoacyl–tRNA and 0.1 A_{260} units of trinucleotides or polynucleotides are added and the mixture is incubated at 25°C for 15 minutes. Two milliliters of iced buffer (tris, KCl, and Mg acetate at the above concentrations) is added and the sample is poured onto a cellulose nitrate filter (H. A. Millipore filter, 25 mm diameter, 0.45 μ pore size) attached to a gentle vacuum. The filter is washed 3 times with 2 ml of the same buffer, dried, and counted in a liquid scintillation counter.

In assaying mammalian tRNA's, it is convenient to use $E. coli$ ribosomes, prepared as described by Nirenberg and Leder (1964). Thus far the authors have been unable to obtain mammalian ribosomes which are sufficiently active to give reliable ribosomal binding data for amino acids other than phenylalanine. For particular purposes, it may be important to perform the binding assay over a range of magnesium concentration (0.01–0.05 M) or polynucleotide concentration (0.05–0.3 A_{260} units/assay). For examples of codon recognition data obtained with mammalian tRNA's, the reader is referred to the studies of Caskey et al. (1968) and of Nishimura and Weinstein (1969).

D. AMINO ACID INCORPORATION INTO PROTEIN: THE TRANSFER REACTION

To assay the properties of a specific tRNA in a protein-synthesizing system, the tRNA is precharged with a labeled amino acid and the transfer of that amino acid into protein, under the direction of a specific mRNA, is determined. Studies first performed by Weisblum et al. (1962, 1965) with isoaccepting species of $Escherichia\ coli$ tRNA^{Leu} demonstrated that these delivered their bound amino acid into protein under the direction of different synthetic mRNA's. Utilizing a subcellular protein-synthesizing system from reticulocytes, it was subsequently demonstrated that isoaccepting species of tRNA also differed in terms of their ability to recognize different leucine codons in the mRNA for the α-chain of rabbit hemoglobin. More recently this approach has been extended to an analysis of arginine tRNA's (Weisblum et al., 1967) and serine tRNA's (Gonano, 1967).

The following is a typical transfer reaction employing reticulocyte or liver ribosomes (Friedman et al., 1968). A 0.4-ml assay system contains:

tris–HCl, pH 7.8, 10 mM; magnesium acetate, 6 mM; KCl, 60 mM; 2-mercaptoethanol, 3 mM; ATP, 6.0 mM; guanosine triphosphate (GTP), 0.03 mM; phosphoenol pyruvate, potassium salt, 3 mM; phosphoenol pyruvate kinase, 12 μg; rat liver or rabbit reticulocyte ribosomes, 10 A_{260} units; and ([14C]) aminoacyl–tRNA (unfractionated), 150 μg. Assays are performed in the absence of added mRNA ("endogenous reaction") and in the presence of 100 μg of synthetic polynucleotides. Samples are incubated at 37°C for 30 minutes and processed for amino acid incorporation into protein (Weinstein, 1968b). With crude preparations of mammalian ribosomes there is no requirement for supernatant proteins since the transfer enzymes are apparently bound to the ribosomes. If one is assaying a purified [14C]-aminoacyl–tRNA, the assay system should also contain a mixture of [12C]-aminoacyl–tRNA's to support polypeptide synthesis.

V. Fractionation of Transfer Ribonucleic Acid and Purification of Individual Species

The major methods currently employed to fractionate tRNA and to purify individual species of tRNA include: countercurrent distribution; electrophoresis; and column chromatography on hydroxylapatite, methylated albumin kieselguhr, DEAE–cellulose, DEAE–Sephadex, benzoylated DEAE–cellulose, salicylated benzoylated DEAE–cellulose, methylated albumin silica, polyacrylamide, or reversed-phase columns. A few of the column chromatography methods which the authors have employed for mammalian tRNA will be described in detail. Most of these columns employ ion-exchange materials, and individual tRNA's are generally eluted by a gradient of increasing salt concentration.

The position of a given tRNA in the eluate can be identified by amino-acylating it with a radioactive amino acid prior to column chromatography, and then assaying column fractions for trichloroacetic acid precipitable radioactivity. For separating aminoacylated tRNA's, the pH of the eluate must be below 7.0 to stabilize the aminoacyl–tRNA bond. If one is looking for minor qualitative differences between two different sources of tRNA, for example, normal liver tRNA[Tyr] versus hepatoma tRNA[Tyr], the liver tRNA is precharged with [14C]-tyrosine, the hepatoma tRNA with [3H]-tyrosine, and the two preparations are mixed together and cochromatographed on the same column. Analysis of radioactivity in the eluate, employing double-isotope counting methods, will give a direct comparison of the elution profiles of the tRNA's from each source. An example of this type of study is given in Fig. 1.

Alternatively, uncharged tRNA can be fractionated by column chromatography and individual species of tRNA identified in the eluate by

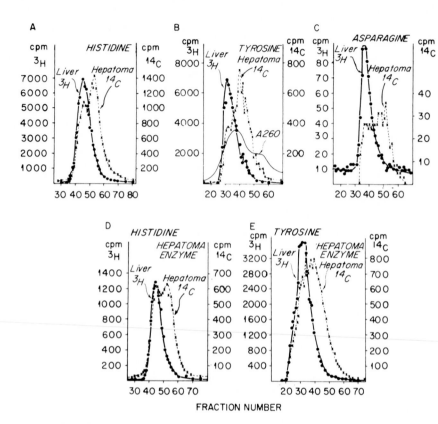

FIG. 1. Methylated albumin kieselguhr column elution profiles of aminoacyl–tRNA's of normal rat liver and Novikoff hepatoma. Hepatoma enzymes were used to charge the tRNA's in D and E, whereas liver enzymes were used for all other profiles. A gradient of 0.3 to 0.7 M NaCl was used in A, B, and D; 0.35–0.6 M NaCl was used in C and E. A typical absorbance (A_{260}) profile is shown in B. For additional details, see Baliga *et al.* (1969).

assaying the amino acid acceptance activity of each fraction. The latter procedure requires a larger amount of material but permits one to analyze simultaneously for several amino acids and is more suitable for preparative purposes. By sequential application of two or three different types of columns, it is usually possible to obtain highly purified samples of a single molecular species of tRNA.

A. METHYLATED ALBUMIN KIESELGUHR

One of the earliest methods developed to fractionate tRNA is MAK column chromatography (Sueoka and Yamane, 1967). It appears to resolve nucleic acids [both RNA and deoxyribonucleic acid (DNA)] on the basis of their G + C content, molecular weight, and configuration. It has been used extensively in double-isotope studies involving the cochromatography of two different sources of aminoacylated tRNA's.

The following procedure for the preparation of MAK is essentially the same as that described by Mandel and Hershey (1960). Five grams of bovine serum albumin (Fraction V) is dissolved in 500 ml of methanol; 4.2 ml of 12 N HCl is added, and the mixture stored in the dark for 3 or more days with occasional shaking. The precipitate is collected by centrifugation at 8000 g for 10 minutes and washed twice with methanol and twice with ether. The residual ether is evaporated, $in\ vacuo$, over KOH. The esterified albumin is pulverized in a mortar and stored in a desiccator over KOH. Twenty grams of kieselguhr suspended in 100 ml of column-starting buffer (0.2 M NaCl in 0.05 M sodium phosphate, pH 6.7) is boiled to expel air and cooled. Then 5 ml of a 1% solution of the esterified albumin in water is added to the kieselguhr with stirring, plus an additional 20 ml of starting buffer.

In a typical experiment, approximately 1 mg of aminoacylated tRNA is applied at room temperature to a 3 cm diameter × 3.5 cm column (a 1 × 10–20 cm column may improve the separation of certain tRNA's) of MAK and the column washed with 80 ml of 0.2 M NaCl in 0.35 M sodium phosphate (pH 6.7). The RNA is eluted with 200 ml of a linear gradient of 0.2 to 1.1 M NaCl in phosphate buffer, at a flow rate of 1.25 ml/minute. The effluent is monitored continuously at 260 mμ through a flow-through cuvette. The 2.5-ml fractions are precipitated by addition of 2.5 ml of cold 10% trichloroacetic acid and 200 μg of carrier DNA, deposited on membrane filters, and washed with 5% trichloroacetic acid. The filters are dissolved in 10 ml of a toluene phosphor solution and counted in a liquid scintillation counter. Typical patterns obtained with tRNA from rat liver and the Novikoff hepatoma are illustrated in Fig. 1. Although the MAK column does not have as high a resolution as some of the columns described below, it does provide a rapid and simple method of screening for gross qualitative changes in tRNA's.

B. DIETHYLAMINOETHYL–SEPHADEX

Chromatography on a DEAE–Sephadex A-50 column is an extremely useful first step in the preparation of larger amounts of a specific tRNA. It has been employed in the fractionation of $Escherichia\ coli$ tRNA (Nishimura $et\ al.$, 1967), yeast tRNA (Takeishi $et\ al.$, 1968), and rat liver tRNA (Nishimura and Weinstein, 1969). It provides a several-fold purification for certain tRNA's from rat liver, and the eluate region enriched with a specific tRNA can then be further fractionated, by one of the other types of columns described below, to yield highly purified

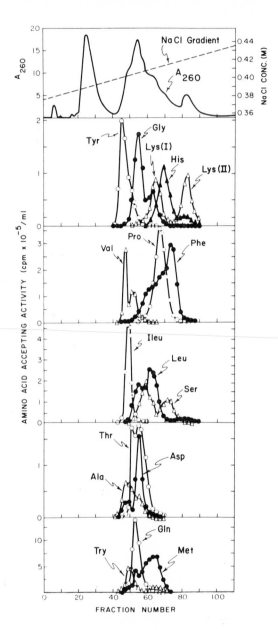

FIG. 2. Diethylaminoethyl–Sephadex column chromatography of rat liver tRNA. The method employed is described in Section IV, B and has been published by Nishimura and Weinstein (1969).

individual tRNA's (Nishimura and Weinstein, 1969). The size of the column and the volume of the elution gradient can easily be scaled up or down to accommodate different loads of tRNA. A slow flow rate is essential for good resolution. A typical procedure for fractionating 50–200 mg of mammalian tRNA is described below and illustrated in Fig. 2.

Diethylaminoethyl–Sephadex A-50 (capacity 3.5 ± 0.5 meq/gm, particle size 40–120 μ, Pharmacia Fine Chemicals) is washed as described by Nishimura et al. (1967) and packed in a 1 × 150-cm column. The column is equilibrated with 0.375 M NaCl in 0.02 M tris–HCl (pH 7.5) and 0.0075 M MgCl$_2$ buffer. The sample, approximately 200 mg of rat liver tRNA, is dissolved in 12 ml of starting buffer and is applied to the column. A linear gradient elution is carried out using 1 liter of 0.525 M NaCl in tris–HCl (pH 7.5) and 0.016 M MgCl$_2$ buffer in the reservoir and 1 liter of the starting buffer in the mixing chamber. The flow rate is 10 ml/hour, each fraction contains 7 ml, and the procedure is done at room temperature. Aliquots (0.03 ml) of each fraction are then assayed for amino acid acceptance capacity in a charging reaction (see Section III).

The results of a typical fractionation are given in Fig. 2. Ninety-eight per cent of the optical density is recovered. An optical density peak which accounts for approximately 30% of the total absorbance is eluted prior to the region of the tRNA's (Fractions 20 to 40). This appears to be a low-molecular-weight contaminant, since it is not precipitated by trichloroacetic acid and moves faster than tRNA on polyacrylamide gel electrophoresis. Assay of the fractions for acceptance capacities for sixteen amino acids indicates that individual tRNA's are eluted as rather sharp peaks which are reasonably well separated from each other. The presence of multiple forms of tRNA for a given amino acid is readily apparent—a finding consistent with the degeneracy and redundancy of tRNA's seen in other species (see Section I). With rat liver tRNA the DEAE–Sephadex procedure results in a 10- to 25-fold purification of tRNA's specific for tyrosine, phenylalanine, valine, serine, and lysine.

C. Benzoylated Diethylaminoethyl–Cellulose

Gillam et al. (1967) have developed a benzoylated DEAE–cellulose (BD–cellulose). The benzoyl residues give this material a high affinity for hydrophobic compounds, and it is, therefore, particularly useful in separating tRNA's or aminoacylated tRNA's bearing highly hydrophobic substituents. With both yeast and rat liver tRNA's, most of the tRNA is eluted from a BD–cellulose column by a 0.4–1.5 M gradient of

NaCl in 0.05 M sodium acetate (pH 5.0) and 0.01 M MgCl$_2$ buffer. Individual tRNA's are distributed through this eluate and resolved to a certain extent from each other. Phenylalanine tRNA, however, is not eluted by the NaCl gradient and requires 10% ethanol in 1.5 M NaCl for elution.

The high affinity of tRNA^{Phe} of yeast, wheat germ, and mammalian tissues results from its content of a highly hydrophobic residue designated "Y" (see Section V). This property provides the basis for a simple two-step method of purifying tRNA^{Phe} (Gillam et al., 1968;

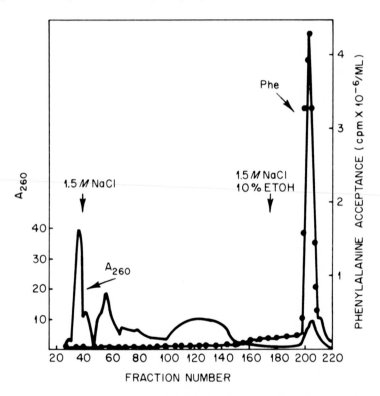

FIG. 3. Benzoylated diethylaminoethyl–cellulose column chromatography of rat liver tRNA. The column (4 × 46 cm) was equilibrated with 0.4 M NaCl, 0.05 M sodium acetate (pH 5.0), and 0.01 M MgCl$_2$, and 18,180 A_{260} units of rat liver tRNA in 100 ml of the initial buffer were applied. The column was then eluted stepwise with 500 ml of the initial buffer; 2500 ml of 1.5 M NaCl, 0.05 M sodium acetate (pH 5.0), 0.01 M MgCl$_2$; and, finally, 1000 ml of 10% ethanol in 1.5 M NaCl, 0.05 M sodium acetate (pH 5.0). 0.01 M MgCl$_2$. The flow rate was 1 ml/min and fractions were approximately 11 ml. All fractions were assayed for absorbance at 260 mμ and for phenylalanine acceptance capacity. Fractions 199–217 were pooled, the tRNA precipitated with ethanol and chromatographed as shown in Fig. 5. For additional details, see Fink et al. (1968).

Fink *et al.*, 1968). In a typical preparation (Fig. 3), a 4 × 46-cm column of BD–cellulose is pre-equilibrated with 0.4 M NaCl in 0.05 M sodium acetate (pH 5.0) and 0.01 M MgCl$_2$. Approximately 1 gm of rat liver tRNA in 100 ml of the same buffer is applied. The bulk of the tRNA is then eluted from the column by applying 500 ml of the initial buffer followed by 2500 ml of 1.5 M NaCl in the same buffer. The column is then eluted with 1 l of 10% ethanol in 1.5 M NaCl, 0.05 M sodium acetate (pH 5.0), and 0.01 M MgCl$_2$. The ethanol region of the eluate contains virtually all of the tRNA^{Phe} together with small amounts of other tRNA's (particularly tRNA^{Ser}). The fractions containing tRNA^{Phe} which are identified by phenylalanine acceptance and/or fluorescence (excitation at 310 mμ and emission at 430 mμ) are pooled and concentrated by ethanol precipitation. Final purification is achieved by rechromatographing this material either on a reversed-phase Freon column (see Fig. 4) or a salicylated BD–cellulose column (Wimmer *et al.*, 1968). With rat liver tRNA this procedure yields tRNA^{Phe} with an acceptance capacity of approximately 1600 $\mu\mu$moles /A_{260} unit (greater than 85% purity).

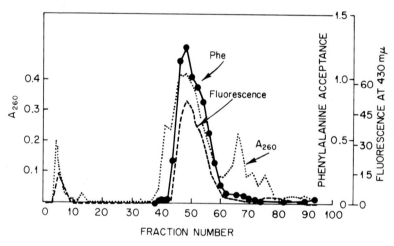

FIG. 4. Further purification of rat liver phenylalanine tRNA on a reversed-phase Freon column. The column (0.3 × 150 cm) was equilibrated with 0.02 M tris–HCl (pH 7.5), 0.01 M MgCl$_2$, 0.15 M NaCl, and 182 A_{260} units of the phenylalanine tRNA region obtained from a benzoylated diethylaminoethyl–cellulose column (Fig. 3) were mixed with 7 ml of water and applied. A linear gradient elution was carried out using 400 ml of 0.02 M tris-HCl (pH 7.5), 0.01 M MgCl$_2$, and 0.15 M NaCl in the mixing chamber and 400 ml of 0.65 M NaCl in the same buffer in the reservoir. The flow rate was 10 ml/hour. A volume of 7.2 ml of effluent was collected per fraction. Fractions were assayed for absorbance at 260 mμ, ^{14}C-phenylalanine acceptance, and for fluorescence at 430 mμ with excitation at 310 mμ. Fluorescence intensity is expressed in arbitrary units. For additional details, see Fink *et al.* (1968).

Gillam *et al.* (1968) have described a general method for purifying specific amino acid tRNA's which takes advantage of the hydrophobic property of BD–cellulose. Crude tRNA is first passed through the column to remove the small amount of tRNA which normally elutes in the ethanol region. The tRNA recovered from the NaCl region is aminoacylated with the appropriate amino acid. This is then chemically converted to a *N*-phenoxyacetyl–aminoacyl–tRNA, which can be separated from all other tRNA's, by virtue of its high affinity for BD–cellulose. The derivatized tRNA is eluted from BD–cellulose with ethanol and the phenoxyacetyl–amino acid removed from the tRNA with mild alkaline treatment.

D. REVERSED-PHASE CHROMATOGRAPHY

Kelmers and his associates at the Oak Ridge National Laboratory have developed several new chromatographic systems for tRNA which have an extremely high degree of resolution and are suitable for both analytical and preparative studies (Kelmers *et al.*, 1965; Weiss and Kelmers, 1967; Weiss *et al.*, 1968). These columns apparently resolve tRNA's on the basis of ion-exchange properties as well as differential solubility between a bound organic phase and a mobile aqueous phase. The columns consist of a quarternary ammonium chloride (which serves as the ion exchanger) dissolved in an organic solvent. The latter is supported, in the form of a thin film, on a hydrophobic diatomaceous earth (Chromosorb W). A sodium chloride gradient is used to elute sequentially individual species of tRNA. Four types of reversed-phase columns have been developed which differ in terms of the nature of the quarternary amine and the organic solvent employed. The suitability of each type varies with the particular tRNA one wishes to resolve. The reversed-phase Freon system (also designated RPC-2) gives excellent resolution of both bacterial (Weiss and Kelmers, 1967) and mammalian tRNA's (Caskey *et al.*, 1968; Yang and Novelli, 1968; Nishimura and Weinstein, 1969; Mushinski and Potter, 1969); the details of this method, derived from that of Weiss and Kelmers (1967), is described below.

The organic phase is prepared by dissolving tricaprylmethylammonium chloride (Aliquat 336 obtained from General Mills, Inc.) in 1,4-tetrachlorotetrafluoropropane (Freon 214, obtained from E. I. du Pont de Nemours and Co.) on a 5% by volume basis. The organic phase is washed successively with two volumes each of 1 M NaOH, 1 M HCl, and 0.5 M NaCl, and dried over silica gel. The organic phase (168 ml) is added dropwise with constant mixing into 300 gm of Chromosorb W (acid washed, dimethyl-dichlorosilane treated, 100–120 mesh size, obtained from Johns-Manville Products Corp.) and the material mixed mechanically for several hours. The mixture can be stored as a slurry in the initial column buffer. The column dimensions, the NaCl gradient, and the temperature during chromatography can be adjusted to suit the load of tRNA and the particular tRNA's to be resolved. If amino-acylated tRNA's are being fractionated, then the elution pH is 4.5, otherwise a tris–HCl buffer (pH 7.5) is employed. The column can be "regenerated" at the end of the run by washing it with 1 M NaCl and then re-equilibrating with the starting buffer. A chromatogram employing rat liver tRNA aminoacylated with ^{14}C-leucine is illustrated in Fig. 5.

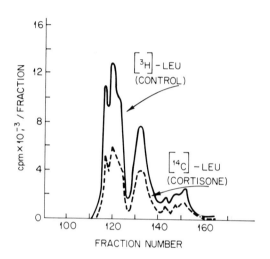

FIG. 5. Cochromatography on a reversed-phase Freon column of liver leucyl–tRNA from control and cortisone-treated rats. The column (0.5 × 130 cm) was equilibrated with 0.2 M NaCl, 0.01 M MgCl$_2$, 0.001 M ethylenediaminetetra-acetate, and 0.01 M sodium acetate, pH 4.5. Equal amounts of tRNA from control and cortisone-treated animals, previously stripped of endogenous amino acids, were charged with [3H] and [14C] leucine, respectively, and mixed. Two milligrams of the mixture was applied to the column, and a linear gradient elution was carried out using 500 ml each of 0.2 and 0.6 M NaCl, buffered as described above. Fractions of 6 ml were collected at a flow rate of 25 ml/hour and absorbance at 260 mμ was measured. Radioactivity in each fraction was deter-mined after trichloroacetic acid precipitation. For additional details, see Agarwal et al. (1969).

E. Criteria for Purity of a Transfer Ribonucleic Acid

In isolating individual species of tRNA for structural and biophysical studies, it is necessary to have criteria for their degree of purity. The theoretical amino acid acceptance capacity of a pure tRNA should be approximately 1.67 nmoles of amino acid/A_{260} unit of tRNA (Hoskinson and Khorana, 1965). This calculation assumes a molecular weight of 30,000 for the tRNA and that a 1 mg/ml solution has an absorbance of 20 at 260 mμ, when measured with a 1 cm path width. The acceptance capacity of the material in question, under optimal conditions of charging, can then be related to the theoretical. The amount of tRNA can also be quantitated by its phosphorous content (Gillam et al., 1968). A fraction of tRNA's may be missing the normal 3' OH adenosine terminus and this will prevent complete aminoacylation. It may be important, therefore, to measure the content of terminal adenosine residues by alkaline hydrolysis and Chelex ion-exchange chromatography (Burtis and Goldstein, 1968). Finally, the purified tRNA should have no, or negligible, acceptance activity for amino acids other than the one in question.

F. ISOACCEPTING SPECIES, DEGENERACY, AND REDUNDANCY

As indicated in Section I, the extensive degeneracy of the genetic code predicts the existence of multiple species of tRNA for the same amino acid, and examples of this are illustrated in Fig. 2. In many cases these isoaccepting species differ in codon recognition, as predicted from the wobble hypothesis (see Crick, 1966b). On the other hand, fractionation studies with *Escherichia coli*, yeast, and mammalian tRNA's indicate several examples in which multiple tRNA's for the same amino acid are resolved, yet they appear to be identical with respect to codon recognition when tested *in vitro* (Söll *et al.*, 1966; Bergquist *et al.*, 1968; Bergquist, 1966; Nishimura and Weinstein, 1969). When this occurs, it is important to consider whether or not the heterogeneity reflects an experimental artifact due to aggregation (Shleich and Goldstein, 1964), partial denaturation (Sueoka *et al.*, 1966; Adams *et al.*, 1967), or the possibility that a fraction of the tRNA is missing adenosine termini which are re-added during assay with crude synthetase preparations (Lebowitz *et al.*, 1966; RajBhandary *et al.*, 1968). There are several examples of what appears to be a true redundancy of tRNA's, i.e., isoaccepting species of tRNA having identical codon recognition, which are not readily attributed to *in vitro* artifacts (Holley *et al.*, 1965; Söll *et al.*, 1966; Bergquist *et al.*, 1968; Nishimura and Weinstein, 1969). In addition, hybridization studies with both yeast DNA (E. Schweizer *et al.*, 1969) and *Drosophilia* DNA (Ritossa *et al.*, 1966) suggest that there is redundancy of the cistrons for tRNA's in the genome. It is likely, therefore, that certain cases of redundant tRNA's seen *in vitro* also exist *in vivo*. The physiological significance of these redundant copies is not entirely clear—there is increasing evidence that they provide an important source of tRNA suppressors in lower organisms (Söll et al., 1966; Bergquist et al., 1968; Garen, 1968; Soll and Berg, 1969). In higher organisms these redundant copies may play an important role in development and differentiation (Weinstein, 1968a; Nishimura and Weinstein, 1969).

V. Structure of Transfer Ribonucleic Acid

A. Determination of the Primary Structure

Holley and co-workers (1965) were the first to obtain the total nucleotide sequence of a single molecular species of tRNA, that of yeast tRNA[Ala]. Since then, the primary structures of at least fourteen other tRNA's, obtained from either *Escherichia coli* or yeast have been elucidated (see Phillips, 1969 for a review of this subject). In addition, the tRNA[Phe] of wheat germ has been sequenced by Dudock et al. (1969). Thus far, there are few sequence studies on mammalian tRNA's, though Staehelin et al. (1968) have determined the total nucleotide sequence of a serine tRNA obtained from rat liver.

The general procedure employed in sequence studies on tRNA has been to digest enzymically the purified tRNA with T1 ribonuclease, which splits adjacent to guanosine residues, yielding oligonucleotide fragments terminating with 3' guanosine monophosphate (GMP). A separate set of fragments is obtained by enzymic digestion of the tRNA with ribonuclease A, which splits adjacent to pyrimidine residues to yield oligonucleotide fragments terminating in 3' uridine monophosphate (UMP) or 3' cytidine monophosphate (CMP). Both sets of oligonucleotide fragments can be separated by DEAE–cellulose column chromatography in 7 M urea and each fragment sequenced by further enzymic or alkaline hydrolysis. Partial enzymic digestion of the native tRNA is also used to obtain larger fragments, sometimes splitting the molecule into approximate halves, and these are then separated and further digested as described above. The oligonucleotide sequences obtained by these various digestion procedures are compared for overlapping sequences and thereby the total primary structure can be derived. For a more detailed discussion of these sequence methods, the reader is referred to Holley et al. (1965), and for a review of the properties of various nucleases used in sequence work, to Egami et al. (1964).

In the above procedure, one relies on optical density methods for detecting oligonucleotide and nucleotide fragments. This requires at least several milligrams of pure tRNA for a complete analysis. Sanger et al. (1965), employing ^{32}P-labeled tRNA, have developed sequence methods which require only microgram amounts of starting material.

The overall strategy is the same as that described above but the oligonucleotide fragments are separated in a two-dimensional system, with ionophoresis on cellulose acetate in the first dimension and ion-exchange chromatography on DEAE paper in the second dimension. Fragments are detected by radioautography and further sequenced. The method has been successfully employed to sequence several tRNA's from $E.$ $coli$ and also $E.$ $coli$ 5 S RNA. A major limitation in the application of this method to mammalian tRNA's is that it requires RNA labeled with ^{32}P at extremely high specific activities. The experience of Forget and Weissman (1967) who employed this method to sequence mammalian 5 S RNA indicates that this probably can be achieved by labeling cells in tissue culture in a low phosphate medium. Recently Székely and Sanger (1969) have described techniques in which oligonucleotides are terminally labeled in $vitro$ with ^{32}P, employing the enzyme polynucleotide kinase, and this approach may prove to be useful for studying RNA's that are not conveniently labeled in the intact cell. The other limitation of the Sanger procedure is that it does not permit complete identification of certain new or unusual minor nucleotide constituents.

B. General Aspects of Primary Structure: the Cloverleaf Model

Sequence data now available on several tRNA's indicate certain striking structural similarities and differences which provide clues to the functional properties of these molecules (Zachau et $al.$, 1966; Fuller and Hodgson, 1967; Madison, 1968; Phillips, 1969). The tRNA's range from 76 to 85 nucleotides in length. All have a C-C-A sequence at the 3' hydroxyl terminus, to which the amino acid is acylated, and a G (or in a few cases a C) residue at the 5' phosphate terminus. When their linear sequences are folded in two dimensions so as to maximize intramolecular Watson–Crick base pairs, all these structures yield the "cloverleaf" configuration originally proposed by Holley et $al.$ (1965) for yeast tRNA^{Ala} (see Fig. 6). The cloverleaf contains three loops of single-stranded regions and four "stems" of double-stranded regions. The "anticodon loop" is designated as such because it contains the expected trinucleotides for base pairing with the related codon. In all cases, there is a U residue immediately to the left (5' side) of the anticodon. In most cases there is a modified A residue, or other rare nucleoside, to the right (3' side) of the anticodon. Two known exceptions to the latter statement are found in a yeast tRNA^{Val} and $E.$ $coli$ tRNA^{FMet}. The left-hand loop, or "DiHU loop," contains the dihydrouridine residues and includes a total of 8 to 12 unpaired base residues. The right-hand loop,

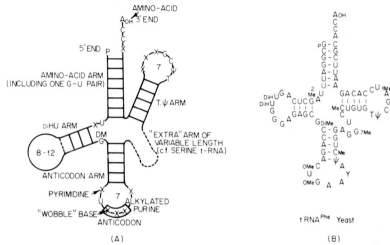

FIG. 6. (A) Generalized cloverleaf structure of tRNA, taken from Fuller and Hodgson (1967). Nucleosides that occur at equivalent positions in all tRNA sequences are denoted as follows: uridine (U), dimethylguanosine (DMG), adenosine (A), cytidine (C), ribothymidine (T), pseudouridine (Ψ). Nucleosides that vary between tRNA's are designated X. The number at the center of each loop indicates the number of nucleotides in the loop. (B) Proposed structure of yeast phenylalanine tRNA, taken from RhajBhandary et al. (1968).

or "T, Ψ, C, G loop," always contains the sequence: ribothymidine–pseudouridine–cytidine–guanosine (or adenosine). In several yeast tRNA's, there is a sequence guanosine–cytidine–dimethylguanosine in the groove between the DiHU loop and the anticodon loop. A small "extra arm" of variable length occurs in several tRNA's near the junction of the anticodon stem and the TΨCG stem and this region frequently contains 7-methyl-guanosine. The modified nucleosides ("minor bases") appear mainly in the loops and frequently in analogous positions in different tRNA's suggesting that they are landmarks in the secondary structure (Zachau et al., 1966).

Aside from the anticodon loop, the functional significance of each region of the tRNA is not known with certainty at the present time. There is suggestive evidence that the DiHU loop, and/or the extra arm, is involved in synthetase recognition and that the TΨCG loop is involved in nonspecific binding to the ribosome. Additional sequence data should help to clarify this problem.

Although only a single mammalian tRNA is available for comparison (Staehelin et al., 1968), its general properties are similar to those described above. Aminoacylation occurs with a mixture of rat liver tRNA[Ser] and yeast synthetase, as well as the converse, despite the fact that the corresponding serine tRNA's of the two species differ in one-fourth of their nucleotide sequences. It is of interest that most of these differences occur in base-paired or stem regions, suggesting that specificity resides in single-stranded regions. Mammalian tRNA^{Ser} contains methylated nucleosides not previously found in *E. coli* or yeast tRNA's (Staehelin *et al.*, 1968).

C. Modified Nucleosides in Transfer Ribonucleic Acid

In addition to the four major nucleosides (adenosine, guanosine, uridine, and cytosine), tRNA's are especially rich in a number of modified nucleosides (the so-called "minor bases"). Several of these were first discovered during the course of sequence analyses and not all of them have been completely characterized. They include various methylated compounds, with methylation on the base residue or on the ribose (Borek and Srinivasan, 1966); pseudouridine (Weiss and Legault-Demare, 1965); dihydrouridine (Holley *et al.*, 1965); thiolated pyrimidine derivatives (Carbon *et al.*, 1968); N^6-(Δ^2-isopentenyl) adenosine (IPA) (Fittler *et al.*, 1968) and its 2-methylthio derivative (Burrows *et al.*, 1968; Nishimura *et al.*, 1969); N-[9-(β-D-ribofuranosyl)-purine-6-ylcarbamoyl] threonine (M. P. Schweizer *et al.*, 1969); and a fluorescent nucleoside "Y," the structure of which has not been determined (RajBhandary *et al.*, 1968; Fink *et al.*, 1969; Dudock *et al.*, 1969). Other unusual nucleosides will, no doubt, be discovered as additional tRNA's are sequenced.

It appears that all of these compounds are synthesized by secondary modifications of the major nucleosides, after the latter are incorporated into a polynucleotide strand. Since this synthesis involves the attachment of residues arising from diverse metabolic pathways, it would appear that the maturation of tRNA's is intimately dependent on intermediary metabolism. This suggests regulatory mechanisms in which the activity of specific tRNA's is linked to various metabolic pathways, and studies along these lines are in progress in several laboratories.

One of the most extensively studied modifications of tRNA is methylation. Borek and his colleagues (Borek and Srinivasan, 1966) were the first to demonstrate that S-adenosylmethionine serves as the donor of these methyl residues and that the reaction can be studied in an *in vitro* system containing S-adenosylmethionine, methylating enzymes, and tRNA that is deficient in methyl groups, as a receptor. The latter is obtained from a "relaxed" strain of *Escherichia coli* which has been allowed to synthesize RNA under conditions of methionine starvation. Several specific tRNA methylases have been purified from *E. coli*, although highly purified methylases have not as yet been obtained from mammalian cells. Borek and Srinivasan (1966) have hypothesized that overmethylation of tRNA may be an important biochemical abnormality in tumor cells. There is some evidence that the crude tRNA of certain tumors is unusually rich in methylated bases (Bergquist and Matthews, 1962; Viale *et al.*, 1968), and it is possible that chromatographic alterations in tRNA's observed in certain tumors may be a consequence of this (Baliga *et al.*, 1969). In addition, a number of studies indicate that extracts obtained from a wide variety of tumors have a several-fold increase in tRNA–methylase activity, when methyl-deficient *E. coli* tRNA is used as an acceptor (see Borek and Srinivasan, 1966; Hacker and Mandel, 1969, for reviews of these studies).

Although these findings are extremely provocative, considerably more work is required to evaluate their significance with respect to cancer. The increase in tRNA–methylase activity may not be unique to tumor extracts, since at least one study suggests increased tRNA–methylase activity in embryonic tissue (Hancock, 1967). As described above, the *in vitro* assay systems for methylation usually employ an unnatural acceptor tRNA and there are very few studies with purified mammalian tRNA methylases. For these reasons it is not clear that the methylases assayed in the *in vitro* system actually overmethylate tRNA's in the intact tumor from which they are obtained. The data suggesting an increased content of methylated bases in the tRNA obtained from certain tumors are difficult to interpret since the results were obtained with total tRNA and may reflect a change in the relative abundance of specific species of tRNA, rather than an overall increase in the degree of methylation. Future studies comparing the structure of a specific tRNA obtained from a normal mammalian tissue to that of the corresponding tRNA of a tumor should help to clarify this point. Capra and Peterkofsky (1968) have described differences in codon recognition between *E. coli* leucyl–tRNA's obtained from normal and methyl-deficient cells. The changes observed are rather subtle, however, and Fleissner (1967) could not detect an effect of methylation on the coding properties of *E. coli* tRNA[Phe]. There is no evidence that tRNA which is "overmethylated" *in vivo* is altered in its codon recognition. At the present time, therefore, the physiological significance of increased tRNA–methylase activity seen in extracts of certain tumors (as well as the general functional significance of tRNA methylation) remains obscure.

Recent studies suggest an intriguing relationship between modifications of the adenosine residue adjacent to the 3' end of the anticodon of tRNA and codon recognition. It appears that in yeast tRNA's this residue is IPA, and in *E. coli* tRNA's it is the 2-methylthio derivative of IPA, in those species of tRNA's of which the anticodons recognize codons that begin with U (Nishimura *et al.*, 1969; Armstrong *et al.*, 1969a; Peterkofsky and Jesensky, 1969). Exceptions to this correlation are yeast tRNA[Phe] (RhajBhandary *et al.*, 1968), wheat germ tRNA[Phe] (Dudock *et al.*, 1969), and probably rat liver tRNA[Phe] (Fink *et al.*, 1969) in which the Y residue occupies this position. These exceptions suggest that the Y residue may be closely related to IPA, and elucidation of its structure will, therefore, be of considerable interest. Results obtained with a preparation of *E. coli* tRNA[Tyr] in which *in vivo* modification of the adenosine residue to produce 2-methylthio–IPA residue is incomplete (Gefter and Russell, 1969), with a preparation of yeast tRNA[Ser] in which the Δ^2-isopentenyl side chain was oxidized selectively with permanganate (Fittler *et al.*, 1968), and with a preparation of yeast tRNA[Phe], which is lacking the Y residue (Thiebe and Zachau, 1968), indicate that the substituted adenosine adjacent to the anticodon is essential for codon recognition, but not for aminoacylation. Studies in progress suggest a similar situation in mammalian tRNA[Phe] (Fink and Weinstein, 1969). The recent finding that tRNA[Ileu] of yeast contains the threonine derivative of adenosine suggests that this unusual nucleoside may play an analogous role in tRNA's that recognize codons beginning with A (Armstrong *et al.*, 1969b).

The presence of IPA in certain *E. coli*, yeast, and mammalian tRNA's is of considerable biological interest since this substance has long been known to be the plant hormone, cytokinin (Helgeson, 1968). The significance of this finding, in terms of the regulation of cell growth, is not clear at the present time.

Although sulfur-containing nucleosides have been identified in *E. coli* and yeast tRNA they have not, as yet, been isolated from mammalian tRNA. Attempts in this laboratory to demonstrate them in rat liver tRNA have thus far been completely negative (Agarwal and Weinstein, 1969, unpublished studies).

D. TERTIARY STRUCTURE

Perhaps the most challenging problem in tRNA chemistry is the elucidation of its three-dimensional or tertiary structure. Indirect techniques which have been employed include changes in absorbance, hydrodynamic measurements, thermal denaturation, circular dichroism, nuclear magnetic resonance, specific chemical modifications, and small-angle scattering in solution (for a review of these studies, see Fresco *et al.*, 1966; Miura, 1967; Smith *et al.*, 1968; Cramer *et al.*, 1968; Ninio *et al.*, 1969). Data obtained with these methods indicate that a considerable amount of tertiary structure does exist in native tRNA, presumably imposed on the basic cloverleaf configuration. The importance of conformational changes with respect to the function of tRNA is indicated by the data of Fresco *et al.* (1966) and Ishida and Sueoka (1968) demonstrating that heat denaturation of certain tRNA's, in the absence of magnesium, will place them in an altered and functionally inactive conformation. The most important break-through in this area has been the recent successful crystallization of several different tRNA's (Clark *et al.*, 1968; Kim and Rich, 1968; Hampel *et al.*, 1968; Fresco *et al.*, 1968; Doctor *et al.*, 1969). X-Ray crystallographic studies, currently underway in several laboratories, should provide definitive information on the tertiary structure of tRNA's. The reader is referred to a paper by Ninio *et al.* (1969) for a discussion of certain currently proposed three-dimensional models.

ACKNOWLEDGMENTS

The authors are indebted to Dr. Susumu Nishimura of the National Cancer Center Research Institute, Tokyo, Japan, for introducing us to several of the techniques described in these studies, while he was a Visiting Scientist at the Institute of Cancer Research of Columbia University.

REFERENCES

Adams, A., Lindahl, T., and Fresco, J. R. (1967). *Proc. Nat. Acad. Sci. U.S.* **57**, 1684.

Agarwal, M. K., and Weinstein, I. B. (1970). *Biochemistry* **9**, 503.

Agarwal, M. K., Hanoune, J., Yu, F. L., Weinstein, I. B., and Feigelson, P. (1969). *Biochemistry* **8**, 4806.

Allende, C. C., and Allende, J. E. (1964). *J. Biol. Chem.* **239**, 1102.

Allende, C. C., Allende, J. E., Gatica, M., Celis, J., Mora, G., and Matamala, M. (1966). *J. Biol. Chem.* **241**, 2245.

Ames, B. N., and Hartman, P. E. (1963). *Cold Spring Harbor Symp. Quant. Biol.* **28**, 349.

Anderson, M. B., and Cherry, J. H. (1969). *Proc. Nat. Acad. Sci. U.S.* **62**, 202.

Anderson, W. F. (1969). *Biochemistry* **8**, 3687.

Armstrong, D. J., Skoog, F., Kirkegaard, L. H., Hampel, A. E., Bock, R. M., Gillam, I., and Tener, G. M. (1969a). *Proc. Nat. Acad. Sci. U.S.* **63**, 504.

Armstrong, D. J., Burrows, W. J., Skoog, F., Roy, K. L., and Söll, D. (1969b). *Proc. Nat. Acad. Sci. U.S.* **63**, 834.

Axel, R., Weinstein, I. B., and Farber, E. (1967). *Proc. Nat. Acad. Sci. U.S.* **58**, 1255.

Baliga, B. S., Borek, E., Weinstein, I. B., and Srinivasan, P. R. (1969). *Proc. Nat. Acad. Sci. U.S.* **62**, 899.

Bergquist, P. L. (1966). *Cold Spring Harbor Symp. Quant. Biol.* **31**, 435.

Bergquist, P. L., and Matthews, R. E. F. (1962). *Biochem. J.* **85**, 305.

Bergquist, P. L., Burns, D. J. W., and Plinston, C. (1968). *Biochemistry* **7**, 1751.

Borek, E., and Srinivasan, P. R. (1966). *Annu. Rev. Biochem.* **35**, 275.

Brunngraber, E. F. (1962). *Biochem. Biophys. Res. Commun.* **8**, 1.

Bruton, C. J., and Hartley, B. S. (1968). *Biochem. J.* **108**, 281.

Buck, C. A., and Nass, M. M. K. (1968). *Proc. Nat. Acad. Sci. U.S.* **60**, 1045.
Burrows, W. J., Armstrong, D. J., Skoog, F., Hecht, S. M., Boyle, J. T. A., and Leonard, N. J. (1968). *Science* **161**, 691.
Burtis, C. A., and Goldstein, G. (1968). *Anal. Biochem.* **23**, 502.
Capra, J. D., and Peterkofsky, A. (1968). *J. Mol. Biol.* **33**, 591.
Carbon, J., David, H., and Studier, M. H. (1968). *Science* **161**, 1146.
Caskey, C. T., Beaudet, A., and Nirenberg, M. (1968). *J. Mol. Biol.* **37**, 99.
Cassio, D., and Waller, J. P. (1968). *Eur. J. Biochem.* **5**, 33.
Chapeville, F., Lipmann, F., von Ehrenstein, G., Weisblum, W. J., Jr., and Benzer, S. (1962). *Proc. Nat. Acad. Sci. U.S.* **48**, 1086.
Clark, B. F. C., Doctor, B. P., Holmes, K. C., Klug, A., Marcker, K. A., Morris, S. J., and Paradies, H. H. (1968). *Nature (London)* **21**, 1220.
Cramer, F., Doepner, H., von der Haar, F., Schlimme, E., and Seidel, H. (1968). *Proc. Nat. Acad. Sci. U.S.* **61**, 1384.
Crick, F. H. C. (1958). *Symp. Soc. Exp. Biol.* **12**, 138.
Crick, F. H. C. (1966a). *Cold Spring Harbor Symp. Quant. Biol.* **31**, 1.
Crick, F. H. C. (1966b). *J. Mol. Biol.* **17**, 394.
Delihas, N. and Staehelin, M. (1966). *Biochim. Biophys. Acta* **119**, 385.
Deutscher, M. P. (1967). *J. Biol. Chem.* **242**, 1123.
Doctor, B. P., Loebel, J. E., and Kellogg, D. A. (1966). *Cold Spring Harbor. Symp. Quant. Biol.* **31**, 543.
Doctor, B. P., Fuller, W., and Webb, N. L. (1969). *Nature (London)* **221**, 58.
Doi, R. H., Kaneko, I., and Goehler, B. (1966). *Proc. Nat. Acad. Sci. U.S.* **56**, 1548.
Dudock, B. S., Katz, G., Taylor, E. K., and Holley, R. W. (1969). *Proc. Nat. Acad. Sci. U.S.* **62**, 941.
Egami, F., Takeishi, K., and Uchida, T. (1964). *Progr. Nucleic Acid Res.* **3**, 59.
Erikson, R. L., and Erikson, E. (1969). *Fed. Proc. Fed. Amer. Soc. Exp. Biol.* **28**, 846.
Fink, L. M., and Weinstein, I. B. (1969) Unpublished results.
Fink, L. M., Goto, T., Frankel, F., and Weinstein, I. B. (1968). *Biochem. Biophys. Res. Commun.* **32**, 963.
Fink, L. M., Nishimura, S., and Weinstein, I. B. (1970). *Biochemistry* **9**, 496.
Fink, L. M., Nishimura, S., and Weinstein, I. B. (1968b). *Proc. Amer. Ass. Cancer Res.* **9**, 21.
Fink, L. M., Goto, T., and Weinstein, I. B. (1969). *Fed. Proc. Fed. Amer. Soc. Exp. Biol.* **28**, 409.
Fittler, F., Kline, L. K., and Hall, R. H. (1968). *Biochemistry* **7**, 940.
Fleissner, E. (1967). *Biochemistry* **6**, 621.
Forget, B. G., and Weissman, S. M. (1967). *Science* **158**, 1695.
Fraenkel-Conrat, H., Singer, B., and Tsugita, A. (1961). *Virology* **14**, 54.
Fresco, J. R., Adams, A., Ascione, R., Henley, D., and Lindahl, T. (1966). *Cold Spring Harbor Symp. Quant. Biol.* **31**, 527.
Fresco, J. R., Blake, R. D., and Langridge, R. (1968). *Nature (London)* **220**, 1285.
Friedman, M., Berezney, R., and Weinstein, I. B. (1968). *J. Biol. Chem.* **243**, 5044.
Fuller, W., and Hodgson, A. (1967). *Nature (London)* **215**, 817.
Galper, J. B., and Darnell, J. E. (1969). *Biochem. Biophys. Res. Commun.* **34**, 205.
Garen, A. (1968). *Science* **160**, 149.
Gefter, M. L., and Russell, R. L. (1969). *J. Mol. Biol.* **39**, 145.
Gillam, I., Millward, S., Blew, D., von Tigerstrom, M., Wimmer, E., and Tener, G. M. (1967). *Biochemistry* **6**, 3043.

Gillam, I., Blew, D., Warrington, R. C., von Tigerstrom, M., and Tener, G. M. (1968). *Biochemistry* **7**, 3459.

Gonano, F. (1967). *Biochemistry* **6**, 977.

Goodman, H. M., Abelson, J., Landy, A., Brenner, S., and Smith, J. D. (1968). *Nature (London)* **217**, 1019.

Grunberger, D., Weinstein, I. B., and Jacobson, K. B. (1969). *Science* **166**, 1635.

Hacker, B., and Mandel, L. R. (1969). *Biochim. Biophys. Acta* **190**, 38.

Hampel, A., Labanauskas, M., Connors, P. G., Kirkegaard, L., RajBhandary, U. L., Sigler, P. B., and Bock, R. M. (1968). *Science* **162**, 1384.

Hancock, R. L. (1967). *Cancer Res.* **27**, 646.

Harada, F., Kimura, F., and Nishimura, S. (1969). *Biochim. Biophys. Acta* **182**, 590.

Helgeson, J. P. (1968). *Science* **161**, 974.

Hodnett, J. L., and Busch, H. (1968). *J. Biol. Chem.* **243**, 6334.

Holland, J. J., Taylor, M. W., and Buck, C. A. (1967). *Proc. Nat. Acad. Sci. U.S.* **58**, 2437.

Holley, R. W., Apgar, J., Everett, G. A., Madison, J. T., Marquisee, M., Merrill, S. H., Penswick, J. R., and Zamir, A. (1965). *Science* **147**, 1462.

Hoskinson, R. M., and Khorana, H. G. (1965). *J. Biol. Chem.* **240**, 2129.

Hung, P. P., and Overby, L. R. (1968). *J. Biol. Chem.* **243**, 5525.

Ikegami, H., and Griffin, A. C. (1969). *Biochim. Biophys. Acta* **178**, 166.

Ishida, T., and Sueoka, N. (1968). *J. Mol. Biol.* **37**, 313.

Kaneko, I., and Doi, R. H. (1966). *Proc. Nat. Acad. Sci. U.S.* **55**, 564.

Kano-Sueoka, T., and Sueoka, N. (1968). *J. Mol. Biol.* **37**, 475.

Kellogg, D. A., Doctor, B. P., Loebel, J. E., and Nirenberg, M. W. (1966). *Proc. Nat. Acad. Sci. U.S.* **55**, 912.

Kelmers, A. D., Novelli, G. D., and Stulberg, M. P. (1965). *J. Biol. Chem.* **240**, 3979.

Khorana, H. G., Buchi, H., Ghosh, H., Gupta, N., Jacob, T. M., Kössel, H., Morgan, R., Narang, S. A., Ohtsuka, E., and Wells, R. D. (1966). *Cold Spring Harbor Symp. Quant. Biol.* **31**, 39.

Kim, S. H., and Rich, A. (1968). *Science* **162**, 1381.

Kirtikar, M. W. D., and Kaji, A. (1968). *J. Biol. Chem.* **243**, 5345.

Kull, F. J., and Jacobson, B. (1969). *Proc. Nat. Acad. Sci. U.S.* **62**, 1137.

Lagerkvist, U., Rymo, L., and Waldenstrom, J. (1966). *J. Biol. Chem.* **241**, 5391.

Lazzarini, R. A. (1966). *Proc. Nat. Acad. Sci. U.S.* **56**, 185.

Lebowitz, P., Ipata, P. L., Makman, M. H., Richards, H. H., and Cantoni, G. L. (1966). *Biochemistry* **5**, 3617.

Lee, J. C., and Ingram, V. M. (1967). *Science* **158**, 1330.

Madison, J. T. (1968). *Annu. Rev. Biochem.* **37**, 131.

Mandell, J. D., and Hershey, A. D. (1960). *Anal. Biochem.* **1**, 66.

Marshall, R. E., Caskey, C. T., and Nirenberg, M. (1967). *Science* **155**, 820.

Mirzabekov, A. D., Grunberger, D., Krutilina, A. I., Holy, A., Bayev, A. A., and Sorm. F. (1968). *Biochim. Biophys. Acta* **166**, 75.

Miura, K. (1967). *Progr. Nucleic Acid Res.* **6**, 39.

Mushinski, J. F., and Potter, M. (1969). *Biochemistry* **8**, 1684.

Ninio, J., Favre, A., and Yaniv, M. (1969). *Nature (London)* **223**, 1333.

Nirenberg, M. W., and Leder, P. (1964). *Science* **145**, 1399.

Nirenberg, M. W., Caskey, T., Marshall, R., Brimacombe, R., Kellogg, D., Doctor, B., Hatfield, D., Levin, J., Rottman, F., Peska, S., Wilcox, M., and Anderson, F. (1966). *Cold Spring Harbor Symp. Quant. Biol.* **31**, 11.

Nishimura, S., and Weinstein, I. B. (1969). *Biochemistry* **8**, 832.
Nishimura, S., Harada, F., Narushima, U., and Seno, T. (1967). *Biochim. Biophys. Acta* **142**, 133.
Nishimura, S., Yamada, Y., and Ishikura, H. (1969). *Biochim. Biophys. Acta* **179**, 517.
Novelli, G. D. (1967). *Annu. Rev. Biochem.* **36**, 449.
Okamato, T., and Kawade, Y. (1967). *Biochim. Biophys. Acta* **145**, 613.
Peterkofsky, A., and Jesensky, C. (1969). *Biochemistry* **9**, 3798.
Phillips, G. R. (1969). *Nature (London)* **223**, 374.
Preddie, E. C. (1969). *J. Biol. Chem.* **244**, 3969.
RajBhandary, U. L., Faulkner, R. D., and Stuart, A. (1968). *J. Biol. Chem.* **243**, 575.
Reeves, R. H., Imura, N., Schwam, H., Weiss, G. B., Schulman, L. H., and Chambers, R. W. (1968). *Proc. Nat. Acad. Sci. U.S.* **60**, 1450.
Ritossa, F. M., Atwood, K. C., and Speigelman, S. (1966). *Genetics* **54**, 663.
Rouge, M. (1969). *Biochim. Biophys. Acta* **171**, 342.
Sanger, F., Brownlee, G. G., and Barrell, B. G. (1965). *J. Mol. Biol.* **13**, 373.
Sarin, P. S., and Zamecnik, P. C. (1964). *Biochim. Biophys. Acta* **91**, 653.
Schweizer, E., MacKechnie, C., and Halvorsen, H. O. (1969). *J. Mol. Biol.* **40**, 261.
Schweizer, M. P., Chheda, G. B., Baczynskyj, L., and Hall, R. H. (1969). *Biochemistry* **8**, 3283.
Seifert, W., Nass, G., and Zillig, W. (1968). *J. Mol. Biol.* **33**, 507.
Shleich, T., and Goldstein, J. (1964). *Proc. Nat. Acad. Sci. U.S.* **52**, 744.
Smith, A. E., and Marcker, K. A. (1968). *J. Mol. Biol.* **38**, 241.
Smith, I. C. P., Yamane, T., and Shulman, R. G. (1968). *Science* **159**, 1360.
Söll, D. J., and RajBhandary, U. L. (1967). *J. Mol. Biol.* **29**, 113.
Söll, D. J., Cherayil, J. D., Jones, D. S., Faulkner, R. D., Hampel, A., Bock, R. M., and Khorana, G. H. (1966). *Cold Spring Harbor Symp. Quant. Biol.* **31**, 51.
Söll, D. J., Cherayil, J. D., and Bock, R. M. (1967). *J. Mol. Biol.* **29**, 97.
Soll, L., and Berg, P. (1969). *Nature (London)* **223**, 1340.
Staehelin, M., Rogg, H., Baguley, B. C., Ginsberg, T., and Wehrli, W. (1968). *Nature (London)* **219**, 1363.
Stent, G. S. (1964). *Science* **144**, 816.
Strehler, B. L., Hendley, D. D., and Hursch, G. P. (1967). *Proc. Nat. Acad. Sci. U.S.* **57**, 1751.
Subak-Sharpe, H., Shepherd, W. M., and Hay, J. (1966). *Cold Spring Harbor Symp. Quant. Biol.* **31**, 583.
Sueoka, N., and Yamane, T. (1967). *Proc. Nat. Acad. Sci. U.S.* **48**, 1454.
Sueoka, N., Kano-Sueoka, T., and Gartland, W. J. (1966). *Cold Spring Harbor Symp. Quant. Biol.* **32**, 571.
Sundharadas, G., Katze, J. R., Söll, D., Konigsberg, W., and Lengyel, P. (1968). *Proc. Nat. Acad. Sci. U.S.* **61**, 693.
Székely, M., and Sanger, F. (1969). *J. Mol. Biol.* **43**, 607.
Takeishi, K., Ukita, T., and Nishimura, S. (1968). *J. Biol. Chem.* **243**, 5761.
Taylor, M. W., Granger, G. A., and Buck, C. A. (1967). *Proc. Nat. Acad. Sci. U.S.* **57**, 1712.
Taylor, M. W., Buck, C. A., and Granger, G. A. (1968). *J. Mol. Biol.* **33**, 809.
Thiebe, R., and Zachau, H. G. (1968). *Eur. J. Biochem.* **5**, 546.
Tonoue, T., Eaton, J., and Frieden, E. (1969). *Biochem. Biophys. Res. Commun.* **37**, 81,

Trávníček, M. (1968). *Biochim. Biophys. Acta* **166**, 757.

Viale, G. L., Fondelli, Restelli, A., and Viale, E. (1968). *Riv. Neurobiol.* **14**, 311.

Vold, B. S., and Sypherd, P. S. (1968). *Proc. Nat. Acad. Sci. U.S.* **59**, 453.

von Ehrenstein, G., and Lipmann, F. (1961). *Proc. Nat. Acad. Sci. U.S.* **47**, 941.

Watson, J. D., and Ralph, R. K. (1967). *J. Mol. Biol.* **26**, 541.

Weinstein, I. B. (1963). *Cold Spring Harbor Symp. Quant. Biol.* **28**, 579.

Weinstein, I. B. (1968a). *Cancer Res.* **28**, 1871.

Weinstein, I. B. (1968b). *Methods Enzymol.* **12B**, 782–787.

Weisblum, B., Benzer, S., and Holley, R. W. (1962). *Proc. Nat. Acad. Sci. U.S.* **48**, 1449.

Weisblum, B., Gonano, F., von Ehrenstein, G., and Benzer, S. (1965). *Proc. Nat. Acad. Sci. U.S.* **53**, 328.

Weisblum, B., Cherayil, J. D., Bock, R. M., and Söll, D. (1967). *J. Mol. Biol.* **28**, 275.

Weiss, J. F., and Kelmers, A. D. (1967). *Biochemistry* **6**, 2507.

Weiss, J. F., Pearson, R. L., and Kelmers, A. D. (1968). *Biochemistry* **7**, 3479.

Weiss, S. B., and Legault-Demare, J. (1965). *Science* **149**, 429.

Williams, L. S., and Neidhardt, F. C. (1969). *J. Mol. Biol.* **43**, 529.

Wimmer, E., Maxwell, I. H., and Tener, G. M. (1968). *Biochemistry* **7**, 2623.

Yang, S. S., and Comb, D. G. (1968). *J. Mol. Biol.* **31**, 139.

Yang, W. K., and Novelli, G. D. (1968). *Proc. Nat. Acad. Sci. U.S.* **59**, 208.

Yaniv, M., and Barrell, B. G. (1969). *Nature (London)* **222**, 278.

Yarus, M., and Berg, P. (1967). *J. Mol. Biol.* **28**, 479.

Yegian, C. D., and Stent, G. S. (1969a). *J. Mol. Biol.* **39**, 45.

Yegian, C. D., and Stent, G. S. (1969b). *J. Mol. Biol.* **39**, 59.

Yoshikami, D., and Keller, E. B. (1969). *Fed. Proc. Fed. Amer. Soc. Exp. Biol.* **28**, 409.

Zachau, H. G., Dutting, H., Feldman, H., Melchers, F., and Karan, W. (1966). *Cold Spring Harbor Symp. Quant. Biol.* **31**, 417.

Zeikus, J. G., Taylor, M. W., and Buck, C. A. (1969). *Exp. Cell Res.* **57**, 74.

Zubay, G. (1962). *J. Mol. Biol.* **4**, 347.

BIOCHEMISTRY

CHAPTER VIII

REGENERATING LIVER:
AN EXPERIMENTAL MODEL FOR THE
STUDY OF GROWTH

EDWARD BRESNICK

I. Introduction

Any study of the etiology of neoplasia is faced with the problem of dissecting away the characteristics which are intimately associated with the neoplasia itself from those which are related more to the process of rapid proliferation. The question, then, of what is a suitable comparative system in the study of the mechanisms underlying carcinogenesis is a crucial one.

A number of interesting experimental models have been employed in this regard. Among these are included: embryonic and neonatal liver, hypertrophied kidney (occurring after unilateral nephrectomy), and regenerating liver. The latter has a number of advantages that make it desirable for investigation.

First, the method of preparation of the model is relatively simple. Second, the amount of tissue that can be obtained for study is of the order of several grams per rat and, hence, is suitable for most investigations. Third, partial hepatectomy is followed by a period of synchronization of the hepatocytes such that approximately 60% or so of the cells will enter mitosis. Few systems in which synchronization of this magnitude can be achieved *in vivo* are available to the investigator. A period of rapid growth ensues which will abate by approximately 2 weeks postoperation. Consequently, not only can rapid proliferation be studied, but the mechanisms responsible for *control* of hepatic growth may be subject to scrutiny. The regenerating liver is particularly suited to the study of one of the most profound problems in cell biology today, "What is responsible for the maintenance of the relative size of organs more or less constant during growth and development?"

This chapter presents available information describing the properties of the regenerating liver model and information concerning the homeostatic mechanisms operative in this model by which the physiology and morphology of this tissue remain constant under a variety of environmental conditions.

A number of very excellent reviews on the subject of liver regeneration have appeared, beginning with that of Fishback (1929) and including the most recent, that of Bucher (1967). Additional material which the serious investigator is encouraged to peruse is in the following: Glinos (1958b); Weinbren (1959); Doljanski (1960); Goss (1964); Steiner *et al.* (1966).

Although hepatectomies have been performed on a variety of species, the most commonly employed animal is the rat; this review will be limited to experiments that involve the latter.

A. HYPERTROPHY, HYPERPLASIA, AND REGENERATION

Three terms which are very often employed in the description of events transpiring after partial hepatectomy are "hypertrophy," "hyperplasia," and "regeneration."

By *hypertrophy* is meant the increase in size or protoplasmic mass of a tissue or organ. *Hyperplasia* implies an increase in the actual number of cells in a tissue. *Regeneration* is the process of growth which is organized to replace a lost structure at the site of its removal. The latter implies a compensation either of a structural nature, as of a *part*, or of a physioolgical nature, as of a *function*.

By definition, the loss of several lobes of liver, which occurs in partial hepatectomy, is *not* accompanied by regeneration, since the original lobes are not replaced during the subsequent weeks. Instead, the residual lobes undergo hypertrophy, restoring the original mass of the tissue (Simpson and Finckh, 1963). New lobules may be formed within the hypertrophic mass, but this process does not constitute regeneration. Restitution, or restoration, would be more appropriate terms for the description of the process which takes place subsequent to partial hepatectomy. Unfortunately, the term, regeneration, although misused has been in common usage for many years, and, hence, will also be employed in the present review.

B. History

The idea of regeneration of liver tissue has its origin in Greek mythology. At the bequest of the Greek goddess, Juno, Prometheus was bound, his abdominal cavity was exposed, and a vulture was sent daily to gnaw upon his liver. The latter underwent at least partial restoration, allowing the creature to continue his daily feast.

An excellent presentation of the historical aspects of liver regeneration has appeared in the review by Fishback published in 1929. In this review, Fishback (1929) notes that the first scientific observers of the phenomenon of liver regeneration were Cruveilhier (quoted by Milne, 1909) and Andral (quoted by Melchior, 1907). However, it was Canalis (quoted by Hess, 1890, in footnote 14) who undertook studies of the regeneration which resulted from the partial ablation of the liver. After removal of small blocks of tissues from the livers of dogs and guinea pigs, he observed proliferation of hepatic cells and new formation of bile ducts.

More extensive studies were carried out in a laboratory of von Podwyssozki (1886). After surgically dissecting small wedges of liver from a wide variety of species including rats, cats, guinea pigs, and rabbits, he noted evidence of regeneration occurring as early as 24 hours postoperatively. In the rat, mitotic figures were seen by $2\frac{1}{2}$ days, with bile ducts sprouting in the scar tissue by the fourth day. The regenerative process took place predominantly from the hepatic cells in the rat.

Removal of approximately 75% of the liver in the rabbit was accomplished by Ponfick in 1890 (see Fishback, 1929). He reported a threefold increase in the amount of restored tissue, the cause of which was attributed to a compensatory stimulation arising from a physiological need. The newly formed tissue performed functionally in a normal manner, although the remaining lobes had lost their former regularity and had increased in size in all directions.

These observations were confirmed by von Meister (1894) in rats. He regarded liver regeneration as a compensatory hypertrophy of the remnant lobes from hyperplasia of their cellular components. Each lobe was considered to possess the power of hypertrophy, manifested upon extirpation of any lobe. The work of von Meister is particularly important since he suggested that the ability of liver to regenerate is potentially infinite by demonstrating that liver was capable of restoring itself after partial hepatectomy for a second or even third time in the same manner as it does after the first.

It is evident that by the beginning of the twentieth century, a great deal of information was already available, particularly related to gross morphological events which occur after hepatectomy. Unfortunately, a technique was still required for the routine hepatectomy in small laboratory animals. Such a procedure was devised by Higgins and Anderson (1931). A discussion of this procedure follows in Section II.

II. Procedure for Partial Hepatectomy

Although the phenomenon of liver regeneration had been known for years prior, it was only after the classic paper of Higgins and Anderson (1931) was published, that definitive studies could be conducted on small laboratory animals. The importance of their study may be ascribed to the documentation of a method for partial hepatectomy in the laboratory rat. One has only to peruse the literature on liver regeneration to appreciate the number of times this paper is cited.

Since their description is so lucid and since their method is so universally applied, Higgins and Anderson's report on the technique is reproduced below:

TECHNIQUE OF PARTIAL REMOVAL (Higgins and Anderson, 1931)

The liver of the rat is a firm, dark red organ and according to Hunt is composed of four main lobes. The median lobe is cleft by a longitudinal fissure, which divides it into a right central and left central lobe. The right central lobe is flanked by the right lateral lobe, which is cleft transversely by a fissure dividing it into two smaller lobes, the posterior one of which caps the anterior pole of the right kidney. The left lateral lobe is a large lobe and lies immediately behind the left central lobe. The caudate lobe is likewise-cleft by a transverse fissure and comprises thereby two smaller lobes which lie within the curvature of the stomach and the lesser omentum. Anatomically, the median lobe, with its two central portions, together with the left lateral lobe, forms somewhat of a unit which lends itself well to surgical removal.

All operations were carried out with the animals under ether anesthesia, and careful asepsis was maintained throughout. Through a median-line incision reaching 3 or 4 cm. posteriorly from the xiphoid process of the sternum the large median lobe of the liver, with the left lateral lobe, was easily delivered, securely ligated by coarse linen and then excised. In this way portions of the hepatic parenchyma ranging in extent from 65 to 75 per-cent of the total liver were removed, leaving within the peritoneum the right lateral lobe and the small caudate, or spigelian, lobe. The abdomen was closed with two layers, one suture of linen being used; the peritoneum and the abdominal muscles were closed in the first layer and the integument in the second. There was no special postoperative care, except that in place of water the animals had access to a 20 per cent solution of dextrose for the first day, after which the normal diet and water were provided. The full diet consisted of known quantities of yellow corn meal, linseed oil meal, crude casein, alfalfa meal, powdered skim milk and salts.

Immediate postoperative complications were not common, and yet, owing essentially to lesions of the lung, which one often encounters in laboratory rats, about 25 per cent of the 220 hepatectomized animals that form the basis for this report died.

In the author's experience, the mortality rate as noted by Higgins and Anderson is slightly high. Over the course of at least several thousand hepatectomies, a mortality of less than 18% was observed. Many of the animals succumb not to the operative procedure per se, but during the course of the anesthesia. A second cause of mortality is in the severance of the ligature that is placed around the blood vessels.

The process of restoration of the liver weight to the preoperative value occurs during a 2-week period. This is apparent from the data which have been extracted from the original paper of Higgins and Anderson (1931) and are presented in Table I. It is evident that within a 24-hour postoperative period, a considerable amount of restoration had occurred.

TABLE I

RESTORATION OF LIVER WEIGHT AFTER PARTIAL HEPATECTOMY[a]

Time after operation	% Liver remaining postoperation
0	29.4
16–24 hr	45.3
24–48 hr	53.3
2–3 days	70.6
4–7 days	74.3
7–14 days	93.0
14–21 days	102

[a] Data obtained from Higgins and Anderson (1931).

III. Cytological Observations

Following partial hepatectomy, the hepatic cells undergo marked alterations in number and size, in the composition of the intracellular organelles, and in their mitotic activity. Some of these alterations may

occur as early as 30 minutes or as late as 28 hours after partial hepatectomy. Many of the ultrastructural changes in regenerating liver are like
those observed in neoplastic cells and consequently reflect the rapid rate
of cell proliferation. Although in many cases, these changes have been
regarded as providing evidence for cellular activity prior to the restoration of the liver mass, it is often difficult to preclude the possibility that
some of the alterations may have arisen as a result of liver damage or
may be due to the restricted food intake occurring postoperatively.
These possibilities must be borne in mind when evaluating the morphological observations of regenerating liver. With this in mind, the
cytological changes that have been observed after partial hepatectomy
will be reviewed. Unless indicated otherwise only the parenchymal cells
will be considered.

A. CELL SIZE

Stowell (1948) has reported that as early as 6 hours after partial
hepatectomy, an increase in the cytoplasmic volume was apparent in
the liver remnant. By 18 to 24 hours later, the increase in cell size had
reached 2.6-times that of the normal hepatocyte. Although the magnitude of the increase was not as great, similar findings were reported by
Harkness (1952), Glinos (1958a), and by Weinbren (1959). By 24 hours
post-hepatectomy, the cell size began to decline, reaching the normal
cytoplasmic volume shortly thereafter. The enlarged cells in the early
regenerating liver tend to crowd into the vascular and extracellular
spaces, thus distorting the normal cellular mosaic. It is interesting that
the cell enlargement coincides with or slightly precedes the burst in
mitotic activity (see p. 354).

1. Cell Surface

During the first 12 hours after partial hepatectomy, widespread
changes take place in the surface of the parenchymal cells (Lane and
Becker, 1966). These include a loss in the sinusoidal microvilli by formation of cytoplasmic sequestra, a loss of contact between intercellular
surfaces, i.e., decreased adhesiveness, and a loss of intercellular materials
resulting in appearance of smooth membranes. The surfaces of cells
lining the bile canaliculus were unaffected.

The surfaces of adult liver cells are functionally highly specialized.
The sinusoidal border has been considered to be an area for endocrine
secretion, whereas the bile canaliculus, for exocrine activity (Bruni and
Porter, 1965). Lane and Becker (1966) have postulated that the changes
in the surfaces may be secondary to a shift of the cell from the synthesis
of protein for cellular maintenance and secretion to the preparation for

cell division. Since the apparatus for the secretion of these proteins is the sinusoidal microvillus, degeneration of this structure would help to achieve the shift in activity.

The alteration in the morphology of the surface of the parenchymal cells during regeneration may be responsible for the elevation in the net electrostatic charge noted by Eisenberg et al. (1962) and by Ambrose et al. (1956). The enhanced electrophoretic mobility of cells from regenerating liver was detectable at 6 hours, was maximal at 24 hours, and was still high by 48 hours post-hepatectomy.

The nature of the chemical effect responsible for the change in the surface of the regenerating rat liver cell and which leads to an increase in electrophoretic mobility was investigated by Chaudhuri and Lieberman (1965). They demonstrated that the increased electrokinetic properties of the liver surface were caused by an elevation in surface neuraminic acid. Furthermore, the neuraminic acid occurred in a bound form, complexed to a molecule which was soluble in 30 to 95% ethanol. The author suggested a mucoprotein rather than a ganglioside as the complexing molecule.

B. Size of Nucleus and of Its Inclusions

Mammalian cells generally appear to maintain constant the ratio of the size of the nucleus to the cytoplasm. Upon the increase in the growth of a cell, the constancy in this ratio can only be achieved in two ways: (a) by *mitosis* or (b) by *nuclear enlargement*.

Stowell (1948) noted that along with the increase in cytoplasmic volume of the cells of regenerating liver, the nuclear volume was similarly enhanced. By 18 to 24 hours postoperation, the volume of the nuclei was 2.2 times that of the normal parenchymal cell nuclear volume. The time of earliest change in nuclear volume was reported as 10 hours by Harkness (1952), whereas Hammarsten (1951) observed the maximal increase by 30 hours, post-hepatectomy.

Not only was the size of the hepatic cell nucleus altered in regenerating liver, but its shape underwent change as well. The nucleus frequently has an irregular outline with ruffled perinuclear membrane in contrast to the smooth periphery of control nuclei (Stenger and Confer, 1966). Occasionally, deep cytoplasmic invaginations were apparent with some evidence of nuclear budding. Inside the nucleus of the hepatic cell after partial hepatectomy, large clumps of chromosomal material and prominent interchromatin granules could be observed. The significance of these nuclear changes is not known, although they may be related to the enhanced synthesis of deoxyribonucleic acid (DNA) which occurs in regenerating liver (see p. 358).

In regenerating liver, the nucleoli were also altered in both size and number. As originally reported by Stowell (1948) and confirmed by Hammarsten (1951), by Bernhard *et al.* (1952), and by Stenger and Confer (1966), the nucleoli were enlarged reaching a maximum size just before the enhanced mitotic activity apparent in regenerating liver.

Stenger and Confer (1966) have reported that in regenerating liver, the nucleoli are frequently in contact with the perinuclear membrane, with prominent small granular components. The changes in appearance and location of the nucleoli may be a reflection of the synthesis of ribosomal ribonucleic acid (RNA) precursors, demonstrable by biochemical techniques, which takes place in this organelle.

Although the size of the hepatic cell nucleoli is reported to increase, St. Mironescu and Dragomir (1967) have reported a reduction in the number of these structures in regenerating liver. The reduction correlated with the variations in mitotic activity, i.e., at lowest value just prior to the mitotic wave. The reduction may have been caused by extrusion of nucleoli or their component parts outside the nuclear environs, by nuclear budding, or by fusion. These authors also observed an accumulation of nucleolini within the nucleoli in regenerating liver.

1. Multinucleated Cells and Polyploidy

Binucleated cells occur with varying frequency in many organs and particularly in normal adult rat liver. Their number decreases in regenerating liver, after the onset of cell division, from the normal liver value of 25–30% to 8–10% (Wilson *et al.*, 1953; see Bucher, 1963). Once regeneration is complete, the percentage of binucleated cells returns to normal.

Concomitant with the shift in binucleated cells noted in regenerating liver, the extent of polyploidy is also increased. In this regard, 70–80% of the normal adult parenchymal nuclei exhibit tetraploidy, whereas 1–2% are octaploid. During regeneration, the tetraploid and octaploid nuclei increased to 90% and 2–4%, respectively (Naora, 1957; Alfert and Geschwind, 1958; Post *et al.*, 1960).

2. Mitotic Activity

Regenerating liver is a model system for studying hyperplasia since the parent normal tissue exhibits such a low rate of cell division. The value for the mitotic activity of normal adult rat liver varies from investigator to investigator, but is in the range of 0.005 to 0.01% of the total parenchymal cell population (Brues and Marble, 1937; Abercrombie and Harkness, 1951). Nevertheless, the total number of liver cells is constantly although slowly expanding; the cell population has been estimated to increase by 0.71% per day (Stevens *et al.*, 1953).

Consequently, the low occurrence of mitotic activity in the slowly increasing population indicates a slow turnover of cells with life-spans in excess of 150 days (Swick *et al.*, 1956).

By 16 to 18 hours after partial hepatectomy, proliferative activity, as seen in radioautographic studies utilizing radioactive precursors of DNA, may be detected among the periportal parenchymal cells (Glinos, 1958a, b). Prior to this time, only a few parenchymal cells become labeled. The proliferative activity rises rapidly from 20 to 24 hours post-operatively with the labeled nuclei extending at first from the periportal region toward the central vein and then more randomly (Grisham, 1960). This period of rapid DNA synthesis is followed by a decline.

Mitotic activity proceeds some 6–8 hours after the incorporation of precursor material into DNA and shows a similar pattern of distribution (Harkness, 1952; Grisham, 1960). An increase in the number of mitotic figures first appears at 24 hours. The number rises sharply to a maximum at 28 to 32 hours postoperatively, then falls off rapidly at first, and more slowly during the next few days. The maximum mitotic activity may reach 3.5% of the total parenchymal cells (Cater *et al.*, 1956; Weinbren, 1959).

The exact timing for these events may differ from investigation to investigation. The reasons for these differences include the presence of secondary mitotic peaks, use of animals of different ages, and time of day the experiments were performed. These factors have been considered in the review by Bucher (1963).

C. CYTOPLASMIC ORGANELLES

Striking alterations in both the form and distribution of cytoplasmic organelles take place during regeneration. Some of these effects, for example, the dispersion of basophilic bodies at the periphery of the lobe (Glinos, 1958a, b), occur within 30 minutes after hepatectomy. Disaggregation of the endoplasmic reticulum with the loss of membrane structures and the appearance of free ribosomes occur 8 hours after the operation (Bernhard and Rouiller, 1956; Aterman, 1961; Davis, 1962; Fisher and Fisher, 1963; Stenger and Confer, 1966). The abundance of free ribosomes in hyaloplasm may be the morphological manifestation of enhanced synthesis of cytoplasmic RNA apparent during regeneration (see p. 369).

The change in the distribution of the rough endoplasmic reticulum is, at first glance, quite surprising. One might anticipate as an end result of this morphological observation a diminution in the capacity for protein synthesis. Yet sufficient data are available which suggest an enhancement in protein synthesis in liver regeneration since microsomes isolated from the latter have an increased ability to incorporate amino acids (Campbell and Greengard, 1957; Hultin and von der Decken, 1957; von der Decken and Hultin, 1958; Hoagland, 1961; Cammarano *et al.*, 1965a). Porter (1957) has supplied the answer to this apparent dilemma by suggesting that ribosomes attached to membranes of endoplasmic reticulum function in the synthesis of "export protein," whereas free ribosomes are devoted to the formation of protein for intracellular use.

Concomitant with the dissolution of the membranes of the endoplasmic reticulum, a marked reduction in the glycogen stores may be noted (Harkness, 1957). Within 2 hours after partial hepatectomy, the liver glycogen is almost completely depleted. The enzymes involved in glycogen metabolism are believed to reside in close proximity to the smooth endoplasmic reticulum (Fouts, 1962). Consequently, the diminution in the amount of glycogen may simply be a reflection in the depletion of the latter membrane structures.

In 24-hour regenerating liver, morphologically distinct mitochondria of elongated dumbbell shape may be observed, comprising 2–6% of the normal mitochondrial population. Within their environs are also found parallel, longitudinally disposed lamellae (Claude, 1967). Characteristically, these dumbbell-shaped structures are also found in intimate contact with expanses of smooth endoplasmic reticulum. The latter envelop and appear to adhere to the elongated middle section of the mitochondria.

Because of the morphological integrity of the mitochondria and their association with the smooth endoplasmic reticulum, Claude (1967) suggested that they represent structures with physiological function rather than degenerative bodies. Their shape also suggested the possible involvement in reduplication of mitochondria. The contact of the endoplasmic reticulum with the mitochondria might also imply the active transport of precursors between the two bodies.

An increase in lipid bodies was most pronounced in regenerating liver, and, frequently, these bodies were associated with multilayered lamellar, myelinlike figures (Stenger and Confer, 1966). The metabolism of regenerating liver is apparently geared to the utilization of lipids instead of glycogen (Simek and Sedlacek, 1965).

The number of microbodies also increases during liver regeneration as first reported by Rouiller and Bernhard (1956) and confirmed by Stenger and Confer (1966). The significance of this observation is not known.

Becker and Lane (1965) observed a marked increase in autophagocytosis during regeneration, particularly in the early postoperative period. These investigators postulated the involvement of the lysosomal system in the preparation for cell division. The mechanism by which the activation of the lysosomal system was accomplished is not known. Support for their hypothosis came from the results of Kent and his associates (1966) who, utilizing iron-laden lysosomes, were able to demonstrate the localization of these bodies around the nucleus and mitotic spindle during cytokinesis and from the results of their own laboratory (Lane and Becker, 1967). The activation of lysosomes took place during periods of maximal nuclear activity. The lysosomes may also function to degrade cytoplasmic structures during regeneration, i.e., endoplasmic reticulum.

The timetable for the appearance of the morphological alterations is offered in Table II.

TABLE II

MORPHOLOGICAL ALTERATIONS DURING REGENERATION AS A FUNCTION OF TIME

Time of appearance after partial hepatectomy (hr)	Type of alteration
0.5–8	Dispersion of cytoplasmic basophilic bodies Disaggregation of endoplasmic reticulum Appearance of free ribosomes Decrease in lipid bodies Loss in glycogen stores Simplification of cell surface Increased lysosomal activity
12–16	Increase in cell size Increase in nuclei and nucleoli Increased DNA synthesis
18–24	Increased mitotic activity

IV. Biochemical Observations

In addition to the number of morphological observations made in liver regeneration, the process has been extensively characterized biochemically. Interestingly enough, it is not clear why the synthesis of DNA is "turned on" and why the subsequent mitosis takes place. However, despite the lack of any key to this process, a presentation of the biochemical changes that have been recorded during regeneration is certainly germane to this discussion.

In this section are presented the effects of liver regeneration upon (*1*) DNA synthesis, (*2*) RNA synthesis, (*3*) enzymes involved in nucleotide metabolism, (*4*) other protein synthesis, and (*5*) lipid synthesis.

A. Deoxyribonucleic Acid Synthesis

Adult liver exhibits a very low mitotic rate (see p. 354), and, consequently, a minimal rate of DNA synthesis (Brues *et al.*, 1944; Furst *et al.*, 1950). This is in marked contrast to the enhanced level of DNA synthesis observed in normal neonatal liver (Kennedy *et al.*, 1958; Bucher *et al.*, 1961). Evidently, the capacity for DNA synthesis did exist in liver at an early stage of development. In both systems, adult and neonatal livers, isotope studies have indicated that once the DNA is made, it is extremely stable, i.e., its turnover is low.

Furst *et al.* (1950) initially observed the enhanced incorporation of adenine into the DNA of regenerating liver. Many subsequent investigations confirmed this observation. A significant elevation of DNA synthesis was detectable 12–18 hours after partial hepatectomy (Swift, 1953; Holmes and Mee, 1954; Nygaard and Rusch, 1955; Hecht and Potter, 1958; Bollum and Potter, 1959). Some discrepancy existed as to

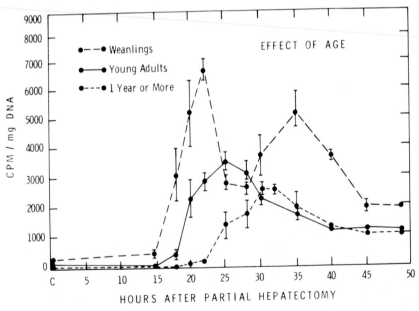

Fig. 1. Effect of age upon DNA synthesis in regenerating liver. Specific activity of DNA 2 hours after intravenous injection of 2-^{14}C-thymidine, at intervals following partial hepatectomy in weanling, young adult (approximately 4 months old), and older rats (12–15 months old) (taken from Bucher, 1963).

the time of maximum synthesis of DNA. The most rapid production of DNA was claimed to occur at 20 to 24 hours after hepatectomy (Nygaard and Rusch, 1955; Cater et al., 1956), at 24 to 30 hours (Hecht and Potter, 1958), or at 30 hours (Hammarsten, 1951; Eliasson et al., 1951). In all cases, however, the period of DNA synthesis was followed 6–8 hours later by mitotic activity (Lesher et al., 1960; Grisham, 1962).

The reasons for the variability in the determination of the time of maximum DNA synthesis during regeneration have been thoroughly examined by Bucher (1963). Some of her data have been reproduced and are presented in Fig. 1. The time of maximum specific activity of DNA is gradually shifted toward the right, i.e., to later times, as a function of increasing age of the rats. Thus, with 24 to 27-day-old rats, the maximum rate is observed at 22 hours; with 200 to 250-gm rats, at 25 hours; with 350 to 400-gm rats, at 32 hours. In addition, the onset of this maximum is progressively more slow as age increases. Furthermore, with the weanling rats, two waves of synthesis are apparent, in a manner reminiscent of DNA synthesis in synchronized cultures of mammalian cells. With the older animals, the waves of synthesis are more or less united, giving a broader and flatter peak. A secondary peak of DNA synthetic activity occurring 12 hours after the first had been reported previously by Cater et al. (1956).

Secondarily, mitotic activity of normal liver, like many other cellular functions, exhibits a profound circadian periodicity (reviewed in Bucher, 1963) and is affected by the duration of illumination and darkness and by feeding habits. The degree of mitosis might vary during a normal cycle by a factor of 10 with a maximum occurring during 0600–1200 hours. Consequently, in meaningful studies on liver regeneration, such factors as diet, illumination and darkness, and the time at which partial hepatectomy had been performed, must be critically controlled and stated.

Bucher (1963) has nicely demonstrated that the increase in DNA synthesis in liver subsequent to hepatectomy is a function of the mass of liver removed in the operation (Fig. 2). Thus, removal of 30% of the total liver mass yields only a barely discernible increase in DNA synthesis. With ablation of 40% of the tissue, one-third of the response is noted as that after a 68% hepatectomy.

1. Rate of DNA Replication in Regenerating Liver

By using radioautography and cytochemistry, Looney and his coworkers (Looney, 1960; Looney et al., 1967) have noted that the rate of DNA synthesis changes during the 8-hour period in which DNA is replicated in regenerating rat liver. In the later study, Looney et al. (1967) measured the changing rate of synthesis of DNA in individual

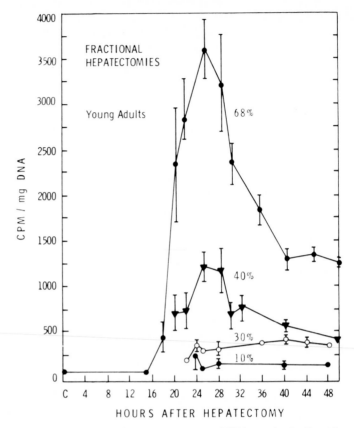

FIG. 2. Effect of fractional hepatectomy upon DNA synthesis. Specific activity of DNA 2 hours after intravenous injection of 2-^{14}C-thymidine at intervals following excision of various lobes (from Bucher, 1963).

cells by radioautography and the changing rate in a total cell population by biochemical techniques. Thus, they were able to calculate the rate of synthesis of DNA at the molecular and chromosomal levels.

Despite the change in the length of the chromosome from early to late metaphase, they were able to calculate the amount of DNA per large chromosome, i.e., 39×10^{-14} gm and the amount per small chromosome, i.e., 6×10^{-14} gm. They assumed and later were able to show that DNA replication occurs at the same rate in liver as in bacteriophage—a point suggested originally on purely hypothetical grounds by Cairns (1963). With some minor assumptions, Looney et al. (1967) demonstrated that at 13 hours after partial hepatectomy, approximately 20 of a possible 200 sites were actively synthesizing DNA in the liver cell; at 17 hours, this number increased to 40; at 21 hours, the period of maximal DNA synthesis, this value rose to 150. These data demonstrate that during the period of DNA synthesis, increasing numbers of sites become engaged in this endeavor, i.e., there is progressive genetic activation.

2. Mitochondrial DNA

Although DNA had been found in subcellular preparations of mitochondria, the observation was not considered important, but was ascribed to contamination by nuclei or by adsorbed DNA. However, with the utilization of highly purified mitochondria, DNA was reported in rat liver by several laboratories (Nass and Nass, 1963; Kalf, 1964; Schneider and Kuff, 1965). The DNA isolated from mitochondria differed markedly from nuclear DNA in various physical and chemical parameters. The nucleotide base compositions were substantially different; mitochondrial DNA exhibited a lower buoyant density and a low melting temperature (Schneider and Kuff, 1965). Furthermore, mitochondrial DNA of liver was circular, reminiscent of a number of DNA viruses (Kroon et al., 1966; Sinclair and Stevens, 1966). The content in rat liver mitochondria was 1.9×10^{-10} μg/mitochondria, representing 14 molecules of DNA of molecular weight 8.7×10^6 for each of the 12×10^{10} mitochondria present in one gram of liver (Schneider and Kuff, 1965). The amount of DNA in the mitochondria of normal rat liver, however, would only account for 1.5% of the DNA present in this tissue.

Electron microscopic studies by Nass et al. (1965) showed the presence of more DNA fibers in the mitochondria of regenerating than of adult resting liver. These morphological studies were confirmed with radioisotope techniques by Schneider and Kuff (1965) using deoxycytidine and thymidine as precursors, and by Nass (1967) with ^{32}P.

Nass (1967) was able to establish an increased rate of incorporation of precursors into mitochondrial DNA after partial hepatectomy as compared with normal liver. The DNA-to-protein ratio in mitochondria of regenerating liver was 2–3 times greater than in resting liver. The total content of mitochondrial DNA in liver was almost completely restored by 2 to 3 days in contrast to nuclear DNA. The mitochondrial DNA from either adult or regenerating livers exhibited metabolic stability. Four hours after the administration of ^{32}P to normal rats, the specific activity of mitochondrial DNA from normal rats was six-fold greater than that of nuclear DNA. In 12-hour regenerating liver, the specific activity of mitochondrial DNA was 18 times greater. At this time, the labeling of the mitochondrial DNA accounted for 50% of the total incorporation of ^{32}P into DNA. In the 24 hour regenerating liver, however, equal specific activities were noted.

It is evident that (a) the synthesis of mitochondrial DNA as judged from these isotope experiments was not synchronous with chromosomal replication and (b) that the mitochondrial DNA was neither a product nor a precursor of nuclear DNA.

3. Deoxyribonucleotide Metabolism

Levels of pyrimidine deoxyribonucleotides are barely detectable in normal liver (Hecht and Potter, 1956; Behki and Schneider, 1962). In regenerating liver, however, a marked elevation in the concentration of these substances has been found. Presumably, these deoxyribonucleosidic compounds will ultimately function as precursors for DNA in regenerating liver.

The mechanism of synthesis of these substances has been the subject of much discussion. In some elegant experiments, Bucher and Oakman (1969) determined the pool size of thymidine triphosphate in control, in 24-hour, and in 45-hour regenerating rat livers. The control levels were difficult to determine and accordingly vary between 0 and 0.88 nmole/mg DNA. The values in 24- and 45-hour regenerating livers were 2.5–4.0 and 3.4–4.1 nmoles/mg DNA, respectively. The total thymidine deoxyribonucleoside and deoxyribonucleotide concentration of normal liver has been estimated as 2 nmoles/mg DNA (Gross and Rabinowitz, 1968). This value is tripled in regenerating liver. The mechanism of synthesis of these deoxyribonucleosides has been the subject of much discussion and has finally been elucidated.

In 1952, Racker postulated the formation of deoxyribonucleotides through the intervention of deoxyribose aldolase, an enzyme believed to function in the catabolism of deoxyribosyl compounds (Racker, 1952) (see Fig. 3). In this sequence of reactions, glyceraldehyde-3-phosphate and acetaldehyde, both arising in carbohydrate metabolism,

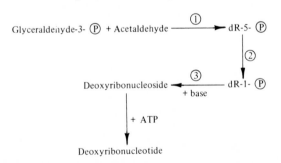

FIG. 3. Deoxyribose aldolase in the synthesis of deoxyribonucleotides. dR-5-(P), deoxyribonucleoside-5-phosphate; ① deoxyribose aldolase; ② mutase; ③ deoxyribonucleoside phosphorylase; ATP, adenosine 5'-triphosphate.

interact to form deoxyribose-5-phosphate. The latter sugar phosphate, in the presence of a specific mutase, is converted to the 1-phosphate derivative. Deoxyribose-1-phosphate interacts with either a purine or pyrimidine base with the resultant transfer of the glycone to yield a deoxyribonucleoside. The latter is phosphorylated by adenosine triphosphate (ATP) and the specific kinase to the deoxyribonucleotide.

Rose and Schweigert (1953), on the other hand, in tracer experiments with various mammalian organs, proposed that the formation of deoxyribonucleotides occurs exclusively by the reduction of ribonucleotides, without the cleavage of the glycosidic linkage. Although evidence obtained from experiments with regenerating liver (Groth and Jiang, 1966) was marshalled to support the position of Racker (1952), convincing evidence is now available from *in vivo* double-isotope experiments with regenerating liver which indicates that deoxyribonucleotides are, indeed, formed by the reduction of ribonucleotides (Larsson and Neilands, 1966).

The exact mechanism for the synthesis of deoxyribonucleotides via the reduction of the ribonucleotides has been clarified by Reichard and his co-workers (reviewed in Larsson and Reichard, 1967). The schema for this reduction is indicated in Fig. 4. The process requires the presence of four different proteins; two enzymes B_1 and B_2 which function in concert in the reductive mechanism; thioredoxin, a small molecular weight protein which undergoes sulfhydryl–sulfide interconversion; and thioredoxin reductase, a flavoprotein which is responsible for the oxidation–reduction reactions between thioredoxin and nicotinamide adenine dinucleotide phosphate (NADP).

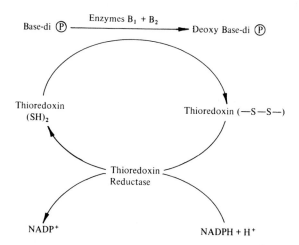

FIG. 4. Deoxyribonucleotide formation via reduction of ribonucleotides.

The ribonucleotide reductase plays an important role in the preparation of the regenerating liver for the synthesis of DNA. Although no cytidine diphosphate reductase activity is demonstrable in normal liver, its activity rises sharply by 24 hours after partial hepatectomy and continues to rise between 24 and 36 hours (King and van Lancker, (1969). The elevated enzyme activity appears to be formed *de novo* since actinomycin D and X-irradiation block this elevation.

The events that transpire during the period of liver regeneration are all geared toward the production of deoxyribonucleotide precursors for the requisite synthesis of DNA. Accordingly, it is not surprising that the activities of enzymes which function in the catabolism of these precursors would diminish after partial hepatectomy. Although pyrimidine deoxyribonucleotides and their di- and triphosphates are detectable in regenerating liver (Schneider, 1957), they are not found in normal liver tissue. Some deoxyribonucleosides, largely deoxycytidine, however, have been reported (Schneider and Brownell, 1957). It has been postulated by Fiala *et al.* (1962) that the absence of deoxyribonucleotides is in part due to the presence of the enzyme, deoxyribonucleotidase. In the 24-hour regenerating liver, deoxyribonucleotidase′activity, localized in the mitochondrial and microsomal fractions, was reduced by one-half (Fiala *et al.*, 1962).

Fritzson (1967), however, has been unable to confirm these results. He has found that the dephosphorylation of deoxyuridine monophosphate, deoxycytidine monophosphate, and thymidine monophosphate occurred largely in the soluble fraction of a liver homogenate and was due mainly to nonspecific acid phosphatase activity. Furthermore, the activity could not be related to the growth rate in regenerating liver.

As mentioned previously (see p. 363), thymidine phosphorylase is looked upon as a catabolic enzyme rather than one that catalyzes the *synthesis* of thymidine (see Fig. 5, enzyme 8). In keeping with the central theme of this section, i.e., preservation of DNA precursors in regenerating liver, the activity of this enzyme is markedly reduced after partial hepatectomy (Okada and Hempelman, 1959; Janion and Shugar, 1961; Bianchi *et al.*, 1961). Furthermore, Maley and Maley (1961a,b) have reported the reduction in the activities of phosphatase and nucleotidase.

The anabolism of thymidine and of its deoxyribonucleotide is greatly accelerated after partial hepatectomy. Thus, thymidylate (TMP) kinase (Bollum and Potter, 1958, 1959; Mantsavinos and Canellakis, 1959; Hiatt and Bojarski, 1960; Weissman *et al.*, 1960; Fausto and van Lancker, 1965) is markedly elevated, beginning at approximately 18 to 23 hours, reaching its maximum level at 36 to 48 hours, and returning to the normal activity by about the fifth day postoperation. Fausto and van Lancker (1965) have reported the appearance in regenerating rat

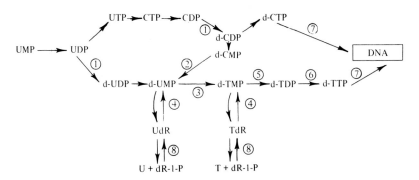

Fig. 5. Deoxyribonucleotide formation. ① Ribonucleotide reductase; ② deoxycytidylate (dCMP) deaminase; ③ (TMP) synthetase; ④ thymidine kinase; reverse reaction catalyzed by phosphatase; ⑤ TMP kinase; ⑥ thymidine diphosphate (TDP) kinase; ⑦ DNA polymerase; ⑧ deoxyribonucleoside (dR) phosphorylase; U, uracil; T, thymine.

liver supernates of a higher proportion of enzyme activity than is found in control supernatant fractions.

The formation of TMP in mammalian systems is accomplished via two enzymic pathways: (a) the conversion of deoxyuridylate (dUMP) to TMP as catalyzed by TMP synthetase (enzyme 3 in Fig. 5) and (b) the phosphorylation of thymidine, catalyzed by thymidine kinase (enzyme 4 in Fig. 5). The substrate for the former enzyme, dUMP, is also formed by two paths—the deamination of deoxycytidylate (dCMP) (enzyme 2 in Fig. 5) and the phosphorylation of deoxyuridine. These interrelations are presented in Fig. 5.

The activities of both TMP synthetase and dCMP deaminase are barely detectable in normal adult liver (Maley and Maley, 1960, 1961a; Myers et al., 1961; Hartmann and Heidelberger, 1961; Beltz, 1962) but rise rapidly by 12 hours post-hepatectomy, reaching a maximum at approximately 24 to 48 hours; thereafter activities fall abruptly. The magnitude of the maximum elevation of activity may be as much as twenty-fold.

a. Thymidine Kinase. The enhancement in the incorporation of thymidine into the DNA of regenerating liver has been reported by a number of laboratories (reviewed in Bucher, 1963). Concomitant with the enhanced incorporation, an increased level of thymidine kinase has been noted prior to the burst in mitotic activity in regenerating liver. The level of activity of this enzyme in normal adult liver is low (Bresnick et al., 1967a) as was noted with dCMP deaminase and TMP synthetase. Thymidine kinase is also responsible for the phosphorylation of deoxyuridine to form deoxyuridylate (Bresnick and Thompson, 1965). Thus, the enhanced phosphorylation of deoxyuridine noted by Sköld (1960) in 36-hour regenerating liver was caused by the increase in thymidine kinase activity.

The elucidation of the function of thymidine kinase in the ordered activities of the hepatocyte has proven an enigma to biochemists for many years. It is believed to comprise part of a "salvage" pathway by which thymidine may be converted to its deoxyribonucleotide for ultimate incorporation into DNA. This is necessary to counterbalance the extremely active dephosphorylating enzyme in liver, thymidine phosphatase (see Fig. 5). In proliferating systems, e.g., regenerating liver, the reduction in the activity of this phosphatase with the concomitant marked elevation in thymidine kinase activity is sufficient to keep the thymidine funneling through the anabolic pathway.

As explicitly stated by Berlin and Schimke (1965) and by Tomkins *et al.* (1965), the net activity of an enzyme is the result of the balance between the synthesis and degradation of the specific protein (Fig. 6).

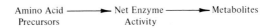

Amino Acid ⟶ Net Enzyme ⟶ Metabolites
Precursors   Activity

FIG. 6. Balance of synthesis and degradation.

Consequently, an experimentally measurable increase in enzymic activity may be the result of an enhanced synthesis of that enzyme or the effect of a decreased catabolism. An investigation of the contribution of the latter to the observed increase in thymidine kinase activity in regenerating liver has been undertaken (Bresnick *et al.*, 1967a). The stability of the messenger RNA responsible for the translation of thymidine kinase was also measured. In these studies, protein synthesis was blocked by cycloheximide, and the decay in enzymic activity was determined in control and regenerating livers. By this experimental procedure, the stability of the enzyme can be ascertained. In addition, messenger RNA synthesis was inhibited by actinomycin D, and the subsequent decay in thymidine kinase activity of control and regenerating liver was measured. The latter was now an indicator of the stability of the messenger RNA. The results of these studies are presented in Table III along with some recent investigations on the enzyme from neonatal rat liver and the Novikoff ascites hepatoma cells (Bresnick and Burleson, 1970).

The data of Table III indicate that the enzyme isolated from the four sources—Novikoff ascites hepatoma cells and neonatal, control adult, and 24-hour regenerating livers—has a similar half-life, i.e., 2.6–3.8 hours, whereas the stability of the messenger RNA varies in proportion to the rate of proliferation of the cell, i.e., the messenger RNA

TABLE III

STABILITY OF TEMPLATE RNA AND OF DEOXYTHYMIDINE KINASE IN
REGENERATING AND CONTROL LIVER

Substance	Half-life (hr)			
	Regenerating	Control	Novikoff	Neonatal liver
Template	7.5	3.0	> 24	> 24
Enzyme	3.7	2.6	3.8	3.5

responsible for the translation of thymidine kinase in the Novikoff cells is more stable than that present in adult liver.

The properties of thymidine kinase partially purified from regenerating liver have been studied (Bresnick et al., 1969) and compared with those of the enzyme isolated by Okazaki and Kornberg (1964) from *Escherichia coli* (see Table IV).

The K_m for thymidine was approximately the same with the enzymes isolated from regenerating rat liver and from the Walker rat carcinosarcoma, but this value differed in a hamster tumor and in *E. coli*. The K_m for thymidine was considerably lower with the enzyme isolated from either adult or fetal rat liver (Table IV). In accordance with these properties, the migration of thymidine kinase isolated from these sources in an electrophoretic field (disc gel electrophoresis at pH 8.8)

TABLE IV

KINETIC CONSTANTS OF THYMIDINE KINASE FROM DIFFERENT SOURCES

Source	K_m Thymidine (mM)	Adenosine 5'-triphosphate (mM)	
		$< 10^{-3} M$	$> 10^{-3} M$
24 hr regenerating rat liver	5.6	20	2.6
SV40-Induced hamster tumor	24	1.5	4.6
Walker rat tumor	6.9[a]	18[a](1)[c]	
Escherichia coli	9.1[b](2)[c]	40[b](3)[c]	
	33[d](3)[c]		
Adult or fetal rat liver	2.5	—(4)[c]	

[a] "Disaggregated" form.

[b] In presence of deoxycytidine diphosphate (0.14 mM).

[c] Key to references: (1) Bresnick et al., 1966b; (2) Iwatzuki and Okazaki, 1969; (3) Okazaki and Kornberg, 1964; (4) Klemperer and Haynes, 1968.

[d] In presence of high adenosine 5'-triphosphate (7.1 mM).

also varied. The regenerating liver enzyme migrated substantially differently from the other enzymes.

Thymidine kinase possesses many of the attributes of a rate-determining enzyme in deoxyribonucleotide metabolism in regenerating liver. For example, its activity and presumably synthesis are markedly elevated after partial hepatectomy. Its activity is inhibited by the distal product of thymidine anabolism, thymidine triphosphate, as reported by Maley and Maley (1962) for chick embryos, by Ives *et al.* (1963) for the Novikoff hepatoma, by Breitman (1963) and this laboratory (Bresnick *et al.*, 1964) for regenerating liver, and by this investigator for embryonic liver and hepatomas (Bresnick *et al.*, 1964). By means of this feedback mechanism (see Fig. 7), thymidine triphosphate can effectively and immediately shut off thymidine anabolism.

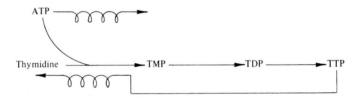

FIG. 7. Feedback mechanism. ATP, adenosine 5′-triphosphate; TMP, thymidylate; TDP, thymidine diphosphate; TTP, thymidine triphosphate.

Not only may thymidine kinase be feedback inhibited by its distal product, but the enzyme is activated by the phosphorylating agent and substrate, ATP. This finding was first made by Okazaki and Kornberg (1964) in *E. coli* and later extended to include the mammalian enzyme as well (Bresnick and Thompson, 1965; Bresnick *et al.*, 1966b). Thus, at low concentrations of ATP, the enzyme is exquisitely sensitive to the inhibitory action of thymidine triphosphate; at higher concentrations of ATP, thymidine kinase is relatively resistant to inhibition. The crucial factors, then, at the enzymic level, are the intracellular concentrations of both ATP and thymidine triphosphate.

b. Other Thymidine Anabolizing Enzymes. Thymidine diphosphate (TDP), once formed through the action of TMP kinase, is immediately phosphorylated by ATP and TDP kinase. The latter activity is appreciable in control adult liver and is elevated even further during regeneration (Bollum and Potter, 1959; Weissman *et al.*, 1960; Chiga *et al.*, 1963).

c. DNA Polymerase. The polymerization of deoxyribonucleotides into DNA, as catalyzed by DNA polymerase, is effectively increased in regenerating liver (Bollum and Potter, 1959). The elevation in enzyme activity is detectable at 18 to 24 hours postoperation, prior to the burst in mitotic activity, but coincident with the enhanced synthesis of DNA, rises to a maximum between 24 and 30 hours after partial hepatectomy, and decreases abruptly thereafter (Bollum and Potter, 1959; Fausto and van Lancker, 1965).

Following these observations on the elevation of this enzyme activity, Mukundan et al. (1963) reported that for the enzyme present in supernatant extracts of regenerating liver, native DNA was more effective as a primer than heat-denatured DNA. For calf thymus DNA polymerase, on the other hand, heat-denatured DNA (Bollum, 1959) was used preferentially.

Iwamura et al. (1968) has recently published an extensive paper in which the nature of DNA polymerase present in extracts of a group of hepatomas from fetal rat liver and from regenerating liver was compared. In their experiments, DNA polymerase from normal adult liver utilized native or heat-denatured DNA as primer equally well. The enzyme from fetal or regenerating livers exhibited higher activities in the presence of heat-denatured DNA.

The enzyme activity was subjected to gel filtration on Sephadex G-100 with the following results. The extract from adult liver was separated into two peaks of enzyme activity: (a) Peak I which exhibited higher activity with heat-denatured DNA and (b) Peak II, the lower molecular weight protein, which utilized only native DNA as primer. Both activities were nearly equal. In regenerating liver extracts, however, Peak I activity was markedly increased and Peak II was unaltered. With fetal liver, only Peak I was apparent. The activity of DNA polymerase was more proportional to DNA synthesis in vivo with heat-denatured DNA as primer. The reason for the difference in the results of Mukundan et al. (1963) and Iwamura et al. (1968) is not understood.

B. RIBONUCLEIC ACID SYNTHESIS

In contrast to the relatively late changes noted in the synthesis of DNA in regenerating liver, i.e., 12–20 hours after partial hepatectomy, alterations in RNA metabolism occur at an earlier stage. Although a net increase in liver RNA is detectable only by 20 hours (Nygaard and Rusch, 1955; Brody and Balis, 1959), enhanced incorporations of nucleotide precursors into this macromolecule are observed by as early as 2 hours postoperation. Thus, Bucher and Swaffield (1969) reported the incorporation of ^{14}C-orotate into RNA of regenerating liver was enhanced by 3 to 6 hours postoperation; Schneider and Potter (1957) and Hecht and Potter (1958) observed an acceleration in the incorporation by the sixth hour. Other investigators using orotate as precursor have also reported the detection of RNA synthesis in regenerating liver by approximately 6 hours (Lieberman *et al.*, 1965; Bucher and Swaffield, 1965; Uchiyama *et al.*, 1966). McArdle and Creaser (1963) reported that the earliest increase in RNA synthesis, as judged by ^{32}P incorporation, was at 1–2 hours postoperation. By using ^{14}C-carbamyl aspartate as precursor, Bresnick (1965) was not able to detect any increase in RNA synthesis in regenerating liver prior to 5 hours.

The maximal rate of RNA synthesis in regenerating liver occurred from 12 to 30 hours postoperatively (Eliasson *et al.*, 1951; Hammarsten, 1951; Nygaard and Rusch, 1955), and RNA synthesis remained elevated for 3 to 6 days (Johnson and Albert, 1952; Nygaard and Rusch, 1955; Hecht and Potter, 1958).

The increased RNA biosynthesis was found in the nucleolar, nuclear, and cytoplasmic fractions (described below) whereas changes in microsomal RNA occurred later (von der Decken and Hultin, 1958). In this regard, the increase in microsomal RNA synthesis probably accounted for the 62% elevation in the RNA content of regenerating liver, as reported by Price and Laird (1950). The observed biochemical effect upon microsomal RNA was confirmed morphologically by Glinos (1958b) who had demonstrated the depletion of cytoplasmic basophilia within a few hours after partial hepatectomy and its subsequent restoration by approximately 24 hours.

The molecular mechanism responsible for the initiation of the elevated synthesis of RNA in regenerating liver is not known. However, there has been some speculation about the possibility of the large increase in the portal blood supply, which is diverted to the remaining liver lobes, as being the principal cause (Tsukada and Lieberman, 1965b; Lieberman *et al.*, 1965). This contention has been questioned by Thomson and Clarke (1965). Although it is conceivable that part of the increase in RNA synthesis may be caused by the increased blood supply, it is very doubtful that this factor alone is totally responsible.

1. Nuclear and Nucleolar RNA

One of the first demonstrable events after partial hepatectomy, is an increase in the incorporation of precursors into nuclear RNA of regenerating liver (Schneider and Potter, 1957; Welling and Cohen, 1960; Fujioka *et al.*, 1963; Bucher and Swaffield, 1965; Muramatsu and Busch, 1965). Muramatsu and Busch (1965) have examined the qualitative composition of the nuclear RNA by zonal sedimentation analysis on sucrose density gradients. Their data (Fig. 8) indicate a marked increase in the 28, 35, and 45 S RNA components of total nuclear RNA in 18-hour regenerating liver. The increase in the 35 and 45 S RNA was

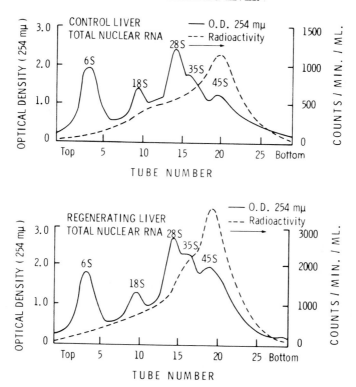

Fig. 8. Sedimentation analysis of nuclear RNA. Nuclear RNA was extracted from control (upper) and 18-hour regenerating liver (lower). Orotic acid-6-^{14}C was injected intravenously 10 minutes prior to killing the animals. Radioactivity was determined in a liquid scintillation counter. The arrow indicates the direction of the sedimentation. The numbers above the peaks indicate the approximate sedimentation coefficients (from Muramatsu and Busch, 1965).

further reflected in the marked elevation of the incorporation of ^{14}C-orotate into these constituents.

The nucleus is the site of transcription of virtually all the RNA made in the cell. Consequently, the RNA components seen on the sucrose density gradients represent transfer, ribosomal, ribosomal precursor, and messenger types. Since ribosomal RNA comprises a large percentage of the total cellular RNA, its synthesis represents a considerable activity in the hepatocyte. One of the major functions, therefore, of the nucleus is in the manufacture ultimately of 18 and 28 S ribosomal RNA components. This process appears to be one of the major functions of the nucleolus (reviewed in Busch and Smetana, 1970).

Ribosomal RNA is constructed first into a large precursor molecule, 45 S RNA, which undergoes a transition into a 35 S RNA component.

The latter is then broken down to the 28 and 18 S RNA ribosomal constituents.

The effect of liver regeneration upon nucleolar function was first implied by Stowell (1949) who observed a marked increase in the size of this organelle after hepatectomy. Thereafter, Swift and co-workers (1956) reported an increase in the RNA content of nucleoli of regenerating liver. The effect of regeneration upon nucleoli can be seen from the data presented in Table V (Muramatsu and Busch, 1965).

TABLE V

COMPOSITION OF NUCLEUS AND NUCLEOLUS AFTER PARTIAL HEPATECTOMY[a]

| | Time after partial hepatectomy (hr) | % of total dry wt. | | | RNA/DNA |
		DNA	RNA	Protein	
Nuclei	0	14.4	3.5	82.0	0.24
	6	15.5	4.1	80.5	0.26
	18	13.1	4.6	82.3	0.35
Nucleoli	0	6.5	9.4	84.0	0.4
	6	4.6	7.6	87.8	1.7
	18	5.4	15.5	79.1	2.9

[a] From Muramatsu and Busch (1965).

No marked alterations occur in the composition of nuclei during the first 6 hours after partial hepatectomy; by 18 hours, the RNA content is elevated. However, in nucleoli, Muramatsu and Busch (1965) have found an elevation in the RNA/DNA by 6 hours although a more substantial increase is noted by 18 hours (see Table V). A similar increase in both nucleolar size and RNA content, beginning at 6 hours after partial hepatectomy, has been reported by Kleinfeld (1966). In her studies, the content of RNA reached 4 times the control value by 20 hours postoperation.

Tsukada and Lieberman (1964) examined the question of nucleolar RNA synthesis during regeneration by employing biochemical techniques. After pulsing with ^{14}C-orotate, they noted a marked increase in the content and in the specific activity of the 35 and 45 S ribosomal precursor RNA components. Similar studies have been performed by Muramatsu and Busch (1965). The kinetics of synthesis of nucleolar RNA compared with nuclear RNA are presented in Table VI. These data have been condensed from the publication of Muramatsu and Busch (1965). Evidently, both nucleolar and nuclear RNA syntheses

TABLE VI

KINETICS OF SYNTHESIS OF NUCLEAR AND NUCLEOLAR RIBONUCLEIC
ACID[a,b]

Time after partial hepatectomy (hr)	Nucleus (cpm/μg)	Nucleolus (cpm/μg)	Nucleolus/nucleus
0	13.5	17.8	1.3
6	21.8	27.9	1.3
18	30.0	35.1	1.2

[a] From Muramatsu and Busch (1965).
[b] Each rat received 2 μcuries of orotate-6-^{14}C, intravenously, 30 minutes before it was killed.

occur simultaneously with a very noticeable elevation by 6 hours after partial hepatectomy.

The kinetics of synthesis and of disappearance of nucleolar 45 S RNA have been studied in 24-hour regenerating liver by Jacob et al. (1967). They showed that the half-lives of disappearance of the 45 S peak of nuclear and nucleolar RNA in regenerating liver were 8 and 4.7 minutes, respectively; the half-lives for control liver were 4.1 and 3.7 minutes, respectively. The rate of synthesis of 45 S nucleolar RNA in normal and regenerating liver was 4 and 16 $\times$ 10^{-15} gm/minute.

The results presented in this section have documented the substantial increases in preribosomal macromolecular components which occur early during liver regeneration. The data suggested that the formation of ribosomes is carried out at this time and may be required for the subsequent translation mechanism through which liver-specific proteins are constructed.

Although the nucleus is the site of synthesis of a considerable amount of rapidly labeled, heterogeneously sedimenting RNA which exhibits template activity in stimulating amino acid incorporation (Bresnick et al., 1967b), the exact physiological function of these macromolecules is obscure. The kinetic studies of Harris (1963) and of Attardi et al. (1966) have indicated that the bulk of this nuclear RNA never leaves the nucleus and is broken down in that organelle. One might speculate that these RNA molecules may be of the messenger variety that would not be expressed at this period of cellular activity.

a. Ribosomes. A gradual increase in the rate of liver ribosome formation occurs during the first 12 hours after partial hepatectomy, reaching a level 10–12 times the normal (Chaudhuri et al., 1967). In control liver, the formation of ribosomes is only partly regulated by the synthesis of protein, as judged by the partial sensitivity of the process to the inhibitor, cycloheximide (Chaudhuri and Lieberman, 1968a), and thus indicating the existence of a pool of preformed ribosomal protein. In regenerating liver, however, the formation of ribosomes is extremely sensitive to inhibition by cycloheximide, implying a total dependence upon protein synthesis.

Chaudhuri and Lieberman (1968b) have calculated that the synthesis of ribosomes takes 2–3 times longer in normal liver, by kinetic determinations of the incorporation of labeled precursors into preribosomal RNA. The ability of regenerating liver to make more ribosomes than normal liver suggests the more efficient use of the 45 S ribosomal precursors and/or the synthesis of new molecules.

b. Ribonucleotide Metabolism. The patterns for ribonucleotide biosynthesis are indicated in Fig. 9. The first precursor in the *de novo* pathway for pyrimidine synthesis is carbamyl phosphate. The latter is important not only in pyrimidine synthesis, but also in the formation of arginine. Until recently, carbamyl phosphate synthetase was considered the enzyme responsible for the synthesis of this important intermediate in nucleic acid and protein syntheses (Cohen, 1962). The enzyme is localized in the liver mitochondria, uses two molecules of ATP, one molecule each of NH_3 and of HCO_3^- as substrates, and requires N-acetylglutamate as a cofactor. Despite the profound activity of this enzyme in liver, no carbamyl phosphate synthetase activity was demonstrable in cell-free preparations of rapidly proliferating systems. In whole cells, however, e.g., Novikoff ascites hepatoma cells, the incorporation of ^{14}C-bicarbonate was demonstrable into the C-2 position of pyrimidines, although rupture of the cell resulted in destruction of this activity (Mayfield et al., 1967).

Recently, this dilemma has been answered with the demonstration of a carbamyl phosphate synthetase-like activity in regenerating liver (Takanishi et al., 1968) and in fetal rat liver (Hager and Jones, 1967). In contrast to the adult liver carbamyl phosphate synthetase, this enzyme is found in a soluble extract of these tissues, is unstable, requires glutamine as the nitrogen donor, and does *not* utilize N-acetylglutamate as cofactor. In the studies of Mayfield et al. (1967), glutamine was highly stimulatory in the incorporation of ^{14}C-bicarbonate into pyrimidines. The hypothesis presently being entertained is that two enzymes are involved in the synthesis of carbamyl phosphate—one which supplies the precursor for arginine synthesis, N-acetylglutamate- requiring carbamyl phosphate synthetase, and, the other, which provides ultimately pyrimidine to the cell, the glutamine-dependent carbamyl phosphate synthetase. The activity of N-acetylglutamate-requiring

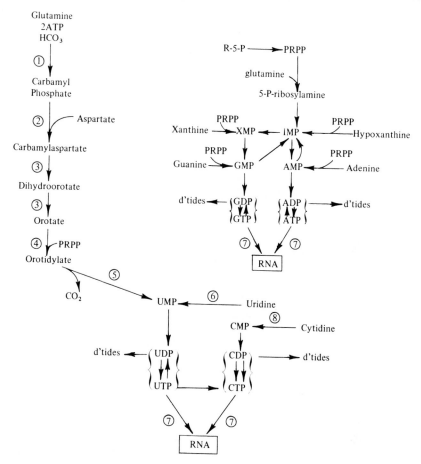

FIG. 9. Ribonucleotide biosynthesis. ① Glutamine-dependent carbamyl phosphate synthetase; ② aspartate transcarbamylase; ③ dihydroorotase and dihydroorotate dehydrogenase; ④ orotidine monophosphate pyrophosphorylase; ⑤ orotidine monophosphate decarboxylase; ⑥ uridine kinase; ⑦ RNA polymerase; ⑧ cytidine kinase. Abbreviations: PRPP, phosphoribosyl pyrophosphate; R-5-P, ribose-5-phosphate; XMP, xanthylic acid; IMP, inosinic acid; d'tides, deoxyribonucleotides; U, uridine; G, guanosine; C, cytidine.

carbamyl phosphate synthetase has also been determined in regenerating liver (Bresnick, 1965). Its activity gradually diminishes during the first 24 hours after partial hepatectomy.

Aspartate transcarbamylase (enzyme 2 in Fig. 9), the next enzyme in the *de novo* pathway for pyrimidine biosynthesis, catalyzes the irreversible transcarbamylation of aspartate by carbamyl phosphate. As reported initially by Calva and Cohen (1959), the activity of this enzyme

TABLE VII

EFFECT OF PARTIAL HEPATECTOMY UPON ACTIVITY OF ENZYMES INVOLVED IN PYRIMIDINE SYNTHESIS[a]

Source regenerating liver	CP Synthetase[b] (nmoles product/ 20 mg/15 min)	Aspartate transcarbamylase (nmoles product/ 20 mg/10 min)	Dihydroorotase and dihydroorotic dehydrogenase (nmoles product/ 20 mg/30 min)	Uridine kinase (nmoles product/ 20 mg/20 min)
Control	37.3 ± 1.5	11 ± 2	2.2 ± 0.2	3.3 ± 0.1
2-hr	39.4 ± 5.6	13 ± 1	2.4 ± 0.2	3.3 ± 0.1
6-hr	30.4 ± 4.6	15 ± 3	2.0 ± 0.4	3.6 ± 0.2
12-hr	30.5 ± 4.5	19 ± 2	2.2 ± 0.1	4.2 ± 0.3
24-hr	29.6 ± 6.3	32 ± 5	3.1 ± 0.3	6.8 ± 0.3

[a] From Bresnick (1965).
[b] CP, carbamyl phosphate.

is elevated in regenerating liver. The kinetics of appearance of the enhanced activity have been more extensively studied (Bresnick, 1965) and are presented in Table VII.

Enzyme activity began to rise by 12 hours after partial hepatectomy and reached a maximum at 48 hours (Bresnick et al., 1967a). In bacterial cells, aspartate transcarbamylase is a site for regulation of pyrimidine biosynthesis (Yates and Pardee, 1957: Beckwith et al., 1962) and is inhibited by the end product, cytidine triphosphate. In rat liver, however, aspartate transcarbamylase activity is not sensitive to pyrimidine end products (Bresnick and Mosse, 1966).

The fluctuation of aspartate transcarbamylase activity in the presence of excess pyrimidines was tested by the administration of large quantities of orotic acid in the diet to control rats and to rats after partial hepatectomy (Bresnick et al., 1968). The specific activity of the liver enzyme was markedly *elevated* after the administration of this pyrimidine, rather than reduced as would be expected if enzyme activity were subject to feedback controls. Furthermore, the elevation in aspartate transcarbamylase activity which is observed in regenerating liver was *not* prevented by orotic acid administration. These experiments conclusively establish the lack of end-product control of this enzyme in rat liver.

It is noteworthy to mention the results obtained with a closely related enzyme (at least functionally), ornithine transcarbamylase (Bresnick et al., 1968). The activity of this liver enzyme is also increased after orotic acid administration; the levels are depressed during regeneration, but this depression is unaltered by orotic acid administration.

The activity of dihydroorotase and dihydroorotic dehydrogenase (enzymes 3 in Fig. 9) is significantly elevated by 24 hours after partial hepatectomy (Bresnick, 1965; Bresnick et al., 1968) (see Table VII). The measure of dihydroorotase activity alone showed maximal activity to occur at 48 hours postoperation with a gradual decline thereafter (Bresnick et al., 1968). This pattern was unaltered by the administration of orotic acid in the diet, again indicating the lack of control of the latter enzyme by pyrimidine end products.

The utilization of orotic acid for nucleotide production is enhanced in regenerating liver (Bresnick, 1965). Although the findings of Blair and Potter (1961) suggested orotidine monophosphate decarboxylase is a site for end-product inhibition, the enhanced formation of uridine monophosphate from orotic acid in partial hepatectomy does not result from an increase in the specific activity of this enzyme, but is due to an increase in orotidine monophosphate pyrophosphorylase.

The "salvage" pathway for production of UMP, i.e., phosphorylation of uridine via the catalysis of uridine kinase (enzyme 6 in Fig. 9) is also elevated in 12 to 24-hour regenerating liver (Sköld, 1960; Bresnick, 1965) (see Table VII).

Although uracil or preformed pyrimidines can be incorporated into ribonucleic acid of liver, the process becomes significant only when these substrates are present at concentrations that can saturate the enzymes associated with the catabolism of pyrimidines (Canellakis, 1957). The experiments of Canellakis (1957) and later of Sköld (1960) and Fritzson (1962) show that an inverse relationship existed between its RNA synthesizing ability and the capacity of a tissue to degrade pyrimidine. In this regard, the nondividing tissue, liver, exhibits a high catabolic capability. The pathway for degradation of uracil is indicated in Fig. 10.

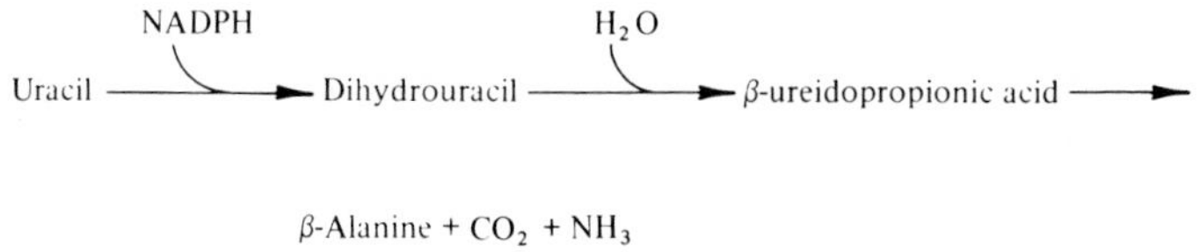

$$\text{Uracil} \xrightarrow{\text{NADPH}} \text{Dihydrouracil} \xrightarrow{H_2O} \beta\text{-ureidopropionic acid} \longrightarrow$$

$$\beta\text{-Alanine} + CO_2 + NH_3$$

FIG. 10. Catabolism of pyrimidine. Dihydrouracil dehydrogenase, dihydrouracil hydrase, and β-ureidopropionic acid decarbamylase catalyze the first, second, and third steps in this pathway, respectively. NADPH, reduced nicotinamide adenine dinucleotide phosphate.

The alterations in pyrimidine ribonucleotide metabolism which ensue in the liver remnant after partial hepatectomy are directed toward the anabolism of these precursors and ultimately toward the production of RNA macromolecules which will be required for the translation of tissue-specific and growth-determining proteins.

It was of interest to determine the effect of inducement of the regenerative state in liver upon the catabolic capabilities of the liver remnant. These studies have been performed by Canellakis et al. (1959), Sköld (1960), and Fritzson (1962). The degradative capacity was markedly diminished. Fritzson (1962) noted a striking parallelism between the activity of dihydrouracil dehydrogenase (see Fig. 10) and the growth rate of the liver. The level of β-ureidopropionic acid decarbamylase, but not that of dihydrouracil hydrase, was also related to the growth rate.

These data are in agreement with the proposal that a homeostatic mechanism controls the rate of RNA synthesis from preformed pyrimidine. Thymine undergoes a similar degradative process. Consequently, DNA synthesis from preformed pyrimidines would also be under the same homeostatic regulatory mechanism.

c. *Ribonuclease Activity*. Several laboratories have reported an increase in ribonuclease activity in rapidly proliferating tissues (Brody,

1957; Roth, 1963; Bresnick *et al.*, 1966a). It was of interest, then, to ascertain the levels of this enzyme during liver regeneration. A sharp rise in enzyme activity was noted after partial hepatectomy which reached a maximum after DNA synthesis had climaxed, i.e., 54 hours after partial hepatectomy, coinciding with the return of the hepatocytes to their normal functions (Maor and Alexander, 1968). Shortman (1962) has examined both ribonuclease and ribonuclease inhibitor activity in regenerating liver and found that at early times, 12 and 24 hours, the former was decreased while the latter was increased.

Chakravorty and Busch (1967) have determined the activity of nuclear alkaline ribonuclease in regenerating liver. The free ribonuclease activity in nuclei increased after partial hepatectomy; this increase was reflected in the determination of nucleolar ribonuclease.

d. RNA Polymerase. The final process in the polymerization of ribonucleoside triphosphates is accomplished by the concerted action of RNA polymerase and the template, DNA. The first report of an elevated activity of this enzyme in regenerating liver appeared in 1962 (Busch *et al.*, 1962) with confirmation arising from the laboratories of Tsukada and Lieberman (1964) and of Vandergoten and Goutier (1966). A significant increase in activity was detected as early as 6 hours after partial hepatectomy with a maximum activity occurring by approximately 12 hours.

An active RNA polymerase from mammalian tissues may be solubilized only with extreme difficulty. This is caused in part by the complex of the enzyme with its deoxyribonucleoprotein template (Weiss, 1960). In this respect, the mammalian and bacterial enzymes differ markedly. The mammalian enzyme is free to transcribe only those regions of the deoxyribonucleoprotein template that are "open." Presumably, during the course of development or differentiation, new regions of the template are exposed for transcription and other regions are "masked."

In regenerating liver, the question arises as to the significance of the elevated level of the "aggregate" RNA polymerase (Weiss, 1960) in the liver remnant. Is the latter caused by an elevation in the amount of enzyme elaborated in the liver or by the exposure of additional loci on the deoxyribonucleoprotein or both? The last possibility appears correct. This conclusion is based largely upon the data of Pogo *et al.* (1966a,b, 1967). These investigators demonstrated the increased availability of DNA sites suggesting a major change in the structure and properties of this macromolecule during gene activation. Analysis of the RNA product revealed a base composition similar to that of ribosomal RNA. These results would agree with the elevated formation of ribosomal RNA and ultimately of ribosomes observed in regenerating liver *in vivo* (see p. 373).

C. SUMMARY OF NUCLEIC ACID CHANGES

A summary of the relationship of the changes in nucleic acids to the mitotic activity in regenerating liver is presented in Fig. 11. Both the maximal synthesis of RNA and DNA precede the burst in cell division occurring after partial hepatectomy. The elevated rate of RNA synthesis persists after cell division has returned to normal preoperative levels.

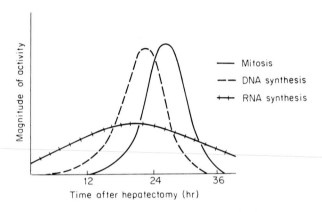

FIG. 11. Kinetics of biochemical changes during regeneration.

D. PROTEIN SYNTHESIS

After partial hepatectomy, the concentration of free amino acids in the liver remnant is altered to accommodate the wave of protein synthesis which is required for the regenerative process. Braun *et al.* (1962) reported an increase in the concentration of amino acids in regenerating liver which reached a maximal elevation at 14 hours after the operation. It has also been reported (Christensen *et al.*, 1948; Ferrari and Harkness, 1954) that by 6 hours postoperation, the hepatic glutamine concentration fell with concomitant increase in glutamic acid, aspartic acid, and lysine. At 20 to 30 hours, glutathione and the other amino acids rose, while aspartate, glutamate, and lysine fell slightly. These data are corroborated by the findings of Wu (1964) who reported in regenerating liver a reduction in the activity of the enzyme that catalyzes the formation of glutamine from glutamic acid and ammonia, glutamine synthetase. The reduction is prompt and is sustained for at least 90 days after hepatectomy.

The net increase in availability of amino acids in regenerating liver was further augmented by a decrease in the catabolism of amino acids during the first postoperative day (Burke, 1962). The activities of dihydroxyphenylalanine (DOPA) decarboxylase (Hawkins and Walker, 1952) and amine oxidase (Thompson and Moss, 1955) remain unchanged for the first 2 days after hepatectomy, but then increase during the next few weeks. Tryptophan pyrrolase (Thompson and Moss, 1955) is depressed by the second postoperative day and returned to its normal preoperative value by 1 week. Glutamate dehydrogenase activity (Greenbaum et al., 1954) is similarly depressed, whereas aspartate transaminase is increased.

Ferrari and Harkness (1954) have reported the detectability of an increment in total protein by about 12 hours postoperation; Price and Laird (1950) observed a 17% increment in protein nitrogen by 24 hours after partial hepatectomy. The maximum rate of increase in protein occurred between 12 and 36 hours, the period in which the free amino acids were most abundant (Gurd et al., 1948; Ferrari and Harkness, 1954).

The regenerating liver is quite unique in that it must produce more proteins than are needed for its own growth. In addition to the responsibility for the production of new liver mass, the liver remnant must take steps to counteract the depletion of plasma proteins that follows partial hepatectomy. However, the residual hepatocytes seem to give first priority to the elaboration of cellular proteins during the early stages of liver regeneration. At a later date, when substantial amounts of the liver mass have been replaced, the switch to the synthesis of plasma proteins is effected.

The increase in the incorporation of labeled amino acids into liver protein in vivo after partial hepatectomy has been extensively reported (reviewed in Harkness, 1957; Campbell, 1958). Maximal incorporation was reached by the third day. In the studies of Aqvist (1951). the specific activity of cytoplasmic proteins after a pulse of ^{15}N-glycine was elevated to a low peak at 26 hours after partial hepatectomy and to a higher maximum by 56 hours. In contrast, the labeling of nuclear proteins occurred maximally at 26 hours with a secondary but lower peak at 56 hours.

A number of studies have been performed in which in vitro systems were employed to demonstrate this point. These systems consisted of a microsomal or ribosomal fraction incubated with a supernatant extract or pH 5 fraction, labeled amino acid, energy source, and various cofactors. When compared to normal, the soluble fraction from regenerating liver (or pH 5 fraction) is more active in promoting amino acid incorporation in the presence of either control or regenerating liver microsomes (Hultin and von der Decken, 1957; Rendi, 1959). The microsomal fraction from regenerating liver was also more active than control in protein synthesis in the presence of either soluble fraction (von der Decken and Hultin, 1958; McCorquodale et al., 1960). The latter was partly due to an increase in ribosome content of these microsomes although normalization on the basis of RNA did not completely remove this difference.

In addition to the increase in ribosome content of the microsomes as a cause for the elevated level, an inhibitor of protein synthesis has been postulated in normal adult rat liver (Hoagland et al., 1964; Scornik et al., 1967). The inhibitor was originally found in cell-free systems, was firmly associated with the endoplasmic reticulum, and its action was reversed by guanosine 5'-triphosphate (GTP). The activity of the inhibitor was much greater in the microsomes from normal liver, and it acted by blocking the transfer of amino acids from aminoacyl–transfer RNA to the nascent polypeptide strands on the polyribosome. For activity, the inhibitor required oxidized glutathione and its action was blocked not only by GTP, but by β-mercaptoethanol and reduced glutathione. Its blockade of protein synthesis was not a reflection of latent GTPase activity and was not due to the sequestration of GTP to macromolecular components.

An additional inhibitor has also been noted by Scornik et al. (1967). The latter, however, was not reversible by GTP and was associated with lysosomes which contaminated the microsomal preparation. The activity of this inhibitor was diminished in regenerating liver although the lysosomal content in the latter as judged by determinations of acid phosphatase was similar to control liver preparations. A greater fragility of the lysosomes or their activation may occur in normal liver.

Recently, another factor contributing to the elevated protein synthesis rate has been reported by Hamburger-Heyd et al. (1967). These investigators have observed a decreased rate of catabolism of ATP, i.e., less ATPase produced by the microsomes of regenerating liver.

As previously mentioned, the microsomes from regenerating liver apparently possess a greater ribosomal content than suitably prepared fractions from control liver. This problem has been examined in greater detail by Tsukada and Lieberman(1965a), Cammarano et al. (1965a), and Bont et al. (1967). These investigators have all demonstrated an increased amount of heavier aggregated polyribosomes in regenerating liver. Bont et al. (1967) have shown the heavier forms to be caused by a greater structural stability which may be related to either the lack of contaminating ribonuclease or to the binding of ribonuclease inhibitor.

Zellis (1967), using polyribosomal preparations, confirmed the enhanced activity of regenerating liver in the incorporation of amino acids into polypeptide material. However, he was unable to demonstrate any difference from control values in the degree of stimulation of protein synthesis with polyribosomes upon the addition of the synthetic "messenger," polyuridylic acid. This finding had been previously reported by Cammarano *et al.* (1965b).

1. Plasma Protein Synthesis

One of the major functions of the liver is in the synthesis of plasma proteins, with the exception of the γ-globulin fraction. In regenerating liver, their synthesis is temporarily inhibited so that the concentrations of the plasma proteins decrease. As a consequence, partial hepatectomy is accompanied by a depression on the first 2 days in the plasma and red blood cell volumes (Lowrance and Chanutin, 1942).

The data of Roberts and White (1949) have been reproduced in Fig. 12. The concentration of albumin, the most abundant protein in liver

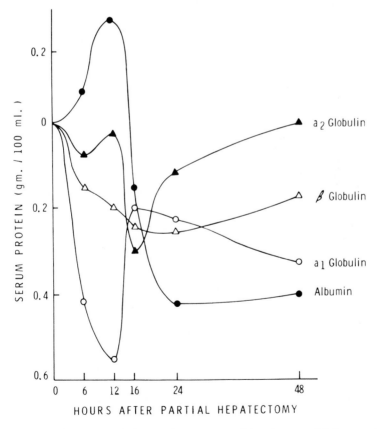

FIG. 12. Changes in serum protein concentration after partial hepatectomy (from Roberts and White, 1949).

undergoes a transient rise during the first 12 hours after partial hepatectomy, followed by a profound drop. The latter remained at this depressed level for at least several days. The globulins showed the depression immediately post-hepatectomy, but returned to more normal values more quickly (Chanutin et al., 1938).

2. Histone Synthesis

Histones are relatively stable molecules, the synthesis of which is largely dependent upon the rate of cell division (Daly et al., 1952; Bloch and Godman, 1955; Lowrance and Butler, 1965). It is known that the synthesis of DNA takes place during the later interphase in mammalian cells (Prescott, 1961). The following questions were entertained: (a) Were histone and DNA syntheses in regenerating liver coordinated? (b) What was the temporal relationship between histone and RNA syntheses? (c) What effect did modification of the histone have upon its biological activity?

The first of these questions has been answered by Holbrook et al. (1962), Butler and Cohn (1963), Umana et al. (1964). Niehaus and Barnum (1965), and Tidwell et al. (1968). Although Holbrook et al. (1962) had concluded that DNA and histone syntheses occurred simultaneously, the other investigators showed the peak of histone synthesis to precede that of DNA. Bloch and Godman (1955) reviewed the earlier data of Bloch (1963) and also concluded that histone synthesis occurred at an earlier time, with the latter becoming associated to DNA immediately after synthesis.

It has recently been found that histones are biologically modified by methylation and/or acetylation. The sequence of events involving histone synthesis and their modification has been ascertained in relation to the regenerative process in liver by Tidwell et al. (1968). Their results indicated that histone synthesis and their methylation were independent processes. Methylation reached a maximum at 30 hours and continued at the elevated rate until 36 hours after partial hepatectomy; thus, the methylation process continued for 6 to 12 hours after DNA synthesis had begun to decline.

Histones are also biologically modified by acetylation (Pogo et al., 1968), and, here, there appears a closer correlation between the sequence of events after partial hepatectomy and the "inactivation" of the histone. Even at 1 hour postoperation, the pattern of acetylation of the arginine-rich histones is altered. A decreased turnover rate of the acetyl group was observed in regenerating liver. The maximal incorporation of tritiated acetate into the arginine-rich histones occurred at 3 to 4 hours post-hepatectomy with a return to the normal level thereafter. On the other hand, the acetylation of the *lysine-rich histones* took place relatively late, i.e., at 16 hours after operation.

These data were in concert with the concept of gene activation occurring at an early time after partial hepatectomy by modification of a protein fraction associated with the DNA. The end result is expressed in the synthesis of new RNA molecules with the capability of translation into enzyme synthesis.

E. Polyamine Synthesis

It has been suggested that the polyamines, spermidine and spermine, may function as physiological stabilizers of nucleic acids (Tabor and Tabor, 1964). Several investigators had decided to test this possibility in the regenerating liver model by ascertaining if any correlation could be found between the rate of synthesis of the polyamines and the early changes in ribonucleic acid metabolism (see p. 369). Dykstra and Herbst (1965) and Raina *et al.* (1966) demonstrated a significant elevation in the levels and in the synthesis of these polyamines. The latter group were able to show the enhanced incorporation of labeled methionine into spermidine as early as 4 to 8 hours post-hepatectomy.

These data have been extended by Russell and Snyder (1968) who reported the marked increase in the activity of the enzyme ornithine decarboxylase which catalyzes the synthesis of putrescine, the immediate precursor of spermidine. Within 1 hour after the operation, the activity of this enzyme had risen threefold and reached 16 times the control level by 16 hours.

Although no physiological role has been definitively ascribed to the polyamines, the kinetics of appearance of ornithine decarboxylase, the rate-limiting enzyme in the synthesis of the polyamines, and the sharp increase in the level of the polyamines at a time preceding the increases in RNA, would certainly suggest a correlation between these two phenomena. However, such a relationship has yet to be proven.

F. Lipid Metabolism

As mentioned previously (see p. 356), the appearance of a fatty liver occurs early during liver regeneration. Changes in the concentration of the lipids in the liver can occur as a result of either an elevation in the rate of hepatic synthesis or a depression in the rate of catabolism of these moieties, or because of an increased rate in the mobilization from extrahepatic sources. The contributions of these possibilities to the overall level of hepatic lipids have been determined in perfused regenerating rat liver by Bartsch and Gerber (1966). These investigators

have shown that the changes in hepatic lipids are caused by an augmented transport of these substances from extrahepatic sources,
confirming the original suggestion of Johnson and Albert (1959). In
the studies of Bartsch and Gerber (1966), the rate of incorporation of
labeled acetate into total lipids decreased in regenerating rat liver. The
individual components of the lipid fraction behaved differently. The
most affected was the turnover of the monounsaturated fatty acids
which were not only synthesized at a lower rate in regenerating liver
but were also degraded more rapidly. In regenerating liver, the qualitative composition appeared to remain the same as in control liver.

The increased mobilization of lipid to regenerating liver exerted a
profound effect upon the respiratory metabolism as observed *in vitro*
with liver slices (Simek *et al.*, 1966). The depressed respiratory quotient,
i.e., below 0.7, is the result of enhanced utilization of fat by the regenerating liver with concomitant formation of ketone bodies. This
result was corroborated by the reduction in the utilization of carbo-
hydrates during this period as would be expected from the marked
loss in liver glycogen.

G. OTHER PROTEINS

The activities of many of the enzymes which function in cellular
respiration are depressed after partial hepatectomy (Novikoff and
Potter, 1948). These include succinoxidase, malic dehydrogenase,
oxalacetate oxidase, and cytochrome reductase. von der Decken and
Hultin (1960) have reported, however, no change in the activity of
NADH– and NADPH–cytochrome c reductase and diaphorase, although
the capacity of regenerating liver preparations to perform certain
oxidative methylations was depressed. It is of interest that Siebert
(1960) and Siebert *et al.* (1961) have reported the concomitant elevation
in glycolytic activity of the nucleus along with the reduction in cytoplasmic glycolysis in regenerating liver.

The observation of the depression in the activity of the enzymes
associated with cell respiration is in concert with the morphological
observations which showed a reduction in the number of mitochondria
per cell during the first week of regeneration (Allard *et al.*, 1952).
Furthermore, the mitochondria of regenerating liver were more resistant
to certain agents that induced swelling, suggesting the involvement of
ATP metabolism (Arcos *et al.*, 1961; Gosch and Arcos, 1961).

An interesting relationship existed between the growth of tissues
and the intracellular concentration of nicotinamide adenine dinucleotide (NAD), more particularly, the rate-limiting enzyme associated
with the synthesis of the latter, NAD pyrophosphorylase. The latter

enzyme which is located within the nucleus of the hepatocyte (Hoge-boom and Schneider, 1952; Branster and Morton, 1956) catalyzes the interaction of nicotinamide mononucleotide and ATP to form NAD. The activity of NAD pyrophosphorylase and the concentration of NAD vary inversely with the growth rate. Thus, in 24-hour regenerating liver, the NAD production is 65% of normal and only 38% by 48 hours after hepatectomy (DeBurgh, 1959). A similar finding was reported by Stirpe and Aldridge (1961).

The relationship between the hepatic concentration of NAD and growth has been examined by Morton (1958). Upon completion of NAD synthesis in the hepatic nucleus, the coenzyme is transferred to the cytoplasm where it is involved in the various dehydrogenations. In the cytoplasm, NAD is also subjected to catabolism by nucleosidases and pyrophosphatases. When the growth rate is stimulated, the cyto-plasmic concentration of NAD is reduced. Upon reaching a critically low value, cell division is stimulated and, concomitantly, an increase in NAD pyrophosphorylase takes place. Through the action of the latter enzyme, the concentration of the coenzyme is returned to normal. Since an important factor in the synthesis of NAD is the concentration of ATP, the balance between the two nucleotides may be critical in the regulation of cellular activities.

V. Regulation of Liver Growth

The suggestion that the initiation of liver regeneration might be dependent upon a specific humoral factor arose from experiments on parabiotic rats, i.e., rats in which a common systemic blood circulation had been established (Christensen and Jacobsen, 1949; Bucher et al., 1951; Wenneker and Sussman, 1951). If one partner of a parabiotic pair is partially hepatectomized, a stimulation of the mitotic activity has been reported to occur in the liver of the unoperated partner, but to a lesser extent than that which takes place in the hepatectomized partner. Similar results have been presented by Bucher et al. (1951) and Islami et al. (1959). The experiments of the former investigator are particularly interesting since they involve the use of sets of parabiotic triplets. The two end partners were partially hepatectomized with the resultant 50-fold increase in the mitotic activity in the liver of the un-operated rat at 48 hours after operation. These data were interpreted as evidence for the presence of a blood-borne factor, although it was uncertain if a new entity was released after partial hepatectomy or if the concentration of a factor present in normal tissue was increased by a failure of the normal breakdown processes in liver.

Not all investigators have found evidence for a humoral factor affecting liver regeneration in parabiotic rats. In this regard, Rogers *et al.* (1961) were unable to measure any increment in mitotic activity or in the rate of incorporation of tritiated thymidine into DNA in partially hepatectomized parabiotic rats. Many factors could be responsible for these apparently contradictory results. One of these had already been discussed by Bucher *et al.* (1951). They noted that the removal of two-thirds of the liver in one member of a parabiotic pair does not result in an overall hepatectomy of 70%, but of 30% instead. Subsequently, Bucher was able to demonstrate that the magnitude of the increase of DNA synthesis in regenerating liver was very dependent upon the extent of hepatectomy (see p. 359). Other factors may also have been instrumental in this discrepancy, e.g., state of fasting of the rats, duration of parabiosis, individual variations. The equivocal results thus described indicate the lack of suitability of this model in answering the question of the existence of a humoral factor. The inability to provide this answer should have been anticipated since (*a*) frequently poor and variable blood circulation was apparent between parabiotic partners, (*b*) immunological reactions were occasionally observed in the partners, and (*c*) functional differences in the status of the liver were apparent.

In addition to the elaboration of a humoral factor after partial hepatectomy, an additional mechanism based upon a hypothesis of Weiss and co-workers has been postulated (Weiss, 1955; Weiss and Kavenau, 1957). Weiss has presumed the presence of specific growth-promoting factors in each cell type, "templates," and of complimentary substances, the "antitemplates," which are produced in sufficient quantity to complex to and inactivate the former. After partial hepatectomy, the capacity to elaborate antitemplates is diminished, thus allowing the intracellular templates to catalyze the growth of the liver remnant. When the number of hepatic cells is restored to the preoperative value, sufficient antitemplate is elaborated to result in an inactivation of the templates present previously in excess. The mechanism represents an environmental feedback control governing the total liver mass.

Some experimental evidence has been obtained which favors the above hypothesis. Glinos and Gey (1952) observed an increase in the fibroblastic growth of primary rat liver explants upon the addition to the culture medium of serum from partially hepectomized rats. In addition, the duration of growth *in vitro* of normal rat fibroblasts was augmented. However, high concentrations of normal rat serum proved inhibitory, suggesting the presence of a normal growth-inhibitory factor.

Friedrich-Freksa and Zaki (1954) reported an increased mitotic activity in the livers of intact rats which had received intraperitoneal injections of serum from partially hepatectomized rats. These results were confirmed by Zimmerman and Celozzi (1961) who observed in addition an increased incorporation of tritiated thymidine and ^{14}C-orotate into liver DNA under these conditions. Instead of normal rats as the recipients, Stich and Florian (1958) injected normal serum into partially hepatectomized rats and reported a reduction in mitotic activity of the regenerating liver. Adibi et al. (1959) observed an even greater increase in the mitotic activity of regenerating liver when the serum from partially hepatectomized rats was injected prior to sacrifice. Furthermore, the serum from the hepatic vein blood was more active than the serum from peripheral blood suggesting the hepatic transport of growth-promoting agent.

However, several investigators have been unable to repeat these results. A summary of results on the effects of serum upon mitotic activity is offered in Table VIII. A solution for this dilemma is provided by Leong et al. (1964) using the technique of heterotopic partial auto-transplantation as modified by Grisham et al. (1964).

In this technique, grafts of liver were located subcutaneously and separated from the liver mass by abdominal wall. The connection between the liver and the graft was only by systemic vasculature. The effect of partial hepatectomy upon DNA synthesis in these auto-grafts was determined by Leong et al. (1964). The results clearly indicated that at least one component responsible for the enhanced DNA synthe-sis was humoral in nature. The study also eliminated the portal blood supply as a necessary factor for hepatic regeneration (Weinbren, 1955). The data of Leong et al. (1964) have been confirmed by Virolainen (1967) who was also able to show that the effect was limited to parenchymal cells, thus indicating a cellular specificity within the liver.

Despite the lack of complete agreement among the investigators in this field utilizing the techniques described above, the presence of a humoral factor during liver regeneration which is responsible for the subsequent enhanced mitotic activity and liver growth is generally accepted. The exact manner in which this effect is accomplished is unknown.

VI. Conclusion

Regenerating liver is an excellent system for the study of the trigger-ing event responsible for cell division. Partial hepatectomy is followed by profound alterations in cellular morphology and biochemistry. These alterations are apparently geared to the central drive of the regenerating liver, i.e., the production of tissue-specific proteins and, ultimately, the replacement of the original liver mass. During this process, some systems of the liver are temporarily suspended so that

TABLE VIII
Effects of Serum on Mitosis[a]

Recipient	Donor	Investigators reporting response of mitosis		
		+	−	±
Normal	Normal	Smythe and Moore (1958) Fisher et al. (1963)	Alston and Thompson (1963)	Friedrich-Freksa and Zaki (1954) MacDonald and Rogers (1961) Leong et al. (1963) Moya (1963)
	Partial hepatectomy	Friedrich-Freksa and Zaki (1954) Smythe and Moore (1958) Hughes (1960) Laguerriere and Laumonier (1960) Van Lancker and Borison (1961) Survis et al. (1962) Fisher et al. (1963)	Alston and Thompson (1963)	MacDonald and Rogers (1961) Peters (1962) Leong et al. (1963) Moya (1963)
Partial hepatectomy	Normal	Smythe and Moore (1958)	Stich and Florian (1958) Weinbren (1959)	Bucher (1958) MacDonald and Rogers (1961) Alston and Thompson (1963)
	Partial hepatectomy	Smythe and Moore (1958) Stich and Florian (1958) Adibi et al. (1959)		MacDonald and Rogers (1961) Leong et al. (1963) Moya (1963)

the catabolism of nucleic acid and protein precursors is significantly depressed. The synthesis of proteins for "export" to extrahepatic systems is also temporarily diminished. Consequently, the regenerating liver model contains all the elements for the regulation of growth and, indeed, a theme directed toward a central goal. The intricate but vital details of this plan are not presently understood. However, a knowledge of these events is required for better understanding of differentiation and of the development of both normal and neoplasic tissues.

ACKNOWLEDGMENTS

The author wishes to acknowledge support from the U.S. Public Health Service (CA-10893P4), American Cancer Society (ACS E-373), National Science Foundation (GB 8010), and the Robert A. Welch Foundation (Q-198), which has made possible much of the original research work presented in this review. The author also wishes to express his sincerest thanks to Mrs. S. S. Burleson for excellent technical assistance.

REFERENCES

Abercrombie, M., and Harkness, R. D. (1951). *Proc. Roy. Soc. Ser. B* **138**, 544.
Adibi, S., Paschkis, K. E., and Canterow, A. (1959). *Exp. Cell Res.* **18**, 396.
Alfert, M., and Geschwind, I. I. (1958). *Exp. Cell Res.* **15**, 230.
Allard, C., DeLamirande, G., and Canterow, A. (1952). *Cancer Res.* **12**, 580.
Alston, W. C., and Thompson, R. Y. (1963). *Cancer Res.* **23**, 901.
Ambrose, E. J., James, A. M., and Lowich, J. H. B. (1956). *Nature (London)* **177**, 576.
Aqvist, S. E. G. (1951). *Acta Chem Scand.* **5**, 1065.
Arcos, J. C., Gosch, H. H., and Zickafoose, D. (1961). *J. Biophys. Biochem. Cytol.* **10**, 23.
Aterman, K. (1961). *J. Pathol. Bacteriol.* **82**, 367.
Attardi, G., Parnas, H., Hwang, M.-I. H., and Attardi, B. (1966). *J. Mol. Biol.* **20**, 145.
Bartsch, G. G., and Gerber, G. B. (1966). *J. Lipid Res.* **7**, 204.
Becker, F. F., and Lane, B. P. (1965). *Amer. J. Pathol.* **47**, 783.
Beckwith, J. R., Pardee, A. B., Austrian, R., and Jacob, F. (1962). *J. Mol. Biol.* **5**, 618.
Behki, R. M., and Schneider, W. C. (1962). *Biochim. Biophys. Acta* **61**, 663.
Beltz, R. E. (1962). *Arch. Biochem. Biophys.* **99**, 304.
Berlin, C. M., and Schimke, R. T. (1965). *Mol. Pharmacol.* **1**, 149.
Bernhard, W., and Rouiller, C. (1956). *J. Biophys. Biochem. Cytol.* **2**, *Suppl.* **4**, 73.
Bernhard, W., Haguenau, A., Groutier, A., and Oberling, C. (1952). *Z. Zellforsch. Mikrosk. Anat.* **37**, 281.
Bianchi, P. A., Butler, J. A. V., Crathorn, A. R., and Shooter, K. V. (1961). *Biochim. Biophys. Acta* **53**, 123.
Blair, D. G. R., and Potter, V. R. (1961). *J. Biol. Chem.* **236**, 2503.
Bloch, D. P. (1963). *J. Cell. Comp. Physiol.* **62**, *Suppl.* **1**, 87.
Bloch, D. P., and Godman, G. C. (1955). *J. Biophys. Biochem. Cytol.* **1**, 17.

Bollum, F. J. (1959). *J. Biol. Chem.* **234**, 2733.
Bollum, F. J., and Potter, V. R. (1958). *J. Biol. Chem.* **233**, 478.
Bollum, F. J., and Potter, V. R. (1959). *Cancer Res.* **19**, 561.
Bont, W. S., Rezelman, G., Meisner, I., and Bloemendal, H. (1967). *Arch. Biochem. Biophys.* **119**, 36.
Branster, M. J., and Morton, R. K. (1956). *Aust. J. Sci.* **19**, 72.
Braun, G. A., Marsh, J. B., and Drabkin, D. L. (1962). *Metab. Clin. Exp.* **11**, 957.
Breitman, T. R. (1963). *Biochim. Biophys. Acta* **67**, 153.
Bresnick, E. (1965). *J. Biol. Chem.* **240**, 2550.
Bresnick, E., and Burleson, S. S. (1970). *Cancer Res.* **30**, 1060.
Bresnick, E., and Mosse, H. (1966). *Biochem. J.* **101**, 63.
Bresnick, E., and Thompson, U. B. (1965). *J. Biol. Chem.* **240**, 3967.
Bresnick, E., Thompson, U. B., Morris, H. P., and Liebelt, A. G. (1964). *Biochem. Biophys. Res. Commun.* **16**, 278.
Bresnick, E., Sage, J., and Lanclos, K. (1966a). *Biochim. Biophys. Acta* **114**, 631.
Bresnick, E., Thompson, U. B., and Lyman, K. (1966b). *Arch. Biochem. Biophys.* **114**, 352.
Bresnick, E., Williams, S. S., and Mosse, H. (1967a). *Cancer Res.* **27**, 469.
Bresnick, E., Lanclos, K., and Eckles, S. (1967b). *Biochemistry* **6**, 2481.
Bresnick, E., Mayfield, E. D., Jr., and Mosse, H. (1968). *Mol. Pharmacol.* **4**, 173.
Bresnick, E., Burleson, S. S., and Mainigi, K. D. (1969). Unpublished observations.
Brody, S. (1957). *Biochim. Biophys. Acta* **24**, 502.
Brody, S., and Balis, M. E. (1959). *Cancer Res.* **19**, 538.
Brues, A. M., and Marble, B. B. (1937). *Arch. Pathol.* **22**. 658.
Brues, A. M., Tracy, M. M., and Cohn, W. E. (1944). *J. Biol. Chem.* **155**, 619.
Bruni, C., and Porter, K. R. (1965). *Amer. J. Pathol.* **46**, 691.
Bucher, N. L. R. (1958). In "Liver Function" (R. W. Brauer, ed.), Publ. No. 4, p. 432. Amer. Inst. Biol. Sci. Washington, D.C.
Bucher, N. L. R. (1963). *Int. Rev. Cytol.* **15**, 245.
Bucher, N. L. R. (1967). *New Eng. J. Med.* **277**, 686, 738.
Bucher, N. L. R., and Oakman, N. J. (1969). *Biochim. Biophys. Acta* **186**, 13.
Bucher, N. L. R., and Swaffield, M. N. (1965). *Biochim. Biophys. Acta* **108**, 551.
Bucher, N. L. R., and Swaffield, M. N. (1969). *Biochim. Biophys. Acta* **174**, 491.
Bucher, N. L. R., Scott, J. J., and Aub, J. C. (1951). *Cancer Res.* **11**, 457.
Bucher, N. L. R., Di Troia, J. F., and Swaffield, M. N. (1961). *Fed. Proc. Fed. Amer. Soc. Exp. Biol.* **20**, 286.
Burke, W. T. (1962). *Cancer Res.* **22**, 10.
Busch, H., and Smetana, K. (1970). "The Nucleolus." Academic Press, New York.
Busch, S., Chambon, P., Mandel, P., and Weill, J. D. (1962). *Biochem. Biophys. Res. Commun.* **7**, 255.
Butler, J. A. V., and Cohn, P. (1963). *Biochem. J.* **87**, 330.
Cairns, J. (1963). *Endeavour* **32**, 141.
Calva, E., and Cohen, P. P. (1959). *Cancer Res.* **19**, 679.
Cammarano, P., Guidice, G., and Lukes, B. (1965a). *Biochem. Biophys. Res. Commun.* **19**, 487.
Cammarano, P., Melli, M., and Novelli, G. D. (1965b). *Biochim. Biophys. Acta* **108**, 329.
Campbell, P. N. (1958). *Advan. Cancer Res.* **5**, 98.
Campbell, P. N., and Greengard, O. (1957). *Biochem. J.* **66**, 47.
Canellakis, E. S. (1957). *J. Biol. Chem.* **227**, 701.

Canellakis, E. S., Jaffe, J. J., Mantsavinos, R., and Krakow, J. S. (1959). *J. Biol. Chem.* **234**, 2096.

Cater, D. B., Holmes, B. E., and Mee, L. K. (1956). *Acta Radiol.* **46**, 655.

Chakravorty, A. K., and Busch, H. (1967). *Cancer Res.* **27**, 789.

Chanutin, A., Hortensine, J. C., Cole, W. S., and Ludwig, S. (1938). *J. Biol. Chem.* **123**, 247.

Chaudhuri, S., and Lieberman, I. (1965). *Biochem. Biophys. Res. Commun.* **20**, 303.

Chaudhuri, S., and Lieberman, I. (1968a). *J. Biol. Chem.* **243**, 29.

Chaudhuri, S., and Lieberman, I. (1968b). *J. Mol. Biol.* **33**, 323.

Chaudhuri, S., Doi, O., and Lieberman, I. (1967). *Biochim. Biophys. Acta* **134**, 479.

Chiga, M., Oda, A., and Holtzer, R. L. (1963). *Arch. Biochem. Biophys.* **103**, 366.

Christensen, B. G., and Jacobsen, E. (1949). *Acta Med. Scand. Suppl.* **234**, 103.

Christensen, H. N., Rothwell, J. T., Sears, R. A., and Streicher, J. A. (1948). *J. Biol. Chem.* **175**, 101.

Claude, A. (1967). *Protoplasma* **63**, 18.

Cohen, P. P. (1962). *In* "The Enzymes" (P. D. Boyer, H. Lardy, and K. Myrbäck, eds.), Vol. 6, p. 477. Academic Press, New York.

Daly, M. M., Allfrey, V. G., and Mirsky, A. E. (1952). *J. Gen. Physiol.* **36**, 173.

Davis, J. M. G. (1962), *Acta Radiol.* **58**, 17.

De Burgh, P. M. (1959). *Aust. J. Sci.* **20**, 86.

Doljanski, T. R. (1960). *Int. Rev. Cytol.* **10**, 217.

Dykstra, W. G., Jr., and Herbst, E. J. (1965). *Science* **149**, 428.

Eisenberg, S., Ben-Or, S., and Doljanski, F. (1962). *Exp. Cell Res.* **26**, 451.

Eliasson, N. A., Hammarsten, E., Reichard, P., Aqvist, S., Thorell, B., and Ehrensvard, G. (1951). *Acta Chem. Scand.* **5**, 431.

Fausto, N., and van Lancker, J. L. (1965). *J. Biol. Chem.* **240**, 1247.

Ferrari, V., and Harkness, R. D. (1954). *J. Physiol. (London)* **124**, 443.

Fiala, S., Fiala, A., Tobar, G., and McQuilla, H. (1962). *J. Nat. Cancer Inst.* **28**, 1269.

Fishback, F. C. (1929). *Arch. Pathol.* **7**, 955.

Fisher, B., Fisher, E. R., and Saffer, E. (1963). *Cancer Res.* **23**, 914.

Fisher, E. R., and Fisher, B. (1963). *Lab. Invest.* **12**, 929.

Fouts, J. R. (1962). *Fed. Proc. Fed. Amer. Soc. Exp. Biol.* **21**, 1107.

Friedrich-Freksa, H., and Zaki, F. G. (1954). *Z. Naturforsch.* **9b**, 394.

Fritzson, P. (1962). *J. Biol. Chem.* **237**, 150.

Fritzson, P. (1967). *Eur. J. Biochem.* **1**, 12.

Fujioka, M., Koga, M., and Lieberman, I. (1963). *J. Biol. Chem.* **238**, 3401.

Furst, S. S., Roll, P. M., and Brown, G. W. (1950). *J. Biol. Chem.* **183**, 251.

Glinos, A. D. (1958a). *In* "Chemical Basis of Development" (W. D. McElroy and B. Glass, eds.), p. 183. Johns Hopkins Press, Baltimore, Maryland.

Glinos, A. D. (1958b). *In* "Liver Function, A Symposium on Approaches to the Quantitative Description of Liver Function" (R. W. Brauer, ed.), Publ. No. 4, p. 425. Amer. Inst. Biol. Sci., Washington, D.C.

Glinos, A. D., and Gey, G. O. (1952). *Proc. Soc. Exp. Biol. Med.* **80**, 421.

Gosch, H. H., and Arcos, J. C. (1961). *Nature (London)* **190**, 272.

Goss, R. J. (1964). "Adaptive Growth." Academic Press, New York.

Greenbaum, A. L., Greenwood, F. C., and Harkness, R. D. (1954). *J. Physiol. (London)* **125**, 251.

Grisham, J. W. (1960). *J. Histochem. Cytochem.* **8**, 330.

Grisham, J. W. (1962). *Cancer Res.* **22**, 842.

Grisham, J. W., Leong, G. F., and Hole, B. V. (1964). *Cancer Res.* **24**, 1474.

Gross, N., and Rabinowitz, M. (1968). *Biochim. Biophys. Acta* **157**, 648.

Groth, D. P., and Jiang, N. (1966). *Biochem. Biophys. Res. Commun.* **22**, 62.

Gurd, F. N., Vars, E. M., and Ravdin, I. S. (1948). *Amer. J. Physiol.* **152**, 11.

Hager, S. E., and Jones, M. E. (1967). *J. Biol. Chem.* **242**, 5674.

Hamburger-Heyd, J., Halbreich, A., and Mager, J. (1967). *Biochem. Biophys. Res. Commun.* **26**, 471.

Hammarsten, E. (1951). *Ciba Found. Conf. Isotop. Biochem.* p. 203.

Harkness, R. D. (1952). *J. Physiol. (London)* **117**, 267.

Harkness, R. D. (1957). *Brit. Med. Bull.* **13**, 87.

Harris, H. (1963). *Progr. Nucl. Acid Res.* **2**, 19.

Hartmann, K. U., and Heidelberger, C. (1961). *J. Biol. Chem.* **236**, 3006.

Hawkins, J., and Walker, J. M. (1952). *Brit. J. Pharmacol.* **7**, 152.

Hecht, L. I., and Potter, V. R. (1956). *Cancer Res.* **16**, 988.

Hecht, L. I., and Potter, V. R. (1958). *Cancer Res.* **18**, 186.

Hess, K. (1890). *Virchows Arch. Pathol. Anat. Physiol.* **121**, 154.

Hiatt, H. H., and Bojarski, T. B. (1960). *Biochem. Biophys. Res. Commun.* **2**, 35.

Higgins, G. M., and Anderson, R. M. (1931). *Arch. Pathol.* **12**, 186.

Hoagland, M. B. (1961). *Cold Spring Harbor Symp. Quant. Biol.* **26**, 153.

Hoagland, M. B., Scornik, O. A., and Pfefferkorn, L. C. (1964). *Proc. Nat. Acad. Sci. U.S.* **51**, 1184.

Hogeboom, G. H., and Schneider, W. C. (1952). *J. Biol. Chem.* **197**, 611.

Holbrook, D. J., Evans, J. H., and Irvin, J. L. (1962). *Exp. Cell. Res.* **28**, 120.

Holmes, B. E., and Mee, L. K. (1954). *Annu. Rep. Brit. Emp. Cancer Campaign* **32**, 281.

Hughes, P. E. (1960). *Australas. Ann. Med.* **9**, 41.

Hultin, T., and von der Decken, A. (1957). *Exp. Cell Res.* **13**, 83.

Islami, A. H., Peck, G. T., and Hubbard, J. C. (1959). *Surg. Gynecol. Obstet.* **108**, 549.

Ives, D. H., Morse, P. A., Jr., and Potter, V. R. (1963). *J. Biol. Chem.* **238**, 1467.

Iwamura, Y., Ono, T., and Morris, H. P. (1968). *Cancer Res.* **28**, 2466.

Iwatzuki, N., and Okazaki, R. (1969). *J. Mol. Biol.* **29**, 139.

Jacob, S. T., Steele, W. J., and Busch, H. (1967). *Cancer Res.* **27**, 52.

Janion, C., and Shugar, D. (1961). *Acta Biochim. Pol.* **8**, 337.

Johnson, R. M., and Albert, S. (1952). *Arch. Biochem. Biophys.* **35**, 340.

Johnson, R. M., and Albert, S. (1959). *J. Biol. Chem.* **234**, 22.

Kalf, G. R. (1964). *Biochemistry* **3**, 1702.

Kennedy, G. C., Pearce, W. M., and Parrot, D. M. V. (1958). *J. Endocrinol.* **17**, 158.

Kent, G., Minick, O. T., Orfei, E., Violini, F. I., and Madera-Orsini, F. (1966). *Amer. J. Pathol.* **49**, 227.

King, C. D., and van Lancker, J. L. (1969). *Arch. Biochem. Biophys.* **129**, 603.

Kleinfeld, R. (1966). *Nat. Cancer Inst. Monogr.* **23**, 369.

Klemperer, H. G., and Haynes, G. R. (1968). *Biochem. J.* **108**, 541.

Kroon, A. M., Borst, P., von Bruggen, E. F. J., and Ruttenberg, G. J. C. M. (1966). *Proc. Nat. Acad. Sci. U.S.* **56**, 1836.

Laguerriere, R., and Laumonier, R. (1960). *C. R. Soc. Biol.* **154**, 286.

Lane, B. P., and Becker, F. F. (1966). *Amer. J. Pathol.* **48**, 183.

Lane, B. P., and Becker, F. F. (1967). *Amer. J. Pathol.* **50**, 435.

Larsson, A., and Neilands, J. B. (1966). *Biochem. Biophys. Res. Commun.* **25**, 222.

Larsson, A., and Reichard, P. (1967). *Progr. Nucl. Acid Res. Mol. Biol.* **7**, 303.

Leong, G. F., Grisham, J. W., and Hole, B. V. (1963). *Fed. Proc. Fed. Amer. Soc. Exp. Biol.* **22**, 192.

Leong, G. F., Grisham, J. W., Hole, B. V., and Albright, M. L. (1964). *Cancer Res.* **24**, 1496.

Lesher, S., Stroud, A. N., and Brues, A. M. (1960). *Cancer Res.* **20**, 1341.

Lieberman, I., Kane, P., and Short, J. (1965). *J. Biol. Chem.* **240**, 3140.

Looney, W. B. (1960). *Proc. Nat. Acad. Sci. U.S.* **46**, 690.

Looney, W. B., Chang, L. O., and Banghart, F. W. (1967). *Proc. Nat. Acad. Sci. U.S.* **57**, 972.

Lowrance, D. J. R., and Butler, J. A. V. (1965). *Biochem. J.* **96**, 53.

Lowrance, P., and Chanutin, A. (1942). *Amer. J. Physiol.* **135**, 606.

McArdle, A. H., and Creaser, E. H. (1963). *Biochim. Biophys. Acta* **68**, 561.

McCorquodale, D. J., Veach, E. G., and Mueller, G. C. (1960). *Biochim. Biophys. Acta* **46**, 335.

MacDonald, R. A., and Rogers, A. E. (1961). *Gastroenterology* **41**, 33.

Maley, F., and Maley, G. F. (1960). *J. Biol. Chem.* **235**, 2968.

Maley, F., and Maley, G. F. (1961a). *Biochim. Biophys. Acta* **47**, 181.

Maley, F., and Maley, G. F. (1961b). *Cancer Res.* **21**, 1421.

Maley, F., and Maley, G. F. (1962). *Biochemistry* **1**, 847.

Mantsavinos, R., and Canellakis, E. S. (1959). *J. Biol. Chem.* **234**, 628.

Maor, D., and Alexander, P. (1968). *Bochim. Biophys. Acta* **157**, 627.

Mayfield, E. D., Jr., Lyman, K., and Bresnick, E. (1967). *Cancer Res.* **27**, 476.

Melchior, E. (1907). *Beitr. Pathol. Anat. Allg. Pathol.* **42**, 479.

Milne, L. S. (1909). *J. Pathol. Bacteriol.* **13**, 127.

Mironescu, St., and Dragomir, C. (1967). *Cancer Res.* **27**, 1819.

Morton, R. K. (1958). *Nature (London)* **181**, 540.

Moya, F. J. (1963). *Esp. Cell Res.* **31**, 457.

Mukundan, M. A., Devi, A., and Sarkar, N. K. (1963). *Biochem. Biophys. Res. Commun.* **11**. 353.

Muramatsu, M., and Busch, H. (1965). *J. Biol. Chem.* **240**, 3960.

Myers, D. K., Hemphill, C. A., and Townsend, C. M. (1961). *Can. J. Biochem. Physiol.* **39**, 1043.

Naora, H. (1957). *J. Biophys. Biochem. Cytol.* **3**, 949.

Nass, M. M. K., Nass, S., and Afzelius, B. A. (1965). *Exp. Cell Res.* **37**, 516.

Nass, S. (1967). *Biochim. Biophys. Acta* **145**, 60.

Nass, S., and Nass, M. M. K. (1963). *J. Cell Biol.* **19**, 593, 612.

Niehaus, U. G., and Barnum, C. P. (1965). *Exp. Cell Res.* **39**, 435.

Novikoff, A. B., and Potter, V. R. (1948). *J. Biol. Chem.* **173**, 223.

Nygaard, O., and Rusch, H. P. (1955). *Cancer Res.* **15**, 240.

Okada, S., and Hempelman, L. H. (1959). *Int. J. Radiat. Biol.* **1**, 305.

Okazaki, R., and Kornberg, A. (1964). *J. Biol. Chem.* **239**, 235.

Peters, R. (1962). *Z. Naturforsch. B.* **17**, 164.

Pogo, A. O., Allfrey, V. G., and Mirsky, A. E. (1966a). *Proc. Nat. Acad. Sci. U.S.* **55**, 805.

Pogo, A. O., Allfrey, V. G., and Mirsky, A. E. (1966b). *Proc. Nat. Acad. Sci. U.S.* **56**, 550.

Pogo, A. O., Littau, V. C., Allfrey, V. G., and Mirsky, A. E. (1967). *Proc. Nat. Acad. Sci. U.S.* **57**, 743.

Pogo, B. G. T., Pogo, A. O., Allfrey, V. G., and Mirsky, A. E. (1968). *Proc. Nat. Acad. Sci. U.S.* **59**, 1337.

Porter, K. R. (1957). *In* "Biological Structure and Function" (T. W. Goodwin and O. Lindberg, eds.), Vol. 1, p. 127. Academic Press, New York.

Post, J., Klein, A', and Hoffman, J. (1960). *AMA Arch. Pathol.* **70**, 314.

Prescott, D. M. (1961). *Int. Rev. Cytol.* **11**, 255.

Price, J. M., and Laird, A. K. (1950). *Cancer Res.* **10**, 650.

Racker, E. (1952). *J. Biol. Chem.* **196**, 347.

Raina, A., Janne, J., and Siimes, M. (1966). *Biochim. Biophys. Acta* **123**, 197.

Rendi, S. (1959). *Biochim. Biophys. Acta* **31**, 266.

Roberts, S., and White, A. (1949). *J. Biol. Chem.* **180**, 505.

Rogers, A. E., Shaka, J. A., Pechet, G., and MacDonald, R. A. (1961). *Amer. J. Pathol.* **39**, 561.

Rose, I. A., and Schweigert, B. S. (1953). *J. Biol. Chem.* **202**, 635.

Roth, J. S. (1963). *Cancer Res.* **23**, 657.

Rouiller, C., and Bernhard, W. (1956). *J. Biophys. Biochem. Cytol.* **2**, *Suppl.* **4**, 355.

Russell, D., and Snyder, S. H. (1968). *Proc. Nat. Acad. Sci. U.S.* **60**, 1420.

Schneider, J. H., and Potter, V. R. (1957). *Cancer Res.* **17**, 701.

Schneider, W. C. (1957). *J. Nat. Cancer Inst.* **18**, 569.

Schneider, W. C., and Brownell, L. W. (1957). *J. Nat. Cancer Inst.* **18**, 579.

Schneider, W. C., and Kuff, E. L. (1965). *Proc. Nat. Acad. Sci. U.S.* **54**, 1650.

Scornik, O. A., Hoagland, M. B., Pfefferkorn, L. C., and Bishop, E. C. (1967). *J. Biol. Chem.* **242** 131.

Shortman, K. (1962). *Biochim. Biophys. Acta* **61**, 50.

Siebert, G. (1960). *In* "The Cell Nucleus" (J. S. Mitchell, ed.), p. 176. Academic Press, New York.

Siebert, G., Bassler, K. H., Hannover, R., Adloff, E., and Beyer, R. (1961). *Biochem. Z.* **334**, 388.

Simek, J., and Sedlacek, J. (1965). *Nature (London)* **207**, 761.

Simek, J., Sedlacek, J., Melka, J., Tusl, M., and Svorcova, S. (1966). *Physiol. Bohemoslov.* **15**, 362.

Simpson, G. E. C., and Finckh, E. S. (1963). *J. Pathol. Bacteriol.* **86**, 361.

Sinclair, J. H., and Stevens, B. J. (1966). *Proc. Nat. Acad. Sci. U.S.* **56**, 508.

Sköld, O. (1960). *Biochim. Biophys. Acta* **44**, 1.

Smythe, R. L., and Moore, R. O. (1958). *Surgery* **44**, 561.

Steiner, J. W., Perz, Z. M., and Taichman, L. B. (1966). *Exp. Mol. Pathol.* **5**, 146.

Stenger, R. J., and Confer, D. B. (1966). *Exp. Mol. Pathol.* **5**, 455.

Stevens, C. E., Daoust, R., and Leblond, C. P. (1953). *J. Biol. Chem.* **202**, 177.

Stich, H. F., and Florian, M. L. (1958). *Can. J. Biochem.* **36**, 855.

Stirpe, F., and Aldridge, W. N. (1961). *Biochem. J.* **80**, 481.

Stowell, R. E. (1948). *Arch. Pathol.* **46**, 164.

Stowell, R. E. (1949). *Cancer Res.* **2**, 121.

Survis, J., Kennedy, R., and Hass, G. M. (1962). *Fed. Proc. Fed. Amer. Soc. Exp. Biol.* **21**, 301.

Swick, R. W., Koch, A. L., and Handa, D. T. (1956). *Arch. Biochem. Biophys.* **63**, 226.

Swift, H. (1953). *Texas Rep. Biol. Med.* **11**, 755.

Swift, H., Rebhun, L., Rasch, E., and Woodard, J. (1956). *In* "Cellular Mechanisms in Differentiation and Growth" (D. Rudnick, ed.), p. 45. Princeton Univ. Press, Princeton, New Jersey.

Tabor, H., and Tabor, C. W. (1964). *Pharmacol. Rev.* **16**, 245.

Takanishi, S., Ito, K., and Tatibana, M. (1968). *Biochem. Biophys. Res. Commun.* **33**, 774.

Thompson, J. F., and Moss, E. M. (1955). *Proc. Soc. Exp. Biol. Med.* **89**, 230.

Thomson, R. J., and Clarke, A. M. (1965). *Nature (London)*, **208**, 392.

Tidwell, T., Allfrey, V. G., and Mirsky, A. E. (1968). *J. Biol. Chem.* **243**, 707.

Tomkins, G. M., Garren, L. D., Howell, R. R., and Peterkofsky, B. (1965). *J. Cell. Comp. Physiol.* **66**, 137.

Tsukada, K., and Lieberman, I. (1964). *J. Biol. Chem.* **239**, 2952.

Tsukada, K., and Lieberman, I. (1965a). *Biochem. Biophys. Res. Commun.* **19**, 702.

Tsukada, K., and Lieberman, I. (1965b). *J. Biol. Chem.* **240**, 1731.

Uchiyama, T., Fausto, N., and van Lancker, J. L. (1966). *J. Biol. Chem.* **241**, 991.

Umana, R., Updike, S., Randall, J., and Dounce, A. L. (1964). In "The Nucleohistones" (J. Bonner and P. O. P. Ts'o, eds.), p. 200. Holden-Day, San Francisco, California.

Vandergoten, R., and Goutier, R. (1966). *Int. J. Radiat. Biol.* **11**, 449.

van Lancker, J. L., and Borison, H. L. (1961). *Biochim. Biophys. Acta* **51**, 171.

Virolainen, M. (1967). *In* "Control of Cellular Growth in Adult Organisms" (H. Teir and T. Rytomaa, eds.), p. 232. Academic Press, New York.

von der Decken, A., and Hultin, T. (1958). *Exp. Cell Res.* **14**, 88.

von der Decken, A., and Hultin, T. (1960). *Exp. Cell Res.* **19**, 591.

von Meister, V. (1894). *Beitr. Pathol. Anat. Allg. Pathol.* **15**, 1.

von Podwyssozki, W., Jr. (1886). *Beitr. Pathol. Anat. Allg. Pathol.* **1**, 259.

Weinbren, K. (1955). *Brit. J. Exp. Pathol.* **36**, 583.

Weinbren, K. (1959). *Gastroenterology* **37**, 657.

Weiss, P. A. (1955). *Symp. Soc. Study Develop. Growth* **12**, 195.

Weiss, P. A., and Kavanau, J. L. (1957). *J. Gen. Physiol.* **41**, 147.

Weiss, S. B. (1960). *Proc. Nat. Acad. Sci. U.S.* **46**, 1020.

Weissman, S. M., Smellie, R. M. S., and Paul, J. (1960). *Biochim. Biophys. Acta* **45**, 101.

Welling, W., and Cohen, J. A. (1960). *Biochim. Biophys. Acta* **42**, 181.

Wenneker, A. S., and Sussman, N. (1951). *Proc. Soc. Exp. Bio. Med.* **76**, 683.

Wilson, M. E., Stowell, R. E., Yokoyama, O., and Tsuboi, K. K. (1953). *Cancer Res.* **13**, 86.

Wu, C. (1964). *Arch. Biochem. Biophys.* **106**, 402.

Yates, R. A., and Pardee, A. B. (1957). *J. Biol. Chem.* **227**, 677.

Zellis, R. (1967). *Biochem. Biophys. Res. Commun.* **29**, 131.

Zimmerman, M., and Celozzi, E. (1961). *Nature (London)* **191**, 1014.

CHAPTER IX

GLYCEROLIPIDS IN THE NEOPLASTIC CELL: METHODOLOGY, METABOLISM, AND COMPOSITION*

FRED SNYDER

I. Introduction

The term "lipids" defines a diverse group of compounds generally soluble in organic solvents, such as hexane, benzene, chloroform, diethyl ether, acetone, methanol, and ethanol, or in combinations of these. Important classes of mammalian lipids are listed below according to their structural formulas or their various functional groups.

1. Hydrocarbons $\quad\quad\quad R$—CH_2—CH_2—CH_3
2. Fatty acids $\quad\quad\quad\quad R$—CH_2—$COOH$
3. Fatty alcohols $\quad\quad\quad R$—CH_2—OH
4. Fatty aldehydes $\quad\quad R$—CH_2—CHO
5. Hydroxy fatty acids

$$\text{(a)}\ \alpha\text{-Hydroxy} \quad\quad R\text{—}CH_2\text{—}\overset{\displaystyle OH}{\underset{\displaystyle H}{C}}\text{—}COOH$$

* Research sponsored by Medical Division, Oak Ridge Associated Universities under contract with U.S. Atomic Energy Commission.

(b) β-Hydroxy

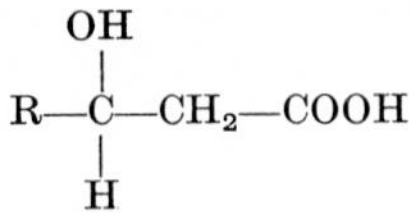

$$\underset{\underset{H}{|}}{\overset{\overset{OH}{|}}{R-C}}-CH_2-COOH$$

6. Alkane-1,2-diols

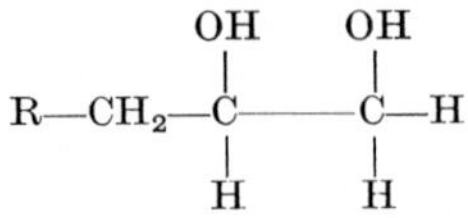

$$R-CH_2-\underset{\underset{H}{|}}{\overset{\overset{OH}{|}}{C}}\quad\underset{\underset{H}{|}}{\overset{\overset{OH}{|}}{C}}-H$$

7. Waxes

(a) Simple waxes

$$R-CH_2-\overset{\overset{O}{\|}}{C}-O-CH_2-R$$

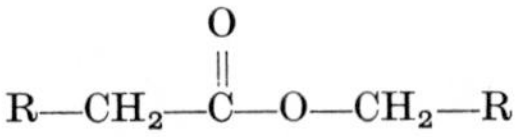

(b) Waxes of alkane-1,2-diols

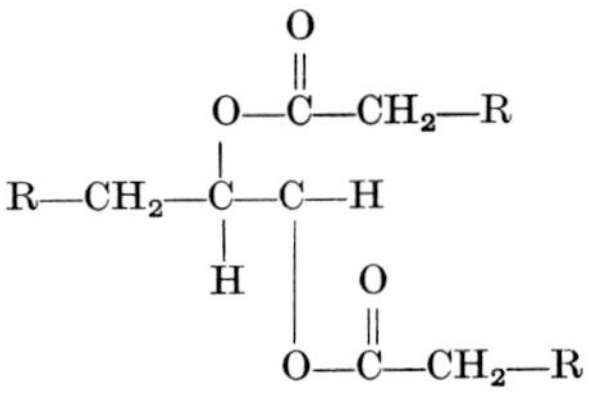

$$R-CH_2-\underset{\underset{H}{|}}{\overset{\overset{O-\overset{\overset{O}{\|}}{C}-CH_2-R}{|}}{C}}-\underset{\underset{O-\overset{\overset{O}{\|}}{C}-CH_2-R}{}}{C}-H$$

8. Monoglycerolipids

$$\begin{array}{l} H_2C-(\text{position 1}) \\ (\text{position 2})-CH \\ H_2C-(\text{position 3}) \end{array}$$

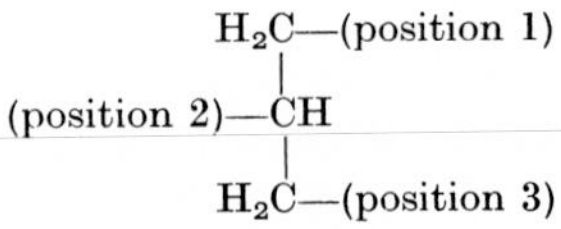

TABLE I

CLASSIFICATION OF MONOGLYCEROLIPIDS

Lipid class	Substituents at the three positions of glycerol		
	1	2	3
(a) Triacylglycerols (triglycerides)	Acyl	Acyl	Acyl
(b) Diacyl alkyl glyceryl ethers (glyceryl ether diesters)	Alkyl	Acyl	Acyl
(c) Diacyl alk-1-enyl glyceryl ethers (neutral plasmalogen)	Alk-1-enyl	Acyl	Acyl
(d) Diacylglycerols (diglycerides)	Acyl	Acyl[a]	Hydroxyl
(e) Monoacyl alkyl glyceryl ethers	Alkyl	Acyl[a]	Hydroxyl
(f) Monoacyl alk-1-enyl glyceryl ethers	Alk-1-enyl	Acyl[a]	Hydroxyl
(g) Monoacylglycerols (monoglycerides)	Acyl[b]	Hydroxyl	Hydroxyl
(h) Alkyl glyceryl ethers	Alkyl	Hydroxyl	Hydroxyl
(i) Alk-1-enyl glyceryl ethers	Alk-1-enyl	Hydroxyl	Hydroxyl
(j) Alkyldihydroxyacetone	Alkyl	Ketone	Hydroxyl

[a] Acyl group can be in 3-position instead of 2-position.
[b] Acyl group can be in 2-position instead of 1-position.

TABLE I (cont.)

CLASSIFICATION OF MONOGLYCEROLIPIDS

Lipid class	Substituents at the three positions of glycerol		
	1	2	3
(k) Choline phosphoglycerides:			
Phosphatidyl choline (lecithin)	Acyl	Acyl	P-choline
Alkyl choline phosphoglyceride	Alkyl	Acyl	P-choline
Alk-1-enyl choline phosphoglyceride (plasmalogen)	Alk-1-enyl	Acyl	P-choline
(l) Ethanolamine phosphoglycerides:			
Phosphatidyl ethanolamine (cephalin)	Acyl	Acyl	P-ethanolamine
Alkyl ethanolamine phosphoglyceride	Alkyl	Acyl	P-ethanolamine
Alk-1-enyl ethanolamine phosphoglyceride (plasmalogen)	Alk-1-enyl	Acyl	P-ethanolamine
(m) Serine phosphoglycerides:			
Phosphatidyl serine	Acyl	Acyl	P-serine
Alkyl serine phosphoglyceride	Alkyl	Acyl	P-serine
Alk-1-enyl serine phosphoglyceride (plasmalogen)	Alk-1-enyl	Acyl	P-serine
(n) Phosphatidic acid	Acyl	Acyl	Phosphate
Alkyl analog of phosphatidic acid	Alkyl	Acyl	Phosphate
Alk-1-enyl analog of phosphatidic acid	Alk-1-enyl	Acyl	Phosphate
(o) Phosphatidyl inositol	Acyl	Acyl	P-inositol
(p) Phosphatidyl inositol diphosphate	Acyl	Acyl	Inositol diphosphate
(q) Galactosyl glyceride	Acyl	Acyl	Galactose
(r) Sulfolipid	Acyl	Acyl	Galactose–SO_4
(s) Phosphonolipid	Acyl	Acyl	Phosphonic acid
Alkyl analog of phosphonolipid	Alkyl	Acyl	Phosphonic acid
(t) Alkyldihydroxyacetone phosphate	Alkyl	Ketone	Phosphate
(u) Acyldihydroxyacetone phosphate	Acyl	Ketone	Phosphate

The monoglycerolipids are classified according to substituents on the three positions of glycerol as shown in Table I. The term "acyl"

$$(-\overset{\overset{\textstyle O}{\|}}{C}-O-CH_2R)$$

refers to esterified aliphatic moieties. "Alkyl"

$$(-C-O-CH_2R)$$

and "alk-1-enyl"

$$(-C-OCH=CHR)$$

are used to describe the α,β carbon bonds adjacent to the O-ether linkage of the hydrocarbon chain attached to the 1-position of glycerol in lipids. Alkyl ethers refer to those compounds that do not have α,β unsaturation in the hydrocarbon chain but may have unsaturation farther out along the chain. Alk-1-enyl ethers refer to those compounds that have α,β unsaturation (vinylic or enol ethers, plasmalogen type) and may also have unsaturation farther out along the chain.

9. Diglycerolipids
    (a) Phosphatidyl glycerol

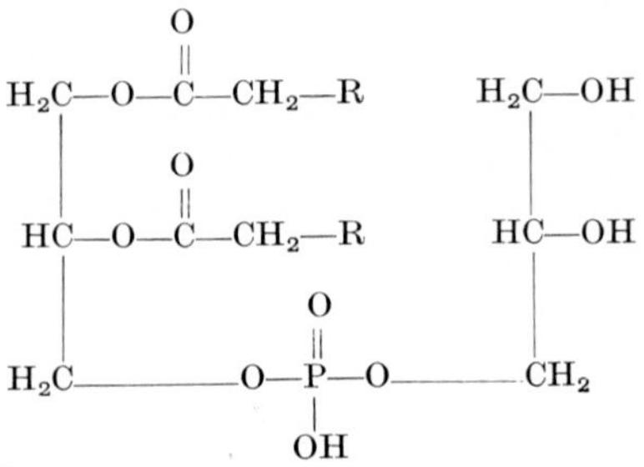

    (b) Diphosphatidyl glycerol (cardiolipin)

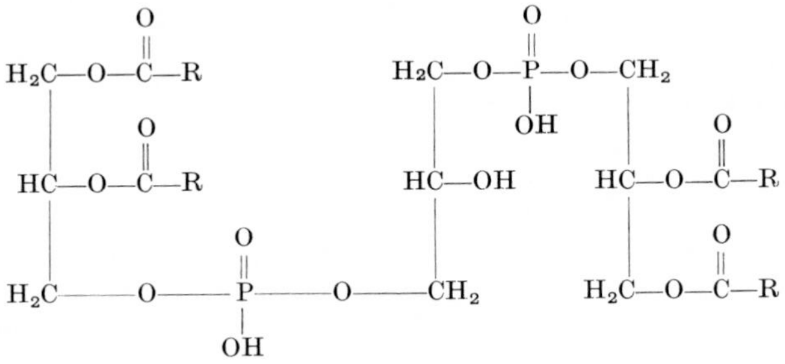

10. Sphingomyelin

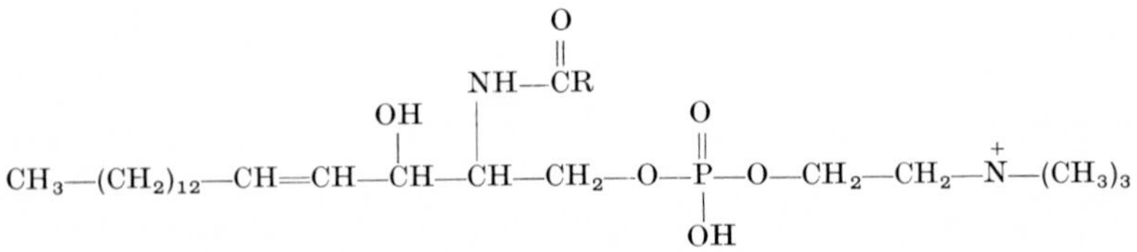

11. Ceramide (N-acyl sphingosine)

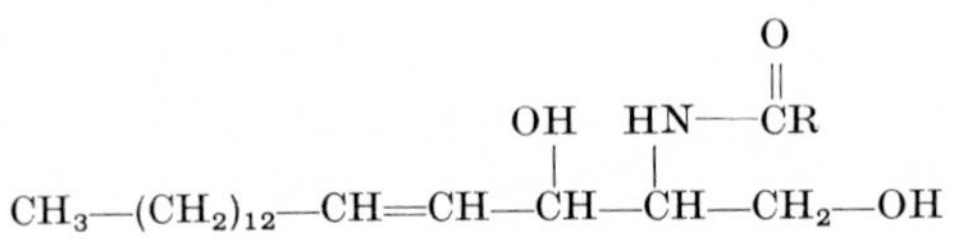

12. Glycolipids
    (a) Cerebrosides: ceramide–$(glucose)_m$–$(galactose)_n$
    (b) Globosides: ceramide–$(glucose)_m$–$(galactose)_n$–$(N\text{-acetylhexosamine})_p$
    (c) Hematosides: ceramide–$(glucose)_m$–$(galactose)_n$–$(sialic\ acid)_q$
    (d) Gangliosides: ceramide–$(glucose)_m$–$(galactose)_n$–$(N\text{–acetylgalactosa-}mine)_p$–$(sialic\ acid)_q$

13. Prostaglandins (E_2)

$$\begin{array}{c}
\text{HOOC}-(\text{CH}_2)_3-\text{CH}=\text{CH}-\text{CH}_2\overset{\text{H}}{\underset{|}{\text{C}}}-\overset{\overset{\text{HO}}{|}}{\text{C}}\diagdown^{\text{H}} \\
\qquad\qquad\qquad\qquad\qquad\qquad |\qquad\diagdown\text{CH}_2 \\
\text{CH}_3(\text{CH}_2)_4\text{CH(OH)}-\text{CH}=\text{CH}\underset{\underset{\text{HO}}{|}}{\overset{\text{H}}{\text{C}}}-\text{C}\diagdown_{\text{H}}
\end{array}$$

Lipids are important structural constituents and sources of energy in cells and they play a vital role in the functional properties of membranes. During cell transformation and malignant growth, the composition and metabolism of lipids undergo drastic alterations (Haven and Bloor, 1956; Lopez, 1956; Kamimae, 1958; Serra, 1960; Galanos and Mitropoulos, 1961; Lettre, 1964). An indexed listing of more than 800 references that pertain to lipid research of cancer tissues (1947–1970) is available (Snyder, 1970a).

II. Methods for Lipid Analyses

A. LIPID EXTRACTION AND PURIFICATION FROM WATER-SOLUBLE CONTAMINANTS

Many organic solvents or combinations of solvents have been used for general and specific extractions of lipids from biological materials. Some solvents, e.g., ethanol or methanol, serve mainly to dehydrate the sample and disrupt the lipoprotein complexes. Excellent solvents for lipids are chloroform or diethyl ether, and the three most widely used lipid extraction procedures are those of Folch et al. (1951, 1957) or Bligh and Dyer (1959), which use combinations of chloroform–methanol, and that of Bloor (1915), which uses ethanol–diethyl ether. These procedures extract lipids directly from a water medium at room temperature. Similar extraction procedures have been carried out on freeze-dried preparations or by Soxhlet extractions at the boiling point of the solvents. The chloroform–methanol extracts are washed directly with water, or a small beaker containing the final extracts is placed in a large beaker of water to permit the methanol (containing nonlipid material) to diffuse into the much larger water phase. Folch et al. (1957) have used metal ions to prevent solubilization of phospholipids. Water-soluble compounds have also been removed from chloroform–methanol extracts by passing the extracts through Sephadex columns (Wells and Dittmer, 1963). Lovern (1957) and Entenman (1961) have reviewed essential steps in the preparation of tissue lipid extracts.

B. CHROMATOGRAPHY

The resolution of lipid classes, of homologous series of lipid classes, and of lipid and nonlipid moieties derived from degradative reaction of complex lipids generally depends on the application of various chromatographic processes. Adsorption and partition (liquid–liquid and liquid–gas) chromatography are most useful in lipid analysis, although ion-exchange and gel filtration (Sephadex) chromatography can sometimes be important auxiliary procedures. The various separation processes occur to some extent during most chromatographic procedures.

Most lipids are associated with proteins in living cells, but discussion of lipoprotein methods and chemistry is beyond the scope of this chapter. A number of texts (Stahl, 1969; Randerath, 1963; Kirchner, 1967; Bobbitt, 1963; Stock and Rice, 1967; Marinetti, 1967, 1969) should be consulted for a broader approach to, and a more extensive bibliography on, the chromatography of lipids. Specific articles on glass-fiber paper chromatography (Hamilton and Muldrey, 1961), on silicic acid-impregnated paper (Marinetti, 1962), on adsorption columns (Wren, 1961), and on chromatography of ether-linked lipids are available (Viswanathan, 1968; Snyder, 1970b).

1. Adsorption Chromatography

Lipid classes are separated by adsorption chromatography on silicic acid or alumina columns, thin-layer chromatoplates, or on silicic acid-impregnated papers or glass-fiber papers. The most useful of these procedures is thin-layer chromatography, since it has much larger load characteristics than the impregnated papers and provides much better resolution than the column procedures. Thin-layer chromatography can be used for both preparative and analytical separations; the chromatographic behavior of lipids on chromatoplates is typical of all separations based on adsorption chromatography.

The diagram in Fig. 1 designates the behavior of representative lipid classes on thin-layer chromatograms in a variety of solvents having a wide range of polarity. It is sometimes advantageous to do a preliminary separation of polar (phospholipids) and nonpolar (neutral lipids) fractions on small columns of silicic acid (Borgström, 1952); the nonpolar lipids are eluted with chloroform or diethyl ether and the polar lipids are then eluted from the columns with methanol.

The nonphosphorus-containing lipids that possess alkyl, alk-1-enyl,

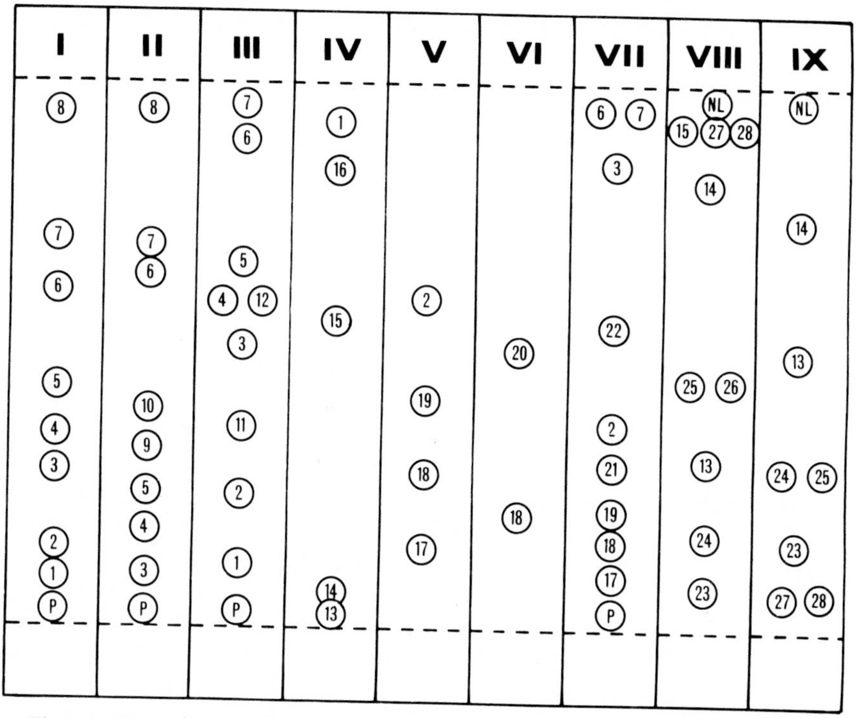

FIG. 1. Typical thin-layer chromatographic systems for separating lipids. The numbers or letters designate the relative R_f's of the following: (P) polar lipid; (1) cholesterol; (2) fatty alcohols; (3) triacylglycerols; (4) diacyl O-alkylglycerols; (5) diacyl O-alk-1-enylglycerols; (6) waxes; (7) cholesteryl esters; (8) hydrocarbons; (9) acyl di-O-alkylglycerols; (10) tri-O-alkylglycerols; (11) fatty acids; (12) fatty aldehydes; (13) phosphatidyl choline; (14) phosphatidyl ethanolamine; (15) cerebrosides; (16) ceramide; (17) monoacylglycerols; (18) O-alkylglycerols (1-isomer); (19) O-alk-1-enylglycerols; (20) O-alkylglycerols (2-isomer); (21) O-alkyldihydroxyacetone; (22) diacylglycerols; (23) lyso phosphatidylcholine; (24) sphingomyelin; (25) phosphatidyl serine; (26) phosphatidyl inositol; (27) phosphatidic acid; (28) cardiolipin. The broken lines locate the origin (lower line) and the solvent front (upper line). The solvent systems (v/v) used were (I) benzene; (II) hexane–diethyl ether (95:5); (III) hexane–diethyl ether–acetic acid (80:20:1); (IV) double development, first in diethyl ether and then in chloroform–methanol (70:30); (V) diethyl ether–water (200:1); (VI) chloroform–methanol (98:2) on silica gel G layers containing borate; (VII) hexane–diethyl ether–methanol–acetic acid (70:30:5:1); (VIII) chloroform–methanol–acetic acid–saline (50:25:8:4); and (IX) chloroform–methanol–ammonium hydroxide (60:35:8). Silica gel G (lanes I–VII) and silica gel HR (lanes VIII and IX) were used as adsorbents.

and acyl moieties are easily subfractionated as intact molecules. In contrast, adequate subfractionation of alkyl, alk-1-enyl, and acyl phospholipids first requires selective removal of the phosphate, phosphoryl base, or both the phosphate and acyl moieties before chromatography. Partition (Gray and MacFarlane, 1958) and argentation (Hoevet et al., 1968) chromatography enrich fractions of alk-1-enyl ether linked phosphoglycerides, but these procedures do not provide separations equivalent to those obtained for the various subclasses of neutral lipids (Snyder, 1969c). Renkonen (1968) approached the problem of subfractionating ester- and ether-linked phospholipids by masking the polar phosphoryl-base moieties of phosphoglycerides with methyl and dinitrophenol groups. Multiple chromatographic developments of these derivatives on layers of silica gel G in toluene–chloroform (2:8, v/v) gave some degree of resolution of alkyl, alk-1-enyl, and acyl phosphoglyceride classes. Kapoulas (1969) has described some solvent systems for thin-layer chromatography that even separate phosphonic acid analogs of phospholipids from the corresponding phosphate esters.

Addition of metals to the adsorbent greatly enhances the versatility of thin-layer chromatography; the metals participate in reversible reactions with organic compounds during chromatography. Silver ions form π-bond complexes with carbon-to-carbon double bonds and fractionate lipid classes on the basis of the number of double bonds that they contain (Fig. 1). Argentation thin-layer chromatography can also separate *cis* and *trans* isomers of fatty acids (Morris, 1966). Arsenite or borate ions form complexes with compounds that have two adjacent free hydroxyl groups; the author (Wood and Snyder, 1967a) has used these ions to resolve 1- and 2-isomers of glyceryl ethers (Fig. 1).

After chromatographic resolution, lipid mass is measured by colorimetric procedures or by photodensitometry of carbon residues formed by spraying the chromatographic layers with H_2SO_4 and charring at 180° to 200°C (Privett et al., 1965) or by "liquid "charring (Marsh and Weinstein, 1966; Snyder and Moehl, 1969). Liquid scintillation spectrometry (zonal profile scans or elution), radioautography, strip scanning, or beta camera analysis are useful in determining the distribution of radioactivity (Snyder and Piantadosi, 1966; Snyder, 1969a) along the chromatographic lane.

2. Partition Chromatography

a. *Liquid–Liquid Chromatography.* Paper chromatography (Macek and Hais, 1965) can identify water-soluble fragments derived from phospholipids after mild alkaline and acid hydrolysis. Dawson and co-workers (1962; Dawson, 1960) have illustrated typical separations of these fragments.

Reverse-phase partition chromatography (Kaufmann and Nitsch, 1954) is the term used when one reverses the polarity of the mobile and stationary phases used in paper chromatography. The support (paper or silicic acid) is impregnated with silicone or a high-boiling hydrocarbon; the mobile phase contains the water or other immiscible solvent. This technique resolves certain homologous classes of lipids according to the nature of the aliphatic moieties, e.g., chain length and *cis-trans* configuration. Problems are encountered with critical pairs, such as linolenic + lauric acid or palmitoleic + linoleic + myristic acids. Quantitation with reverse-phase systems is difficult, although some stationary phases can be removed at reduced pressures and relatively low temperatures. Conventional procedures quantitate the lipids remaining behind. However, liquid columns combined with conventional gas chromatographic detectors are best for quantitation (Karmen, 1967).

b. Gas–Liquid Chromatography. (*i*) *General.* Gas–liquid chromatography separates lipids of a homologous series according to functional groups, molecular weight, carbon numbers, and degree of unsaturation. Most lipids are generally converted to derivatives of lower-vapor pressure before ideal separations are obtained. However, under certain conditions, high-temperature chromatography (300°–400°C) combined with temperature programming has successfully resolved lipids with molecular weights of 700 to 1200.

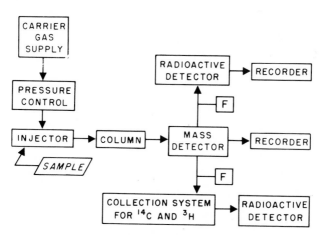

Fig. 2. The essential components of a typical gas–liquid chromatograph equipped for radioassay. Organic compounds leaving the mass detector can be radioassayed in a continuous flow system or after collection. The furnaces (F) containing a suitable catalyst are available when conversion of the organic compounds to $^{14}CO_2$ and ^3H_2O is desired.

Figure 2 is a block diagram showing the main components of a gas–liquid chromatograph equipped for radioassay. The packing in the column contains an inert support, e.g., Chromosorb W, coated with a liquid phase. Nonpolar liquid phases, such as silicone, separate a homologous series of compounds mainly according to molecular weight and determine the total number of carbon atoms that a compound contains. Polar phases, such as polyesters, separate compounds according to functional groups, unsaturation, and molecular weight. The organic compounds can be measured quantitatively as they emerge from the columns by hydrogen flame, argon ionization, thermal conductivity, electron capture, or density balance detectors. A recent book on the theory and applications of gas chromatography has been edited by Kroman and Bender (1968). Commercially available gas-flow splitters can direct a portion of the effluent stream emerging from the column into devices that monitor or collect radioactivity in the gas stream; investigators use both combustion and noncombustion techniques in conjunction with gas–liquid chromatography radioassay measurements (see Snyder, 1969a).

(ii) *Separation of intact lipid classes and determination of carbon numbers.* High-temperature gas–liquid chromatography of intact lipid classes or of fragments of high-molecular-weight lipids was initially applied to the analysis of triglycerides (Kuksis and Brekenridge, 1966). Investigators have now used these procedures in the analysis of diacyl glyceryl ethers (Wood and Snyder, 1969), diglyceride acetates (Renkonen, 1966; Wood et al., 1969), diol lipids (Wood and Baumann, 1968), and phospholipids (Kuksis et al., 1967). High-temperature methods are generally not quantitative for phospholipids (fragmentation occurs), but these compounds can first be converted to neutral glycerides with phospholipase C. Their acetates are then prepared and analyzed by high-temperature gas–liquid chromatography (Renkonen, 1966). One can calculate the number of carbon atoms in the total aliphatic moieties from appropriate standards.

(iii) *Resolution of aliphatic moieties according to chain length and number of double bonds.* The resolution of aliphatic chains attached to glycerol or glycol requires masking of the free hydroxyl groups with appropriate derivatives (e.g., isopropylidene, acetates) or preparation of derivatives from the aliphatic moieties (methyl esters of fatty acids, dimethyl acetals of aldehydes, or acetates of fatty alcohols) after they are removed from the glycerol or glycol lipids. The preparation of derivatives is described in Section III, B. Direct analysis of intact fatty acids (Metcalfe, 1960) and fatty aldehydes (Wood and Harlow, 1969) is also possible. These analyses provide information about the carbon chain lengths, degree of unsaturation, molecular weight, and functional groups; they can usually resolve all major homologs of acyl, O-alkyl, and O-alk-1-enyl moieties derived from naturally occurring lipids (Fig. 3). Table II lists some specific conditions used for gas–liquid chromatography of various derivatives of lipids containing acyl, O-alkyl, and O-alk-1-enyl groups. These methods of chromatography combined with the chemical procedures listed in the next section can generally identify most lipid molecules.

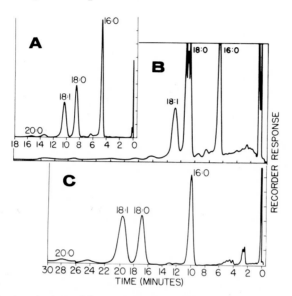

FIG. 3. The resolution of long-chain fatty aldehydes (A), long-chain fatty alcohols (B), and O-alkylglycerols (C) by gas–liquid chromatography. The numbers above each peak designate the chain length and number of double bonds. The fractions were isolated from lipids of neoplastic tissues.

TABLE II

EXAMPLES OF TYPICAL CONDITIONS[a] FOR GAS-LIQUID CHROMATOGRAPHY OF GLYCEROLIPID MOIETIES

Lipid class	Derivative	Temperature (°C)
Glyceryl ethers	Isopropylidenes	200
Fatty acids	Methyl esters	175–200
Fatty alcohols	Acetates	180–200
Fatty aldehydes	Dimethyl acetals	175–200
	None (intact)	175

[a] Six-foot columns containing a stationary phase of 10% EGSS-X (ethylene glycol succinate silicone polymer) on a support of Gas Chrom-P (silane treated). The stationary phase, precoated on the support, is available from Applied Science Laboratories, P.O. Box 440, State College, Pa., 16801.

III. Chemistry of Glycerolipids

This section describes reactions that fragment glycerolipids into their constituent parts and that are useful in preparing derivatives of these constituents for subsequent analyses and identification. The organic portion and/or its derivatives can be analyzed for the number of carbon atoms, the degree of unsaturation, and the functional groups present, whereas the inorganic portions (phosphate or sulfate) can be quantitated by colorimetric procedures. Application of these methods to the stereospecific and positional analysis of glycerolipids, including determination of double-bond locations of the aliphatic moieties, has provided significant information on the structural relationships of lipid classes. A number of useful texts on the chemistry of lipids should be consulted for more complete details (Deuel, 1951; Hanahan, 1960; Ansell and Hawthorne, 1964). Several recent reviews specifically cover the ether-linked lipids (Thompson and Kapoulas, 1969; Piantadosi and Snyder, 1970; Snyder, 1970b).

A. Degradation of Complex Lipids into Constituent Parts

1. Acidic and Alkaline Hydrolysis

A number of excellent papers (Dawson, 1960; Dawson et al., 1962; Wells and Dittmer, 1966; Marinetti, 1962) describe the hydrolysis of common lipid classes under acidic and alkaline conditions. Lovern (1957) provides a condensed version of the basic essentials, virtues, and inherent problems of these methods. The main features of acidic and basic hydrolytic procedures used in lipid research are summarized below.

a. *Acid Hydrolysis.* Strong acid hydrolysis with HCl or H_2SO_4 removes ethanolamine, serine, choline, sphingosine, and fatty acids from phosphoglycerides. Hydrolysis is generally carried out in aqueous solutions of HCl or H_2SO_4 (6 N) or methanolic solutions of HCl or H_2SO_4 (5–10%). Hydrolytic procedures range from several minutes to longer than a day, depending upon the class of lipid undergoing hydrolysis.

Acid hydrolysis cleaves O-alk-1-enyl bonds (plasmalogens) completely, producing long-chain fatty aldehydes. Even mild acid hydrolysis with acetic acid cleaves O-alk-1-enyl linkages or can produce cyclic acetals with lyso plasmalogens (Davenport and Dawson, 1961; Pietruszko and Gray, 1962). However, acetic acid does not alter the O-alk-1-enyl linkage in organic solvent systems used for thin-layer chromatography.

$$H_2C-O\diagdown$$
$$\quad\quad | \quad\quad \diagup CH-CH_2-R$$
$$HC\diagdown O\diagup$$
$$\quad | $$
$$H_2C-O-\circled{P}-ethanolamine$$

It is important to note that acetic acid will cause acetylation of free hydroxyl groups and promotes the hydrolysis of cardiolipins to yield diglycerylphosphate and diglyceride.

Acid hydrolysis (HCl or H_2SO_4 at 100°C) of O-alkyldihydroxyacetone phosphate and O-alkyldihydroxyacetone liberates fatty alcohols that have been identified by gas–liquid chromatography as acetate derivatives (Snyder et al., 1970d). The ether linkage in the enol form of these ketone-containing compounds is an alkenyl type and, therefore, acid-labile.

$$H_2C-OCH_2R \quad\quad\quad HC-OCH_2R$$
$$\quad | \quad\quad\quad\quad\quad\quad\quad\quad \|$$
$$C=O \quad\longleftrightarrow\quad COH \quad\xrightarrow{\quad H^+\quad}\quad ROH+[glyceraldehyde\text{-}3\text{-}P]$$
$$\quad | \quad\quad\quad\quad\quad\quad\quad\quad |$$
$$H_2C-phosphate\ or\ OH \quad H_2C-phosphate\ or\ OH$$
$$(O\text{-alkyldihydroxyacetone} \quad (enol\ form\ of$$
$$lipid) \quad\quad\quad O\text{-alkyldihydroxyacetone}$$
$$\quad\quad\quad\quad lipid)$$

b. *Alkaline Hydrolysis.* Alkaline hydrolysis with methanolic or ethanolic solution of NaOH or KOH splits ester linkages of fatty acids, choline, ethanolamine, and serine from glycerolipids, but it is not very effective for the hydrolysis of amide, glycosidic, acetal, O-alkyl, or O-alk-1-enyl bonds. Acyl migration can occur during dephosphorylation of diacyl phosphatides, and Bevan et al. (1953) have suggested a mechanism for this.

The phosphoric ester linkage in O-alkyl glycerophosphoric acid is resistant to alkaline hydrolysis and cyclic phosphate compounds can be formed (Carter et al., 1958):

$$H_2C-OR$$
$$\quad | $$
$$HC\diagdown O\diagdown \quad O$$
$$\quad | \quad\quad \| $$
$$H_2C\diagdown O\diagup P-OH$$

The phosphoryl choline linkage in sphingomyelins also resists most alkaline hydrolysis procedures, although a saturated solution of barium hydroxide (Brante, 1949) can quantitatively liberate choline and inorganic phosphate from sphingomyelin. Thompson (1967) has used alkaline hydrolysis to remove small amounts of acyl glycerolipids from phosphonolipids. The products of alkaline hydrolysis are water-soluble compounds, including soaps and nonsaponifiable lipids. Partitioning between water and diethyl ether separates them from one another. Acidification of the total mixture before or during ether extraction liberates the free fatty acids from the soaps and also liberates fatty aldehydes from all O-alk-1-enyl-linked lipids; the fatty acids and aldehydes then enter the ether phase with other nonsaponifiable lipids, mainly cholesterol and O-alkylglycerols.

The conditions for mild alkaline hydrolysis are extremely critical, since variations will produce different types and different quantities of water soluble hydrolytic products. Careful timing of a reaction can yield intermediate products that are useful in identifying the original compound and also in providing important intermediates for subsequent enzyme studies. Lovern (1957) has pointed out that hydrolysis of phosphatidyl choline with 0.2 N NaOH gives mainly glycerylphosphorylcholine during a 15-minute hydrolysis at 37°C or during a 2-hour hydrolysis at room temperature but that hydrolysis with 1 N methanolic NaOH at room temperature for 1 hour gives an almost equal mixture of glycerylphosphorylcholine and phosphorylcholine (the phosphorylcholine being extremely resistant to further hydrolysis) and that hydrolysis of phosphatidyl choline with 0.5 N KOH in ethanol for 15 minutes at 37°C yields free choline and glycerophosphate. Prolonged alkaline hydrolysis (> 1 hour) of O-alkyldihydroxyacetone phosphate and O-alkyldihydroxyacetone yields fatty alcohols (Wykle and Snyder, 1970); these compounds are stable (Snyder et al., 1970d) under milder conditions (15 minutes).

2. Lithium Aluminum Hydride Reduction

Lithium aluminum hydride (Thompson and Lee, 1965; Hanahan et al., 1963; Wood and Snyder, 1968) removes acyl- and phosphoryl-base groups from lipids, the acyl groups being reduced to fatty alcohols in the process. Alkyl– and alk-1-enyl–ether groupings and unsaturated bonds are unaffected by $LiAlH_4$ reduction. Its application to the quantitative analysis of O-alkyl and O-alk-1-enyl lipids is shown in Scheme 1.

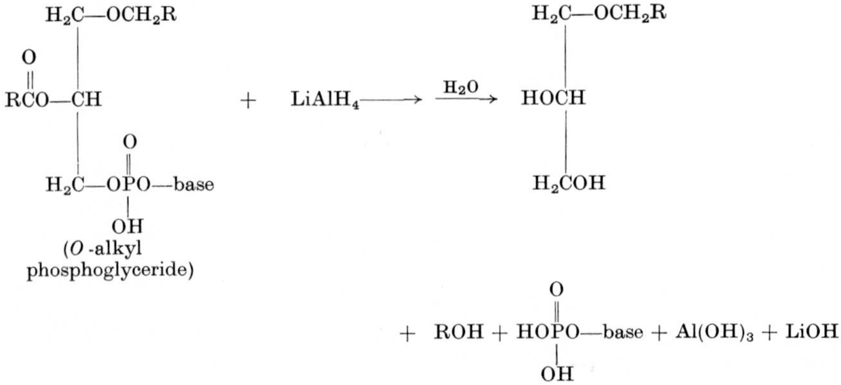

SCHEME 1

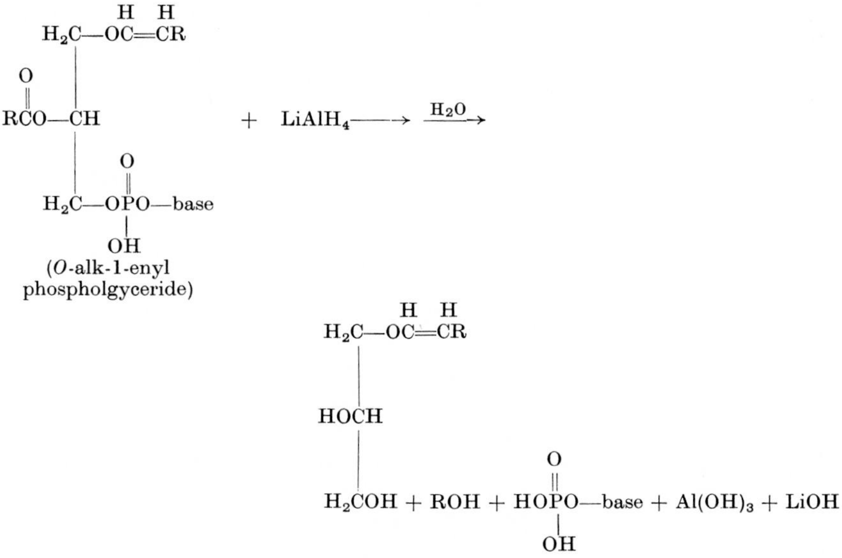

$$\begin{array}{c} \overset{H\ \ H}{H_2C-OC=CR} \\ | \\ \overset{O}{\underset{\|}{}} \quad | \\ RCO-CH \qquad\qquad + \ LiAlH_4 \longrightarrow \xrightarrow{H_2O} \\ | \quad \overset{O}{\underset{\|}{}} \\ H_2C-OPO-base \\ | \\ OH \\ (O\text{-alk-1-enyl} \\ \text{phospholgyceride}) \end{array}$$

$$\begin{array}{c} \overset{H\ \ H}{H_2C-OC=CR} \\ | \\ HOCH \\ | \qquad\qquad\qquad\qquad O \\ \qquad\qquad\qquad\qquad \underset{\|}{} \\ H_2COH + ROH + HOPO-base + Al(OH)_3 + LiOH \\ | \\ OH \end{array}$$

SCHEME 1 (continued)

This reaction is also useful for analysis of diacyl and monoacyl glyceryl ethers.

3. Grignard Reagent

Acyl moieties can be removed from glycerolipids by CH_3CH_2MgBr (Yurkowski and Brockerhoff, 1966). The latter compound causes random deacylation with a minimum of acyl migration:

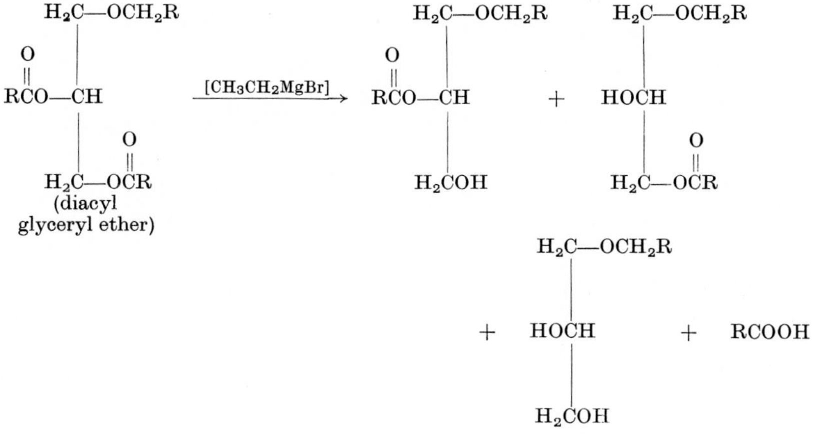

$$\begin{array}{c} H_2C-OCH_2R \\ | \\ \overset{O}{\underset{\|}{}} \quad | \\ RCO-CH \qquad \xrightarrow{[CH_3CH_2MgBr]} \\ | \quad \overset{O}{\underset{\|}{}} \\ H_2C-OCR \\ (\text{diacyl} \\ \text{glyceryl ether}) \end{array}$$

$$\begin{array}{ccc} H_2C-OCH_2R & & H_2C-OCH_2R \\ | & & | \\ \overset{O}{\underset{\|}{}}\ | & & \\ RCO-CH & + & HOCH \\ | & & | \quad \overset{O}{\underset{\|}{}} \\ H_2COH & & H_2C-OCR \end{array}$$

$$\begin{array}{c} H_2C-OCH_2R \\ | \\ + \quad HOCH \qquad + \quad RCOOH \\ | \\ H_2COH \end{array}$$

4. Cleavage of Ether Bonds

Hydriodic acid cleaves alkyl ethers at high temperatures.

$$\begin{array}{l} H_2C-OCH_2R \\ | \\ HOCH \\ | \\ H_2COH \end{array} \quad + \quad HI \longrightarrow RCH_2I + \text{glycerol}$$

(O-alkylglycerol)

Guyer et al. (1963) have used gas–liquid chromatography to measure the alkyl iodides formed by this procedure. However, it is not recommended for structural studies, since HI can attack on either side of double bonds, forming isomeric products (Hanahan, 1965). Enzymes can cleave alkyl glyceryl ethers (Tietz et al., 1964; Pfleger et al., 1967) but they have not yet been purified. Acids readily cleave O-alk-1-enyl bonds to form glycerol and long-chain fatty aldehydes.

$$\begin{array}{l} \quad\quad\quad H \;\; H \\ H_2C-OC{=}CCH_2R \\ | \\ HOCH \\ | \\ H_2COH \end{array} \quad \xrightarrow{[H^+]} \quad \begin{array}{l} O \\ \| \\ RC \\ H \end{array} \;+\; \text{glycerol}$$

(O-alk-1-enylglycerol)

Gas–liquid chromatography is used to analyze the intact fatty aldehydes (Wood and Harlow, 1969) or their dimethyl acetals (Farquhar, 1962). Acid hydrolysis can be carried out in a test tube (Anderson et al., 1969a) or directly on thin-layer chromatograms with acidic fumes or sprays in conjunction with a "separation–reaction–separation" technique (Schmid and Mangold, 1966; Owens, 1966; Horrocks, 1968; Viswanathan et al., 1968a,b).

5. Lipases and Phosphatases

Purified pancreatic lipase hydrolyzes acyl moieties from the 1- and 3-positions of acyl-substituted glycerols (Desnuelle and Savary, 1963; Mattson and Volpenhein, 1961), but contaminants in commercial preparations can cause hydrolysis at the 2-position as well (Mattson and Volpenhein, 1968). Purified pancreatic lipase also removes the acyl group at position 1 of phosphoglycerides (de Haas et al., 1965) but has no effect on the O-alkyl or O-alk-1-enyl moieties. However, diacyl glyceryl ethers do serve as substrates (Snyder and Piantadosi, 1968). The action of lipase on glycerolipids is depicted in Scheme 2. These reactions are useful in structural analyses of glycerolipids, e.g., pancreatic lipase can be used to prepare 1,2-alkylacyl and 1,3-alkylacyl (by presence of H$^+$) derivatives of glycerol from diacyl glyceryl ethers for standards and substrates in metabolic studies (Snyder and Piantadosi, 1968).

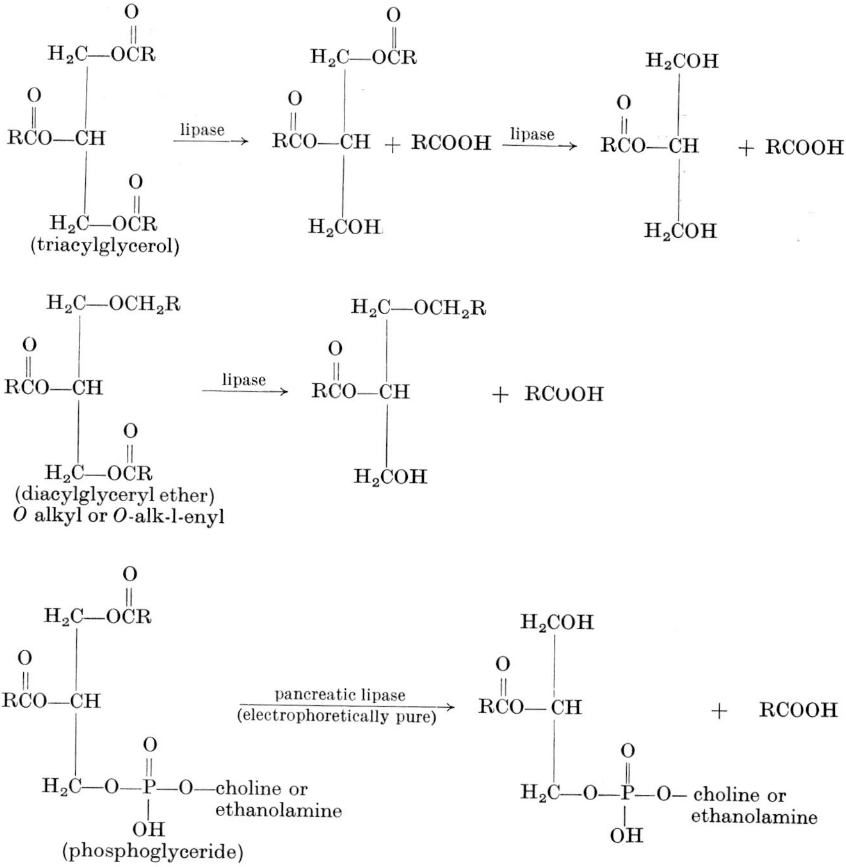

$$
\begin{array}{ccc}
\underset{\text{(triacylglycerol)}}{\begin{array}{c} \overset{O}{\underset{\|}{H_2C-OCR}} \\ \overset{O}{\underset{\|}{RCO-CH}} \\ \overset{O}{\underset{\|}{H_2C-OCR}} \end{array}}
& \xrightarrow{\text{lipase}} &
\begin{array}{c} \overset{O}{\underset{\|}{H_2C-OCR}} \\ \overset{O}{\underset{\|}{RCO-CH}} + RCOOH \\ H_2COH \end{array}
\xrightarrow{\text{lipase}}
\begin{array}{c} H_2COH \\ \overset{O}{\underset{\|}{RCO-CH}} + RCOOH \\ H_2COH \end{array}
\end{array}
$$

$$
\underset{\substack{\text{(diacylglyceryl ether)} \\ O \text{ alkyl or } O\text{-alk-l-enyl}}}{\begin{array}{c} H_2C-OCH_2R \\ \overset{O}{\underset{\|}{RCO-CH}} \\ \overset{O}{\underset{\|}{H_2C-OCR}} \end{array}}
\xrightarrow{\text{lipase}}
\begin{array}{c} H_2C-OCH_2R \\ \overset{O}{\underset{\|}{RCO-CH}} \\ H_2COH \end{array} + RCOOH
$$

$$
\underset{\text{(phosphoglyceride)}}{\begin{array}{c} \overset{O}{\underset{\|}{H_2C-OCR}} \\ \overset{O}{\underset{\|}{RCO-CH}} \\ \underset{\underset{OH}{|}}{H_2C-O-P-O-}\text{choline or}\\ \text{ethanolamine} \end{array}}
\xrightarrow[\text{(electrophoretically pure)}]{\text{pancreatic lipase}}
\begin{array}{c} H_2COH \\ \overset{O}{\underset{\|}{RCO-CH}} \\ \underset{\underset{OH}{|}}{H_2C-O-P-O-}\text{choline or}\\ \text{ethanolamine} \end{array} + RCOOH
$$

SCHEME 2

Specificities of the phospholipases for linkages in phosphoglycerides can be illustrated as follows:

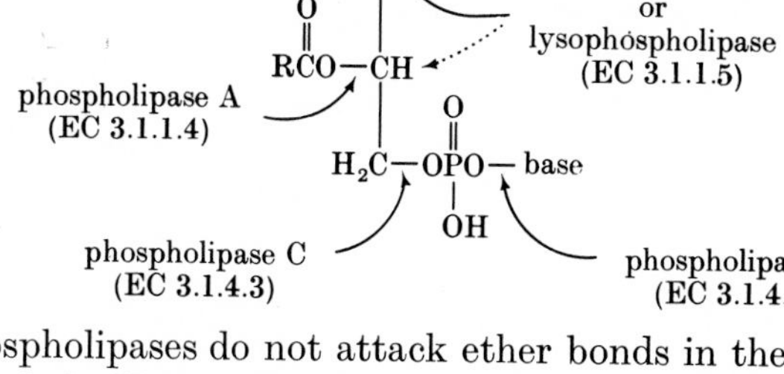

These phospholipases do not attack ether bonds in the 1-position. Van Deenen and de Haas (1966) have written an excellent review on the phospholipases, and there are further details in Ansell and Hawthorne's

(1964) book on phospholipids. Phospholipases are generally sluggish with ether-linked glycerolipids as substrates. Lands and Hart (1965) found that phospholipase D (cabbage) is inert with ether-linked substrates, whereas Hack and Ferrans (1959) and Slotboom (Slotboom *et al.*, 1967; Slotboom, 1968) reported that, under their conditions, it could slowly attack alk-1-enyl phosphoglycerides. In contrast, phospholipase D from *Bacillus cereus* is extremely active with ether-containing lipids under similar conditions (van Golde and van Deenen, 1967).

The author (Snyder *et al.*, 1970d) found that alkaline phosphatase from *Escherichia coli* can remove the phosphate moiety from O-alkyldihydroxyacetone phosphate, which could not be accomplished by alkaline or acid hydrolysis. The reaction proceeds as follows:

$$
\begin{array}{ccc}
\text{H}_2\text{C—OCH}_2\text{R} & & \text{H}_2\text{C—OCH}_2\text{R} \\
| & & | \\
\text{C=O} & \xrightarrow[\text{phosphatase (pH 8.5)}]{\text{bacterial alkaline}} & \text{C=O} \quad + \quad \text{P}_i \\
| & & | \\
\text{H}_2\text{C—O}\,ⓟ & & \text{H}_2\text{COH}
\end{array}
$$

6. Oxidation Reactions

a. Permanganate–Periodate Oxidation. Permanganate–periodate solutions oxidize double bonds and split the carbon-to-carbon bond between two adjacent hydroxyl groups but have no effect on ether bonds (Hanahan *et al.*, 1963). Monocarboxylic acids and dicarboxylic acids are the product.

$$
\begin{array}{l}
\quad\quad\quad\quad\;\; \text{H} \;\; \text{H} \\
\text{H}_2\text{C—O(CH}_2)_8\text{C=C(CH}_2)_7\text{CH}_3 \\
\text{HOCH} \\
| \\
\text{H}_2\text{COH} \\
(O\text{-alkylglycerol})
\end{array}
\quad + \quad \text{KMnO}_4 \quad + \quad
\begin{array}{l}
\text{KIO}_4 \rightarrow \text{CH}_3(\text{CH}_2)_7\text{COOH} \\
\\
+ \quad \text{H}_2\text{C—O(CH}_2)_8\text{COOH} + \text{HCOOH} \\
\quad\quad\; | \\
\quad\quad\; \text{COOH}
\end{array}
$$

The methyl esters of the products can be analyzed by gas-liquid chromatography.

b. Chromic Acid Oxidation. Chromic acid oxidation, in conjunction with gas–liquid chromatographic analysis, can determine the location of double bonds in lipid molecules (Hallgren and Larsson, 1962). A specific example of its application in glyceryl ether analysis is

$$
\begin{array}{l}
\quad\quad\quad\quad \text{H} \;\; \text{H} \\
\text{H}_2\text{C—O(CH}_2)_8\text{C=C(CH}_2)_7\text{CH}_3 \\
\text{H}_3\text{COCH} \\
| \\
\text{H}_2\text{COCH}_3 \\
(\text{dimethoxy-}O\text{-alkylglycerol})
\end{array}
\; + \; \text{H}_2\text{CrO}_4 \longrightarrow
\begin{array}{l}
\text{H}_2\text{C—CO(CH}_2)_8\text{COOH} \\
\text{H}_3\text{COCH} \\
| \\
\text{H}_2\text{COCH}_3
\end{array}
\; + \; \text{CH}_3(\text{CH}_2)_7\text{COOH}
$$

One analyzes the monocarboxylic acids produced as their methyl esters, and the glyceryl ether fragments as their dimethoxy and methyl ester derivatives.

   c. Periodate Oxidation. Periodate oxidation of glyceryl ethers containing two adjacent hydroxyl groups produces formaldehyde and an acetaldehyde derivative containing an alkyl ether moiety:

$$
\begin{array}{c}
H_2C\text{---}OCH_2R \\
| \\
HOCH \\
| \\
H_2COH \\
(O\text{-alkylglycerol})
\end{array}
\quad + \quad HIO_4 \quad \longrightarrow \quad
\begin{array}{c}
H_2C\text{---}OCH_2R \\
| \\
HC{=}O
\end{array}
\quad + \quad H_2C{=}O
$$

This reaction has been used to measure colorimetrically the glycerol liberated from lipids—chromatropic acid forms a colored complex with the formaldehyde (Karnovsky and Brumm, 1955). The acetaldehyde containing the ether-linked aliphatic moiety is analyzed directly by gas–liquid chromatography (Mangold and Baumann, 1967).

   Periodate oxidation of O-alkyldihydroxyacetone produces O-alkyl glycolic acid which can be reduced by $LiAlH_4$ to the O-alkyl ethylene glycol (Snyder *et al.*, 1970d). The acetate of the glycol is isolated by gas–liquid chromatography. These reactions are essential for identifying the ketone intermediates involved in the biosynthesis of glyceryl ethers.

   d. Ozonolysis. The aliphatic ether moieties of naturally occurring glyceryl ethers are almost exclusively saturated or monoenoic (Snyder, 1969b), and this has simplified the task of determining the location of double bonds in such molecules. Ozonolysis and reduction (Adams catalyst) procedures determine the location of double bonds in fatty acids (Privett and Nickell, 1962) and ether-linked side chains (Snyder and Blank, 1969; Ramachandran *et al.*, 1968). The reductive-ozonolysis reaction for an isopropylidene derivative of a glyceryl ether is

$$
\begin{array}{c}
\overset{H\ \ H}{H_2C\text{---}O(CH_2)_8C{=}C(CH_2)_7CH_3} \\
HC\diagdown^{O}\diagdown_{}CH_3 \\
\diagup C \\
H_2C\diagdown_{O}\diagup \diagdown CH_3
\end{array}
\quad + \quad O_3 \quad \longrightarrow \quad \overset{H_2}{\longrightarrow} \quad
\begin{array}{c}
H_2C\text{---}O(CH_2)_8CHO \\
HC\diagdown^{O}\diagdown_{}CH_3 \\
\diagup C \\
H_2C\diagdown_{O}\diagup\diagdown CH_3
\end{array}
$$

$$+$$
$$CH_3(CH_2)_7CHO$$

(isopropylidene of
O-alkylglycerol)

The isopropylidene derivatives of the glyceryl ether aldehyde fragments and the fatty aldehyde fragments are analyzed by gas–liquid chromatography. Ramachandran *et al.* (1968) have applied reductive ozonolysis to determine the location of double bonds in alkyl iodides after hydriodic acid cleavage of the ether linkage in glyceryl ethers. The number of double bonds in *O*-alk-1-enyl chains can be measured in the acids or alcohols formed from the aldehydes liberated by acid hydrolysis.

B. Derivatives of Functional Groups in Glycerolipids

In general, it is necessary to prepare derivatives of functional groups of lipids for gas–liquid chromatography and other identification purposes. Hydroxyl groups can form acetates, trifluoroacetates, and trimethylsilyl ethers; these derivatives are useful in the analysis of partial glycerides (Wood *et al.*, 1965), glyceryl ethers (Blomstrand and Gürtler, 1959; Wood and Snyder, 1966), hydroxy fatty acids (Radin, 1965), and fatty alcohols (VandenHeuvel *et al.*, 1965). Acetone can react with adjacent hydroxyl groups to form isopropylidene derivatives, which are useful in the analysis of glyceryl ethers (Hanahan *et al.*, 1963) and hydroxy fatty acids (Wood, 1967). Hallgren and Larsson (1962) prepared dimethoxy derivatives of such compounds. Typical derivatives of hydroxy compounds are structures I–V.

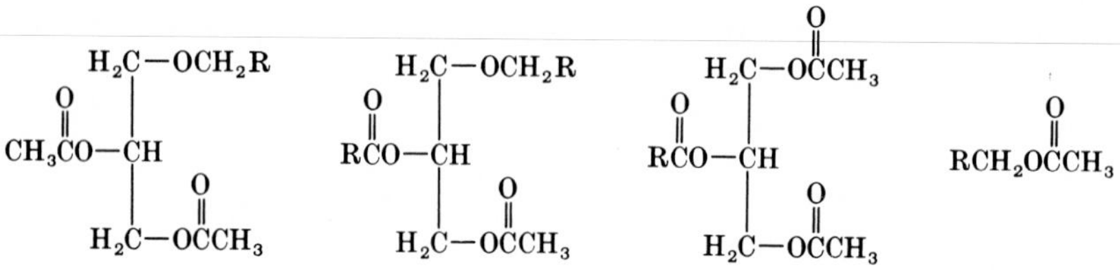

(acetates)
I

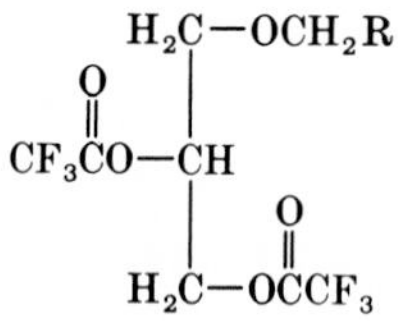

(trifluoroacetates)
II

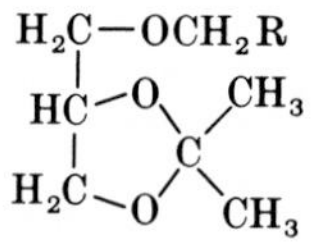

(isopropylidenes)
III

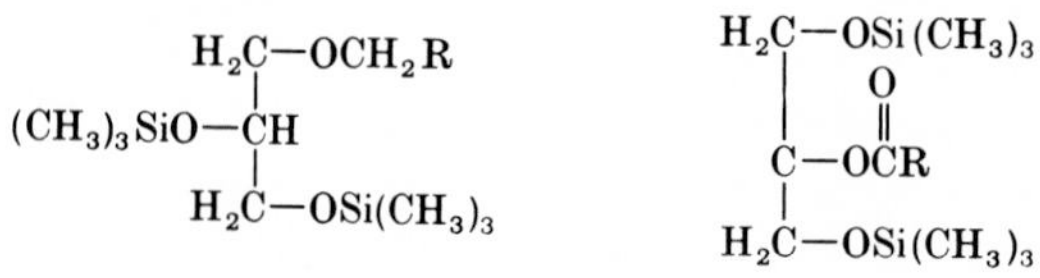

(trimethylsilyl ethers)
IV

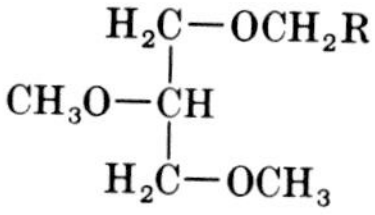

$$H_2C-OCH_2R$$
$$CH_3O-CH$$
$$H_2C-OCH_3$$

(dimethoxy derivative)
V

Direct or transesterification can methylate carboxyl groups, forming methyl esters.

$$O$$
$$\|$$
$$RCH_2C-OCH_3$$
(methyl ester)

This reaction can be either acid- (James, 1960) or base-catalyzed (Morgan et al., 1963). The methyl esters of fatty acids are readily resolved by gas–liquid chromatography.

Alkyl iodide derivatives (RCH_2I) obtained from glyceryl ethers by the cleavage of O-alkyl bonds with hydriodic acid are also useful in gas–liquid chromatographic analysis (Guyer et al., 1963).

Many workers have used dimethyl acetals of long-chain fatty aldehydes in gas–liquid chromatographic analysis. These derivatives are prepared by refluxing the aldehydes or total lipids containing O-alk-1-enyl groups with methanolic hydrogen chloride (Farquhar, 1962). The reaction proceeds as follows:

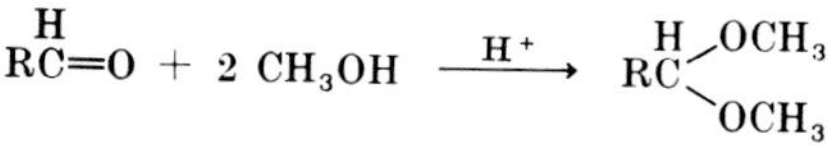

$$RC{=}O + 2\ CH_3OH \xrightarrow{\ H^+\ } RC\langle{}^{OCH_3}_{OCH_3}$$

Methyl esters of the fatty acids liberated also form, but the difference in polarity and retention time between methyl esters and dimethyl acetals is generally sufficient for resolution.

Fatty aldehydes derived from alk-1-enyl glyceryl ethers are reduced by $LiAlH_4$ to fatty alcohols; the acetates of the fatty alcohols can be analyzed by gas-liquid chromatography. Chromic acid oxidizes aldehydes to acids, but this procedure is not satisfactory with unsaturated compounds, since it degrades the unsaturated chains (Gray, 1967).

IV. Biochemical Studies of Lipids in Neoplasms

A. Enzymic Pathways for Glycerolipids and Their Precursors

1. Enzymic Synthesis of Glycerolipids

a. Acylglycerol Lipids. Glycerolipids with acyl moieties originate from a-glycerophosphate (Kennedy, 1953) and under some conditions from dihydroxyacetone-P (Hajra, 1968). The reactions are illustrated in

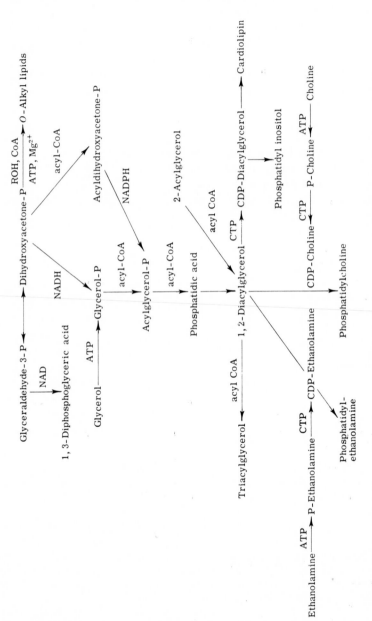

Fig. 4. The biosynthesis of acyl glycerolipids. NAD—nicotinamide adenine dinucleotide; ATP—adenosine triphosphate; CTP—cytidine triphosphate; CoA—coenzyme A; NADPH—reduced nicotinamide adenine dinucleotide phosphate; CDP—cytidine diphosphate.

Fig. 4. The phosphatidic acid and diacylglycerols depicted in this figure are key intermediates in the biosynthesis of triglycerides and phosphoglycerides. The thiokinase activates the fatty acids as coenzyme A (CoA) derivatives (Kornberg and Pricer, 1953), and the acyl transferases catalyze the essential acylation steps. Cytidine derivatives of P-choline or P-ethanolamine (Kennedy and Weiss, 1956) and cytidine diphosphate diglyceride (Kiyasu *et al.*, 1960) are required for the formation of phosphoglycerides. Rossiter (1968) has reviewed the metabolism of phospholipids.

b. O-Alkylglycerol Lipids. The author and colleagues, Snyder *et al.*, 1970a,d) have recently elucidated the formation of ether bonds in glycerolipids. The enzymic system was first isolated from neoplasms (Snyder *et al.*, 1969b,c; Wykle and Snyder, 1969b; Wykle and Snyder, 1969a) and then found in some normal cells (Snyder *et al.*, 1969a,

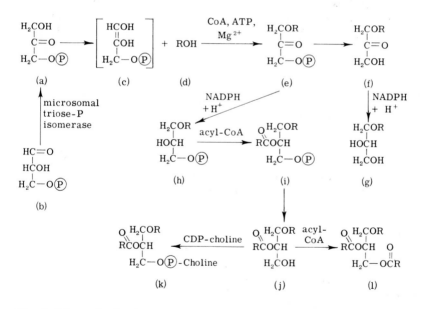

FIG. 5. Biosynthesis of *O*-alkyl lipids. The compounds depicted in the scheme are (a) dihydroxyacetone-P; (b) *O*-glyceraldehyde-3-P; (c) enol form of compounds (a) and (b); (d) long-chain fatty alcohol; (e) *O*-alkyldihydroxyacetone-P; (f) *O*-alkyldihydroxyacetone; (g) *O*-alkylglycerol; (h) *O*-alkylglycerol-P; (i) *O*-alkyl analog of phosphatidic acid; (j) 1-*O*-alkyl 2-acylglycerol; (k) *O*-alkyl choline phosphoglyceride; and (l) diacyl glyceryl ether. ATP—adenosine triphosphate; CoA—coenzyme A; NADPH—reduced nicotinamide adenine dinucleotide phosphate; CDP—cytidine diphosphate.

1970b; Kapoulas and Thompson, 1969; Friedberg and Greene, 1969; Hajra, 1969). The reaction between long-chain fatty alcohols and dihydroxyacetone-P, catalyzed by microsomal enzymes, yields O-alkyl lipids (Fig. 5) only when CoA, adenosine triphosphate (ATP), and Mg^{++} are present as cofactors. A microsomal reductase and reduced nicotinamide adenine dinucleotide phosphate (NADPH) reduce the O-alkyl-dihydroxyacetone-P and O-alkyldihydroxyacetone synthesized in this system. The cell-free system requires cytidine diphosphate choline or cytidine diphosphate ethanolamine for the biosynthesis of O-alkyl phospholipids (Snyder et al., 1970e). Acylation of alkyl glyceryl ethers occurs in vivo and in vitro (see review by Snyder, 1969b). Cell-free systems isolated from numerous tissues acylate 1-O-alkylglycerols in the 3-position only (Snyder et al., 1970c). Acylation of the 2-position on the 1-isomer of alkyl glyceryl ethers only occurs when a phosphate moiety is in the 3-position (Snyder et al., 1970d).

c. *O-Alk-1-enylglycerol Lipids.* No one has yet found a cell-free system that synthesizes plasmalogens. Data obtained in vivo suggest that O-alkyl bonds are direct precursors of plasmalogens (Thompson, 1968; Keenan et al., 1961; Friedberg and Greene, 1967; Horrocks and Ansell,

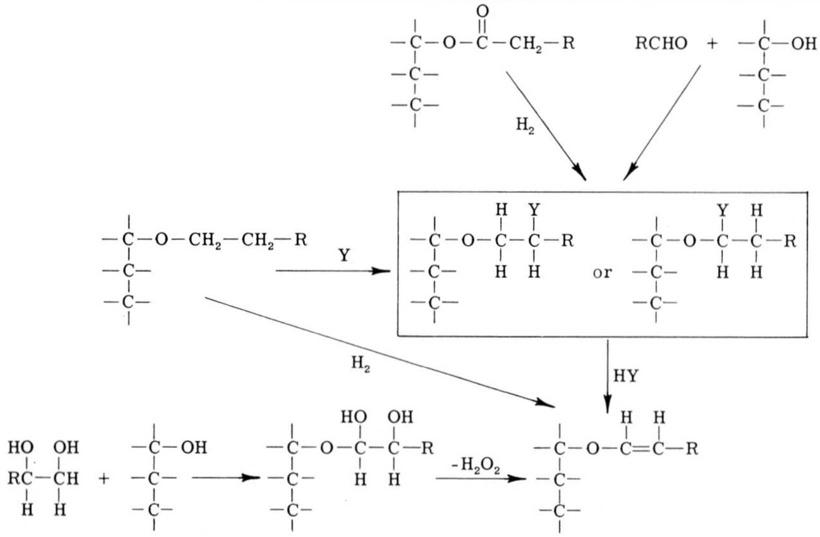

FIG. 6. Possible routes for the biosynthesis of plasmalogens. The 2-position of the glycerolipid molecule could contain a hydroxyl or acyl group and the 3-position could contain a phosphate or phosphoryl base group. The Y moiety designates a hydroxyl, methoxy, amino, or other substituted group on the O-alkyl chain.

1967; Wood and Healy, 1970; Wykle *et al.*, 1970; Blank *et al.*, 1970), but fatty acids (Bickerstaffe and Mead, 1967) and fatty aldehydes (Ellingboe and Karnovsky, 1967; Hagen and Goldfine, 1967; Bell and White, 1968) have also been implicated as precursors of the O-alk-1-enyl moiety. Figure 6 shows several possible routes for plasmalogen biosynthesis.

Acylation reactions of O-alk-1-enyl-linked lipids do occur. For example, 1-O-alk-1-enyl glycero-3-phosphorylcholine is a substrate for acyl-CoA–phospholipid transferase in erythrocytes from humans and in sarcoplasmic reticulum from rabbits (Waku and Lands, 1968); however, this reaction does not occur in microsomes of rat liver (Lands and Hart, 1965). Kiyasu and Kennedy (1960) reported that a particulate fraction of rat liver could catalyze the transfer of cytidine diphosphate choline or cytidine diphosphate ethanolamine to 1-O-alk-1-enyl-2-acylglycerols. These reactions indicate that the transferases involved cannot distinguish between acyl and alk-1-enyl substituents on the substrates. Others have confirmed these experiments in homogenates of brain (McMurray, 1964) and in a particulate fraction from ox heart (Poulos *et al.*, 1968).

2. Enzymic Degradation of Glycerolipids

a. Acylglycerol Lipids. Lipase and phospholipases remove acyl moeities of lipids. Pancreatic lipase hydrolyzes acyl moieties from the 1- and 3-positions of glycerolipids (Snyder and Piantadosi, 1968) and the 1-position of phosphoglycerides unless contaminating enzymes are present (de Haas *et al.*, 1965). Phospholipase A catalyzes the hydrolysis of fatty acids from the 2-position of phosphoglycerides, and phospholipase B is thought to catalyze the hydrolysis from both the 1- and 2-positions or only from lysophosphoglycerides. The dual specificity of phospholipase B might be due to phospholipase A contamination. Other phospholipases can catalyze the hydrolysis of the entire phosphoryl-base moiety (phospholipase C) or the base portion only (phospholipase D). These lipolytic reactions are thought to occur in most living cells. (For details, see Ansell and Hawthorne, 1964, and Section III,A,5 of this chapter.)

b. O-Alkylglycerol Lipids. Enzymes in rat liver (Tietz *et al.*, 1964) and in some other mammalian cells (Pfleger *et al.*, 1967) can cleave O-alkyl bonds; neoplastic cells appear to lack this enzyme (Soodsma *et al.*, 1970). The reaction depicted requires molecular oxygen, tetrahydropteridine, and NADPH as cofactors, and the products are glycerol and fatty aldehydes.

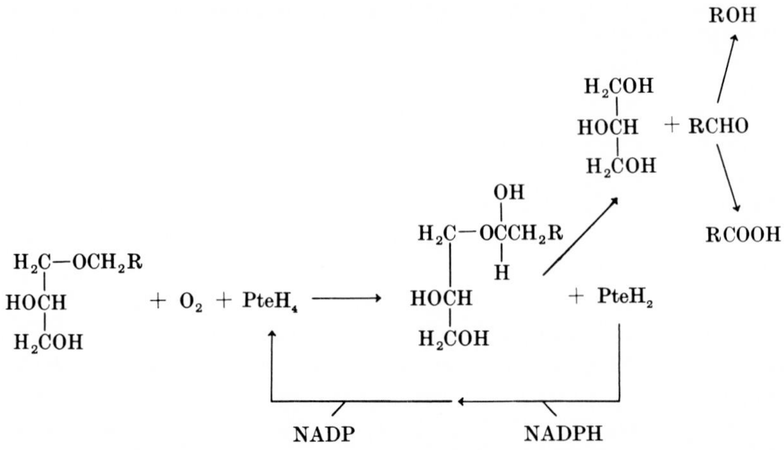

$$
\begin{array}{c}
H_2COH \\
| \\
HOCH \quad + \ RCHO \\
| \\
H_2COH
\end{array}
\nearrow \quad \xrightarrow{\quad} \quad ROH
$$

The reaction scheme:

$$
\begin{array}{ccc}
H_2C-OCH_2R & & \overset{OH}{\underset{H}{H_2C-OCCH_2R}} \\
| & & | \\
HOCH & + \ O_2 + PteH_4 \longrightarrow & HOCH \quad + \ PteH_2 \\
| & & | \\
H_2COH & & H_2COH
\end{array}
$$

ROH

+ RCHO

RCOOH

NADP   NADPH

The fatty aldehydes are rapidly converted to fatty acids in the presence of nicotinamide adenine dinucleotide (NAD), but fatty aldehydes and fatty alcohols form when NAD is absent. Acylated glyceryl ethers serve as substrates for pancreatic lipase, which does not attack the ether bond (Snyder and Piantadosi, 1968).

c. O-Alk-1-enylglycerol Lipids. Enzymes from liver (Warner and Lands, 1961) and brain (Ansell and Spanner, 1965) can catalyze the cleavage of ether bonds in plasmalogens.

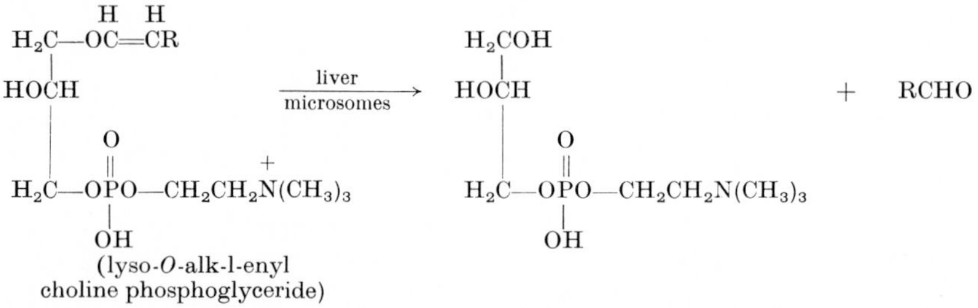

$$
\begin{array}{ccc}
\overset{H \ \ H}{H_2C-OC=CR} & & H_2COH \\
| & & | \\
HOCH & \xrightarrow[\text{microsomes}]{\text{liver}} & HOCH \qquad\qquad + \quad RCHO \\
| & & | \\
\underset{OH}{H_2C-O\overset{O}{\overset{||}{P}}O-CH_2CH_2N(CH_3)_3} & + & \underset{OH}{H_2C-O\overset{O}{\overset{||}{P}}O-CH_2CH_2N(CH_3)_3}
\end{array}
$$

(lyso-*O*-alk-1-enyl
choline phosphoglyceride)

The microsomal enzyme in liver uses 1-*O*-alk-1-enyl glycerylphosphorylcholine alone as substrate; no other cofactors are required. However, phospholipids are important in reactivating alk-1-enyl glycerylphosphorylcholine hydrolase (Ellingson and Lands, 1968).

Acetone powders of brain contain an enzyme similar to the one found in the liver preparation; but it hydrolyzes 1-*O*-alk-1-enyl-2-acyl-glycerylphosphorylethanolamine, although the lyso derivative is also attacked to a lesser extent (Mg^{++} was required as a cofactor).

$$
\begin{array}{ccc}
\overset{\text{H H}}{H_2C-OC=CR} & & H_2COH \\[4pt]
\underset{RCO-CH}{\overset{O}{\overset{\|}{}}} & \xrightarrow[\text{(acetone powder)}]{\text{brain}} & \underset{RCO-CH}{\overset{O}{\overset{\|}{}}} \quad\quad + \quad RCHO \\[4pt]
\underset{OH}{H_2C-O\overset{O}{\overset{\|}{P}}O-CH_2CH_2NH_2} & & \underset{OH}{H_2C-O\overset{O}{\overset{\|}{P}}O-CH_2CH_2NH_2}
\end{array}
$$

(O-alk-1-enyl ethanolamine
phosphoglyceride)

Thiele (1959) has also reported nonspecific enzymic cleavage of ether bonds in plasmalogens. All the phospholipases can use O-alk-1-enyl phosphatides as substrates under certain conditions, but generally the reaction rates are slower than when the diacyl analogs are used as substrates (Snyder, 1969b).

3. Metabolism of Glycerolipid Precursors

a. *Glycero-3-phosphate and Dihydroxyacetone Phosphate.* Glycerol can be phosphorylated by ATP with glycerokinase (Kennedy, 1953; Bublitz and Kennedy, 1954), an enzyme present in liver, heart, kidney, intestines, and lactating mammary glands, but absent in adipose tissue or muscle. However, in tissues that lack glycerokinase, α-glycerophosphate dehydrogenase reduces dihydroxyacetone-P to glycerophosphate with reduced NAD (NADH) (Meyerhof and Kiessling, 1933).

Aldolase forms dihydroxyacetone-P from fructose-1,6-diphosphate during glycolysis. The other triose-P produced, D-glyceraldehyde-3-P, is in equilibrium with the dihydroxyacetone-P under the influence of triose-P isomerase (Meyerhof et al., 1936a,b). However, this equilibrium favors the dihydroxyacetone-P formation by approximately 96 to 4 for triose-P isomerase in Ehrlich ascites cells, even though more glyceraldehyde-3-P is found in the intact cells (Garfinkel and Hess, 1964). Glyceraldehyde-3-P dehydrogenase (NAD-dependent) oxidizes the glyceraldehyde-3-P to 1,3-diphosphoglyceric acid; the dihydroxyacetone-P (via triose-P isomerase) is also oxidized by this mechanism.

The enzymes responsible for these interconversions (Fig. 4) are located in the soluble protein fraction of the cytoplasm. However, significant quantities of triose-P isomerase, apparently not a contaminant, have been found in mitochondria (Boxer and Shonk, 1960) and microsomes (Rao et al., 1968; Wykle and Snyder, 1969b). 1-Hydroxy-3-chloro-2-propanone phosphate (Hartman, 1968, 1970) and glycidol phosphate (Rose and O'Connell, 1969) are effective inhibitors of this P-isomerase. The 1-hydroxy-3-chloro-2-propanone phosphate has been extremely useful in studies of lipid metabolism (Wykle and Snyder, 1969b).

b. Fatty Acids. Fatty acids are synthesized by two separate systems (Green and Allmann, 1968a). Mitochondria synthesize fatty acids by an enzymic sequence similar to, but in the reverse direction of, the reactions involved in β-oxidation; elongation of existing fatty acids occurs, and ATP, NADH, and NADPH are the cofactor requirements. However, the main site of fatty acid synthesis is in the soluble portion of the cell, where fatty acid synthetases catalyze the formation of palmitic acid from acetyl CoA and malonyl CoA; NADPH, ATP, Mn^{++}, and bicarbonate are the cofactor requirements. The fatty acid synthetase in mammals is a multienzyme complex that contains bound 4'-phosphopantetheine as an acyl-group carrier. The protein-bound sulfhydryl grouping is called acyl carrier protein (ACP). In lower forms of life, the ACP can be dissociated from the synthetase and can participate as a substrate in lipid synthesis, but in mammals the fatty acids must be hydrolyzed from ACP before they can be metabolized.

Enzymes that oxidize fatty acids two carbons at a time (β-oxidation) are located in mitochondria (Green and Allmann, 1968b). A fatty acid can be oxidized completely to acetyl-CoA units that can then be enzymically converted to CO_2 and water via the tricarboxylic acid cycle. Complete β-oxidation of palmitic acid produces ninety-six high-energy bonds. Fatty acids are also degraded by α-oxidation and ω-oxidation; both pathways are relatively minor compared to β-oxidation in liver (Antony and Landau, 1969).

c. Interconversions of Fatty Acids, Fatty Aldehydes, and Fatty Alcohols. Very few data are available on the interconversions of fatty acids, fatty aldehydes, and fatty alcohols. No cell-free systems for these interconversions have been reported in mammals except those occurring during the biocleavage of glyceryl ethers (Tietz *et al.*, 1964; Pfleger *et al.*, 1967). However, Kolattukudy (1970) has recently reported a cell-free system from *Euglena gracilis* that reduces long chain fatty acids to fatty alcohols. Sand and Schlenk (1969) have found reactions in fishes that converted fatty acids to fatty alcohols.

4. Regulation of Glycerolipids in Tumors

Essentially nothing is known about regulatory mechanisms that influence glycerolipids in tumors. Tissue cultures appear to be useful systems for investigating regulatory factors that control the distribution of the acyl, O-alkyl, and O-alk-1-enyl moieties attached to glycerol. Fibroblasts grown in suspension cultures accumulate the ether-linked lipids (Anderson *et al.*, 1969b), but the same cells grown in monolayers do not (Cheng *et al.*, 1967). Disorders in feedback control of precursors,

intermediates, or products need to be considered in the metabolism of
ether-linked lipids in neoplastic cells, since other studies indicate that
feedback regulation involved in cholesterol metabolism (Siperstein,
1966) and lipogenesis (Elwood and Morris, 1968) is absent in hepatomas.

B. Lipid Characteristics of Neoplastic Cells

1. Glycerolipids

Many investigations have dealt with glycerolipids of neoplastic cells
and other tissues of animals bearing tumors (Haven and Bloor, 1956;
Lopez, 1956; Kamimae, 1958; Serra, 1960; Galanos and Mitropoulos,
1961; Lettre, 1964; Snyder, 1970a). The only consistent pattern so far
is that diacyl glyceryl ethers (Figs. 7 and 8) and other ether-linked lipids

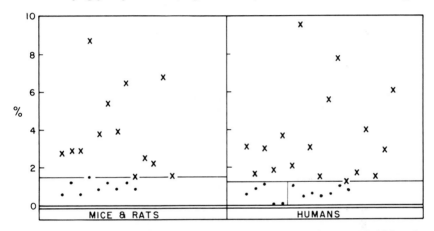

Fig. 7. The percentage of O-alkyl-linked lipids in the total neutral lipid fraction
of a variety of normal (black dots) and neoplastic (crosses) tissues from mice,
rats, and humans. Each value of total glyceryl ethers is for a different normal
tissue or tumor. (For the detailed analysis of the samples summarized in this chart,
see Snyder and Wood, 1968, 1969.) The horizontal lines drawn between 1.5 and
2.0% designate an arbitrary separation of the values for normal tissues and tumors.

are elevated in cancer cells. Present evidence indicates that the glyceryl
ether lipids are closely associated with neoplasia and cell transformation
to the extent that they may be considered a marker for malignant
tumors. Snyder and co-workers (1966) used saponification and thin-
layer chromatography of total lipid extracts from rat or mouse tumors
and from a human lymphosarcoma and found high levels of diacyl
glyceryl ethers. More rigorous procedures characterized these compounds
in Ehrlich ascites cells (Wood and Snyder, 1967b) and in the Walker-256
tumor and the human lymphosarcoma (Bollinger, 1967). The general
pattern of high quantities of diacyl glyceryl ethers (and ether-linked

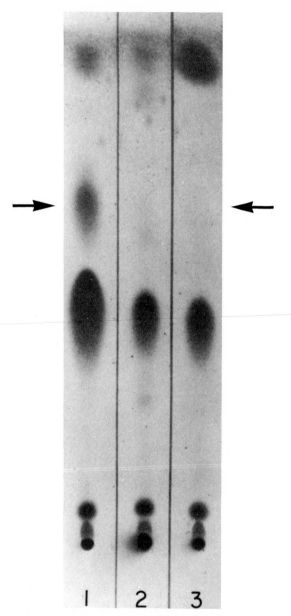

Fig. 8. A typical thin-layer chromatogram of total lipid extracts from a neoplasm (lane 1—Walker 256 carcinosarcoma), normal liver (lane 2), and normal blood (lane 3). The arrows designate the location of the diacyl-*O*-alkylglycerols (glyceryl ether diesters). The area directly below the arrows represents the R_f of triacylglycerols (triglycerides). The solvent system used for development of the chromatogram was hexane–diethyl ether (90:10, v/v) and the adsorbent was silica gel G.

phosphoglycerides) was later substantiated in a wide variety of tumors from animals (Snyder and Wood, 1968) and humans (Snyder and Wood, 1969). High levels of ether-linked lipids are also found in fibroblasts grown in suspension cultures (Anderson *et al.*, 1969b). Normal tissues (Wood and Snyder, 1968) and tissues undergoing rapid cellular proliferation (embryonic tissues, regenerating liver, or pouch granulomas; unpublished data) do contain some ether-linked lipids, but not to the same extent as neoplasms. The higher level of diacyl glyceryl ethers and ether-linked phosphoglycerides occurs only in Morris hepatomas that have fast growth rates (Snyder *et al.*, 1969d).

Neoplastic tissues also contain high levels of ether-linked phosphoglycerides but their presence is not a marker as the ether-linked neutral lipids are. The O-alkyl and O-alk-1-enyl glyceryl ethers (Fig. 3) of both normal and neoplastic cells consist mainly of 16:0, 18:0, and 18:1 O-hydrocarbon moieties (Snyder, 1969c). In view of the precursor role of long-chain fatty alcohols in the biosynthesis of O-alkyl lipids, it is significant that much higher levels of fatty alcohols have been found in neoplasms than in normal tissues (Blank and Snyder, 1970). The fatty alcohols and the O-alkyl groups of the glyceryl ethers contained similar carbon chains (16:0, 18:0, and 18:1) (see Fig. 3). The role that ether-linked lipids play in living cells is not known, although those that exist as phospholipids appear to be important structural components of membranes. On the other hand, the high levels of diacyl glyceryl ethers in neoplastic cells might simply reflect the extreme "reductive" state of tumor cells since the formation of fatty alcohols (from fatty acids) and of glyceryl ethers requires hydrogen transfer reactions via NADPH. Such reactions provide a mechanism for oxidizing NADPH at the substrate level. Several reviews have covered the biochemistry of O-alkyl and O-alk-1-enyl lipids (Rapport and Norton, 1962; Hanahan and Thompson, 1963; Klenk and Debuch, 1963; Goldfine, 1968; Snyder, 1969b; Piantadosi and Snyder, 1970).

2. Characteristics of Lipids Not Containing Glycerol

a. *Malignolipin* (Kosaki *et al.*, 1958). This poorly defined compound was thought for a number of years to be a unique lipid of tumors and certain tissues of tumor-bearing animals. Kosaki and co-workers (1958) originally proposed that the structure of malignolipin was

$$(CH_3)_3N-(CH_2)_2-O-\overset{\overset{\displaystyle O}{\|}}{\underset{\underset{\displaystyle OH}{|}}{P}}-NH(CH_2)_3-\underset{\underset{\displaystyle COR}{|}}{N}-(CH_2)_4NH(CH_2)_4NH(CH_2)_3NH_2$$

(with OH on the first carbon)

since they found phosphoric acid, choline, spermine, and fatty acid to be present in equimolar amounts. Many papers have been published on malignolipin (see bibliography compiled by Snyder, 1970a). However,

Petering *et al.* (1967) found that malignolipin was a heterogeneous mixture of compounds consisting of lipid (ranging up to C_{24} fatty acids) loosely associated with three amines. One of the amines was L(+)-glutamic acid and another appeared to be aspartic acid, but none of the purified amines contained phosphorus; picrates of the amines or intact malignolipin contained sodium and potassium. Petering and co-workers (1967) were also unable to confirm the antigenicity or validity of the blood tests originally attributed to malignolipin.

b. Cytolipin H. Immunologically active lipids have been isolated from tumor tissues (Rapport and Graf, 1955; Rapport *et al.*, 1955, 1958a,b,c, 1959, 1960, 1961, 1964; Hakim, 1956, 1959; Rapport and Graf, 1957; Graf *et al.*, 1961; Graf and Rapport, 1961; Rapport, 1962; Witz, 1964; Hakomori *et al.*, 1967), but they are also found in certain healthy tissues. A large effort in the search for immunologically active lipids in malignant cells has centered on cytolipin H; it has been characterized as a glycosphingolipid, containing residues of fatty acids, sphingosine, glucose, and galactose (Rapport *et al.*, 1959).

c. Carcinolipin. Hradec and Stroufová (1960) have reported that a carcinogenic sterol esterified with a branch chain fatty acid, "carcinolipin," occurs as a natural constituent of tissues. Carcinolipin was originally found in egg yolks (Hradec, 1958), and its name was coined because of its carcinogenic properties (Hradec and Kruml, 1960). It stimulates the incorporation of amino acids into microsomal proteins; this appears to be characteristic of many carcinogenic substances (Hradec, 1961). Hradec and Dolejš (1968) recently identified carcinolipin as cholesteryl methyl hexadecanoate.

3. Biomembranes

Our knowledge of the lipids of membranes comprising cell surfaces and organelles has revealed little about their specific functions except that they are important structural components (Rothfield and Finkelstein, 1968; Fleischer and Rouser, 1965). Khadzhiolov (1965) has recently reviewed intracellular membranes and carcinogenesis, in Russian. Wallach *et al.* (1960) concluded that the individual phosphatides in the organelles of Ehrlich ascites cells were not distinctive from those found in normal cells. However, Bergelson and co-workers (1968) obtained data suggesting that the specificities of phospholipids in organelles (Fleischer and Rouser, 1965) is lost in cancer cells. Theise and Bielka (1968) reported that the lipids of microsomes from normal rat liver and hepatomas differ quantitatively but not qualitatively; the microsomes of hepatomas contained less phospholipids than did those of normal liver although they contained greater proportions of aminophosphatides and plasmalogens. So far, no specific patterns of lipids have evolved from these limited studies on the lipid composition of organelles in tumors, but it is possible that differences between the membrane systems of normal and cancer cells reflect the invasive character of malignant cells (Abercrombie and Ambrose, 1962).

Ether-linked glycerolipids are found in membranes (Pfleger *et al.*, 1968; Cotman *et al.*, 1969), and the author and co-workers (Pfleger *et al.*, 1968) have speculated that the ether bond might be important to the stability and orientation of lipid protein configurations in biomembranes. The high levels of ether lipids in neoplastic cells might thus permit them to withstand otherwise hostile environments.

REFERENCES

Abercrombie, M., and Ambrose, E. J. (1962). *Cancer Res.* **22**, 525.

Anderson, R. E., Garrett, R. D., Blank, M. L., and Snyder, F. (1969a). *Lipids* **4**, 327.

Anderson, R. E., Cumming, R. B., Walton, M., and Snyder, F. (1969b). *Biochim. Biophys. Acta* **176**, 491.

Ansell, G. B., and Hawthorne, J. N. (1964). *In* "Phospholipids—Chemistry, Metabolism and Function," Vol. III. Elsevier, New York.

Ansell, G. B., and Spanner, S. (1965). *Biochem. J.* **94**, 252.

Antony, G. J., and Landau, B. R. (1969). *J. Lipid Res.* **9**, 267.

Bell, O. E., Jr., and White, H. B., Jr. (1968). *Biochim. Biophys. Acta* **164**, 441.

Bergelson, L. D., Dyatlovitskaya, E. V., Torkhovskaya, T. I., Sorokina, I. B., and Gorkova, N. P. (1968). *Fed. Eur. Biochem. Soc. Lett.* **2**, 87.

Bevan, T. H., Brown, D. A., Gregory, G. I., and Malkin, T. (1953). *J. Chem. Soc. London*, p. 127.

Bickerstaffe, R., and Mead, J. F. (1967). *Biochemistry* **6**, 655.

Blank, M. L., and Snyder, F. (1970). *Lipids* **5**, 337.

Blank, M. L., Wykle, R. L., Piantadosi, C., and Snyder, F. (1970). *Proc. Amer. Assoc. Cancer Res.* **11**, 9.

Bligh, E. G., and Dyer, W. J. (1959). *Can. J. Biochem. Physiol.* **37**, 911.

Blomstrand, R., and Gürtler, J. (1959). *Acta Chem. Scand.* **13**, 1466.

Bloor, W. R. (1915). *J. Biol. Chem.* **22**, 133.

Bobbitt, J. M. (1963). "Thin-Layer Chromatography." Reinhold, New York.

Bollinger, J. (1967). *Lipids* **2**, 143.

Borgström, B. (1952). *Acta Physiol. Scand.* **25**, 101.

Boxer, G. E., and Shonk, C. E. (1960). *Biochim. Biophys. Acta* **37**, 194.

Brante, G. (1949). *Acta Physiol. Scand.* **18**, Suppl. 63.

Bublitz, C., and Kennedy, E. P. (1954). *J. Biol. Chem.* **211**, 851.

Carter, H. E., Smith, D. B., and Jones, D. N. (1958). *J. Biol. Chem.* **232**, 681.

Cheng, S., Piantadosi, C., and Snyder, F. (1967). *Lipids* **2**, 193.

Cotman, C., Blank, M. L., Moehl, A., and Snyder, F. (1969). *Biochemistry*, **8**, 4606.

Davenport, J. B., and Dawson, R. M. C. (1961). *Biochem. J.* **79**, 10P.

Dawson, R. M. C. (1960). *Biochem. J.* **75**, 45.

Dawson, R. M. C., Hemington, N., and Davenport, J. B. (1962). *Biochem. J.* **84**, 497.

de Haas, G. H., Sarda, L., and Roger, J. (1965). *Biochim. Biophys. Acta* **106**, 638.

Desnuelle, P., and Savary, P. (1963). *J. Lipid Res.* **4**, 369.

Deuel, H. J., Jr. (1951). "The Lipids: Their Chemistry and Biochemistry," Vol. I. Wiley (Interscience), New York.

Ellingboe, J., and Karnovsky, M. L. (1967). *J. Biol. Chem.* **242**, 5693.

Ellingson, J. S., and Lands, W. E. M. (1968). *Lipids* **3**, 111.

Elwood, J. C., and Morris, H. P. (1968). *J. Lipid. Res.* **9**, 337.

Entenman, C. (1961). *J. Amer. Oil Chem. Soc.* **38**, 534.

Farquhar, J. W. (1962). *J. Lipid Res.* **3**, 21.

Fleischer, S., and Rouser, G. (1965). *J. Amer. Oil Chem. Soc.* **42**, 588.

Folch, J., Ascoli, I., Lees, M., Meath, J. A., and LeBaron, F. N. (1951). *J. Biol. Chem.* **191**, 833.

Folch, J., Lees, M., and Sloane Stanley, G. H. (1957). *J. Biol. Chem.* **226**, 497.

Friedberg, S. J., and Greene, R. C. (1967). *J. Biol. Chem.* **242**, 5709.

Friedberg, S. J., and Greene, R. C. (1969). *J. Amer. Oil Chem. Soc.* **46**(8), Abstr. No. 82.

Galanos, D. S., and Mitropoulos, K. A. (1961). *Chim. Chon.* **26**, 42.

Garfinkel, D., and Hess, B. (1964). *J. Biol. Chem.* **239**, 971.

Goldfine, H. (1968). *Annu. Rev. Biochem.* **37**, 303.

Graf, L., and Rapport, M. M. (1961). *Cancro* **14**, 415.

Graf, L., Rapport, M. M., and Brandt, R. (1961). *Cancer Res.* **21**, 1532.

Gray, G. M. (1967). *In* "Lipid Chromatographic Analysis" (G. V. Marinetti, ed.), Vol. I, pp. 401–463. Dekker, New York.

Gray, G. M., and MacFarlane, M. G. (1958). *Biochem. J.* **70**, 409.

Green, D. E., and Allmann, D. W. (1968a). *In* "Metabolic Pathways" (D. M. Greenberg, ed.), Vol. II, pp. 37–67. Academic Press, New York.

Green, D. E., and Allmann, D. W. (1968b). *In* "Metabolic Pathways" (D. M. Greenberg, ed.), Vol. II, pp. 1–36. Adademic Press, New York.

Guyer, K. E., Hoffman, W. A., Horrocks, L. A., and Cornwell, D. G. (1963). *J. Lipid Res.* **4**, 385.

Hack, M. H., and Ferrans, V. J. (1959). *Hoppe-Seyler's Z. Physiol. Chem.* **315**, 157.

Hagen, P-O, and Goldfine, H. (1967). *J. Biol. Chem.* **242**, 5700.

Hajra, A. K. (1968). *J. Biol. Chem.* **243**, 3458.

Hajra, A. K. (1969). *Biochem. Biophys. Res. Commun.* **37**, 486.

Hakim, A. A. (1956). *Exp. Med. Surg.* **14**, 211.

Hakim, A. A. (1959). *Naturwissenschaften* **46**, 84.

Hakomori, S.-I., Koscielak, J., Bloch, K. J., and Jeanloy, R. W. (1967). *J. Immunol.* **98**, 31.

Hallgren, B., and Larsson, S. (1962). *J. Lipid Res.* **3**, 31.

Hamilton, J. G., and Muldrey, J. E. (1961). *J. Amer. Oil Chem. Soc.* **38**, 582.

Hanahan, D. J. (1960). "Lipide Chemistry." Wiley, New York.

Hanahan, D. J. (1965). *J. Lipid Res.* **6**, 350.

Hanahan, D. J., and Thompson, G. A., Jr., (1963). *Annu. Rev. Biochem.* **32**, 223.

Hanahan, D. J., Ekholm, J., and Jackson, C. M. (1963). *Biochemistry* **2**, 630.

Hartman, F. C. (1968). *Biochem. Biophys. Res. Commun.* **33**, 888.

Hartman, F. C. (1970). *Biochemistry* **9**, 1776.

Haven, F. L., and Bloor, W. R. (1956). *Advan. Cancer Res.* **4**, 237.

Hoevet, S. P., Viswanathan, C. V., and Lundberg, W. O. (1968). *J. Chromatogr.* **34**, 195.

Horrocks, L. A. (1968). *J. Lipid Res.* **9**, 469.

Horrocks, L. A., and Ansell, G. B. (1967). *Lipids* **2**, 329.

Hradec, J. (1958). *Nature* **182**, 52.

Hradec, J. (1961). *Biochim. Biophys. Acta* **47**, 149.
Hradec, J., and Dolejš, L. (1968). *Biochem. J.* **107**, 129.
Hradec, J., and Kruml, S. (1960). *Nature (London)* **185**, 55.
Hradec, J., and Stroufová, A. (1960), *Biochim. Biophys. Acta* **40**, 32.
James, A. T. (1960). *Methods Biochem. Anal.* **8**, 1.
Kamimae, T. (1958). *Shinryo* **11**, 949.
Kapoulas, V. M. (1969). *Biochim. Biophys. Acta* **176**, 324.
Kapoulas, V. M., and Thompson, G. A. Jr. (1969). *Biochim. Biophys. Acta* **187**, 594.
Karmen, A. (1967). *In* "Separation Techniques in Chemistry and Biochemistry" (R. A. Keller, ed.), pp. 345–355. Dekker, New York.
Karnovsky, M. L., and Brumm, A. F. (1955). *J. Biol. Chem.* **216**, 689.
Kaufmann, H. P., and Nitsch, W. H. (1954). *Fette, Seifen, Anstrichm.* **56**, 154.
Keenan, R. W., Brown, J. B., and Marks, B. H. (1961). *Biochim. Biophys. Acta* **51**, 226.
Kennedy, E. P. (1953). *J. Biol. Chem.* **201**, 399.
Kennedy, E. P., and Weiss, S. B. (1956). *J. Biol. Chem.* **222**, 193.
Khadzhiolov, A. A. (1965). *Usp. Sovrem. Biol.* **60**, 215.
Kirchner, J. G. (1967). *Tech. Org. Chem.* **12**.
Kiyasu, J. Y., and Kennedy, E. P. (1960). *J. Biol. Chem.* **235**, 2590.
Kiyasu, J. Y., Paulus, H., and Kennedy, E. P. (1960). *Fed. Proc. Fed. Amer. Soc. Exp. Biol.* **19**, 233.
Klenk, E., and Debuch, H. (1963). *Progr. Chem. Fats Other Lipids* **6**, 3–29.
Kolattukudy, P. E. (1970). *Biochemistry* **9**, 1095.
Kornberg, A., and Pricer, W. E., Jr. (1953). *J. Biol. Chem.* **204**, 345.
Kosaki, T., Ikeda, T., Kotani, Y., Nakagawa, S., and Saka, T. (1958). *Science* **127**, 1176.
Kroman, H. S., and Bender, S. R., eds. (1968). "Theory and Application of Gas Chromatography in Industry and Medicine." Grune & Stratton, New York.
Kuksis, A., and Breckenridge, W. C. (1966). *J. Lipid Res.* **7**, 576.
Kuksis, A., Marai, L., and Gornall, D. A. (1967). *J. Lipid Res.* **8**, 352.
Lands, W. E. M., and Hart, P. (1965). *Biochim. Biophys. Acta* **98**, 532.
Lettre, H. (1964). *Fette, Seifen, Anstrichm.* **66**, 885.
Lopez, M. (1956). *Tumori* **42**, 616.
Lovern, J. A. (1957). "The Chemistry of Lipids of Biochemical Significance." Wiley, New York.
Macek, K., and Hais, I. M., eds. (1965). "Stationary Phase in Paper and Thin-Layer Chromatography," 2nd Int. Chromatogr. Symp., Liblice, 1964. Elsevier, New York.
McMurray, W. C. (1964). *J. Neurochem.* **11**, 315.
Mangold, H. K., and Baumann, W. J. (1967). *In* "Lipid Chromatographic Analysis" (G. V. Marinetti, ed.). Vol. I, pp. 339–359. Dekker, New York.
Marinetti, G. V. (1962). *J. Lipid Res.* **3**, 1.
Marinetti, G. V., ed. (1967). "Lipid Chromatographic Analysis," Vol. I. Dekker, New York.
Marinetti, G. V., ed. (1969). "Lipid Chromatographic Analysis," Vol. II. Dekker, New York.
Marsh, J. B., and Weinstein, D. B. (1966). *J. Lipid Res.* **7**, 574.
Mattson, F. H., and Volpenhein, R. A. (1961). *J. Lipid Res.* **2**, 58.
Mattson, F. H., and Volpenhein, R. A. (1968). *J. Lipid Res.* **9**, 79.
Metcalfe, L. D. (1960). *Nature (London)* **188**, 142.

Meyerhof, O., and Kiessling, W. (1933). *Biochem. Z.* **264**, 40.

Meyerhof, O., Lohmann, K., and Schuster, P. H. (1936a). *Biochem. Z.* **286**, 319.

Meyerhof, O., Lohmann, K., and Schuster, P. H. (1936b). *Biochem. Z.* **286**, 301.

Morgan, T. E., Hanahan, D. J., and Ekholm, J. (1963). *Fed. Proc. Fed. Amer. Soc. Exp. Biol.* **22**, 414.

Morris, L. J. (1966). *J. Lipid Res.* **7**, 717.

Owens, K. (1966). *Biochem. J.* **100**, 354.

Petering, H. G., Van Giessen, G. J., Buskirk, H. H., Crim, J. A., Evans, J. S., and Musser, E. A. (1967). *Cancer Res.* **27**, 7.

Pfleger, R. C., Piantadosi, C., and Snyder, F. (1967). *Biochim. Biophys. Acta* **144**, 633.

Pfleger, R. C., Anderson, N. G., and Snyder, F. (1968). *Biochemistry* **7**, 2826.

Piantadosi, C., and Snyder, F. (1970). *J. Pharm. Sci.* **59**, 283.

Pietruszko, R., and Gray, G. M. (1962). *Biochim. Biophys. Acta* **56**, 232.

Poulos, A., Hughes, B. P., and Cumings, J. N. (1968). *Biochim. Biophys. Acta* **152**, 629.

Privett, O. S., and Nickell, E. C. (1962). *J. Amer. Oil Chem. Soc.* **39**, 414.

Privett, O. S., Blank, M. L., Codding, D. W., and Nickell, E. C. (1965). *J. Amer. Oil Chem. Soc.* **42**, 381.

Radin, N. S. (1965). *J. Amer. Oil Chem. Soc.* **42**, 569.

Ramachandran, S., Sprecher, H. W., and Cornwell, D. G. (1968). *Lipids* **3**, 511.

Randerath, K. (1963). "Thin-layer Chromatography." Academic Press, New York.

Rao, G. A., Sorrels, M. F., and Reiser, R. (1968). *Biochem. Biophys. Res. Commun.* **31**, 252.

Rapport, M. M. (1962). *J. Biol. Chem.* **237**, 1056.

Rapport, M. M., and Graf, L. (1955). *Cancer* **8**, 538.

Rapport, M. M., and Graf, L. (1957). *Cancer* **10**, 438.

Rapport, M. M., and Norton, W. T. (1962). *Annu. Rev. Biochem.* **31**, 103.

Rapport, M. M., Graf, L., and Alonzo, N. (1955). *Cancer* **8**, 546.

Rapport, M. M., Graf, L., and Alonzo, N. F. (1958a). *Cancer* **11**, 1136.

Rapport, M. M., Graf, L., Skipski, V. P., and Alonzo, N. (1958b). *Nature (London)* **181**, 1803.

Rapport, M. M., Alonzo, N. F., Graf, L., and Skipski, V. P. (1958c). *Cancer* **11**, 1125.

Rapport, M. M., Graf, L., Skipski, V. P., and Alonzo, N. (1959). *Cancer* **12**, 438.

Rapport, M. M., Graf, L., and Alonzo, N. (1960). *J. Lipid Res.* **1**, 301.

Rapport, M. M., Graf, L., and Yariv, J. (1961). *Arch. Biochem. Biophys.* **92**, 438.

Rapport, M. M., Graf, L., and Schneider, H. (1964). *Arch. Biochem. Biophys.* **105**, 431.

Renkonen, O. (1966). *Biochim. Biophys. Acta* **125**, 288.

Renkonen, O. (1968). *J. Lipid Res.* **9**, 34.

Rose, I. A., and O'Connell, E. L. (1969). *J. Biol. Chem.* **244**, 6548.

Rossiter, R. J. (1968). In "Metabolic Pathways" (D. M. Greenberg, ed.), Vol. II, pp. 69–115. Academic Press, New York.

Rothfield, L., and Finkelstein, A. (1968). *Annu. Rev. Biochem.* **37**, 463.

Sand, D. M., and Schlenk, H. (1969). *J. Amer. Oil Chem. Soc.* **46**(8), Abstr. No. 107.

Schmid, H. H. O., and Mangold, H. K. (1966). *Biochim. Biophys. Acta* **125**, 182.

Serra, J. A. (1960). *Acta Unio Int. Contra Cancrum* **16**, 955.

Siperstein, M. D. (1966). *In* "Developmental and Metabolic Control Mechanisms and Neoplasia", 19th Annu. Symp. Fundam. Cancer Res. Anderson Hosp. and Tumor Inst., 1965, pp. 427–451. Williams & Wilkins, Baltimore, Maryland.

Slotboom, A. J. (1968). "Kleine der A 4," p. 1. V.R.B.-Offsetdrukkerij, Groningen.

Slotboom, A. J., de Haas, G. H., and van Deenen, L. L. M. (1967). *Chem. Phys. Lipids* **1**, 192.

Snyder, F. (1969a). *Isotop. Radiat. Technol.* **6**, 381.

Snyder, F. (1969b). *Progr. Chem. Fats Other Lipids* **10**, 287–335.

Snyder, F. (1969c). *Advan. Exp. Med. Biol.* **4**, 609–621.

Snyder, F. (1970a). *U.S. At. Energy Comm. Rep.* **ORAU–111**.

Snyder, F. (1970b). *In* "Progress in Thin-Layer Chromatography and Related Methods" (A. Niederwieser and G. Pataki, eds.). Ann Arbor-Humphrey Sci. Publ., Ann Arbor, Michigan. Vol. 2, p. 105.

Snyder, F., and Blank, M. L. (1969). *Arch. Biochem. Biophys.* **130**, 101.

Snyder, F., and Moehl, A. (1969). *Anal. Biochem.* **28**, 503.

Snyder, F., and Piantadosi, C. (1966). *Advan. Lipid Res.* **4**, 257–283.

Snyder, F., and Piantadosi, C. (1968). *Biochim. Biophys. Acta* **152**, 794.

Snyder, F., and Wood, R. (1968). *Cancer Res.* **28**, 972.

Snyder, F., and Wood, R. (1969). *Cancer Res.* **29**, 251.

Snyder, F., Cress, E. A., and Stephens, N. (1966). *Lipids* **1**, 381.

Snyder, F., Malone, B., and Blank, M. L. (1969a). *Biochim. Biophys. Acta* **187**, 302.

Snyder, F., Malone, B., and Wykle, R. L. (1969b). *Biochem. Biophys. Res. Commun.* **34**, 40.

Snyder, F., Wykle, R. L., and Malone, B. (1969c). *Biochem. Biophys. Res. Commun.* **34**, 315.

Snyder, F. Blank, M. L., and Morris, H. P. (1969d). *Biochim. Biophys. Acta* **176**, 502.

Snyder, F., Malone, B., and Blank, M. L. (1970a). *J. Biol. Chem.* **245**, 1790.

Snyder, F., Malone, B., and Cumming, R. B. (1970b). *Can. J. Biochem.* **48**, 211.

Snyder, F., Piantadosi, C., and Malone, B. (1970c). *Biochim. Biophys. Acta* **202**, 244.

Snyder, F., Blank, M. L., Malone, B., and Wykle, R. L. (1970d). *J. Biol. Chem.* **245**, 1800.

Snyder, F., Blank, M. L., and Malone, B. (1970e). *J. Biol. Chem.* **245**, 4016.

Soodsma, J. F., Piantadosi, C., and Snyder, F. (1970). *Cancer Res.,* **30**, 309.

Stahl, E., ed. (1969). "Thin-Layer Chromatography." Springer-Verlag, New York.

Stock, R., and Rice, C. B. F., eds. (1967). "Chromatographic Methods." Chapman & Hall, London.

Theise, H., and Bielka, H. (1968). *Arch. Geschwulstforsch.* **32**, 11.

Thiele, O. W. (1959). *Hoppe-Seyler's Z. Physiol. Chem.* **316**, 137.

Thompson, G. A., Jr. (1967). *Biochemistry* **6**, 2015.

Thompson, G. A., Jr. (1968). *Biochim. Biophys. Acta* **152**, 409.

Thompson, G. A., Jr., and Kapoulas, V. M. (1969). *Methods Enzymol.* **14**, p. 668.

Thompson, G. A., Jr., and Lee, P. (1965). *Biochim. Biophys. Acta* **98**, 151.

Tietz, A., Lindberg, M., and Kennedy, E. P. (1964). *J. Biol. Chem.* **239**, 4081.

van Deenen, L. L. M., and de Haas, G. H. (1966). *Annu. Rev. Biochem.* **35**, 157.

VandenHeuvel, W. J. A., Gardiner. W. L., and Horning, E. C. (1965). *J. Chromatogr.* **19**, 263.

van Golde, L. M. G., and van Deenen, L. L. M. (1967). *Chem. Phys. Lipids* **1**, 157.

Viswanathan, C. V. (1968). *Chromatogr. Rev.* **10**, 18.

Viswanathan, C. V., Phillips, F., and Lundberg, W. O. (1968a). *J. Chromatogr.* **35**, 66.

Viswanathan, C. V., Basilio, M., Hoevet, S. P., and Lundberg, W. O. (1968b). *J. Chromatogr.* **34**, 241.

Waku, K., and Lands, W. E. M. (1968). *J. Biol. Chem.* **243**, 2654.

Wallach, D. F. H., Soderberg, J., and Bricker, L. (1960). *Cancer Res.* **20**, 397.

Warner, H. R., and Lands, W. E. M. (1961). *J. Biol. Chem.* **236**, 2404.

Wells, M. A., and Dittmer, J. C. (1963). *Biochemistry* **2**, 1259.

Wells, M. A., and Dittmer, J. C. (1966). *Biochemistry* **5**, 3405.

Witz, I. (1964). *Brit. J. Cancer,* **18**, 397.

Wood, R. (1967). *Lipids* **2**, 199.

Wood, R., and Baumann, W. J. (1968). *J. Lipid Res.* **9**, 733.

Wood, R., and Harlow, R. D. (1969). *J. Lipid Res.* **10**, 463.

Wood, R., and Healy, K. (1970). *Biochem. Biophys. Res. Commun.* **38**, 205.

Wood, R., and Snyder, F. (1966). *Lipids* **1**, 62.

Wood, R., and Snyder, F. (1967a). *Lipids* **2**, 161.

Wood, R., and Snyder, F. (1967b). *J. Lipid Res.* **8**, 494.

Wood, R., and Snyder, F. (1968). *Lipids* **3**, 129.

Wood, R., and Snyder, F. (1969). *Arch. Biochem. Biophys.* **131**, 478.

Wood, R., Baumann, W. J., Snyder, F., and Mangold, H. K. (1969). *J. Lipid Res.* **10**, 128.

Wood, R., Raju, P. K., and Reiser, R. (1965). *J. Amer. Oil Chem. Soc.* **42**, 161.

Wren, J. J. (1961). *Chromatogr. Rev.* **3**, 111–133.

Wykle, R. L., and Snyder, F. (1969a). *J. Amer. Oil Chem. Soc.* **46**(8), Abstr. No. 109.

Wykle, R. L., and Snyder, F. (1969b). *Biochem. Biophys. Res. Commun.* **37**, 658.

Wykle, R. L., and Snyder, F. (1970). *J. Biol. Chem.* **245**, 3047.

Wykle, R. L., Blank, M. L., Piantadosi, C., and Snyder, F. (1970). *Fed. Proc. Fed. Amer. Soc. Exp. Biol.* **29**, 674.

Yurkowski, M., and Brockerhoff, H. (1966). *Biochim. Biophys. Acta* **125**, 55.

COCARCINOGENS

CHAPTER X

ISOLATION AND CHARACTERIZATION OF THE
COCARCINOGENIC PRINCIPLES FROM CROTON OIL

ERICH HECKER

I. Introduction

Croton oil is a multicomponent mixture of lipids. It may be obtained either by extraction or by expression of the seeds of *Croton tiglium* L. (family Euphorbiaceae), a leafy shrub native to Southeast Asia. The oil is toxic to bacteria, insects, amphibia, fish, and other vertebrates including mammals. Used internally it is a drastic cathartic and on skin it is an irritant and vesicant. Diluted with a suitable inactive vehicle, it was used as counterirritant. However, it acts so powerfully that, in human medicine, the oil is deemed unsafe for use either as a cathartic or as a counterirritant.

The well-known irritant properties of croton oil led Berenblum (1941a,b) to the detection of an augmentational effect of croton oil in tumorigenesis on mouse skin induced by carcinogenic aromatic hydrocarbons. After an important modification of Berenblum's original experiment by Mottram (1944), Berenblum and Shubik (1947a,b) devised their experiment of treating the skin of mice with one single subcarcinogenic dose of a carcinogenic aromatic hydrocarbon followed by repeated applications of croton oil. From the results of this and similar experiments, the "two-stage hypothesis" of skin carcinogenesis was derived (Berenblum, 1947).

In the years to follow this hypothesis became one of the most important although controversial approaches in the biological analysis of the mechanism of chemical carcinogenesis. The interpretation of the first or "initiation" stage of Berenblum experiments as the result of an essentially irreversible biological event (Berenblum and Shubik, 1949) was readily accepted. However, the interpretation of the second or "promotion" stage remained controversial especially after a weak but definite tumorigenic or even carcinogenic activity of croton oil was detected. If, in Berenblum experiments, croton oil would exert its augmentational effect by induction of an essentially irreversible biological response of mouse skin, it would be just another carcinogen. However, if the augmentational effect of the oil would be due to an essentially reversible response of mouse skin, a special type of multifactorial carcinogenesis would be apparent which could truly be called cocarcinogenic activity (definition: Shear 1938; for reviews, see Berenblum, 1954, 1964; Salaman, 1958; Graffi and Bielka, 1959; Druckrey, 1959; Nakahara, 1961; Saffioti and Shubik, 1963; Boutwell, 1964; Graffi, 1964; Salaman and Roe, 1964). Only in the latter case can the Berenblum experiment be considered as one of the most advanced models for detailed investigation of the biochemical mechanism of chemical carcinogenesis at the molecular level (Hecker, 1963b, 1966a, 1968c; Van Potter, 1964).

Numerous efforts have been made to characterize the active principles of croton oil. Toward the end of the nineteenth century, several investigators attributed the vesicant properties of croton oil to an acid called "crotonol" or "crotonol acid." It was believed to be related to oleic acid, although it was not obtained as a well-defined compound. Subsequently from the ethanol-soluble fraction of croton oil, Dunstan and Boole (1895) obtained a neutral, resinous, and strongly vesicant mass which they called "croton resin." They speculated that some sort of a lactone was the active principle of their croton resin. Boehm (1915a,b) reported a modified procedure for preparation of a croton resin, and investigated its acute toxicity in frogs and rabbits. In one of his preparations, Boehm (1923) obtained a crystalline compound which he called "phorbol," because it was isolated from the seed oil of an Euphorbiacea. Using simple liquid distribution techniques, investigations on the toxic and vesicant principles of croton oil and croton resin were carried on by Boehm and Flaschenträger (1930), Cherbuliez et al. (1932a,b), Flaschenträger (1935), Spies (1935), and Flaschenträger and Wigner (1942). Further, the detection of the cocarcinogenic activity of croton oil in 1941 stimulated additional investigations aimed at the isolation of its active principles (Saffiotti and Shubik, 1963).

In all trials up to 1961, a successful resolution of croton oil was not accomplished. Also, based upon the relatively poor experimental evidence available, contradictory views developed regarding the biological activities of croton oil. Cherbuliez *et al.* (1932a,b) attempted to separate the cathartic from the vesicant activity by simple liquid distribution methods. Boehm *et al.* (1935) described a synthetic acetate of phorbol and found it to be toxic to frogs and rabbits, whereas phorbol as such revealed to be nontoxic. Also Flaschenträger and his co-workers developed a method to obtain phorbol from croton oil directly (Flaschenträger, 1935; Flaschenträger and Wigner, 1942). Using the techniques described by Cherbuliez *et al.* (1932a,b), Berenblum (1941a,b) separated croton resin from the remainder of the oil and found quantitative differences in the cocarcinogenic activities of these two portions. Using paper chromatographic methods, Danneel and Weissenfels (1955) claimed to have separated the irritant from the cocarcinogenic activity of the oil. By column chromatography, Gwynn (1955) separated a number of fractions all of which produced gross epidermal hyperplasia, but only two of them appeared to have cocarcinogenic activity. Sicé (1958) found that the cocarcinogenic activity of croton oil does not result from its vesicant activity; moreover, he saw no parallelism between the cocarcinogenic activity of the oil and epidermal inflammation or hyperplasia. Lijinsky (1958, 1961), employing high vacuum distillation techniques, concluded that croton oil may contain several cocarcinogens.

Thus, for a final evaluation of the interrelationships between the biological activities of croton oil and, in particular, for a more precise definition of its cocarcinogenic activity, the isolation and chemical characterization of its active principles remained of special importance. To achieve this goal, a systematic fractionation of the oil was required which could be controlled carefully by suitable biological assays.

In fractionation experiments of croton oil started in 1958, multiplicative liquid distribution methods (Hecker, 1955a, 1963a) were introduced as separation methods of choice and combined—at certain stages—with a mild column-chromatographic procedure (Hecker, 1962a,b). As analytical procedures, thin-layer and gas-liquid chromatographic analyses of the fractions as well as their optical rotation proved to be useful. To evaluate the fractions biologically, three standardized assays were developed (Hecker, 1963c): (*a*) estimation of the acute toxicity in frogs, (*b*) estimation of the irritant activity on the mouse ear, and (*c*) estimation of the cocarcinogenic activity in Berenblum experiments on the skin of the backs of mice.

II. Biological Assays for the Followup of the Fractionation

For estimation of the acute toxicity, the weighed sample of toxic material is dissolved in as little as possible of ethanol and filled up to the desired volume with polyethylene glycol 400. The final solution is approximately 10% alcoholic. Of this solution 0.5 ml/50 gm frog is injected into the lymph sac of *Rana esculenta* L. weighing between 30 and 60 gm. Groups of 6 to 8 frogs are used, with control groups receiving only 0.5 ml of the 10% ethanolic solvent. According to the pathological effects observed, the frogs injected may be divided in two groups (Hecker, (1963c):

1. Frogs dying within 12 hours develop progressive immobility. The lymph sac and the thighs appear swollen and in severe cases lose their contours. They exhibit diffuse or localized hemorrhage in the ventral skin and in the skin of the thighs. In most cases the stomach is filled with bloody mucus.

2. Frogs that do not die within 12 hours show less marked immobility and symptoms of the lymph sac and skin. The stomach of such frogs is usually empty. These frogs may die later, presumably because of secondary lesions.

The number of frogs dying is counted within 6 to 12 hours after the injection. From the results of the assay the lethal dose for 50% of the frogs (LD_{50}) is calculated and expressed in milligrams or micrograms per 50 gm frog (see Charts 1 and 2).

For estimation of the irritant activity the inner surface of the outer ear of mice is treated and the degree of redness developing subsequently is evaluated.

Entering at its root the ear of mice contains three pairs of blood vessels (one artery and vena each). The middle pair is developed most markedly, exhibiting 3–5 branches. It provides the blood supply primarily for the upper edge of the ear and its middle parts. Both other pairs are less branched and supply the lower edges of the ear. Between these pairs of blood vessels, a network of anastomoses is observed.

According to the standard procedure (Hecker *et al.*, 1966a), in male and female SIM mice, 3 months of age, one ear is treated with 0.006 ml of an acetone solution of the irritant material. The other ear remains untreated and is used as a reference in order to evaluate the degree of ear redness. Five solutions are prepared in geometric progression by a factor of 2 (Table I). Twenty-four hours after application of the irritant, the ears treated exhibit various degrees of redness which may be classified as follows (Table I): ($^+$) slight reddening of the main vessels, without reddening of areas in between; ($^{++}$) marked reddening of the main vessels with beginning reddening of the areas in between; and ($^{+++}$) intense reddening of the entire ear often combined with macroscopically visible hyperplasia. The reddening of the ears is reversible. Thus, after its disappearance the mice may be used again, with the formerly treated ear as a reference.

In reading the degree of ear redness, SIM mice proved to be more suitable than NMRI mice. Furthermore, experience is required for

TABLE I

STANDARD PROCEDURE FOR ESTIMATION OF THE IRRITANT UNIT[a]

Croton oil GP 6, 1958, dose/ear (μg)	Males	Females
0.6	—	+
1.2	+	+
2.4	+ +	+ +
4.8	+ + +	+ +
9.6	+ + +	+ + +

[a] From Hecker *et al.*, 1966a.

evaluation of redness with satisfactory reproducibility (Hecker *et al.*, 1966a). The dose causing an ear redness of the degree $^{++}$ is defined as an irritant unit (IU) and is expressed in micrograms per ear (see Charts 1 to 4). The IU thus determined is usually reproducible within a factor of 2 to 3 (Hecker *et al.*, 1966a). Prior to the standard procedure the IU was estimated in a preliminary standard procedure which neglected possible sex differences (Hecker, 1963c; IU^+, Charts 1 and 2).

For estimation of the cocarcinogenic activity, in Berenblum experiments young mice are used in order to speed up the appearance of tumors. In the standard procedure (Hecker, 1963c; Hecker and Bresch, 1965), 4-week-old mice, born within 72 hours, are immunized against ectromelia by intraperitoneal injection of 0.1 ml of pox lymph; the mice are then distributed randomly into Macrolon cages (type II, with wire cover), 7 mice per cage. They are kept at $21 \pm 1\,°C$ and 50–60% relative humidity on wood shavings to be changed 2 times per week. Hope farm standard laboratory diet R.M.H. and water are accessible *ad libitum*.

At 6 weeks of age, in groups of 28 mice (4 cages; 14 males, 14 females) the backs are shaved (approx. 6 cm^2). One week later the initiating dose of the carcinogenic aromatic hydrocarbon dissolved in 0.1 ml of acetone is applied; after one week the application of the cocarcinogen is started. The single dose is dissolved in 0.1 ml of acetone and administered 2 times weekly for at least 12 weeks (Monday and Thursday or Tuesday and Friday). Mortality is practically zero within 12 weeks. During the entire experiment, every week the mice are weighed and the tumors counted. All tumors 1 mm in diameter or more are recorded. At the end of the twelfth week of treatment, i.e., after twenty-four applications the cocarcinogenic activity is expressed as tumor rate (i.e., number of surviving mice with at least one tumor per number of survivors) in per cent and as average tumor yield (i.e., total number of tumors per number of survivors, (see Tables II, IV, VII and X).

In the standard procedure with NMRI mice, 25.6 μg, i.e., 0.1 μM of 7,12-dimethylbenz[a]anthracene (DMBA) are used as subcarcinogenic (Hecker, 1966a) initiating dose. In the initial stages of the fractionation procedure, 12/12 SIM mice and 300 μg of DMBA were used in a standardized manner (Hecker, 1963c) similar to that described above (see Table II).

TABLE II

COCARCINOGENIC ACTIVITIES AT VARIOUS STAGES OF THE
FRACTIONATION OF CROTON OIL AND OF THE HYDROPHILIC
PORTION OF CROTON OIL[a]

	Cocarcinogenic activity[b]		
	Single dose (μg/application)	Tumor rate[c] (%)	Average tumor yield[c] (tumors/survivor)
Croton oil GP6, 1958	500	100	9.6
Hydrophilic portion	50 (500)	83 (18)	4.0 (0.5)
Neutral fraction	50 (500)	100 (60)	9.6 (0.9)
Factor group A[d]	5	100	10.2
Factor group B[d]	5	100	11.2

[a] From Hecker et al., 1965a.

[b] Estimated by the standard procedure on SIM mice (Hecker, 1963c). Initiator: 300 μg 7,12-dimethylbenz[a]anthracene. Numbers in parentheses refer to data obtained for the less active side fractions.

[c] After 12 weeks (24 applications).

[d] Head and tail fraction of chromatography not assayed.

III. Phorbol Esters from Croton Oil

A. RESOLUTION OF CROTON OIL INTO ITS HYDROPHILIC AND HYDROPHOBIC PORTIONS

In the fractionation of croton oil the acute toxicity in frogs is used to relate the biological data of earlier investigators to the irritant and cocarcinogenic activities of croton oil, some of its fractions and subfractions. The estimation of irritant activity is considered a rapid, although preliminary, measure for possible cocarcinogenic activity of one and the same fraction until the latter activity is established separately in the more time-consuming assay for cocarcinogenic activity.

The fractionation procedure (Chart 1) is started with a sample of croton oil (GP 6, 1958)* exhibiting an LD_{50} of 5 mg/50 gm frog, an IU^+ of 0.4 µg/ear, and a specific rotation of $[a]_D + 7°$ (Hecker, 1962a,b, 1963b; Hecker et al., 1964a). In the standard Berenblum experiment, with a single dose of 500 µg, its tumor rate is 100%, with an average tumor yield of 9.6 tumors per survivor (see Table II).

In the flow schemes (Charts 1 to 5), vertical arrows indicate the sequence of the fractions with increasing biological activity; horizontal arrows the elimination of less active side fractions. Percentages are given by weight; optical activities are given as specific rotation $[a]_D$ determined in 1% dioxane solution at 24° to 28°C. Relative migration rates (R_f) refer to thin-layer chromatography.

CROTON OIL GP 6 1958 (100%)
(LD_{50}: 5 mg/50 gm frog; IU^+: 0.4 µg/ear)
$[a]_D + 7°$

O'Keeffe distribution | →hydrophobic portion (95%)
(IU^+: 38 µg/ear; $[a]_D + 6°$)

HYDROPHILIC PORTION (5%)
(IU: 0.15 µg/ear; $[a]_D + 17°$)

Na_2CO_3 | →acid fraction (1%)
(IU^+: 5 µg/ear; $[a]_D + 5°$)

NEUTRAL FRACTION (4%)
(IU^+: 0.15 µg/ear; $[a]_D + 29°$)

CHART 1. Initial stages of the fractionation of croton oil (Hecker et al., 1964a, 1965a). Irritation units (IU^+) estimated in the preliminary standard procedure (Hecker, 1963c).

In the first stage of the fractionation procedure, by an O'Keeffe distribution, croton oil is separated into its hydrophobic (95%) and its hydrophilic (5%) portions (Chart 1). The O'Keeffe distribution is a steady-state multiplicative liquid distribution procedure employing repetitive feeding of the mixture in the center of the distribution battery (Hecker, 1955a). It is primarily a preparative separation method (Hecker, 1955a, 1961, 1963a). O'Keeffe distributions may be

---

* GP 6 indicates that the oil satisfies the requirements specified in the German Pharmacopoea, 6th ed.; 1958 indicates the year when the oil was purchased.

performed in either one of two different schemes—procedure 1 or 2. If z is the number of elements used to perform procedure 1, a certain separation efficiency is obtained. In procedure 2, 2 times z elements are required to obtain that same separation efficiency. However, procedure 2 is advantageous with respect to the number of feedings per cycle (Hecker, 1963a, 1965). Consequently, procedure 1 with one feeding per cycle is used primarily with hand-operated batteries* (Hecker, 1957); procedure 2 with two feedings per cycle is primarily used with automatic batteries (von Metzsch, 1959; Alderweireldt, 1961†; Post and Craig, 1963‡).

For the O'Keeffe distribution (Chart 1), procedure 1 is used with a hand operated battery. Each element is filled with $V_u = 300$ ml of upper and $V_l = 300$ ml of lower phase of a solvent system obtained by equilibration of petroleum ether (37), methanol (30), water (0.3) parts by volume. Fifty-ml portions of croton oil are fed into the central element of the battery. The first distribution cycle $N = 1$ is started by equilibration of the phases (transfer n = 1) and finished by phase transport (end of second transfer n = 2). The second distribution cycle $N = 2$ is started with another 50 ml of croton oil feed and so on. The upper and lower phases leaving the battery during distribution cycles $N = 1$ and $N = 2$ do not contain material and may be discarded. All phases leaving the battery during the subsequent distribution cycles are collected. After removal of the solvents, the petroleum ether-rich upper phases yield the hydrophobic portion, the methanol-rich lower phases the hydrophilic portion of the oil.

In this manner, 1 liter of croton oil may be separated into its hydrophobic and hydrophilic portions within 6 to 8 hours (Hecker, 1962a, 1965). Although the latter represents only about 5% of the original oil, its IU^+ has decreased to about one-third of that of the original oil, indicating an approximately threefold increase of irritant activity (Chart 1). Also the optical (Chart 1) and the cocarcinogenic activities (Table II) of the hydrophilic portion are considerably increased. The hydrophobic portion representing 95%, i.e., almost all the material, is biologically and optically less active than the original oil. Consequently, by O'Keeffe distribution, almost the entire biological activities from croton oil are transferred to the hydrophilic portion.

---

* Manufacturer: E. Bühler, Scientific Instruments, Reutlingerstr. 6, 74 Tübingen, Germany.

† Manufacturer: Quickfit Laborglas G.m.b.H., Hüttenstr. 8, Wiesbaden-Schierstein 62, Germany.

‡ Manufacturer: H. O. Post, Scientific Instruments, Co., Inc. 69–57 Juniper Boulevard South, Middle Village, New York 11379, U.S.A.

B. FRACTIONATION OF THE HYDROPHILIC PORTION OF CROTON OIL

Treatment of the hydrophilic portion with sodium carbonate yields 1% of an acid fraction of relatively little biological and optical activities (Chart 1; Table II). The residual neutral fraction resembles 4% of the original oil and practically all of its biological activity (Chart 1; Table II).

In the next stage of the fractionation procedure the neutral fraction is subjected to a column chromatography on silica gel deactivated with 13% (by weight) of water using carbon tetrachloride–ether mixtures as eluents (Chart 2; Fig. 1). After a rather big head fraction of relatively little irritant but high optical activity (Chart 2), a broad band B leaves the column (Fig. 1). It is clearly separated from a subsequent broad band A. Finally with acetone as eluent, a biologically relatively inactive tail fraction leaves the column (Chart 2).

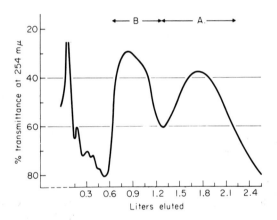

FIG. 1. Chromatography of the hydrophilic fraction from croton oil on deactivated silica gel. Eluent—carbon tetrachloride–ether mixtures; elution curve recorded at 254 mμ. (From Hecker and Bresch, 1965; Hecker and Schairer, 1967.)

In thin-layer chromatography, the material contained in bands A and B each exhibits a single spot with R_f values of 0.3 and 0.4, respectively (see Chart 2). On silica gel Merck HF 254 the spots may be recognized in UV light (254 mμ) and both develop a dark brown color after spraying with vanillin–sulfuric acid followed by exposure to 110°C. The material of both bands exhibits practically identical LD_{50}, IU^+, and optical (Chart 2) as well as cocarcinogenic activities (Table II). The increase in the biological activities from the stage of croton oil to that of the bands A and B roughly corresponds to the decrease in material. Thus, the material contained in both bands together represents

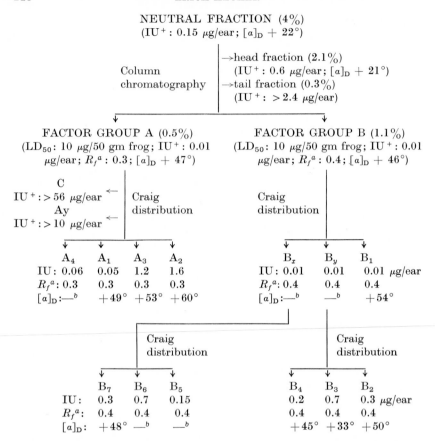

NEUTRAL FRACTION (4%)
(IU⁺: 0.15 μg/ear; [a]_D + 22°)

Column
chromatography

→head fraction (2.1%)
(IU⁺: 0.6 μg/ear; [a]_D + 21°)
→tail fraction (0.3%)
(IU⁺: > 2.4 μg/ear)

FACTOR GROUP A (0.5%)
(LD₅₀: 10 μg/50 gm frog; IU⁺: 0.01
μg/ear; R_f^a: 0.3; [a]_D + 47°)

FACTOR GROUP B (1.1%)
(LD₅₀: 10 μg/50 gm frog; IU⁺: 0.01
μg/ear; R_f^a: 0.4; [a]_D + 46°)

C
IU⁺: > 56 μg/ear
Ay
IU⁺: > 10 μg/ear

Craig
distribution

Craig
distribution

	A₄	A₁	A₃	A₂		B_x	B_y	B₁
IU:	0.06	0.05	1.2	1.6	IU: 0.01	0.01	0.01 μg/ear
R_f^a:	0.3	0.3	0.3	0.3	R_f^a: 0.4	0.4	0.4
[a]_D:	—^b	+49°	+53°	+60°	[a]_D: —^b	—^b	+54°

Craig
distribution

Craig
distribution

	B₇	B₆	B₅		B₄	B₃	B₂
IU:	0.3	0.7	0.15	0.2	0.7	0.3 μg/ear
R_f^a:	0.4	0.4	0.4	0.4	0.4	0.4
[a]_D:	+48°	—^b	—^b	+45°	+33°	+50°

CHART 2. Fractionation of the hydrophilic portion of croton oil (continued) (Hecker *et al.*, 1964a, 1965a; Hecker and Bresch, 1965; Hecker and Kubinyi, 1965; Clarke and Hecker, 1965b; Hecker and Schairer, 1967). Irritation units (IU⁺) estimated by the preliminary standard procedure (Hecker, 1963c); IU, by the standard procedure (Hecker *et al.*, 1966a).

^a System methylene chloride–acetone = 3/1; silica gel Merck 254 HF.
^b Not determined because of scarcity of compound.

practically the entire biological activity of croton oil. In particular, this result indicates that the toxic principle is identical with the irritant and co-carcinogenic principles (Hecker, 1962b, 1963b; Hecker *et al.*, 1964a,b,c).

Since 1958, the fractionation procedure of the hydrophilic portion from croton oil was simplified gradually. The number of stages employed between the O'Keeffe distribution and the column chromatography has been reduced considerably. In its most advanced version, samples of about 40 gm of the hydrophilic portion are being chromatographed directly on a column of 3.5 kg of deactivated silica gel (150 ×

7 cm), thus eliminating even the stage of sodium carbonate extraction (Hecker and Schairer, 1967). Similar modifications have been reported also by Meyer (1966) and Meyer-Bertenrath (1968). Recently also, separations of 4 to 5 gm portions of the alcoholic extract of croton oil by dry column chromatography have been described (Ocken, 1969).

1. Isolation and Resolution of the Croton Oil Factor Groups A and B

Although in thin-layer chromatography the material contained in the chromatographic bands A and B appeared to be uniform, further resolution of both bands was achieved by Craig distribution procedures (Chart 2).

In contrast to steady-state liquid distribution procedures, such as the O'Keeffe distribution, Craig distribution procedures are nonsteady-state liquid distribution methods employing single feeding at the beginning of the battery (Hecker, 1955a; Craig et al., 1956). Primarily they are analytical separation procedures (Hecker, 1961, 1963a).

Depending on the particular separation problem to be solved by Craig distribution, the fundamental procedure may be extended by either recycling or by the single or double withdrawal procedure, thus increasing the separation efficiency (Hecker, 1955a; Craig et al., 1956). Assuming a linear partition isotherm of the compounds distributed, the effectiveness of separations by Craig distributions may be judged by "theoretical" distribution curves (Hecker, 1955a; Craig et al., 1956). They may be calculated, (see for example, Fig. 2) according to standard procedures (Hecker, 1955a, 1965; Craig et al., 1956) from the partition number G corresponding to the number r of the fraction which contains the maximum of the band and the total number n of transfers used.

Craig distributions for resolving bands A and B are performed in automatic batteries: a battery with $z = 200$ elements, each holding 25 ml of stationary phase (von Metzsch, 1953) along with batteries of $z = 1020$ elements (Craig and King, 1958), one holding 3 ml and another holding 10 ml of stationary phase.* The material to be separated is introduced in as few elements as possible (Table III). At the beginning of the distribution, longer settling periods are usually used than those recorded in Table III. In the Craig distributions of factor groups B_y and B_x (Chart 2), it was convenient to finish the distribution with a complement of double-phase withdrawal to remove most of the high-boiling di-n-butyl ether from the more important fractions. Distribution curves are constructed by the weighed-sample method

* Manufacturer: H. O. Post, Scientific Instruments, Co., Inc., South Juniper Boulevard, Middle Village, New York 11379, U.S.A.

TABLE III

SPECIFICATION OF CRAIG DISTRIBUTIONS USED FOR FURTHER
RESOLUTION OF THE CHROMATOGRAPHIC BANDS A AND B[a,b]

Craig distribution of fractions[b]	Battery type	V	No. of transfers n	No. of complete shaking movements	Settling period (min)	No. of tubes receiving sample
Band A	Craig	12/10	1600	20	3.0	13
Band B	von Metzsch	25/25	450	20	3	1
Factor group B_y	Craig	5/3	2500	20	1.5	6
Factor group B_x	Craig	3/3	3020	20	1.5	3

[a] From Hecker and Bresch, 1965; Hecker and Kubinyi, 1965; Clarke and Hecker, 1965b, Hecker and Schairer, 1967.

[b] For systems and procedures, see Figs. 2 to 6, showing the individual distribution patterns.

(Hecker, 1955a; Craig et al., 1956) the sample consisting of the material of between 2 and 5 neighboring fractions. The average fraction weights thus obtained are plotted against the number of the middle fractions (see Figs. 2–6, 17–19, 21).

In a preliminary Craig distribution (Hecker et al., 1964b) using a carbon tetrachloride system and $n = 270$ transfers the material from the chromatographic band A is resolved to give two bands, A_1 and A_x (Fig. 2).

As a criterion of purity of individual fractions of the distribution, "theoretical" distribution curves cannot be used since the partition isotherms of the croton oil factors are nonlinear in the systems and concentration ranges used (Hecker and Bresch, 1965; Hecker and Kubinyi, 1965; Clarke and Hecker, 1965b). Also thin-layer chromatography is not useful as a criterion of purity since it does not separate croton oil factors within one factor group. Finally, as a criterion of purity following rigorous hydrolysis of individual fractions and subsequent methylation, gas-liquid chromatography of the methyl esters thus obtained was used. It is based upon the assumption that each croton oil factor contains only one long-chain fatty acid, the purity and identity of which is determined (Hecker and Kubinyi, 1965). As a criterion of purity and for identification of long-chain fatty acid moieties, this procedure is satisfactory as confirmed by subsequent degradative work.

Using the same solvent system as in the preliminary distribution (Fig. 2), resolution of the factors of the A group is improved employing

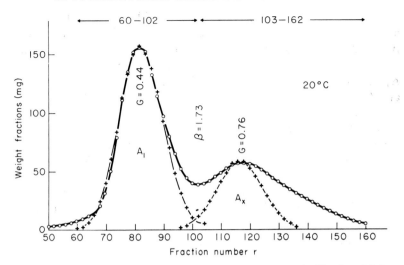

FIG. 2. Preliminary Craig distribution of factor group A. Single withdrawal procedure: $z = 200$; $n = 270$; $V = 25/25$; system carbon tetrachloride (2), methanol (1), water (0.15). (—○—) Experimental: (—×—) calculated according to Hecker (1955a). (From Hecker and Bresch, 1965.)

$n = 1600$ transfers (Chart 2; Fig. 3). In thin-layer chromatography, the materials contained in bands A_1–A_4, and A_y, as they are collected from the battery, exhibit impurities of higher R_f value which are being formed from the main compounds by autoxidation during the Craig distribution. Thus, it is preferred to run the distribution of croton oil factors under an atmosphere of nitrogen. Furthermore fractions $r = 708$–780 and $r = 880$–964 are contaminated with small amounts

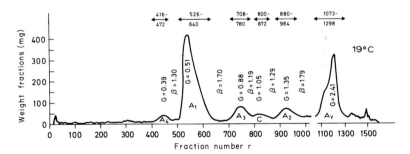

FIG. 3. Craig distribution of factor group A. Single withdrawal procedure: $z = 1020$; $n = 1600$; $V = 12/10$; system carbon tetrachloride (2), methanol (1), water (0.15). Fractions $r = 0$–1020 represent the average weight of four neighboring fractions r to $r-3$ plotted against $r-2$; fractions $r = 1021$–1600 represent the average weight of nine neighboring fractions. (From Hecker and Schairer, 1967.)

of band C. On thin-layer plates, C is not visible under UV light. However, in contrast to the brown color mainly developed by the spots of bands A_2 and A_3 in staining with vanillin–sulfuric acid, C′ may be recognized by a rose color reaction. By thick-layer chromatography the croton oil factors A_1–A_4 and compound C may be freed from autoxidation products and thus be obtained in a chromatographically (gas-liquid) pure state.

From all croton oil factors of the A group, A_1 is the main constituent (Fig. 3). They all exhibit identical R_f values and similar optical activities (Chart 2). Also they are highly irritant (Chart 2) and exhibit various cocarcinogenic activities (Table IV). Bands C and A_y are not irritant in the doses assayed (Chart 2).

Since A_y appeared to represent a mixture of inactive compounds, it was not further fractionated. Compound C was crystallized and identified as 1-monopalmitine.

The material from the chromatographic band B is separated into three bands B_1, B_y, and B_x by Craig distribution in a carbon

TABLE IV

COCARCINOGENIC ACTIVITIES OF THE CROTON OIL FACTORS
ISOLATED FROM THE HYDROPHILIC PORTION[a]

Factor	Cocarcinogenic activity[b]	
	Tumor rate[c] (%)	Average tumor yield[c,d] (tumors/survivor)
A_1	82	3.6
A_2	8	0.3
A_3	29	0.6
A_4	64	2.6
B_1	71	3.1
B_2	86	6.2
B_3	61	3.0
B_4	64	2.3
B_5	32	2.0
B_6	29	1.0
B_7	57	2.4

[a] From Hecker, 1962c; Clarke and Hecker, 1965a,b; Hecker and Schairer, 1967.

[b] Estimated by the standard procedure on NMRI mice (Hecker and Bresch, 1965). Initiator: 0.1 μM 7,12-dimethylbenz[a]anthracene.

[c] After 12 weeks (24 applications).

[d] Cocarcinogens group A: 0.02 μM per application; cocarcinogens group B: 10 μg per application.

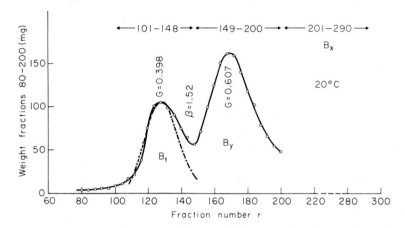

FIG. 4. Craig distribution of factor group B. Single withdrawal procedure: $z = 200$; $n = 450$; $V = 25/25$; system carbon tetrachloride (2), methanol (1), water (0.15). (—○—) Experimental; (—×—) calculated according to Hecker, 1955a. Withdrawn fractions $n = 201-290$ pooled to give fraction B_x. (From Hecker and Kubinyi, 1965.)

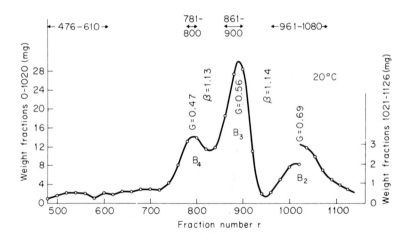

FIG. 5. Craig distribution of factor group B_y. Single phase withdrawal procedure: $z = 1020$; $n = 2500$; $V = 5/3$; system cyclohexane (15), n-dibutyl ether (5), nitromethane (16), methanol (4). Fractions $r = 0-1020$ represent the average weight of two neighboring fractions r and $r-1$ plotted against $r-1$; fractions 1021–1126 represent the average weight of three neighboring fractions. (From Clarke and Hecker, 1965b.)

tetrachloride–methanol–water system, employing $n = 450$ transfers
(Hecker et al., 1964c) (Chart 2; Fig. 4). From band B_1, chromatographically (gas liquid) pure material is obtained. The material from fractions
$r = 149$–200 (B_y) and $r = 201$–290 (B_x) has to be fractionated further,
partially with recombinations of fractions. However, from the entire
fractionation procedure of the B group (Clarke and Hecker, 1965a,b),
only the more important stages will be discussed. B_y is fractionated further by Craig distribution using a nonaqueous solvent system
and $n = 2500$ transfers (Chart 2). From the fractions $r = 961$–1080,
partially withdrawn from the battery (Fig. 5), a new croton oil factor
B_2 is obtained. Fractions $r = 861$–900 and $r = 781$–800 remaining
on the battery contain B_3 and B_4 as additional new croton oil factors.
Similarly B_x is resolved in a Craig distribution (Chart 2) using a
different nonaqueous solvent system and $n = 3020$ transfers yielding
the chromatographically (gas liquid) pure factors B_5, B_6 and B_7 (Fig. 6).
Again, as observed in the A group, the main compounds in fractions

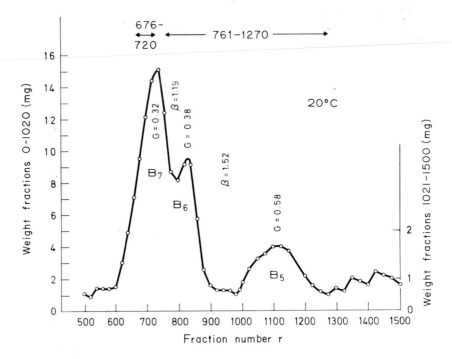

FIG. 6. Craig distribution of factor group B_x. Single withdrawal procedure
for $n = 2000$ transfers; double withdrawal procedure for further $n = 1020$
transfers; $z = 1020$; $V = 3/3$; system cyclohexane (13), n-dibutyl ether (7),
nitromethane (20). Fractions $r = 0$–1020 represent the average weight of three
neighboring fractions; fractions $r = 1021$–1500 of five neighboring fractions.
(From Clarke and Hecker, 1965b.)

of the distributions may form autoxidation products which have to be removed by thick-layer chromatography.

From all croton oil factors of the B group, B_1 and B_2 represent the main constituents. The factors B_1–B_7 all exhibit practically the same R_f values in thin-layer chromatography and, so far as determined, similar optical rotations (see Chart 2). All of them exhibit irritant (Chart 2) and cocarcinogenic activities (Table IV) of various degrees.

In other fractionation trials employing combinations of column chromatography, Craig distribution, and thick-layer chromatography, the biologically active "amorphous materials A and C" (Van Duuren et al., 1963a,b,c, 1966; Van Duuren and Orris, 1965; Van Duuren, 1969) and a crystallized compound C-3 (Arroyo and Holcomb, 1965a,b) have been isolated from croton oil.

2. Characterization of the Croton Oil Factor Groups A and B

Ten out of the eleven chromatographically (gas liquid) pure (see Table V) croton oil factors from the hydrophilic portion have been obtained as resinous, amorphous compounds. Only croton oil factor A_1 crystallized.

TABLE V

PURITIES AND CHEMICAL DATA CHARACTERIZING THE CROTON
OIL FACTORS ISOLATED FROM THE HYDROPHILIC PORTION[a]

Croton oil factor	Purity by g.l.c.[b] (%)	R_f[c]	Crystalline derivative[d]	Melting point (°C)	Molecular formula[d]
A_1	99	0.3	NPABE	86–87	$C_{49}H_{63}N_3O_{11}$
			2,4-DNP	106–108	$C_{42}H_{58}N_4O_{11}$
A_2	97	0.3	—[e]	—	—
A_3	91	0.3	—[e]	—	—
A_4	92	0.3	—[e]	—	—
B_1	97	0.4	2,4-DNP	109–110	$C_{43}H_{60}N_4O_{11}$
B_2	97	0.4	2,4-DNP	20–121	$C_{41}H_{56}N_4O_{11}$
B_3	98	0.4	NPABE	90–91	$C_{48}H_{54}N_3O_{11}$
B_4	96	0.4	NPABE	150–152	$C_{47}H_{59}N_3O_{11}$
B_5	94	0.4	—	—	—
B_6	95	0.4	NPABE	94–98	$C_{46}H_{55}N_3O_{11}$
B_7	98	0.4	NPABE	148–150	$C_{45}H_{55}N_3O_{11}$

[a] Hecker and Bresch, 1965; Hecker and Kubinyi, 1965; Clarke and Hecker, 1965b; Hecker and Schairer, 1967.

[b] Gas-liquid chromatography.

[c] Methylenechloride–acetone = 3:1; silica gel "Merck HF 254."

[d] By micro- or ultramicrocombustion analyses. NPABE = 4-(4-phenylazo)-benzoic acid ester; 2,4-DNP = 2,4-dinitrophenylhydrazone from corresponding aldehyde.

[e] No derivative prepared from factors as isolated.

All factors are sensitive to acid and alkali and to oxidative agents. They are practically insoluble in water and easily soluble in most organic solvents. From solution in volatile organic solvents such as petroleum ether or methylenechloride, they may be obtained as brittle foams which can be broken to give light amorphous powders softening below 100°C. These powders and even crystals of A_1 hold all kinds of organic solvents very strongly. Thus, the croton oil factors as such are not suitable for micro- or submicrocombustion analysis. However, reaction of the factors with the acid chloride of 4-(4-nitrophenylazo)benzoic acid (NPAB) (Hecker, 1955b) yields crystalline NPAB monoesters (NPABE) from which correct elemental analyses (Table V) may be obtained (Hecker et al., 1964a,b,c). Also amorphous aldehydes may be prepared from the croton oil factors by oxidation with manganese dioxide (Hecker et al., 1964a,b,c) the 2,4-dinitrophenylhydrazones of which yield correct elemental analyses (Table V). Because of the high molecular weights of these derivatives and also because of their tendency to solvate strongly with all kinds of solvents, extrapolations from their equivalent molecular formulas as obtained by combustion analyses to that of the factors themselves must be considered somewhat uncertain.

The ultraviolet (UV), infrared (IR), and nuclear magnetic resonance (NMR) spectra of all croton oil factors are very similar in type and rather unspecific (Hecker, 1962b; Hecker et al., 1964a,b,c). As typical examples the spectra of croton oil factor A_1 are recorded in Figs. 7 to 9.

The UV spectra (see Fig. 7) exhibit a maximum absorption or

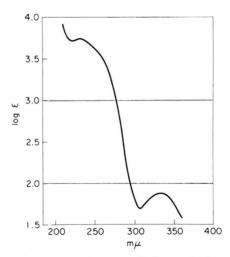

FIG. 7. Ultraviolet spectrum of croton oil factor A_1 in ethanol, $\lambda_{max} = 232$ and 333 mμ, $\epsilon_{max} = 5400$ and 73. (From Hecker and Bresch, 1965.)

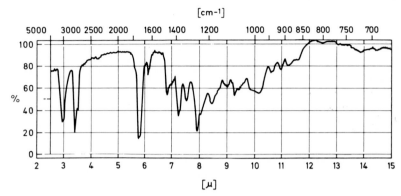

FIG. 8. Infrared spectrum of croton oil factor A_1 in potassium bromide. (From Hecker and Bresch, 1965.)

at least an inflection at about 230 mμ and a further maximum at about 330 mμ, indicating the presence of an a,β-unsaturated carbonyl group. The IR spectra (see Fig. 8) show bands in the region below 3 μ typical for hydroxyl groups, a broad or even split band between 5.75 and 5.85 μ characteristic for carbonyls of esters and ketones, and a band between 6.1 and 6.15 μ indicating a double bond conjugated with a carbonyl group. In the NMR spectrum (see Fig. 9), intense signals appear around $\delta = 1.3$ ppm due to long-chain aliphatic acyl residues. In the NMR spectra of factors A_1–A_4, B_4 and B_7, a singlet at $\delta = 2.00$ ppm indicates the presence of an acetyl group. By proton exchange in deuterium oxide in the NMR spectra of all factors, signals disappear partially or completely at about $\delta = 3.9$, 4.3, and 5.4 ppm, indicating the presence of three free hydroxyl groups.

Independent confirmative evidence for the molecular formulas is obtained by mass spectrometry of the croton oil factors. Here the

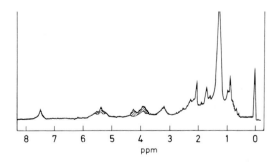

FIG. 9. Nuclear magnetic resonance spectrum of croton oil factor A_1 in carbon tetrachloride with tetramethyl silane as internal standard ($\delta = 0$ ppm). Shaded signals: protons exchanging in deuterium oxide. (From Hecker and Bresch, 1965.)

molecules of solvents solvated are volatilized well before the molecules of the factors themselves. On the other hand, care must be taken to protect the sensitive molecules of the factors from thermal degradation before they are ionized. At first, with reasonable intensity, the molecular ions were obtained only in the comparatively mild (electron addition) mass spectrometry developed by von Ardenne *et al.* (1961, 1963) for croton oil factors A_1, B_3–B_7 (Hecker *et al.*, 1964b; Clarke and Hecker, 1965a,b). For croton oil factors B_1 and B_2 (Hecker *et al.*, 1964c), A_2–A_4 (Hecker and Schairer, 1967), and later on for all others, satisfactory mass spectra have been obtained by conventional (electron impact) high-resolution mass spectrometry.*

As a typical example, the mass spectrum of croton oil factor A_1 is reproduced in Fig. 10. With careful techniques employed especially

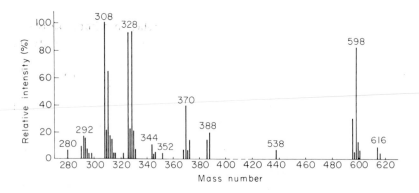

Fig. 10. Mass spectrum (von Ardenne type) of croton oil factor A_1. Temperature of evaporator, 120°C. (From Hecker and Bresch, 1965.)

during the heating procedure in the spectra of all factors, the molecular ion is apparent with reasonable intensity. Fragment ions arising from loss of water and of acid moieties appear as more or less intense lines (in Fig. 10, for example, $m/e = 598$, 538, 388). They permit calculation of the molecular weight of the fatty acid moieties [in Fig. 10, for example, some fragment ions lose 60 mass units (acetic acid) and 228 mass units (tetradecanoic acid)]. After the loss of 18 mass units (water) and the fatty acid moieties, the fragmentation of all factors channels into the same pattern starting with the fragment ion $m/e = 328$ (Fig. 10). This may be assigned to an entity, "parent alcohol minus 2 H_2O," and indicates the presence of the same diterpenoid parent alcohol $C_{20}H_{28}O_6$ in all croton oil factors.

---

* Mass spectrometer CEC 110B, Consolidated Electrodynamics Corp., 360 Sierra Madre Villa, Pasadena, California, U.S.A.; Bell and Howell, G.m.b.H., Friedberg (Hessen) 636, Germany.

In Table VI the results of mass spectrometric analyses of the croton oil factors are summarized. In all factors the long-chain fatty acid discovered by mass spectrometry is identical with the fatty acid identified by the gas-liquid chromatographic method used for proof of purity of the factors. Most interestingly, the croton oil factors A_2 and B_7 and A_3 and B_4 exhibit identical molecular formulas and contain the same acid moieties (see Table VI).

Chemical degradation of the croton oil factors is carried out by reduction with lithium aluminum hydride (Hecker et al., 1964a,b,c; Clarke and Hecker, 1965a). This procedure leads to a mixture of three alcohols; in ether–water, two of them partition into the ether phase and one into the water phase.

The alcohols from the ether phase are reacted with 3,5-dinitrobenzoic acid chloride to yield a mixture of 3,5-dinitrobenzoates. These are separated to identify the individual esters as in factors B_1–B_7 (Hecker et al., 1964c; Hecker and Kubinyi, 1965; Clarke and Hecker, 1965a,b). Also from such mixtures the long-chain fatty alcohols may be characterized as NPAB esters as, for example, in factor A_1 (Hecker et al., 1964a,b; Hecker and Bresch, 1965).

From all croton oil factors, one and the same water-soluble and extremely sensitive alcohol, $C_{20}H_{30}O_6$, mp = 220°–223°C, is obtained.

TABLE VI

MASS SPECTROMETRIC CHARACTERIZATION OF THE FACTORS
ISOLATED FROM THE HYDROPHILIC PORTION OF CROTON OIL[a]

Croton oil factor	R_f[b]	Molecular formula	Acyl residues identified as	Parent alcohol
A_1	0.3	$C_{36}H_{56}O_8$	Acetic, tetradecanoic	
A_2	0.3	$C_{32}H_{48}O_8$	Acetic, decanoic	
A_3	0.3	$C_{34}H_{52}O_8$	Acetic, dodecanoic	
A_4	0.3	$C_{38}H_{60}O_8$	Acetic, hexadecanoic	
B_1	0.4	$C_{37}H_{58}O_8$	(+)-S-2-methylbutyric, dodecanoic	
B_2	0.4	$C_{35}H_{54}O_8$	(+)-S-2-methylbutyric, decanoic	$C_{20}H_{28}O_6$
B_3	0.4	$C_{35}H_{52}O_8$	Tiglic, decanoic	
B_4	0.4	$C_{34}H_{52}O_8$	Acetic, dodecanoic	
B_5	0.4	$C_{33}H_{50}O_8$	(+)-S-2-methylbutyric, octanoic	
B_6	0.4	$C_{33}H_{48}O_8$	Tiglic, octanoic	
B_7	0.4	$C_{32}H_{48}O_8$	Acetic, decanoic	

[a] Hecker and Bresch, 1965; Hecker and Kubinyi, 1965; Clarke and Hecker, 1965b; Hecker and Schairer, 1967.

[b] Methylenechloride–acetone = 3:1; silica gel "Merck HF 254."

It may be characterized by mass spectrometry of its tetraacetate, $C_{28}H_{38}O_{10}$, mp = 189°C. In the alcohol and its tetraacetate the α,β-unsaturated carbonyl group that is contained in all croton oil factors is no longer present. Thus, the water-soluble alcohol $C_{20}H_{30}O_6$ is the dihydro product of a parent alcohol $C_{20}H_{28}O_6$. It is the diterpene parent of all croton oil factors and carries an α,β-unsaturated carbonyl group (Hecker et al., 1964a,b,c; Clarke and Hecker, 1965a). The molecular formula $C_{20}H_{28}O_6$ of this diterpene parent is reminiscent of that proposed for phorbol as prepared directly from croton oil ($C_{20}H_{28-30}O_6$; Flaschenträger, 1935).

Indeed, phorbol obtained directly from croton oil according to the procedure outlined in Section IV exhibits a mass spectrometric fragmentation pattern similar (Fig. 11) to that of the croton oil

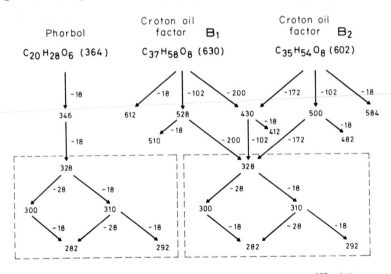

18 = H_2O, 28 = CO or C_2H_4, 102 = methyl butyric acid, 172 = decanoic acid, 200 = dodecanoic acid

FIG. 11. Fragmentation of phorbol and the croton oil factors B_1 and B_2 by conventional mass spectrometry. (From Hecker and Kubinyi, 1965.)

factors. Moreover, below the fragment ion, i.e., $m/e = 328$, "parent alcohol minus 2 H_2O," they are identical (Hecker et al., 1964a,b,c). Similarly the synthetic acetate of phorbol (Boehm et al., 1935) is identified as a phorbol triacetate. By lithium aluminum hydride reduction of this triacetate the water-soluble and extremely sensitive crystalline alcohol, $C_{20}H_{30}O_6$, mp = 220°–223°C, is obtained (Hecker et al., 1964a,b,c).

Thus, it is established unequivocally that the toxic, irritant, and cocarcinogenic principles from croton oil are diesters of phorbol, each factor containing a short and a long-chain fatty acid (see Table VI).

As are the croton oil factors, so also their parent alcohol phorbol is extremely sensitive to acid, alkali and oxygen. It reduces Tollen's and Fehling's reagents. Also it exhibits a remarkable tendency to solvate with organic solvents, e.g., 1 mole of ethanol (Hoppe *et al.*, 1969). Phorbol is relatively nontoxic to frogs, also it is not irritant and not cocarcinogenic (Table VII). Phorbol triacetate exhibits some activity in all three assays (Table VII): it is more toxic than croton oil but less toxic than croton oil factor A_1. However, it is less irritant and cocarcinogenic than both croton oil and A_1.

Besides mass spectrometry, other modern techniques of natural product chemistry, such as NMR, UV, and IR spectrometry and circular dichroism (CD) combined with purposeful chemical reactions have been used to derive the functionality of the new tetracyclic diterpene phorbol (Hecker *et al.*, 1964a,b,c, 1965c). The partial structures and structural elements thus obtained (Hecker, 1966a; Hecker *et al.*, 1966c; Bartsch *et al.*, 1966) have been interlinked to obtain its

TABLE VII

Toxic, Irritant, and Cocarcinogenic Activities for
Croton Oil, Phorbol, Phorbol Triacetate, and Croton Oil
Factor A_1

Compound	LD_{50} (mg/50 mg frog)	IU^a (μg/ear)	Cocarcinogenic activity[b]		
			Single dose (μg/ application)	Tumor rate[c] (%)	Average tumor yield[c] (tumors/ survivor)
Croton oil GP6, 1958	6^d	2.4^d	500^e	64	4.0
Phorbol	$> 5^f$	$> 100^g$	$183^{h,i}$	0	0
Phorbol triacetate	0.15^f	39^g	490^h	4	0.04
Croton oil factor A_1	0.01^f	0.05^g	10^i	93	5.6

[a] Irritation units (IU) estimated in the standard procedure (Hecker *et al.*, 1966a).

[b] Estimated in the standard procedure on NMRI mice (Hecker and Bresch, 1965). Initiator: 0.1 μM 7,12-dimethylbenz[a]anthracene.

[c] At the end of 12 weeks (24 applications).

[d] Hecker, 1963c.

[e] Clarke and Hecker, 1965.

[f] Hecker *et al.*, 1964a.

[g] Hecker *et al.*, 1966a.

[h] Hecker, 1962c.

[i] Hecker, 1966a.

final chemical structure (Fig. 12), as published in 1966 (Hecker, 1966b, 1967, Hecker *et al.*, 1967).

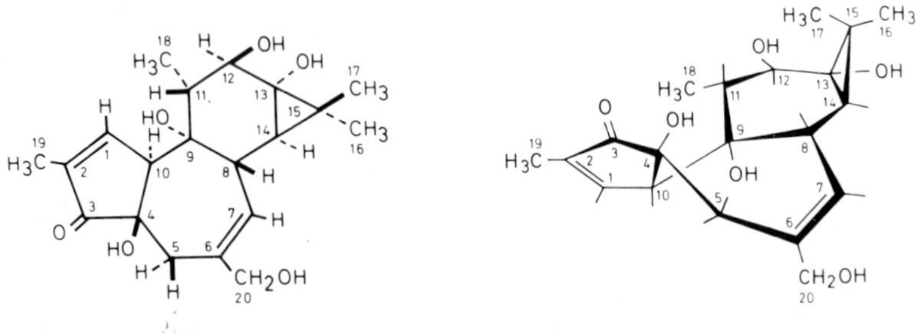

Fig. 12. Structure and stereochemistry of phorbol, the diterpene parent of the croton oil factors A_1–A_4 and B_1–B_7. (From Hecker, 1967; Hecker *et al.*, 1967; Gschwendt and Hecker, 1968a,b; Hoppe *et al.*, 1967; Pettersen *et al.*, 1967.)

Phorbol is a tetracyclic diterpene of complicated and rather peculiar structure. Its six oxygen functions reside in a tertiary 1,2-unsaturated 3,4 ketol (acyloin) group in the five-membered ring, in a 6,7-unsaturated primary alcohol group at C-20 attached to the seven-membered ring, in a 12,13-glycol group interlinking the six- and three-membered rings, and, finally, in a tertiary hydroxyl group at C-9, interlinking the six- and the seven-membered rings of the diterpene skeleton. The molecule exhibits eight centers of asymmetry (C atoms 4, 8, 9, 10, 11, 12, 13, and 14), the relative configurations of which are established (excepting that at C-10) by NMR, circular dichroic measurements, and certain chemical reactions (Hecker *et al.*, 1967; Kreibich and Hecker, 1967, 1968a,b; Bartsch and Hecker, 1967, 1968; Bartsch *et al.*, 1968; Gschwendt and Hecker, 1967, 1968a,b, 1969, Gschwendt *et al.*, 1968). Thus, for example, the five- and the six-membered rings are connected with the seven-membered ring in trans configuration. Together with the conformation of the molecule as deduced by NMR measurements (Gschwendt and Hecker, 1968a,b, 1969), the three-dimensional structure of phorbol (Fig. 12, right) is obtained. As may be seen from Dreiding models of this structure, phorbol is a rigid, nonflexible molecule. Its five-membered ring is not entirely planar and rather strained through its trans connection with the seven-membered ring, which also fixes the latter in an envelope conformation (Fig. 12). The six-membered ring is fixed in the half-chair conformation (see Fig. 12) imposed on it primarily by the planar cis-linked cyclopropane ring.

The recognition of the chemical structure of phorbol was complicated by a number of unusual difficulties. Thus, because of the sensitivity of the molecule and its tendency to solvate all kinds of organic solvents the problem of its molecular formula and the more so of its functionality and chemical structure remained unsettled for a long time (Flaschenträger, 1935; Thomas and Marxer, 1958; Kauffmann and Neumann, 1959; Kauffmann *et al.*, 1959). Based upon the results of quantitative hydrogenation of phorbol and its triacetate, its diterpene nature was recognized and a tetracyclic hydroaromatic structure for phorbol was proposed in 1964 (Hecker *et al.*, 1964a,b, 1965c). This structure was supported by NMR data (Hecker *et al.*, 1965c, 1966b) and by the generation of azulenes in dehydrogenation and dehydration of phorbol and 3-deoxy-3β-hydroxyphorbol (Hecker *et al.*, 1965c; Härle *et al.*, 1967). Further, in agreement with the general chemical experience at that time it was assumed that the reducing properties of phorbol toward Fehling's and Tollen's reagents are due to a secondary 1,2-ketol group (Flaschenträger, 1935; Kauffmann and Neumann, 1959; Hecker *et al.*, 1965c). Finally the production of equivalent amounts of acetone by reaction of phorbol with lead tetraacetate as claimed by Kauffmann *et al.* (1959) was accounted for by an appropriate ditertiary 1,2-glycol group involving the cyclopropanol hydroxyl (Hecker *et al.*, 1965c). On the other hand, based upon results of dehydrogenation of phorbol with a palladium catalyst, Arroyo and Holcomb (1965a) proposed a tricyclic hydroaromatic structure for phorbol. Later they accepted the tetracyclic ring system proposed by Hecker *et al.* (1965c), but translocated two of its structural elements (Arroyo and Holcomb, 1965b). This translocation, however, was not in agreement with NMR spectroscopic data (Hecker *et al.*, 1966b). Subsequent to their first structural proposal, the Heidelberg group found that phorbol does not contain a reducing secondary but rather a (nonreducing) tertiary 1,2-ketol group. Further, the reducing properties of phorbol were demonstrated to be due to the tertiary cyclopropanol group which up to that time was not known as a reducing group for both Tollen's reagent and Fehling's solution. Also the production of acetone in the reaction with lead tetraacetate as claimed by Kauffmann *et al.* (1959) was not reproducible (Hecker, 1966a; Bartsch *et al.*, 1966; Hecker *et al.*, 1966c). With this chemical information and additional circular dichroic key information, the interlinking of the structural elements and partial structures of phorbol as proposed in 1965 (Hecker *et al.*, 1965c) was revised to yield the correct chemical structure (Fig. 12; Hecker, 1966b, 1967; Hecker *et al.*, 1967).

The phorbol structure (Fig. 12) was confirmed and completed with respect to the relative configuration at C-10 by X-ray diffraction analysis (Hoppe *et al.*, 1967, 1969; Hecker *et al.*, 1969; Pettersen *et al.*, 1967, 1968). Further, the absolute configuration of the molecule, as indicated in Fig. 12, was established by X-ray diffraction analysis (Hoppe *et al.*, 1967).

From the structure of phorbol and certain of its chemical reactions, it follows that phorbol triacetate is the phorbol-12, 13, 20-triacetate. Further, the extremely sensitive alcohol from reductive degradation of the croton oil factors and of phorbol-12,13,20-triacetate is 3-deoxy-3β-hydroxyphorbol (Hecker *et al.*, 1967; Gschwendt and Hecker, 1967). A full account of the chemistry of phorbol is beyond the scope of this article. For more detailed chemical information, see review by Hecker (1971).

With the clarification of the structure of phorbol, two problems remain regarding the chemistry of the croton oil factors isolated. (*a*) Which two hydroxyls of phorbol are esterified in these phorbol diesters and, more specifically (*b*), which kind of isomerism is involved in the two pairs of croton oil factors, A_2/B_7 and A_3/B_4, with different R_f values but, nevertheless, with the same acid moieties and identical molecular formulas (see Table VI)?

The analytical methods applied indicate that in all croton oil factors the primary hydroxyl group of phorbol is free. In addition, they contain two free tertiary hydroxyls. From the two ester functions present in the croton oil factors, one is associated with the secondary hydroxyl of the 1,2-glycol group of phorbol. Thus one out of the three tertiary hydroxyls in phorbol must carry a second acyl residue. Unlike the tertiary hydroxyl groups at C-4 and C-9 the tertiary cyclopropanol hydroxyl is easily acetylated with acetic acid anhydride–pyridine at room temperature (Hecker *et al.*, 1965c; von Szczepanski *et al.*, 1967). Further from the primary ester group, at C-20 the acyl group may be selectively removed by acid-catalyzed transesterification to yield, for example, from phorbol-12,13,20-triacetate and phorbol-12,13-diacetate (von Szczepanski *et al.*, 1967). These and some other findings on selective reactivities of the hydroxyls at C-12, C-13, and C-20 strongly suggest that both hydroxyls in the 12,13-glycol group of phorbol may be esterified in the croton oil factors isolated.

Further information comes from experiments aimed at the partial synthesis of mixed phorbol-12,13-diesters. The synthetic concept as developed to solve the remaining problems of identification is summarized in Fig. 13. As shown on the left side of the figure, partial synthesis starts from phorbol (I) as obtained from croton oil (see Section IV). Esterification with either long-chain fatty acid chlorides or with acetic acid anhydride yields phorbol-12,13,20-triacylates (IIa) or phorbol-12,13,20-triacetate (IIb), respectively. In the next step by base-catalyzed transesterification, the phorbol-12-monoesters (IIIa and IIIb) are prepared. Acetylation of IIIa and IIIb with long-chain fatty acid chlorides or acetic anhydride, respectively, yields the corresponding mixed functional 12,13,20-triesters (IVa and IVb). Finally, in IVa and IVb the ester groups at C-20 are removed selectively by

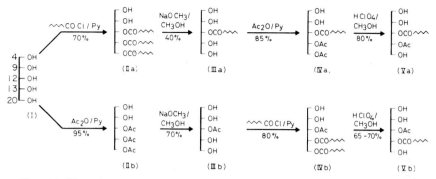

Fig. 13. Reaction sequences for partial synthesis of isomeric phorbol-12,13-diesters from phorbol. Py = pyridine. (From Bartsch et al., 1966; Bresch et al., 1968.)

acid-catalyzed transesterification. Depending on the starting material used, this reaction sequence yields either phorbol-12,13-diesters of the type Va, i.e., 12-O-acyl-phorbol-13-acetates or of the type Vb, i.e., 12-O-acetyl-phorbol-13-acylates with the positions of the acyl residues inverted. In this manner from the croton oil factors isolated those carrying an acetyl group as short-chain acid moiety have been identified with the corresponding phorbol-12,13-diester prepared synthetically (Hecker et al., 1965b; Hecker, 1966a, 1967).

In their physical and chemical properties phorbol-12,13-diesters of type Va and Vb exhibit characteristic differences as summarized in Table VIII. For example, the diesters of type Va all show the same R_f value. However, it is smaller than the R_f value of the diesters of

TABLE VIII

CHEMICAL PROPERTIES OF ISOMERIC PHORBOL-12,13-DIESTERS
TYPE Va AND Vb[a]

Properties	Type Va	Type Vb
R_f value[b]	0.3	0.4
NPAB-20-ester[c]	m.p. below 100°C	m.p. above 140°C
Mass spectrum[d]	M-⌇⌇COO˙	M-CH₃COO˙
	M-CH₃COOH	M-⌇⌇COOH
Infrared spectrum	1710 cm⁻¹	1705 and 1736 cm⁻¹

[a] Hecker and Schairer, 1967; Bresch et al., 1968; Hecker, 1968a,b.
[b] Methylenechloride–acetone = 3:1; silica gel "Merck HF 254."
[c] NPAB = 4-(4-nitrophenylazo)benzoic acid; m.p. = melting point.
[d] M = molecular ion; ⌇⌇COOH-long-chain fatty acid, ⌇⌇COO˙ = corresponding radical.

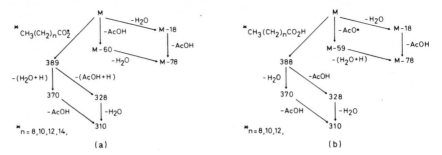

FIG. 14. General fragmentation pattern of phorbol-12,13-diesters of type Va(a) and type Vb(b) given by conventional high-resolution mass spectrometry. (From Hecker and Schairer, 1967; Bresch *et al.*, 1968.)

Type Vb which, in turn, is the same for all esters of this type. There is also a characteristic difference of the two types of positional isomers with respect to the melting points of their NPAB-20-esters, although the existence of different modifications of NPAB esters is observed (Hecker *et al.*, 1965b; Bresch *et al.*, 1968). As a rule, type Va NPAB esters melt below 100°C, whereas type Vb NPAB esters melt above 140°C. Further, in mass spectrometric fragmentation, an acyloxy residue attached to C-12 of phorbol leaves the molecule as a radical, whereas an acyloxy residue attached to C-13 leaves the molecule

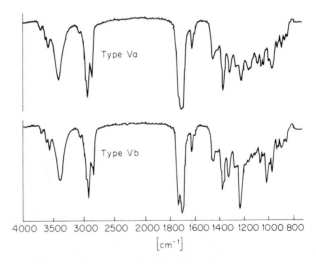

FIG. 15. Infrared spectra of the positionally isomeric phorbol-12,13-diesters type Va, e.g., 12-*O*-decanoyl-phorbol-13-acetate, and type Vb, e.g., 12-*O*-acetyl-phorbol-13-decanoate, in methylene chloride. (From Hecker and Schairer, 1967; Bresch *et al.*, 1968.)

as complete acid (see Table VIII and Fig. 14). Also, the IR spectra of 12-O-acyl-phorbol-13-acetates exhibit a rather broad carbonyl band around 1700 cm^{-1} but those of 12-O-acetyl-phorbol-13-acylates exhibit two clearly separated bands in the carbonyl region (Table VIII and Fig. 15). This difference is seen in IR spectra measured both in potassium bromide and in methylene chloride.

Based upon these findings and mass spectrometric reinvestigation of several of the isolated croton oil factors with acyl residues other than acetyl, they are classified chemically as follows. Factor group A carries the long-chain fatty acid residue in the 12-position and the short-chain fatty acid residue in the 13-position. In factor group B, the positions of long- and short-chain fatty acid residues are inverted. Consequently, the pairs of factors A_2/B_7 and A_3/B_4 are positional isomers, as indicated in Table IX. Croton oil factor A_2 is 12-O-decanoyl-phorbol-13-acetate, whereas croton oil factor B_7 is the corresponding positional isomer. Similarly the factor A_3 carries its dodecanoyl moiety in the 12-position and its acetyl moiety in the 13-position. In factor B_4 the position of both acid residues is inverted (see Fig. 16).

Thus, the occurrence of the two factor groups B and A in the hydrophilic fraction of croton oil is fully understood. Obviously, within one and the same factor group, variable lengths of the long-chain acyl residues do not cause a significant alteration in the R_f values of individual phorbol-12,13-diesters (Table IX). However, the position of the long-chain acyl residue in the phorbol moiety exerts a remarkable influence on the R_f value. This interesting effect must be due to the

TABLE IX

IDENTIFICATION AS POSITIONAL ISOMERS OF THE CROTON OIL FACTORS A_2/B_7 AND A_3/B_4 ISOLATED FROM THE HYDROPHILIC FRACTION[a]

Croton oil factor isolated	$R_f{}^b$	Identical with synthetic phorbol-12,13-diester carrying acyloxy residues at	
		C-12	C-13
A_2	0.3	Decanoic	Acetic
B_7	0.4	Acetic	Decanoic
A_3	0.3	Dodecanoic	Acetic
B_4	0.4	Acetic	Dodecanoic

[a] From Bartsch et al., 1966; Hecker, 1967, 1968a,b; Bresch et al., 1968.
[b] Methylenechloride–acetone = 3:1; silica gel "Merck HF 254."

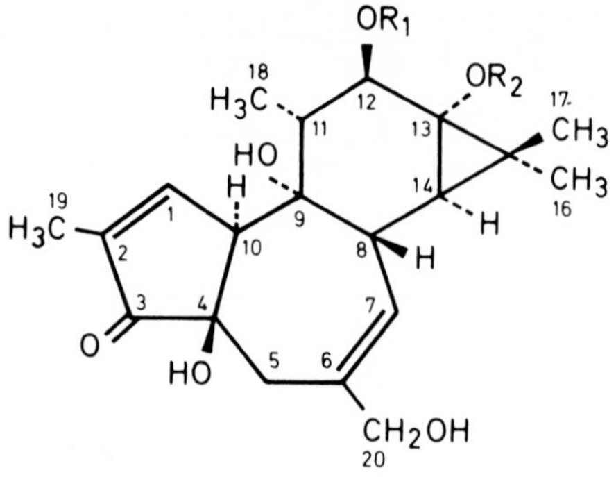

Phorbol : $R_1 = R_2 = H$
Factor group A and A' : R_1 = long , R_2 = short chain fatty acid residue
Factor group B and B' : R_1 = short , R_2 = long chain fatty acid residue

FIG. 16. Structure and stereochemistry of the cocarcinogenic phorbol-12,13 diesters from croton oil. (From Hecker et al., 1965b; Hecker, 1967; Bresch et al., 1968.)

trans-configuration of the 12,13-glycol diester group (Fig. 16), allowing for a discrimination of the isomers by the thin-layer phase, depending on the position of a long-chain acyl residue.

By direct comparison of thin-layer chromatograms and mass spectra of authentic samples the "amorphous material C" isolated by Van Duuren and co-workers (see Section III,B) was found essentially pure and identical to croton oil factor A_1 (Hecker, 1968a,b). However, mass spectrometry of their "amorphous material A" revealed a mixture consisting mainly of croton oil factors B_1, B_2, B_4, and B_7 together with small amounts of croton oil factor A_1 (Hecker, 1968a,b).

According to the physical and chemical data reported for compound C-3 (Arroyo and Holcomb, 1965a,b), it is identical with croton oil factor A_1. Yet it is somewhat puzzling how in a simple one-step reaction followed by thin-layer chromatographic purification (Arroyo and Holcomb, 1965a,b) a pure sample of croton oil factor A_1, alias C-3, could have been obtained.

C. Activation and Fractionation of the Hydrophobic Portion of Croton Oil

The neutral fraction from croton oil, obtained following O'Keeffe distribution and subsequent removal of the acids from the hydrophilic portion, contains practically all the biological and optical activity of the oil whereas the hydrophobic portion and the acid fraction exhibit rather low biological and optical activities (see Charts 1 and

CROTON OIL GP 6 1967 (100%)
IU: 2.8 μg/ear; phorbol: 1.25%)

O'Keeffe   →neutral fraction (4.9%)
distribution   (IU: 0.7 μg/ear; phorbol: 0.5%)

HYDROPHOBIC PORTION (94%)
(IU: 23 μg/ear; phorbol: 0.6%)

transesterification   H$^+$

ACTIVATED HYDROPHOBIC PORTION (93%)
(IU: 2.2 μg/ear; phorbol: 0.55%)

O'Keeffe   →hydrophobic fraction (79%)
distribution   (IU: > 70 μg/ear; phorbol: 0%)

HYDROPHILIC FRACTION (12%)
IU: 0.3 μg/ear; phorbol: 0.6%)

CHART 3. Activation of the hydrophobic portion of croton oil and initial stages of the fractionation of the activated hydrophobic portion (Hecker, 1968a,b; Schmidt and Hecker, 1968). Irritation units (IU) estimated by the standard procedure (Hecker et al., 1966a).

3; Table II). However, the hydrophobic portion of the oil contains phorbol and most surprisingly, it exhibits an even higher phorbol content than the neutral fraction (Chart 3).

Knowing about the low irritant as well as cocarcinogenic activity of phorbol-12,13,20-triacetate (Table VII) and other triacylates (Hecker, 1968a,b; Thielman and Hecker, 1969a), it may be suspected that, as sources of phorbol, the hydrophobic portion contains some sort of phorbol-12,13,20-triesters. If this were true, an acid-catalyzed trans-esterification of the hydrophobic portion should selectively set free the alcohol group in 20-position (see Fig. 13). Indeed, by acid-catalyzed transesterification of the hydrophobic portion obtained from croton oil (GP, 1967) an "activated hydrophobic portion" is obtained (Chart 3). It exhibits an IU of approximately 1/10 of that of the hydrophobic portion i.e. comparable to that of the original oil (Hecker, 1968a,b; Schmidt and Hecker, 1968).

1. Isolation and Resolution of the Croton Oil Factor Groups A' and B'

The activated hydrophobic portion (Chart 3) may be subjected to a fractionation procedure analogous to that of croton oil (Charts 1 and 2). Thus, by O'Keeffe distribution from the activated hydrophobic portion a hydrophobic and a hydrophilic fraction are obtained. The latter carries the entire phorbol content and irritant activity (Chart 3). The hydrophobic fraction contains no phorbol and is practically inactive. In the next stage, by column chromatography of the hydrophilic fraction (Chart 4), practically inactive head and tail fractions as well as two highly active factor groups A′ and B′ are obtained. Together these factor groups contain essentially all the irritant activity of the activated hydrophobic portion (Chart 4).

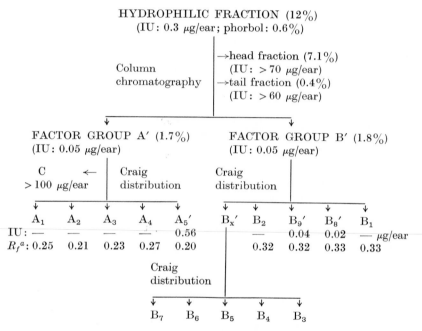

CHART 4. Fractionation of the activated hydrophobic portion from croton oil (continued) (Hecker, 1968a,b; Hecker, 1970c). Irritation units (IU) estimated by the standard procedure (Hecker *et al.*, 1966a).

  [a] System chloroform–ethyl acetate = 2:3; silica gel Merck HF 254.

Factor group A′ is further resolved by Craig distribution employing the solvent system and machinery (Table III) already used for resolution of factor group A (Fig. 3). A distribution pattern is obtained which is almost identical with that of the factor group A (Fig. 17). Using gas chromatographic and mass spectrometric techniques, as described in Section III,B,1, the croton oil factors A_1–A_4 as isolated already from factor group A were identified in the fractions of the distribution pattern. Also the band C of monopalmitine is present (Fig. 17). Further the band corresponding to A_y of the distribution pattern (Fig. 3) is identified as a new croton oil factor $A_5′$ (Hecker, 1968a,b; Schmidt and Hecker, 1968). Factor $A_5′$ is a relatively weak

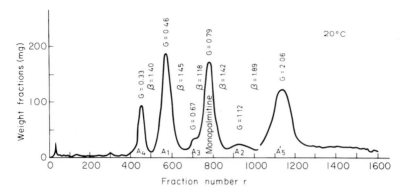

Fig. 17. Craig distribution of factor group A′. Single withdrawal procedure; $z = 1020$; $n = 1600$; $V = 12/10$; system carbon tetrachloride (2), methanol (1), water (0.15). Fractions $r = 0$–1020 represent the average weight of four neighboring fractions r to r-3 plotted against r-2; fractions $r = 1021$–1600 represent the average weight of nine neighboring fractions. (From Hecker, 1968a,b; Schmidt and Hecker, 1968; Hecker, 1970c.)

irritant (Chart 4) and also a weak cocarcinogen (Table X). From the similarity of the band A_y obtained in the Craig distribution of factor group A (Fig. 3) and $A_5′$ (Fig. 17), respectively, it may be suspected that contained in the band A_y might also be one or more phorbol-12,13-diesters of relatively weak irritant activity (see also Chart 2.)

TABLE X

COCARCINOGENIC ACTIVITIES OF THE CROTON OIL FACTORS
ISOLATED FROM THE ACTIVATED HYDROPHOBIC PORTION[a]

Factor	Cocarcinogenic activity[b]	
	Tumor rate[c] (%)	Average tumor yield[c] (tumors/survivor)
$A_5′$	14[d]	0.3
$B_8′$	42[e]	1.0
$B_9′$	32[e]	0.8
Fraction D′	Under investigation	
Fraction E′	Under investigation	

[a] From Hecker, 1970a,b,c,d.

[b] Assayed by the standard procedure on NMRI mice (Hecker and Bresch, 1965); initiator: 0.1 μM 7,12-dimethylbenz[a]anthracene.

[c] After 12 weeks (24 applications).

[d] Cocarcinogen, 0.06 μM per application.

[e] Cocarcinogen, 0.02 μM per application.

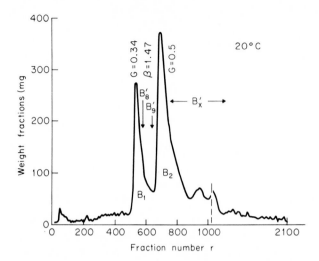

Fɪɢ. 18. Craig distribution of factor group B′. Single withdrawal procedure; $z = 1020$; $n = 2100$; $V = 10/10$; system carbon tetrachloride (2), methanol (1), water (0.15). Fractions $r = 0$–1020 represent the average weight of four neighboring fractions r to r-3 plotted against r-2; fractions $r = 1021$–1600 represent the average weight of nine neighboring fractions. (From Schmidt and Hecker 1968; Hecker 1970c.)

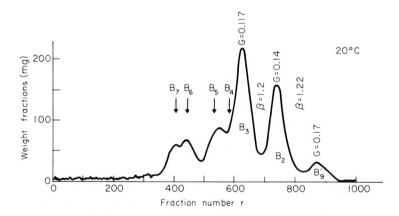

Fɪɢ. 19. Craig distribution of fraction B_x'. Single withdrawal procedure; $z = 1020$; $n = 6000$, $V = 12/10$; system petroleum ether (2), carbon tetra- chloride (0.4), methanol (1.75), water (0.1). Fractions $r = 0$–1020 represent the average weight of four neighboring fractions r to r-3 plotted against r-2; fractions $r = 1021$–1600 represent the average weight of nine neighboring fractions. (From Schmidt and Hecker, 1968; Hecker, 1970c.)

Factor group B' may be resolved further by Craig distribution (Chart 3). In the first distribution (Fig. 18) essentially two bands are obtained. From the band G = 0.34 by column chromatography on a silica gel–silver nitrate column the factor B_1, obtained already from the factor group B of the hydrophilic portion, may be isolated and identified using gas chromatographic and mass spectrometric techniques. In addition, the new croton oil factor B_8' is obtained in small amounts (Schmidt and Hecker, 1968).

To further resolve the material above fraction $r = 600$ (Fig. 18), it is redistributed in a different solvent system using $n = 6000$ transfers (Fig. 19). Thus another new croton oil factor B_9' was isolated. Besides B_9', the factors B_2–B_7 isolated from the factor group B of the hydrophilic portion are being identified (Chart 4; Schmidt and Hecker, 1968). Both of the new croton oil factors B_8' and B_9' exhibit considerable irritant (Chart 4) and cocarcinogenic activities (Table X).

2. Characterization of the Croton Oil Factor Groups A' and B'

Using the techniques described in Section III,B,2, the new croton oil factor A_5' is identified as 12-O-tiglyl-phorbol-13-butyroate. The factors B_8' and B_9' are recognized as 12-O-tiglyl- and 12-O-butyroyl-phorbol-13-dodecanoate, respectively (Table XI).

As in the hydrophilic portion of croton oil, and also in the activated hydrophobic portion, croton oil factor A_1 is the most abundant phorbol-12,13-diester followed by B_1 and B_2. The successful activation and fractionation of the hydrophobic portion indicate that in croton oil, besides phorbol-12,13-diesters accounting for approximately 50% of the phorbol content, nearly the same amount of phorbol is present as phorbol-12,13,20-triesters. In the O'Keeffe distribution of croton oil the biologically active 12,13-diesters preferentially concentrate in the hydrophilic, and the 12,13,20-triesters in the hydrophobic portion

TABLE XI

MASS SPECTROMETRIC CHARACTERIZATION OF THE NEW FACTORS
ISOLATED FROM THE ACTIVATED HYDROPHOBIC PORTION OF CROTON OIL[a]

Croton oil factor	R_f[b]	Molecular formula	Acyl residues identified as	Parent alcohol
A_5'	0.3	$C_{29}H_{40}O_8$	Tiglic, butyric	
B_8'	0.4	$C_{37}H_{56}O_8$	Tiglic, dodecanoic	$C_{20}H_{28}O_6$
B_9'	0.4	$C_{36}H_{56}O_8$	Butyric, dodecanoic	

[a] Schmidt and Hecker, 1968; Hecker 1970a,b,c.
[b] Methylene chloride–acetone (3:1); silica gel Merck HF_{254}.

of the oil. Since, in the acid catalyzed transesterification stage of the hydrophobic portion, the acyl residues esterified with OH-20 of the phorbol molecules are transferred to methanol, the nature of the acyl residues remains unknown.

IV. Further Diterpene Esters and Diterpenes from Croton Oil

By base-catalyzed transesterification, phorbol may be obtained directly from croton oil as colorless crystals. They are separated from a viscous filtrate, which mainly consists of glycerol, the parent alcohol of the mass of the lipids of croton oil, and of residual phorbol.

To prepare phorbol (Hecker et al., 1966c, improved) croton oil (500 gm) is agitated in a shaking machine under nitrogen with a solution of 55 gm of $Ba(OH)_2 \cdot 8 H_2O$ in 2.25 liters of methanol for 10 to 12 hours. Subsequently the solution is filtered to remove the precipitate of barium soaps and kept in the rotary evaporator until no more methanol volatilizes (temperature of bath, 40°C). The oily residue is dissolved in 2 liters of water and extracted 2 times, each with 500 ml of ether. The remaining aqueous phase contains phorbol and is adjusted to pH 5 with 2 N sulfuric acid. After addition of 40 ml of a saturated solution of sodium sulfate the preparation is kept at 4°C. After 12 hours it is filtered from the precipitated barium sulfate, adjusted to pH 7 with 2 N sodium hydroxide, and extracted with 500 ml ethyl acetate followed by 500 ml of ether. The aqueous phase is kept in the rotary evaporator until no more water volatilizes (temperature of bath, 45°C). The viscous residue is "digested" with 100 ml of ethanol and separated from sodium sulfate by suction through a filter plate. The sodium sulfate remaining on the filter is extracted with warm ethanol until a sample boiled with several milliliters of HCl gives no or only a very slight red color ("phorbol reaction" according to Flaschenträger, 1935). From the filtrate, the ethanol is partly removed until 50 to 60 ml of an oily residue remain. This preparation is stored at 4°C. Crystallization of phorbol usually starts spontaneously. If not, the preparation may be too viscous and has to be diluted with a little ethanol. Also, inoculation with phorbol may induce crystallization. After 4 weeks the crystals of the solvate "alcohol phorbol," i.e., phorbol · C_2H_5OH (Hoppe et al., 1969) are separated from their mother liquor by suction. The resulting mass is spread on a clay dish and stored under nitrogen in a dessicator at 4°C. Thus, 5.5–6.1 gm of pure white phorbol · C_2H_5OH are obtained. Since this solvate is not stable, it is converted to phorbol by dissolving 5.8 gm of phorbol · C_2H_5OH in 100 ml of water at 60°C. From this solution in the rotary evaporator (temperature of bath, 60°C), water is removed until crystals begin to separate. This preparation is kept at 4°C for 1 week, and the crystals are collected by suction (4.4 gm of phorbol). From the filtrate, additional phorbol may be obtained by further removal of water in the rotary evaporator and precipitation of the remaining solution by bringing it to 30% (by volume) of acetone.

In the filtrate of alcohol phorbol, besides glycerol and residual phorbol, other alcohol moieties may be expected which occur in the lipids of croton oil and which, in the procedure to prepare phorbol, partition preferably into the water phase. Indeed, in thin-layer chromatography, besides the spots from glycerol and phorbol, several other spots may be seen by both UV light and after staining with vanillin–sulfuric acid. The most intense of these additional spots has an R_f value slightly smaller than that of phorbol, whereas three rather faint spots exhibit R_f values larger than that of phorbol (Hecker et al., 1966c, Jacobi et al., 1970).

After acetylation of the filtrate from phorbol preparations with an excess of acetic acid anhydride–pyridine and subsequent removal of the glycerol triacetate formed, a resinous residue is obtained. From the latter, by chromatography on silica gel columns, besides some phorbol-12,13,20-triacetate a new triacetate is isolated (Hecker et al., 1968). This new compound is isomeric with phorbol-12,13,20-triacetate and exhibits a melting point different from that of phorbol-12,13,20-triacetate; also, its spectral data are slightly but definitely different from those of phorbol-12,13,20-triacetate. Moreover—and contrary to phorbol-12,13,20-triacetate (Schairer et al., 1968)—with hot acetic acid anhydride–pyridine the new triacetate yields a tetraacetate that is sensitive to light (Hecker et al., 1968). From comparison of physical and chemical data, this tetraacetate is identical with a tetraacetate preparation believed to be a phorbol tetraacetate (Arroyo and Holcomb, 1965b). In fact, however, this tetraacetate is not identical either with authentic phorbol-9,12,13,20-tetraacetate (Schairer et al., 1968) or with authentic phorbol-4,12,13,20-tetraacetate (Hecker, 1970c).

By irradiation with UV light of 254 mμ the new triacetate is converted to "lumiphorbol triacetate." Analysis of the NMR spectrum of the latter reveals a most interesting cagelike structure formed by internal cycloaddition (Hecker et al., 1968; Härle and Hecker, 1971). This structure is confirmed by X-ray diffraction analysis (Hecker et al., 1968). Together with additional chemical evidence (Jacobi et al., 1970) the structure of lumiphorbol triacetate proves that the new triacetate is the 4a-epimer of phorbol-12,13,20-triacetate, i.e., 4a-phorbol-12,13,20-triacetate (Fig. 21a). In contrast to phorbol its 3,4-ketol group may be acylated with pyridine as catalyst to yield for example 4a-phorbol-4,12,13,20-tetraacetate (Fig. 21, Hecker *et al.*, 1968; Jacobi *et al.*, 1971).

To obtain further clues as to the presence of additional diterpene parent alcohols in the filtrate of phorbol preparations, the glycerol was removed more mildly by O'Keeffe distribution using an *n*-butanol–water system (hand-operated battery with $z = 5$ elements holding 50 ml of stationary phase; Section III,A). Thus, whereas the glycerol is removed with the water-rich phases (Chart 5), from the butanol-rich phases a resinous material is obtained. The latter is acetylated and subjected to a Craig distribution ($n = 1600$ transfers) in a carbon tetrachloride–methanol–water solvent system. In Fig. 20 the bands with the distribution numbers $G = 3.56$ and 2.12 represent 4a-phorbol-12,13,20-triacetate (Fig. 21) and phorbol-12,13,20-triacetate, respectively. Of the remaining three bands, that with $G = 1.15$ is 4a-phorbol-4,12,13,20-tetraacetate (Fig. 21). Most interestingly, the material with $G = 0.95$ is a new diterpene 4-deoxy-4a-phorbol-12,13,20-triacetate (Fig. 21). It may also be obtained from both phorbol-12,13,20-triacetate

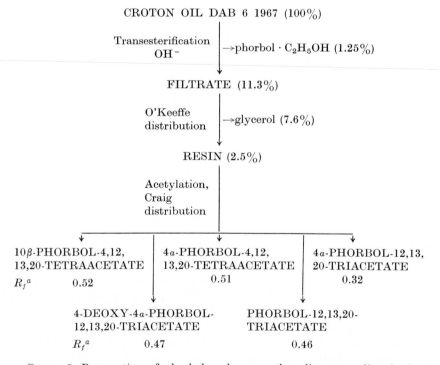

CHART 5. Preparation of phorbol and some other diterpenes directly from croton oil (Hecker *et al.*, 1966c; Schmidt and Hecker, 1968).

([a]) System chloroform–ethylacetate = 2:3: silica gel Merck HF 254.

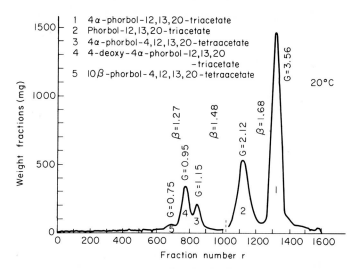

FIG. 20. Craig distribution of the "acetylated resin" obtained from the filtrate of phorbol preparations. Single phase withdrawal procedure: $z = 1020$, $n = 1600$; $V = 10/10$; system carbon tetrachloride (2), methanol (1), water (0.13). Fractions $r = 0$–1020 represent the average weight of four neighboring fractions r to r-3 plotted against r-2; fractions $r = 1021$–1600 represent the average weight of nine neighboring fractions. (From Hecker, 1970c.)

(Gschwendt *et al.*, 1968) and 4α-phorbol-12,13,20-triacetate (Jacobi *et al.*, 1970) by reduction with zinc–acetic acid. The small band with $G = 0.75$ (Fig. 20) is the tetraacetate of another epimer of phorbol, 10β-phorbol-4,12,13,20-tetraacetate (Fig. 21b). 10β-Phorbol may be obtained by treatment of phorbol with sodium methoxide in methanol under carefully controlled conditions (Hecker, 1970c).

In contrast to phorbol in both 4α- and 10β-phorbol (*cis*-phorbols) the five-membered ring is planar and the conformations of their seven-membered rings are rather flexible as indicated by spectroscopic data (Jacobi *et al.*, 1970; Hecker, 1970c). Thus for example, in Dreiding models of 4α-phorbol, a conformation may be demonstrated which allows a parallel orientation of the double bonds of the molecule on its β-side as it is required for formation of lumiphorbol-12,13,20-triacetate.

The appearance of acetates of two epimers of phorbol, i.e., 4α- and 10β-phorbol, and of the new diterpene 4-deoxy-4α-phorbol in the filtrates of preparations of phorbol from croton oil poses the problem whether these compounds do occur naturally in croton oil as parent alcohols of some lipids or, alternatively, if they are merely artificial side products formed during the alkali-catalyzed transesterification procedure.

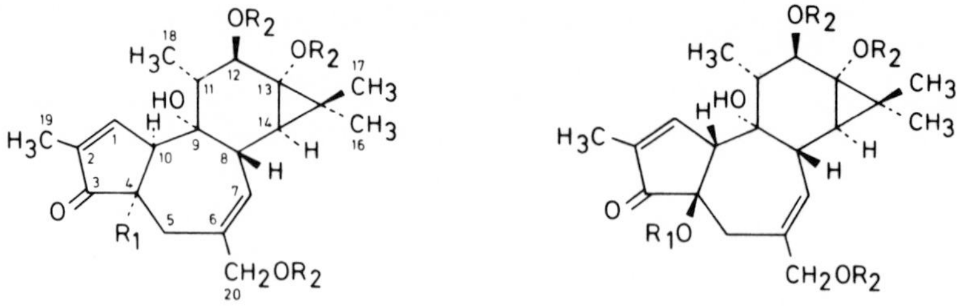

a R_1 = OH, R_2 = COCH$_3$: 4 α - phorbol - 12,13, 20 - triacetate
     R_1 = OCOCH$_3$, R_2 = COCH$_3$: 4 α - phorbol - 4, 12, 13, 20 - tetraacetate
     R_1 = H, R_2 = COCH$_3$: 4 - deoxy - 4 α - phorbol - 12,13, 20 - triacetate

b R_1 = R_2 = COCH$_3$: 10 β - phorbol - 4,12,13, 20 - tetraacetate

FIG. 21. Structure of some acetates of 4a-, 10β- and 4-deoxy-4a-phorbol iso-lated from the "acetylated resin" obtained from the filtrate of phorbol prepar-ations. (From Hecker, 1970c.)

If phorbol-12,13,20-triacetate is exposed to conditions similar to those used in the alkali-catalyzed transesterification of croton oil, 4a-phorbol (Hecker et al., 1968; Schmidt and Hecker, 1968; Jacobi et al., 1970) as well as 10β-phorbol (Hecker, 1970c) form. Thus, these epimers are at least partially produced during the transesterification procedure of phorbol esters contained in croton oil. However, alkali-catalyzed transesterification of phorbol esters or of croton oil is not adequate to deoxigenate phorbol in 4-position. Consequently, either 4-deoxyphorbol or 4-deoxy-4a-phorbol is to be considered as a native companion diterpene of phorbol in croton oil. The corresponding esters may not have been detected during the fractionations of croton oil (Charts 1 to 4) because of the scarcity and/or weak biological activity of these esters.

To evaluate this proposition, the hydrophilic and the hydrophobic portion of croton oil (see Chart 1) both were subjected to base-catalyzed transesterification in methanol in a manner similar to that of croton oil itself. Besides spots from phorbol, 4a- and 10β-phorbol, thin-layer chromatograms of both batches of parent alcohols thus obtained exhibit spots of 4-deoxy-4a-phorbol. In the head fraction obtained from the column chromatography of the activated hydrophobic portion the corres-ponding esters may be located (see Chart 4). Rechromatography of this fraction on silica gel with petroleum–ether mixtures yields two bands D' and E' containing several 4-deoxy-4a-phorbol-12,13-diesters. Ac-cording to their relative R_f values, the bands D' and E' correspond to the factor groups A' and B', respectively. Both of these new factor groups D′ and E′ do not exhibit irritant activities with doses up to 100 μg/ear (Hecker, 1970a,b,c,d). Their cocarcinogenic activities are presently under investigation (see Table X). These results and the relatively high amount and optical activity of the corresponding head fraction obtained in the fractionation of the hydrophilic portion (Chart 2) suggest that this fraction also contains 12,13-diesters of the 4-deoxy derivative of phorbol. Whether these native esters have 4-deoxy-4α-phorbol or 4-deoxyphorbol or both as parent alcohol has not been evaluated as yet. Since with zinc–acetic acid both phorbol and 4α-phorbol-12,13,20-triacetate yield solely 4-deoxy-4α-phorbol-12,13,20-triacetate, it may be suspected that 4-deoxyphorbol esters would epimerize even under mild acetic or alkaline conditions such as are used during the fractionation of both the hydrophilic and the hydrophobic portion of croton oil (Charts 1–4).

From the results of the preparation of parent alcohols directly from croton oil (Chart 5), a balance sheet of its diterpene constituents may be prepared (Table XII). Phorbol accounts for 3.4% and

TABLE XII

ESTIMATION OF RELATIVE AMOUNTS
OF PHORBOL, ITS 4-DEOXY DERIVATIVE, AND THEIR
ESTERS CONTAINED IN CROTON OIL[a]

Diterpenes	Isolated directly from croton oil (%)	Diesters	
		Calculated[d] (%)	Isolated[d] (%)
Phorbol	3.4[b]	5.6	5.5[e]
4-Deoxy derivative	0.29[c]	0.52	0.27[f]

[a] From Hecker, 1970c.
[b] Total of phorbol, 4α- and 10β-phorbol, calculated from the amount of crystalline phorbol and the amount of acetates isolated from phorbol mother liquor.
[c] Calculated from the amount of acetate isolated from phorbol mother liquor.
[d] Assuming an average molecular weight of 600 per diester.
[e] Total 12,13-diesters isolated from the hydrophilic and the hydrophobic portions.
[f] Total esters isolated from the hydrophobic portion only.

its 4-deoxy derivative for 0.29% of the weight of native croton oil. Assuming an average molecular weight of 600 per diester of phorbol and its 4-deoxy derivative, respectively, the percentage of parent alcohols corresponds to 5.6% and 0.52% of diesters, respectively

(Table XII). The total phorbol-12,13-diesters actually isolated from the hydrophilic (Chart 2) and the hydrophobic (Chart 4) portions is 5.5%, indicating a satisfactory yield from the isolation procedure. According to Table XII the ratio of phorbol diesters to diesters of the 4-deoxy derivative is roughly 10:1. Thus, it may be concluded that the hydrophilic portion contains approximately the same amount of diesters of the 4-deoxy derivatives as isolated from the hydrophobic portion, i.e., a total of 0.54% in croton oil. This figure is in satisfactory agreement with the figure calculated (see Table XII).

V. Conclusion

Fourteen different phorbol-12,13-diesters, A_1–A_4, A_5', B_1–B_7, B_8', and B_9' have been isolated from croton oil. Each of these diesters occurs in the hydrophobic portion as phorbol-12,13,20-triester with an unknown acyl residue in 20-position. Together these 12,13,20-triesters represent roughly 50% of the entire phorbol content of croton oil. They exhibit little if any irritant and cocarcinogenic activity.

Eleven of the phorbol-12,13-diesters isolated, A_1–A_4 and B_1–B_7, occur in the hydrophilic portion. They account roughly for another 50% of the phorbol content of croton oil. All of them exhibit irritant and cocarcinogenic activities to a greater or lesser extent. Throughout the entire isolation procedure it is impossible to divorce the irritant from the cocarcinogenic activity. 12-O-Tetradecanoyl-phorbol-13-acetate (TPA, croton oil factor A_1^*) is the most abundant of the biologically active phorbol-12,13-diesters; it is also the most irritant and cocarcinogenic phorbol-12,13-diester of the oil (Hecker, 1968a,b). Furthermore, it is highly toxic to frogs. Thus, it may be concluded that the phorbol-12,13-diesters A_1–A_4 and B_1–B_7 represent essentially all of the toxic, irritant, and cocarcinogenic factors of croton oil.

With the pure and molecularly uniform active principles of croton oil at hand the classic problem of the interrelationships between irritant and cocarcinogenic activities may be reinvestigated (Hecker, 1970a, b,c,d). Also the basic question may be answered as to whether reversible or irreversible biological events caused by phorbol-12,13-diesters produce their augmentational effect in Berenblum experiments (Hecker, 1966a; Hecker, 1968a,b). Further, new and most interesting problems as to the interrelationships between the chemical structure of phorbol derivatives and their biological activities come up (Thielmann and Hecker, 1969a). Last but not least phorbol derivatives will be of

---

* Phorbol and croton oil factor A_1 (TPA) are commercially available from Th. Schuchardt GmbH & Co., Chemische Fabrik, 8 Munich 80, P.O. Box 801549, Germany.

outstanding interest for a deeper understanding of the mechanism of tumorigenesis and carcinogenesis at both the biological (Hecker, 1966a, 1968a,b) and the molecular level (e.g., Weissmann *et al.*, 1967; Hecker and Paul, 1968; Paul and Hecker, 1969; Hecker and Bresch, 1969; Kreibich and Hecker, 1970a,b).

REFERENCES

Alderweireldt, F. (1961). *Anal. Chem.* **33**, 1920.

Arroyo, E. R., and Holcomb, I. (1965a) *Chem. & Ind. (London)* p. 350.

Arroyo, E. R., and Holcomb, I. (1965b). *J. Med. Chem.* **8**, 672.

Bartsch, H., and Hecker, E. (1967). *Angew. Chem.* **79**, 994; *Angew. Chem. Intern. Ed. Engl.* **6**, 974.

Bartsch, H., and Hecker, E. (1968). *Aktuel. Probl. Cancerol.* **2**, 162.

Bartsch, H., Bresch, H., Gschwendt, M., Härle, E., Kreibich, G., Kubinyi, H., Schairer, H. U., von Szczepanski, C., Thielmann, H. W., and Hecker, E. (1966). *Z. Anal. Chem.* **221**, 424.

Bartsch, H., Snatzke, G., and Hecker, E. (1968). *Z. Naturforsch.* **23b**, 1453.

Berenblum, I. (1941a). *Cancer Res.* **1**, 44.

Berenblum, I. (1941b). *Cancer Res.* **1**, 807.

Berenblum, I. (1947). *Brit. Med. Bull.* **4**, 343.

Berenblum, I. (1954). *Advan. Cancer Res.* **2**, 129.

Berenblum, I. (1964). *In* "Cellular Control Mechanism and Cancer" (P. Emmelot and O. Mühlbock, eds.), p. 259. Elsevier, Amsterdam.

Berenblum, I., and Shubik, P. (1947a). *Brit. J. Cancer* **1**, 379.

Berenblum, I., and Shubik, P. (1947b). *Brit. J. Cancer* **1**, 383.

Berenblum, I., and Shubik, P. (1949). *Brit. J. Cancer* **3**, 384.

Boehm, R. (1915a). *Arch. Exptl. Pathol. Pharmakol.* **79**, 138.

Boehm, R. (1915b). *Arch. Pharm.* **253**, 574.

Boehm, R. (1923). Quoted in Boehm and Flaschenträger (1930), Boehm *et al.* (1935), and Flaschenträger (1935).

Boehm, R., and Flaschenträger, B. (1930). *Arch. Exptl. Pathol. Pharmakol.* **157**, 115.

Boehm, R., Flaschenträger, B., and Lendle, L. (1935). *Arch. Exptl. Pathol. Pharmakol.* **177**, 212.

Boutwell, R. (1964). *Progr. Exptl. Tumor Res.* **4**, 207.

Bresch, H., Kreibich, G., Kubinyi, H., Schairer, H. U., Thielmann, H. W., and Hecker, E. (1968). *Z. Naturforsch.* **23b**, 538.

Cherbuliez, E., Ehninger, E., and Bernhard, K. (1932a). *Helv. Chim. Acta* **15**, 658.

Cherbuliez, E., Ehninger, E., and Bernhard, K. (1932b). *Helv. Chim. Acta* **15**, 855.

Clarke, E., and Hecker, E. (1965a). *Naturwissenschaften* **52**, 446.

Clarke, E., and Hecker, E. (1965b). *Z. Krebsforsch.* **67**, 192.

Craig, L. C., and King, T. P. (1958). *Federation Proc.* **17**, 1126.

Craig, L. C., King, T. P., and Scheibel, E. G. (1956). *Tech. Org. Chem.* ed. by A. Weissberger, 2nd ed., Interscience Publ., New York **3**, Part I, 149.

Danneel, R., and Weissenfels, N. (1955). *Naturwissenschaften* **42**, 128.

Druckrey, H. (1959). *In* "Physiologische Chemie" (B. Flaschenträger and E. Lehnartz, eds.), Vol. II, Part 2c, p. 1 (see p. 232). Springer, Berlin.

Dunstan, W. R., and Boole, L. E. (1895). *Pharm. J.* **55**, 5; *Pharm. Zentralhalle* **36**, 537 and 799 (1895); *Proc. Roy. Soc.* **58**, 238 (1895).

Flaschenträger, B. (1935). "Festschrift Heinrich Zangger," Vol. II, p. 857. Verlag Rascher, Zürich.

Flaschenträger, B., and Wigner, G. (1942). *Helv. Chim. Acta* **25**, 569.

Graffi, A. (1964). *Sitzber. Deuts. Akad. Wiss. Berlin, Kl. Med.* No. 2.

Graffi, A., and Bielka, H. (1959). "Probleme der experimentellen Krebsforschung." Akad. Verlagsges., Leipzig.

Gschwendt, M., and Hecker, E. (1967). *Angew. Chem.* **79**, 994; *Angew. Chem. Intern. Ed. Engl.* **6**, 974.

Gschwendt, M., and Hecker, E. (1968a). *Aktuel. Probl. Cancerol.* **2**, 170.

Gschwendt, M., and Hecker, E. (1968b). *Z. Naturforsch.* **23**b, 1584.

Gschwendt, M., and Hecker, E. (1969). *Z. Naturforsch.* **24**b, 80.

Gschwendt, M., Härle, E., and Hecker, E. (1968). *Z. Naturforsch.* **23**b, 1579.

Gwynn, R. H. (1955). *Brit. J. Cancer.* **9**, 445.

Härle, E., and Hecker, E. (1971). *Ann. Chem.* (in preparation).

Härle, E., Koch, W., and Hecker, E. (1967). *Chem. Ber.* **100**, 795.

Hecker, E. (1955a). "Verteilungsverfahren im Laboratorium." Verlag Chemie, Weinheim.

Hecker, E. (1955b). *Chem. Ber.* **88**, 1666.

Hecker, E. (1957). *Chem.-Ing.-Tech.* **29**, 23.

Hecker, E. (1961). *Z. Anal. Chem.* **181**, 284.

Hecker, E. (1962a). *Chemiker. Ztg.* **86**, 272.

Hecker, E. (1962b). *Angew. Chem.* **74**, 722; *Angew. Chem. Intern. Ed. Engl.* **1**, 602.

Hecker, E. (1962c). Unpublished data.

Hecker, E. (1963a). *Naturwissenschaften* **50**, 165 and 290.

Hecker, E. (1963b). *Mitt. Max-Planck-Ges.* Nos. 1–2, p. 41.

Hecker, E. (1963c). *Z. Krebsforsch.* **65**, 325.

Hecker, E. (1965). *In* "Handbuch der Lebensmittelchemie" (I. Schormüller, ed.), Vol. II, Part 1, p. 713. Springer, Berlin.

Hecker, E. (1966a). *In* "Molekulare Biologie des malignen Wachstums" (H. Holzer and A. W. Holldorf, eds.), p. 105. Springer, Berlin.

Hecker, E. (1966b). *Proc. 10th Intern. Cancer Congr., Tokyo, 1966* Abstracts, p. 17.

Hecker, E. (1967). *Naturwissenschaften* **54**, 282.

Hecker, E. (1968a). *Cancer Res.* **28**, 2338.

Hecker, E. (1968b). *Planta Med.* Suppl. 1968, p. 24.

Hecker, E. (1968c). *Arzneimittel-Forsch.* **18**, 978.

Hecker, E. (1970a). *Proc. 10th Intern. Cancer Congr., Houston, 1970* (in press).

Hecker, E. (1970b). *Proc. Intern. Symp. Pharmacognosy Phytochem., Munich, 1970* (in press).

Hecker, E. (1970c). *Symp. Naturally Occurring Carcinogens, Prague, 1970,* Abstract p. 2.

Hecker, E. (1970d). *First Congr. European Assoc. Cancer Res.,* Brussels, 1970, Abstracts p. 5.

Hecker, E. (1971). *Fortschr. Chem. Org. Naturstoffe* (in preparation).

Hecker, E., and Bresch, H. (1965). *Z. Naturforsch.* **20**b, 216.

Hecker, E., and Bresch, H. (1969). *Proc. Am. Assoc. Cancer Res.* p. 37.

Hecker, E., and Kubinyi, H. (1965). *Z. Krebsforsch.* **67**, 176.

Hecker, E., and Paul, D. (1968). *Z. Krebsforsch.* **71**, 153.

Hecker, E., and Schairer, H. U. (1967). *Z. Krebsforsch.* **70**, 1.

Hecker, E., Bresch, H., and Meyer, J. G. (1964a). *Abstr. Papers, 1st World Fat Congr., Hamburg*, 1964, p. 176; see also *Fette, Seifen, Anstrichmittel* (1965). 67, 78.

Hecker, E., Bresch, H., and von Szczepanski, C. (1964b). *Angew. Chem.* 76, 889; *Angew. Chem. Intern. Ed. Engl.* 3, 747.

Hecker, E., Kubinyi, H., and Bresch, H. (1964c). *Angew. Chem.* 76, 889; *Angew. Chem. Intern. Ed. Engl.* 3, 747.

Hecker, E., Jarczyk, H., Meyer, J. G., Bresch, H., and Brachmann, I. (1965a). *Z. Krebsforsch.* 66, 478.

Hecker, E., Kubinyi, H., Schairer, H. U., von Szczepanski, C., and Bresch, H. (1965b). *Angew. Chem.* 77, 1076; *Angew. Chem. Intern. Ed. Engl.* 4, 1072.

Hecker, E., Kubinyi, H., von Szczepanski, C., Härle, E., and Bresch, H. (1965c). *Tetrahedron Letters* p. 1837.

Hecker, E., Immich, H., Bresch, H., and Schairer, H. U. (1966a). *Z. Krebsforsch.* 68, 366.

Hecker, E., Kubinyi, H., Bresch, H., and von Szczepanski, C. (1966b). *J. Med. Chem.* 9, 246.

Hecker, E., von Szczepanski, C., Kubinyi, H., Bresch, H., Härle, E., Schairer, H. U., and Bartsch, H. (1966c). *Z. Naturforsch.* 21b, 1204.

Hecker, E., Bartsch, H., Bresch, H., Gschwendt, M., Härle, E., Kreibich, G., Kubinyi, H., Schairer, H. U., von Szczepanski, C., and Thielmann, H. W. (1967). *Tetrahedron Letters* p. 3165.

Hecker, E., Härle, E., Schairer, H. U., Jacobi, P., Hoppe, W., Gassmann, J., Röhrl, M., and Abel, H. (1968). *Angew. Chem.* 80, 913; *Angew. Chem. Intern. Ed. Engl.* 7, 890.

Hecker, E., Bartsch, H., Kreibich, G., and von Szczepanski, C. (1969). *Ann. Chem.* 725, 130.

Hoppe, W., Brandl, F., Strell, I., Röhrl, M., Gassmann, J., Hecker, E., Bartsch, H., Kreibich, G., and von Szczepanski, C. (1967). *Angew. Chem.* 79, 824; *Angew. Chem. Intern. Ed. Engl.* 6, 809.

Hoppe, W., Zechmeister, K., Röhrl, M., Brandl, F., Hecker, E., Kreibich, G., and Bartsch, H. (1969). *Tetrahedron Letters* p. 667.

Jacobi, P., Härle, E., Schairer, H. U., and Hecker, E. (1970). *Ann. Chem.* (in press).

Kauffmann, T., and Neumann, H. (1959). *Chem. Ber.* 92, 1715.

Kauffmann, T., Eisinger, A., Jasching, W., and Lenhardt, K. (1959). *Chem. Ber.* 92, 1727.

Kreibich, G., and Hecker, E. (1967). *Angew. Chem.* 79, 993; *Angew. Chem. Intern. Ed. Engl.* 6, 973.

Kreibich, G., and Hecker, E. (1968a). *Aktuel. Probl. Cancerol.* 2, 155.

Kreibich, G., and Hecker, E. (1968b). *Z. Naturforsch.* 23b, 1444.

Kreibich, G., and Hecker, E. (1970a). *Z. Krebsforsch.* 74, 448.

Kreibich, G., Süss, R., Kinzel, V., and Hecker, E. (1970b). *Z. Krebsforsch.* 74, 383.

Lijinsky, W. (1958). *Biochem. J.* 70, 5P.

Lijinsky, W. (1961). *Abstr. Commun., 5th Intern. Congr. Biochem., Moscow*, 1961 p. 9.

Meyer, J. G. (1966). *Experientia* 22, 482.

Meyer-Bertenrath, J. G. (1968). *Experientia* 24, 1295.

Mottram, J. C., (1944). *J. Pathol. Bacteriol.* 56, 181.

Nakahara, W. (1961). *Progr. Exptl. Tumor Res.* 2, 158.

Ocken, P. R. (1969). *J. Lipid Res.* 10, 460.

Paul, D., Hecker, E. (1969). *Z. Krebsforsch.* **73**, 149; see also *Cancer Res.* **29**, 1218 (1969).

Pettersen, R. C., Ferguson, G., Crombie, L., Games, M. L., and Pointer, D. J. (1967). *Chem. Commun.* pp. 716–717.

Pettersen, R. C., Birnbaum, G. I., Ferguson, G., Islam, K. M. S., and Sime, I. G. (1968). *J. Chem. Soc. B* p. 980.

Post, O., and Craig, L. C. (1963). *Anal. Chem.* **35**, 641.

Saffiotti, U., and Shubik, P. (1963). *Natl. Cancer Inst. Monograph* **10**, p. 489.

Salaman, M. H. (1958). *Brit. Med. Bull.* **14**, 116.

Salaman, M. H., and Roe, F. J. C. (1964). *Brit. Med. Bull.* **20**, 139.

Schairer, H. U., Thielmann, H. W., Gschwendt, M., Kreibich, G., Schmidt, R., and Hecker, E. (1968). *Z. Naturforsch.* **23**b, 1430.

Schmidt, R., and Hecker, E. (1968). *Fette, Seifen, Anstrichmittel* **70**, 851.

Shear, M. B. (1938). *Am. J. Cancer* **33**, 499.

Sicé, I. (1958). *Arch. Intern. Pharmacodyn.* **115**, 408.

Spies, J. R. (1935). *J. Am. Chem. Soc.* **57**, 180–182.

Thielmann, H. W., and Hecker, E. (1969). *Fortschritte Krebsforsch.* p. 171. Schattauer Verlag, Stuttgart-New York.

Thomas, A. F., and Marxer, A. (1958). *Experientia* **14**, 320.

Van Duuren, B. L. (1969). *Progr. Exptl. Tumor Res.* **11**, 31.

Van Duuren, B. L., and Orris, L. (1965). *Cancer Res.* **25**, 1871.

Van Duuren, B. L., Orris, L., and Arroyo, E. R. (1963a). *Proc. Am. Assoc. Cancer Res.* p. 69

Van Duuren, B. L., Orris, L., and Arroyo, E. R. (1963b). *J. Med. Chem.* **6**, 616.

Van Duuren, B. L., Orris, L., and Arroyo, E. R. (1963c). *Nature* **200**, 1115.

Van Duuren, B. L., Sivak, A., Segal, A., Orris, L., and Lengseth, L. (1966). *J. Natl. Cancer Inst.* **37**, 519.

Van Potter, R. (1964). *Cancer Res.* **24**, 1085.

von Ardenne, M., Steinfelder, K., and Tümmler, R. (1961). *Angew. Chem.* **73**, 136.

von Ardenne, M., Steinfelder, K., and Tümmler, R. (1963). *Experientia* **19**, 178.

von Metzsch, F. A. (1953). *Chem.-Ing.-Tech.* **25**, 66.

von Metzsch, F. A. (1959). *Chem.-Ing.-Tech.* **31**, 262.

von Szczepanski, C., Schairer, H. U., Gschwendt, M., and Hecker, E. (1967). *Ann. Chem.* **705**, 199.

Weissmann, G., Troll, W., Van Duuren, B. L., and Sessa, G. (1967). *J. Clin. Invest.* **46**, 1131.

AUTHOR INDEX

Numbers in italics refer to the pages on which the complete references are listed.

SUBJECT INDEX

A

Acetaldehyde, deoxyribose formation and, 362

Acetate, labeled, regenerating liver and, 386

Acetic acid,
croton oil fractions and, 458, 459, 465, 467
lipid hydrolysis by, 410–411

Acetone, lipid derivatives and, 418

2-Acetylaminobiphenyl, hydroxylation of, 222

2-Acetylaminofluorene,
hydroxylation of, 222
transfer ribonucleic acids and, 223, 314

2-Acetylaminophenanthrene, hydroxylation of, 222–223

2-Acetylaminostilbene, hydroxylation of, 222

Acetyl coenzyme A, fatty acid synthesis and, 426

N-Acetylglutamate, carbamyl phosphate synthetase and, 374

Acid hydrolysis, lipids, 410-411

Acid phosphatase, regenerating liver, 382

Actinomycin D, regenerating liver and, 364, 366

Acyl carrier protein, fatty acid synthesis and, 426

Acylglycerol lipids,
biosynthesis, 419–421
enzymatic degradation of, 423

Adenosine, transfer ribonucleic acid and, 334, 335, 337–338.

Adenosine diphosphate,
concentration, determination of, 167
mitochondrial respiration and, 163, 167

Adenosine monophosphate,
cyclic, protein release and, 236

Adenosine triphosphatase, regenerating liver and, 382

Adenosine triphosphate,
amino acid activation and, 317–318
aminoacyl transfer ribonucleic acid, and 196

formation, respiration and, 163–164
thymidine kinase and, 367, 368

S-Adenosylmethionine, transfer ribonucleic acid and 222, 336–337

Adenovirus 7,
infection, transfer ribonucleic acid and, 314

Age, liver regeneration and, 359

Age distribution, cell cycle and, 15–18, 34, 40, 41, 49, 53

Alanine,
transfer ribonucleic acid, 225
structure, 219, 220–221, 333

Albumin, partial hepatectomy and, 383–384

Aldolase, lipid precursors and, 425

Alkaline hydrolysis, lipids, 411-412

Alkaline phosphatase, lipid degradation and, 416

Alkane–1, 2–diols, structure, 400

O-Alkyldihydroxyacetone phosphate,
hydrolysis,
acid, 411, 419
alkali, 412
enzymatic, 416

O-Alk-l-enylglycerol lipids,
biosynthesis of, 422–423
enzymatic degradation of, 424–425

O-Alkylglycerol lipids,
biosynthesis of, 421–422
enzymatic degradation of 423–424

Alumina Cγ-gel, transfer enzymes and, 197

Amino acid(s),
acceptance, assay of, 320–321
concentration in regenerating liver, 380–381
incorporation into protein: the transfer reaction, 322–323
Novikoff ascites cell labeling and, 256–258
uptake by ascites cells, 276–277

Amino acid-incorporating systems,
enzymes and related factors, 231–240.
liver, 202–207
assay procedure, 204–205
regenerating liver, 381–382

3 5282 00234 9804